# A TREATISE ON TRIGONOMETRIC SERIES

VOLUME I

N. K. BARY

# A Treatise on Trigonometric Series

VOLUME I

*Authorized translation by*

MARGARET F. MULLINS

A Pergamon Press Book

THE MACMILLAN COMPANY
NEW YORK
1964

THE MACMILLAN COMPANY
60 Fifth Avenue
New York 11, N.Y.

This book is distributed by
THE MACMILLAN COMPANY
pursuant to a special arrangement with
PERGAMON PRESS LIMITED
Oxford, England



Library of Congress Catalog Card Number 63–12682

This is an authorized translation of the original volume
*Тригонометрические ряды* (Trigonometricheskiye ryady),
published in 1961 by Fizmatgiz, Moscow

# CONTENTS

# CONTENTS OF VOLUME II

# TRANSLATOR'S PREFACE

Miss Nina Bary's 900 page monograph *Trigonometricheskiye Ryady* (Trigonometric Series) was published in Moscow in 1961, the year of her death. Two years previously when her book was at the proof stage, the important two-volume 2nd edition of Prof. A. Zygmund's work of the same title was published by the Cambridge University Press. Whilst both works deal comprehensively with the classical theory of Fourier series, they are quite different in their styles of presentation and also differ apprcciably in their selected coverage of the field.

Miss Bary's monograph develops the subject of trigonometric series very carefully in the sense of giving proofs, or references to where proofs can be found, of all the elementary theorems; in other words, her book is written for students as well as research workers, although it includes in the later chapters a comprehensive account of all contributions right up to 1959 of advances in those topics which she has selected (see Author's Preface). Her thoroughness has the result too that any mathematical phrase or terminology which appears strange to the English reader is completely defined and therefore understandable.

In particular, the monograph includes much of the recent researches of Miss Bary herself (the problem of uniqueness, null-series, sets of measure zero, best approximations) and her compatriots, P. L. Ul'yanov (*A*-integration, rearrangement of trigonometric systems), D. E. Men'shov (limits of indetermination, universal trigonometric series), S. B. Stechkin (absolute convergence, best approximations) and others.

The English translation with the title *A Treatise on Trigonometric Series* is published in two volumes, the first of which is suitable for University students and the second for advanced students and research workers. The two volumes will serve further as a reference work and source-book for libraries. Each volume contains the complete Contents List and Bibliography; Vol. I includes Problems added to the end of each Chapter by Professor P. L. Ul'yanov in January 1963 and contains its own Index; Vol. II includes an Index covering both volumes. In the Bibliography, numbers referring to books and monographs are prefixed by the lettcr A.

I wish to thank Mr. M. G. Woollett M.A. for his valuable assistance in clarifying a number of mathematical points and assisting me with the technical editing and my husband Dr. B. P. Mullins for help with many aspects of the work involved in the translation.

Farnborough, Hants. MARGARET F. MULLINS

# AUTHOR'S PREFACE

THE well-known book by A. Zygmund, *Trigonometrical Series*,[A. 35] contains a more or less exhaustive account of all the results using the theory of trigonometric series that had been obtained up to 1935†. Since then the interest of mathematicians in trigonometric series has not diminished and the progress achieved has been so considerable that it seems necessary to report the present state of our knowledge in this field.

The range of questions which should be considered is so large that it is immediately necessary to limit this. Therefore, I completely exclude Fourier integrals,†† trigonometrical series of several variables††† and I only touch very briefly on the investigation of best approximations of functions by trigonometric polynomials.

Furthermore I refer to orthogonal systems only in those cases where it seems simpler to derive a theorem in the theory of trigonometric series from more general theorems concerning orthogonal systems; if the transfer of theorems into general orthogonal systems requires specialized investigation, I confine myself to formulating them for trigonometric series††††.

In spite of the limitations imposed on the material published here, there still remains very much to include. When in 1915 N. N. Lusin wrote his excellent dissertation "The integral and trigonometric series"[A. 15] [A. 16] in which a whole series of essential problems were solved and propounded, he said that "the concept of the Fourier series is not a completely definite and rigid one, although it does depend entirely on the concept of the integral. By using in the Fourier formulae the increasingly general definitions of the integral (Cauchy, Riemann, Dirichlet, Harnack, Lebesgue, Denjoy) we develop an increasingly large class of trigonometric series". In the present book, the words "Fourier series" will always mean the Fourier–Lebesgue series. It is known that trigonometric series exist which converge at every point but which possess a sum which is non-integrable not only according to Lebesgue but also according to Denjoy in the sense that the integral was defined by Denjoy himself and by A. Ya. Khinchin in 1916. In order to be able to express the coefficients of such a series by its sum according to Fourier formulae, Denjoy later devised a new process: totalization with two indices.[A. 4]

---

† The English edition of Zygmund's book was printed in 1935; the Russian translation appeared in 1939 (Note added at proof stage:— Recently a fundamental monograph by Zygmund, *Trigonometric Series*, has appeared, 2nd Edition, Cambridge, 1959).

†† Specialized books have been devoted to this subject, e.g. Titchmarsh.[A. 31]

††† Fundamental references to this question can be found in Hobson's book[A. 11] Vol. II and Tonelli's book.[A. 32] An account of modern results, in my opinion, is premature at the present moment, since the theory of multiple trigonometric series has as yet been insufficiently studied.

†††† The general theory of orthogonal systems is given in a book by Kaczmarz and Steinhaus, the Russian translation of which contains additional material describing the present state of this theory and appeared in 1958.

I have found it impossible in my book to discuss this theme, though it is very important, as it would have taken up too much space. Moreover, I do not refer to the Fourier–Denjoy series even if the Denjoy integral is understood to be that of the original definition; it was necessary to devote very many pages to describing the material on the Fourier–Lebesgue series and general trigonometric series (that is, non-Fourier series). Although at first after the creation of the Lebesgue integral it was customary to think that sets of measure zero could always be neglected, today the position is clearly completely the reverse; in a whole series of problems in the theory of trigonometric series certain sets of measure zero behave in the same way as sets of positive measure. Thus, although previously very little could be said concerning general trigonometric series, now a whole series of interesting reports have been devoted to them, in which not only new results but also essentially new methods have appeared (in particular, the theory of numbers sometimes plays an important role in the theory of trigonometric series).

The foregoing remarks are intended to explain, even if incompletely, the field covered by this book. It is true that if I had wished to shorten it, I could have done so by means of abbreviated descriptions, but I have consciously refrained from doing this. It seems to me that, recently, authors of mathematical works too frequently misuse the words "easily seen", as a result of which the reader often does not understand the proofs of theorems or misses some important facts. I have tried to make the account completely understandable to undergraduates and research students. This refers especially to the material of Chapter I. I assume that it can be understood by anyone who knows only the theory of the Lebesgue integral from the normal course on the theory of functions at universities.† The later chapters contain more profound researches on the theory of trigonometric series; in order to understand them, additional material is sometimes necessary. For the reader's convenience, the proofs of a number of theorems to which I refer in the text are given in the Appendix. In the Introductory Material reference is made to extremely elementary theorems in analysis, in the theory of series and in the theory of functions, which I use systematically in the text; I make reference to the most suitable textbooks where their proofs can be found. The introductory material is written in the form of separate theorems, but I did not aim at formulating them in the most general form, but only in the way which is required in the later text.

I wish to acknowledge most sincerely my debt to P.L. Ul'yanov who read through the whole book and made a number of valuable remarks both as regards the selection of material and the correction of errors. Also in many instances he gave his own proofs of the theorems of other authors.

N. BARY

December 27th, 1957

† For example, from the book by P.S. Aleksandrov and A.N. Kolmogorov[A.1] or the book by Natanson.[A.23]

THIS WORK IS DEDICATED
TO THE MEMORY OF MY TEACHER,
NIKOLAI NIKOLAYEVICH LUSIN

# NOTATION

$[a, b]$ denotes the set of all values of $x$ such that $a \leqslant x \leqslant b$; correspondingly, $(a, b]$ for $a < x \leqslant b$; $(a, b)$ for $a < x < b$ and $[a, b)$ for $a \leqslant x < b$.

$[x]$ is the integral part of the number $x$.

$(x) = x - [x]$.

$\{x\}$ is the difference between $x$ and the nearest integer (whether below or above $x$).

$x = x_0 \pmod{a}$ shows that the difference $x - x_0$ is divisible by $a$.

$\uparrow$ monotonically non-decreasing; $\downarrow$ monotonically non-increasing; $\uparrow a$ (or $\downarrow a$) tending towards $a$, monotonically non-decreasing (or correspondingly non-increasing).

$f(x) \in C[a, b]$ signifies that $f(x)$ is continuous in $[a, b]$.

$f(x) \in L[a, b]$ signifies that $f(x)$ is summable in $[a, b]$.

$f(x) \in L^p[a, b)$ signifies that $f(x)$ is summable to the power $p$ in $[a, b]$.

$$\|f\|_{L^p[a,b]} = \left\{\int_a^b |f|^p\,dx\right\}^{1/p}, \quad 1 \leqslant p \leqslant \infty; \quad \|f\|_{C[a,b]} = \max_{a \leqslant x \leqslant b} |f(x)|.$$

If it is clear which interval is concerned then the brief notation $\|f\|_p$ or $\|f\|_C$ will be used.

$\|f\|_\infty$ see §9 of Introductory Material.

$f(x) \in \operatorname{Lip}\alpha$ signifies that constant $C$ exists such that $|f(x_1) - f(x_2)| \leqslant C|x_1 - x_2|^\alpha$ for any $x_1$ and $x_2$ in the interval for which $f(x)$ is defined.

$o, O, \sim, \approx$ see § 11 of Introductory Material.

$\sigma(f)$ is the Fourier series of the function $f(x)$.

$x \in E$ indicates that the point $x$ belongs to the set $E$.

$E_1 \subset E_2$ indicates that any point of $E_1$ belongs to $E_2$.

# INTRODUCTORY MATERIAL

## 1. ANALYTICAL THEOREMS

### § 1. Abel's transformation

If $u_0, u_1, \ldots, v_0, v_1, \ldots, v_n, \ldots$ are any real numbers, let us assume that

$$V_n = v_0 + v_1 + \cdots + v_n.$$

Then for any values of $m$ and $n$ we find that

$$\sum_{k=m}^{n} u_k v_k = \sum_{k=m}^{n-1} (u_k - u_{k+1}) V_k + u_n V_n - u_m V_{m-1} \tag{1.1}$$

(under the condition that if $m = 0$, $V_{-1} = 0$).

This formula which is known as *Abel's transformation* can be proved immediately; it is only necessary to note that $v_k = V_k - V_{k-1}$, to substitute this expression in the left-hand side and to regroup the terms.

At $m = 0$, we obtain as a particular case,

$$\sum_{k=0}^{n} u_k v_k = \sum_{k=0}^{n-1} (u_k - u_{k+1}) V_k + u_n V_n. \tag{1.2}$$

The importance of formulae (1.1) and (1.2) becomes clear if it is noted that they play the same kind of role as integration by parts; in the same way as it is sometimes convenient to convert a calculation of the integral $\int u\, dv$ into a calculation of the integral $\int v\, du$, here by supposing that

$$\Delta u_k = u_k - u_{k+1},$$

$$\Delta V_k = V_k - V_{k+1},$$

we can rewrite (1.1) in the form

$$\sum_{k=m}^{n-1} \Delta u_k V_k = - \sum_{k=m}^{n} u_k \Delta V_{k-1} + u_m V_{m-1} - u_n V_n, \tag{1.3}$$

that is, we can convert a calculation of one of the given sums into the other, which frequently proves useful.

It becomes especially convenient when one of the given sequences decreases monotonically (since from $u_k \downarrow$ it follows that $\Delta u_k \geqslant 0$ for all values of $k$).

From Abel's transformation, we can obtain directly a corollary.

COROLLARY. *When all values of* $u_k \geqslant 0$ *and* $u_k \downarrow$, *but* $|V_k| \leqslant M$ *for* $m \leqslant k \leqslant n$, *then*

$$\left| \sum_{k=m}^{n} u_k v_k \right| \leqslant 2u_m M. \tag{1.4}$$

In fact,

$$\left| \sum_{k=m}^{n} u_k v_k \right| \leqslant M \left| \sum_{k=m}^{n-1} (u_k - u_{k+1}) + u_n + u_m \right| \leqslant 2u_m M.$$

We will now consider the case when instead of numbers $v_n$ we have functions $v_n(x)$ defined in a certain interval $[a, b]$. Supposing that

$$V_n(x) = v_0(x) + \cdots + v_n(x),$$

we obtain the lemma:

ABEL'S LEMMA. *If* $u_n \downarrow 0$ *and*

$$|V_n(x)| \leqslant M, \quad a \leqslant x \leqslant b,$$

*then the series*

$$\sum_{n=0}^{\infty} u_n v_n(x)$$

*converges uniformly in* $[a, b]$ *and for its sum* $S(x)$ *the inequality holds*

$$|S(x)| \leqslant M u_0, \quad a \leqslant x \leqslant b. \tag{1.5}$$

Indeed let us suppose

$$S_n(x) = \sum_{k=0}^{n} u_k v_k(x).$$

Then according to formula (1.2)

$$S_n(x) = \sum_{k=0}^{n} (u_k - u_{k+1}) V_k(x) + u_n V_n(x), \tag{1.6}$$

whence

$$S_n(x) - u_n V_n(x) = \sum_{k=0}^{n} (u_k - u_{k+1}) V_k(x).$$

Since

$$|(u_k - u_{k+1}) V_k(x)| \leqslant (u_k - u_{k+1}) M, \quad a \leqslant x \leqslant b, \tag{1.7}$$

and the series

$$\sum_{k=0}^{\infty} M(u_k - u_{k+1})$$

with non-negative terms converges (since $u_n \downarrow 0$) and has the sum $Mu_0$, then the series

$$\sum_{k=0}^{\infty} (u_k - u_{k+1}) V_k(x)$$

converges absolutely and uniformly in $[a, b]$. Then from $u_n \downarrow 0$ and (1.6) it follows that $S_n(x)$ tends uniformly in $[a, b]$ to a certain function $S(x)$ for which (1.5) holds and the lemma is proved.

Abel's Lemma can be generalized, but first of all we must introduce a definition.

DEFINITION. A sequence of numbers $\{u_n\}$ is of *bounded variation* if

$$\sum_{n=0}^{\infty} |\Delta u_n| < +\infty . \tag{1.8}$$

It is clear that if $u_n \downarrow 0$, then condition (1.8) is satisfied.

Abel's Lemma continues to hold if the condition $u_n \downarrow 0$ is replaced by the condition: the sequence $\{u_n\}$ is of bounded variation.

In fact, the proof completely holds if $|u_k - u_{k+1}| = |\Delta u_k|$ is substituted for $u_k$ $u_{k+1}$ in the right-hand side of (1.7).

## § 2. Second mean value theorem

*If $f(x)$ and $g(x)$ are two functions which are Riemann-integrable in a given interval $[a, b]$, then if $f(x)$ is monotonic in $[a, b]$, the formula holds*

$$\int_a^b f(x)\, g(x)\, dx = f(a) \int_a^{\xi} g(x)\, dx + f(b) \int_{\xi}^b g(x)\, dx, \tag{2.1}$$

*where $a \leqslant \xi \leqslant b$.*

In the case when $f(x)$ is not only monotonic in $[a, b]$, but also non-negative in this interval, the formula is simplified and takes the form

$$\int_a^b f(x)\, g(x)\, dx = f(a) \int_a^{\xi} g(x)\, dx, \quad \text{if} \quad f(x)\downarrow, \tag{2.2}$$

and

$$\int_a^b f(x)\, g(x)\, dx = f(b) \int_{\xi}^b g(x)\, dx, \quad \text{if} \quad f(x)\uparrow \tag{2.3}$$

(see, for example, Fikhtengol'ts, ref. A.7).

## § 3. Convex curves and convex sequences

DEFINITION 1. Curve $y = \varphi(x)$ is called *convex* if for any two of its points $A$ and $B$ all the points of the arc $AB$ lie either below the chord $AB$ or on it (Fig. 1). Analogously the curve is called *concave* if all the points of the arc lie either above the chord or on it.

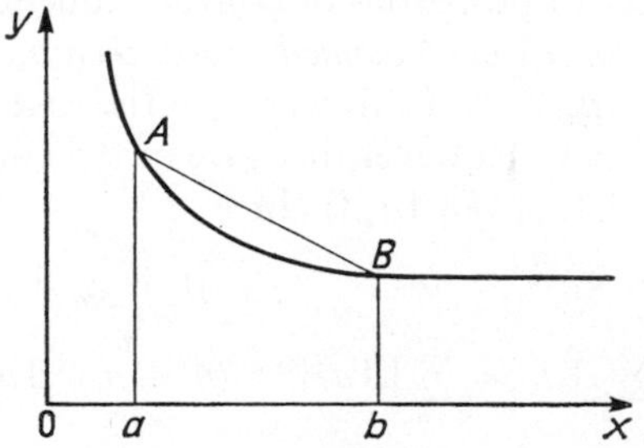


FIG. 1

For example, if $\varphi(x)$ has a continuous first-order derivative and $\varphi''(x) \geqslant 0$ in $[a, b]$, then $\varphi(x)$ is convex in this interval.

Indeed, if $a < x < b$, then for any $h > 0$ provided that it is sufficiently small for $x + h$ and $x - h$ to still lie in $(a, b)$, we have

$$\varphi(x+h) - \varphi(x) = h\varphi'(x_1), \quad \text{where} \quad x < x_1 < x + h;$$
$$\varphi(x-h) - \varphi(x) = -h\varphi'(x_2), \quad \text{where} \quad x - h < x_2 < x.$$

Therefore

$$\varphi(x+h) + \varphi(x-h) - 2\varphi(x) = h[\varphi'(x_1) - \varphi'(x_2)] = h(x_1 - x_2)\varphi''(\xi) \geqslant 0.$$

(Here $x - h < \xi < x + h$.) Thus

$$\varphi(x+h) + \varphi(x-h) - 2\varphi(x) \geqslant 0,$$

that is,

$$\varphi(x) \leqslant \frac{\varphi(x+h) + \varphi(x-h)}{2},$$

whence it follows that, since $\varphi(x)$ is continuous, any point of the arc of the curve between $x - h$ and $x + h$ lies below or on the chord, that is, the curve is convex.

THEOREM. *If $F(x)$ is a convex function in $[a, b]$, then it can be represented in the form*

$$F(x) = F(a) + \int_a^x \varphi(t)\,dt, \tag{3.1}$$

*where $\varphi(t)$ is a non-decreasing function in $[a, b]$. Conversely, any function $F(x)$ which can be represented in this form is convex in $[a, b]$.*

See, for example, Natanson, Ref. A.23, p. 547.

We should now become more acquainted with the properties of convex functions; but we will at present discuss only those connected with the concept of a convex sequence.

DEFINITION 2. A sequence $\{a_n\}$ $(n = 0, 1, \ldots)$ is called *convex* if, supposing that

$$\Delta a_n = a_n - a_{n+1},$$
$$\Delta^2 a_n = \Delta a_n - \Delta a_{n+1},$$

we have

$$\Delta^2 a_n \geqslant 0 \quad (n = 0, 1, 2, \ldots).$$

It is clear that if the curve $y = \varphi(x)$ is convex in $0 \leqslant x < +\infty$, then the points $a_n = \varphi(n)$ form a convex sequence.

Let us indicate a number of properties of convex sequences.

(1) *If a sequence $\{a_n\}$ is convex and bounded above, then $a_n \downarrow$.*

It must be proved that $\Delta a_n \geqslant 0$. If this were not the case, then there would exist a value of $m$ such that $\Delta a_m < 0$. However, because of the convexity, at any $k \geqslant m$ we would have $\Delta a_k < 0$ and $|\Delta a_k| \geqslant |\Delta a_m|$; since

$$a_n - a_m = (a_n - a_{n-1}) + (a_{n-1} - a_{n-2}) + \cdots + (a_{m+1} - a_m)$$
$$= -\sum_{k=m}^{n-1} \Delta a_k = \sum_{k=m}^{n-1} |\Delta a_k| \geqslant (n - m)|\Delta a_m| \to \infty$$

at $n \to \infty$, but $a_n$ is bounded above; therefore we have a contradiction.

(2) *If* $\{a_n\}$ *is convex and* $a_n \to 0$, *then* $a_n \downarrow 0$.

It follows from $a_n \to 0$ that $a_n$ is bounded above; then from the previous property $a_n \downarrow$; this fact together with $a_n \to 0$ gives $a_n \downarrow 0$.

(3) *If* $\{a_n\}$ *is convex and bounded, then*

$$n\,\Delta a_n \to 0 \tag{3.2}$$

*and*

$$\sum (n+1)\,\Delta^2 a_n < +\infty. \tag{3.3}$$

We have already seen that under these conditions $a_n \downarrow$. Because of the lower bound, the numbers $a_n$ possess a finite limit. Let

$$\lim a_n = a;$$

then

$$a_0 - a = (a_0 - a_1) + (a_1 - a_2) + \cdots + (a_n - a_{n+1}) + \cdots,$$

where the series on the right-hand side has monotonic decreasing terms and converges. Therefore $n\,\Delta a_n \to 0$ by virtue of the well-known theorem from the theory of numerical series.

Also, using Abel's transformation, we find

$$\sum_{m=0}^{n} \Delta a_m = \sum_{m=0}^{n} 1 \cdot \Delta a_m = \sum_{m=0}^{n-1} (m+1)\,\Delta^2 a_m + (n+1)\,\Delta a_n,$$

and since $(n+1)\,\Delta a_n \to 0$ but

$$\sum_{m=0}^{n} \Delta a_m = a_0 - a_n \to a_0 - a \quad \text{at} \quad n \to \infty,$$

then

$$\sum_{m=0}^{n-1} (m+1)\,\Delta^2 a_m \to a_0 - a, \quad \text{i.e. the series} \quad \sum_{m=0}^{\infty} (m+1)\,\Delta^2 a_m$$

converges, which is the required proof.

*Note*. If $\{a_n\}$ is convex, and $a_n \to 0$, then the hypothesis just proved is even more true.

# II. NUMERICAL SERIES, SUMMATION

## § 4. Series with monotonically decreasing terms

THEOREM 1. (Cauchy's theorem). *If* $u_n \downarrow 0$, *then the series*

$$\sum_{n=1}^{\infty} u_n \quad \text{and} \quad \sum_{n=1}^{\infty} 2^n u_{2^n}$$

*converge or diverge simultaneously.*

Because $u_n$ is monotonic, we have for any $k$

$$2^{k-1}u_{2^k} \leqslant \sum_{n=2^{k-1}+1}^{2^k} u_n \leqslant 2^{k-1}u_{2^{k-1}}$$

and it should be noted that

$$\sum_{n=1}^{\infty} u_n = u_1 + \sum_{k=1}^{\infty} \sum_{s=2^{k-1}+1}^{2^k} u_s.$$

THEOREM 2. *If* $a_n \downarrow 0$ *and* $\sum_{n=1}^{\infty} a_n = +\infty$, *then taking* $\Delta a_n = a_n - a_{n+1}$, *we have*

$$\sum_{n=1}^{\infty} n\,\Delta a_n = +\infty.$$

Let us assume $u_n = \sum_{k=1}^{\infty} k\,\Delta a_k$. Because $a_n \downarrow 0$ we have $\Delta a_k \geqslant 0$ $(k = 1, 2, \ldots)$. This signifies that all $u_n \geqslant 0$. It must be proved that $u_n \to \infty$. If this were untrue then

$$u_n \uparrow a, \quad \text{where} \quad a \neq +\infty.$$

Then $u_n = a - \varepsilon_n \downarrow 0$ and therefore since

$$u_n - u_{n-1} = n\,\Delta a_n = (a - \varepsilon_n) - (a - \varepsilon_{n-1}) = \Delta\varepsilon_{n-1},$$

then

$$\Delta a_n = \frac{\Delta\varepsilon_{n-1}}{n}.$$

Because $a_n \to 0$ and $\Delta\varepsilon_k \geqslant 0$ we have

$$a_n = \sum_{k=n}^{\infty} \Delta a_k = \sum_{k=n}^{\infty} \frac{\Delta\varepsilon_{k-1}}{k} \leqslant \frac{1}{n} \sum_{k=n}^{\infty} \Delta\varepsilon_{k-1} = \frac{1}{n}\varepsilon_{n-1},$$

and therefore $na_n \to 0$.

But using Abel's transformation for the sum expressed by $u_n$ we find

$$u_n = \sum_{k=1}^{n} k\,\Delta a_k = a_1 + a_2 + \cdots + a_n + a_{n+1},$$

and since $u_n \to a$ and $na_n \to 0$, then

$$a_1 + a_2 + \cdots + a_n \to a,$$

which contradicts the condition $\sum a_n = +\infty$.

The following definition is introduced for future application.

DEFINITION 1. Let $\sum u_n$ be a convergent series with $u_n \downarrow 0$. We will assume

$$r_n = \sum_{k=n}^{\infty} u_k.$$

It is said that this *series satisfies condition* (*L*), if

$$r_n = O(u_n). \tag{4.1}$$

If the terms of the series decrease not more slowly than a certain geometrical procession, i.e. if

$$u_{n+1} \leqslant \theta u_n, \quad 0 < \theta < 1,$$

then it satisfies condition $(L)$, but the converse conclusion is obviously inaccurate, as can be proved by this example:

$$u_{2n-1} = u_{2n} = \theta^n, \quad n = 1, 2, \ldots; \quad 0 < \theta < 1.$$

We will show that if the series satisfies condition $(L)$, for any $\theta < 1$, then it is possible to partition it into a finite number of series $l$ ($l$ varies with $\theta$) such that the terms of each of them decrease not more slowly than a geometrical progression with common ratio $\theta$.

Indeed, condition (4.1) signifies that

$$r_n < c u_n,$$

where $c$ is a constant. Let $\theta$ be given. We will choose a number $l$ such that

$$l = \left[\frac{c}{\theta}\right].$$

Because the numbers $u_n$ decrease monotonically and using (4.2) we have

$$(l + 1)\, u_{n+1} \leqslant \sum_{k=n}^{k=n+l} u_k \leqslant \sum_{k=n}^{\infty} u_k \leqslant c u_n, \tag{4.3}$$

and therefore due to (4.3)

$$u_{n+1} \leqslant \frac{c}{l+1} u_n \leqslant \theta u_n.$$

Therefore all $l$ series

$$u_1 + u_{1+l} + u_{1+2l} + \cdots,$$

$$u_2 + u_{2+l} + u_{2+2l} + \cdots,$$

$$\cdots\cdots\cdots\cdots\cdots\cdots$$

$$u_l + u_{2l} + u_{3l} + \cdots,$$

into which our series $\sum_{k=1}^{\infty} u_k$ can be partitioned decrease not more slowly than a geometrical progression with common ratio $\theta$.

We will now prove a theorem.

THEOREM 3. *If a series $\sum u_n$ satisfies condition $(L)$ then*

$$\sum_{k=1}^{n} \frac{1}{u_k} = O\left(\frac{1}{u_n}\right). \tag{4.4}$$

In fact, we have from the definition

$$u_n = r_n - r_{n+1},$$

and therefore from $r_n/u_n < c$

$$\frac{r_n}{r_n - r_{n+1}} < c,$$

whence

$$r_n < c(r_n - r_{n+1}),$$

that is

$$cr_{n+1} < (c-1)\, r_n$$

or

$$r_{n+1} < \theta r_n, \quad \text{where} \quad \theta = \frac{c-1}{c} < 1.$$

But then

$$u_n \sum_{k=1}^{n} \frac{1}{u_k} \leqslant r_n \sum_{k=1}^{n} \frac{c}{r_k} \leqslant c\left[\frac{r_n}{r_1} + \frac{r_n}{r_2} + \cdots + \frac{r_n}{r_n}\right]$$
$$\leqslant c(1 + \theta + \cdots + \theta^{n-1}) = O(1),$$

which signifies that (4.4) is proved.

DEFINITION 2. It is said that *an increasing sequence of natural numbers*

$$n_1 < n_2 < \cdots < n_k < \cdots$$

*satisfies condition* (*L*), if the series $\sum 1/n_k$ satisfies condition (*L*), that is,

$$\sum_{k=m}^{\infty} \frac{1}{n_k} = O\left(\frac{1}{n_m}\right). \tag{4.5}$$

In particular, this occurs for one important class of sequences known as lacunary.

DEFINITION 3. The sequence of natural numbers

$$n_1 < n_2 < \cdots < n_k < \cdots$$

is called a *lacunary sequence*, if there exists a $\lambda > 1$ such that

$$\frac{n_{k+1}}{n_k} \geqslant \lambda \quad (k = 1, 2, \ldots). \tag{4.6}$$

It is clear that any type of lacunary sequence satisfies condition (*L*), since

$$n_{k+s} \geqslant \lambda^s n_k \quad (s = 1, 2, \ldots),$$

and therefore

$$\sum_{k=m}^{\infty} \frac{1}{n_k} \leqslant \frac{1}{n_m} \sum_{s=0}^{\infty} \frac{1}{\lambda^s} = O\, \frac{1}{n_m}.$$

In the general case, a sequence satisfying condition (*L*) can be partitioned into a finite number of lacunary sequences (since it can be partitioned into a finite number of sequences, the terms of which increase not more slowly than the terms of a certain increasing geometrical progression).

*Note* 1. If the sqeuence $\{n_k\}$ satisfies condition (*L*), then the sequence $\{n_k^2\}$ also does so. In fact

$$\sum_{k=m}^{\infty} \frac{1}{n_k^2} \leqslant \frac{1}{n_m} \sum_{k=m}^{\infty} \frac{1}{n_k} = \frac{1}{n_m}\, O\left(\frac{1}{n_m}\right) = O\left(\frac{1}{n_m^2}\right).$$

*Note* 2. If the sequence $\{n_k\}$ satisfies condition $(L)$, then

$$\sum_{k=1}^{m} n_k = O(n_m). \tag{4.7}$$

In fact, from the condition we have

$$\sum_{k=m}^{\infty} \frac{1}{n_k} < C\frac{1}{n_m}, \tag{4.8}$$

where $C$ is a constant. It is clear that $C > 1$.

Let us suppose

$$r_m = \sum_{k=m}^{\infty} \frac{1}{n_k}.$$

Then $1/n_m = r_m - r_{m+1}$ and (3.8) takes the form

$$r_m < C(r_m - r_{m+1}),$$

whence

$$r_{m+1} < \frac{C-1}{C} r_m$$

or supposing that $\theta = (C-1)/C$,

$$r_{m+1} < \theta r_m \quad (m = 1, 2, \ldots), \tag{4.9}$$

where $0 < \theta < 1$. But

$$\frac{1}{n_m} < r_m$$

and, on the other hand, from (4.8) $r_m < C/n_m$, therefore

$$n_m < \frac{C}{r_m}.$$

Whence

$$\frac{1}{n_m} \sum_{k-1}^{m} n_k < r_m \sum_{k=1}^{m} \frac{C}{r_k} = C\left[1 + \frac{r_m}{r_{m-1}} + \frac{r_m}{r_{m-2}} + \cdots + \frac{r_m}{r_1}\right]$$

$$< C[1 + \theta + \theta^2 + \cdots] = \frac{C}{1-\theta} = K,$$

where $K$ is a constant, which proves (4.7).

## § 5. Linear methods of summation

There exists a whole series of methods permitting the "sum" of an increasing series to be expressed; these methods are called *methods of series summation.* The most generally used are the linear methods of summation which are devised on the following principle; let $A$ be a given matrix with an infinite number of rows and columns

$$A = \left\| \begin{matrix} a_{00} \dots a_{0n} \dots \\ a_{10} \dots a_{1n} \dots \\ \dots\dots\dots\dots \\ a_{n0} \dots a_{nn} \dots \\ \dots\dots\dots\dots \end{matrix} \right\| .$$

Instead of considering the usual partial sums $S_n$ of the series $\sum_{n=0}^{\infty} u_n$, we consider the quantities

$$\sigma_n = \sum_{k=0}^{\infty} a_{nk} S_k, \tag{5.1}$$

supposing that the series on the right-hand sides of these equalities converge $(n = 0, 1, 2, \dots)$; if there exists a limit

$$\lim_{n\to\infty} \sigma_n = S,$$

then the value $S$ is called the "*sum*" of the series $\sum_{k=0}^{\infty} u_n$ and we say that the method, definable by a matrix, *sums* the series $\sum u_n$ to a value $S$.

Methods defined in this way are called *linear* because if a series $\sum u_n$ is summable by such a method to the sum $S$, then the series $\sum Cu_n$, where $C$ is a constant, is summable to $CS$ and if a series $\sum v_n$ is summable to $S_1$, then the series $\sum (u_n + v_n)$ is summable to $S + S_1$.

The method of summation is usually called *regular*, if any convergent series is summable by this method to the value $S$ which is its sum in the classical meaning of the word, that is,

$$S = \lim_{n\to\infty} S_n.$$

Toeplitz[1] proved that *for the regularity of the linear method, definable by a matrix $A$, it is necessary and sufficient for the following three conditions it be fulfilled*:

(1) $\lim\limits_{n\to\infty} a_{nk} = 0 \quad (k = 0, 1, \dots)$

(2) *If* $A_n = a_n + a_{n1} + \cdots + a_{nk} + \cdots$, *then* $\lim\limits_{n\to\infty} A_n = 1$.

(3) *If* $K_n = \sum_{k=0}^{\infty} |a_{nk}|$, *then* $K_n < C \, (n = 1, 2, \dots)$, *where $C$ is a constant.*

These are usually known as "*Toeplitz' conditions*" and the matrices satisfying them are known as *T-matrices.*

We will not prove that these conditions are necessary for the regularity of the method (in this connection, see Hardy, ref. A8); but their sufficiency can instantly be proved. Indeed, let

$$S = \lim_{n\to\infty} S_n.$$

Let us assume that $S_n = S + \varepsilon_n$, then $\varepsilon_n \to 0$ as $n \to \infty$. But

$$\sigma_n = \sum_{p=0}^{\infty} a_{np} S_p = S \sum_{p=0}^{\infty} a_{np} + \sum_{p=0}^{\infty} a_{np}\varepsilon_p = SA_n + \sum_{p=0}^{\infty} a_{np}\varepsilon_p .$$

Since $A_n \to 1$ as $n \to \infty$ from condition (2), it remains to prove that $\lim\limits_{n\to\infty} \sum\limits_{p=0}^{\infty} a_{np}\varepsilon_p = 0$.

It is given that $\varepsilon > 0$; we choose $N$ so large that $|\varepsilon_p| < \varepsilon$ for $p > N$, then

$$\left|\sum_{p=0}^{\infty} a_{np}\varepsilon_p\right| \leqslant \left|\sum_{p=0}^{N} a_{np}\varepsilon_p\right| + \varepsilon \sum_{p=N+1}^{\infty} |a_{np}| .$$

In the first sum the number of terms is finite, $a_{np} \to 0$ as $n \to \infty$, all the numbers $\varepsilon_p$ are bounded; this signifies that as $n \to \infty$ this sum tends to 0; the second sum does not exceed $\varepsilon C$, where $C$ is a constant from condition (3) and $\varepsilon$ is taken as being arbitrarily small, therefore the first part can be made as small as desired with increase in $n$, which proves the theorem.

The matrix $A$ is usually named *positive*, if all $a_{nk} \geqslant 0$ $(k = 0, 1, \ldots, n = 0, 1, \ldots)$. It is clear that if Toeplitz' second condition is fulfilled for a positive matrix, then the third condition is also fulfilled.

Matrix $A$ is called a *$T^*$-matrix* if it satisfies the first two Toeplitz conditions but under no circumstances satisfies the third (this is impossible in the case of positive matrices by virtue of the foregoing remarks).

We will make yet another general remark regarding $T$-matrices; if $S_k$ does not tend to a limit, then $\lim\limits_{k_n\to\infty} S_{k_n} = S$ exists, where $\{k_n\}$ is some increasing sequence of natural numbers. We can then say that the sequence $S_k$ is summable to $S$ by some Toeplitz method. In fact, if we assume

$$a_{n\,k_n} = 1, \quad n = 0, 1, 2, \ldots,$$

$$a_{nk} = 0, \quad \text{if } k \neq k_n,$$

then the matrix obtained satisfies all three Toeplitz conditions and in this case $\sigma_n = \sum a_{nk} S_k = S_{k_n} \to S$ as $n \to \infty$, that is, the sequence $S_n$ is summable to $S$ by this method.

## § 6. Method of arithmetic means [or $(C, 1)$]

As the simplest example of methods definable by $T$-matrices, we will consider the classical case, namely, the method of arithmetic means (or $(C, 1)$†), introduced by Cesàro. Cesàro proposed ascribing a sum $S$ to a divergent series, if $\lim \sigma_n = S$ where

$$\sigma_n = \frac{S_0 + \cdots + S_n}{n+1},$$

and proved the regularity of this method of summation.

† The notation $(C, 1)$ will be understood when the concept of the $(C, \alpha)$ methods is introduced (see Appendix, § 9).

If it is assumed that

$$a_{n_k} = \begin{cases} \dfrac{1}{n+1} & (k = 0, 1, \dots, n), \\ 0 & (k > n), \end{cases}$$

then the method of arithmetic means is defined by the matrix $A = \| a_{nk} \|$ and it is evident at once that the three Toeplitz conditions are satisfied here, that is, $A$ is a $T$-matrix.

*Note 1.* The method of arithmetic means (or method $(C, 1)$) is also completely regular, that is, if

$$S_n \to +\infty$$

then also

$$\sigma_n \to +\infty .$$

In fact, if $M$ is any number, then it is possible to find a value of $N$ such that $S_n > M$ for $n \geqslant N$. Then

$$\sigma_n = \frac{S_0 + \cdots + S_N}{n+1} + \frac{S_{N+1} + \cdots + S_n}{n+1}.$$

To first term tends to zero as $n \to \infty$ and for the second we have

$$\frac{S_{N+1} + \cdots + S_n}{n+1} > M \frac{n-N}{n+1} > \frac{M}{2},$$

if only $n > 2N + 1$, and therefore $\sigma_n$ can become as large as desired if $n$ is sufficiently great, that is, $\sigma_n \to \infty$, which is thus proved.

*Note 2.* Whilst referring to method $(C, 1)$, one formula must be mentioned which will latter be used frequently, namely: if $S_n$ are the partial sums and $\sigma_n$ are the arithmetic means for the series $\sum u_k$, then

$$S_n - \sigma_n = \frac{1}{n+1} \sum_{k=1}^{n} k u_k. \tag{6.1}$$

In fact,

$$S_n - \sigma_n = S_n - \frac{S_0 + \cdots + S_n}{n+1} = \frac{1}{n+1} \sum_{k=0}^{n} (S_n - S_k)$$

$$= \frac{1}{n+1} \sum_{k=0}^{n} (u_{k+1} + \cdots + u_n) = \frac{1}{n+1} \sum_{k=0}^{n} k u_k.$$

## § 7. Abel's method

Let $\sum_{k=0}^{\infty} u_k$ be a numerical series and $x$ be a real number, $0 \leqslant x < 1$.

We say that the series $\sum_{k=0}^{\infty} u_k$ is *summable by Abel's method* to the value $S$ (or briefly: summable $A$ to the value $S$), if $\sum_{k=0}^{\infty} u_k x^k$ converges for $0 \leqslant x < 1$ and

$$\lim_{x \to 1} \sum_{k=0}^{\infty} u_k x^k = S. \tag{7.1}$$

Condition (7.1) can be written in another form. For this purpose we note that for $0 \leqslant x < 1$ we have the identity

$$\sum_{k=0}^{\infty} u_k x^k = (1 - x) \sum_{k=0}^{\infty} S_k x^k. \tag{7.2}$$

In fact, if $0 \leqslant x < 1$, the series on the left of (7.2) converges. Let us take any $r$ such that $x < r < 1$. Then, since $\sum_{k=0}^{\infty} u_k r^k$ converges, a value of $C$ can be found such that $|u_k r^k| \leqslant C\ (k = 0, 1, \ldots)$.

Therefore

$$|S_n x^k| \leqslant C x^n \left(1 + \frac{1}{r} + \frac{1}{r^2} + \cdots + \frac{1}{r^n}\right) < \frac{C}{1 - r} x^n \frac{1}{r^n},$$

and this expression tends to zero as $n \to \infty$. But using Abel's transformation

$$\sum_{k=0}^{n} u_k x^k = \sum_{k=0}^{n-1} S_k (x^k - x^{k+1}) + S_n x^n = (1 - x) \sum_{k=0}^{n} S_k x^k + S_n x^n$$

and since $S_n x^n \to 0$, (7.2) is proved. The proof is analogous if the convergence of the series on the right-hand side of (7.2) is assumed.

Therefore, condition (7.1) can also be written in the form

$$\lim_{x \to 1} (1 - x) \sum_{k=0}^{\infty} S_k x^k = S \tag{7.3}$$

and it can be said that the series is summable to the value $S$ by Abel's method, if (7.3) is fulfilled.

Let us prove what takes place.

FROBENIUS'S THEOREM. *If a series is summable $(C, 1)$ to a value $S$, then it is summable by Abel's method to the same value.*

In fact since

$$(n + 1)\, \sigma_n = S_0 + S_1 + \cdots + S_n,$$

then, applying Abel's transformation to the right-hand side of (7.2), we find

$$\sum_{k=0}^{\infty} u_k x^k = (1 - x)^2 \sum_{k=0}^{\infty} (k + 1)\, \sigma_k x^k. \tag{7.4}$$

But since for $0 < x < 1$ we have

$$\frac{1}{(1 - x)^2} = \sum_{k=0}^{\infty} (k + 1)\, x^k$$

or

$$1 = (1 - x)^2 \sum_{k=0}^{\infty} (k + 1)\, x^k, \tag{7.5}$$

then multiplying both sides of (7.5) by $S$ and subtracting from (7.4), we obtain

$$\sum_{k=0}^{\infty} u_k x^k - S = (1-x)^2 \sum_{k=0}^{\infty} (k+1)(\sigma_k - S)\, x^k$$
$$= (1-x)^2 \sum_{k=0}^{N} (k+1)(\sigma_k - S)\, x^k$$
$$+ (1-x)^2 \sum_{N+1}^{\infty} (k+1)(\sigma_k - S)\, x^k. \qquad (7.6)$$

If $\varepsilon$ is given, then it is possible to choose $N$ such that

$$|\sigma_{k+1} - S| < \varepsilon \quad \text{for} \quad k \geqslant N,$$

and then the second sum on the right-hand side of (7.6) is less than $\varepsilon$, whilst the first sum tends to zero, since the number of terms in it is fixed. Thence (7.1) is fulfilled and the theorem is proved.

In order to compare Abel's method with the linear methods of summation already mentioned, then any sequences $r_n$, where $r_n \to 1$ as $n \to \infty$, could be considered instead of the continuous parameter $r$. However, it is more worthwhile to consider the aggregate of functions $a_k(x)$, where $k = 0, 1, 2, \ldots$ and $0 \leqslant x < 1$, instead of the matrices $\| a_{nk} \|$. If we let

$$\sigma(x) = \sum_{k=0}^{\infty} a_k(x)\, S_k,$$

assuming that the series in the first part converges as $x \to 1$ and if

$$\lim_{x \to 1} \sigma(x) = S,$$

then it is possible to consider $S$ as the "sum" of the series $\sum u_k$, definable by this method of summation with the continuous parameter $x \to 1$.

In the same way as the regularity of the methods definable by Toeplitz matrices was proved, we see that this method will be regular if the conditions are fulfilled:

(1) $\lim_{x \to 1} a_k(x) = 0 \quad (k = 0, 1, \ldots)$.

(2) If $A(x) = \sum_{0}^{\infty} a_k(x)$, $0 \leqslant x < 1$, then $A(x) \to 1$ as $x \to 1$.

(3) If $\sum_{k=0}^{\infty} |a_k(x)| = f(x)$, then $|f(x)| < C$, $0 \leqslant x < 1$, where $C$ is a constant.

In particular, *Abel's method is regular*, since in this case

$$a_k(x) = x^k - x^{k+1},$$

and it is immediately evident that all three cases are satisfied. Moreover, Abel's method is *completely regular*, since if $S_k \to +\infty$, then it is possible for any $M$ to find $k_0$ such that $S_k > M$ at $k > k_0$;

then

$$(1-x)\sum_{k=0}^{\infty} S_k x^k = (1-x)\sum_{k=0}^{k_0} S_k x^k + (1-x)\sum_{k=k_0+1}^{\infty} S_k x^k$$

$$> (1-x)\sum_{k=0}^{k_0} S_k x^k + M x^{k_0+1}.$$

If $x \to 1$, then the first term of the right-hand side is $o(1)$, because $k_0$ is fixed, and the second tends to $M$; therefore $(1-x)\sum S_k x^k$ can be made greater than any previously given value if $x$ is sufficiently close to 1, and this signifies that $\sum u_n$ is summable $A$ to $+\infty$.

Whilst considering method $A$ it would also be very useful to consider yet another method of summation closely connected with it. Namely, instead of real numbers

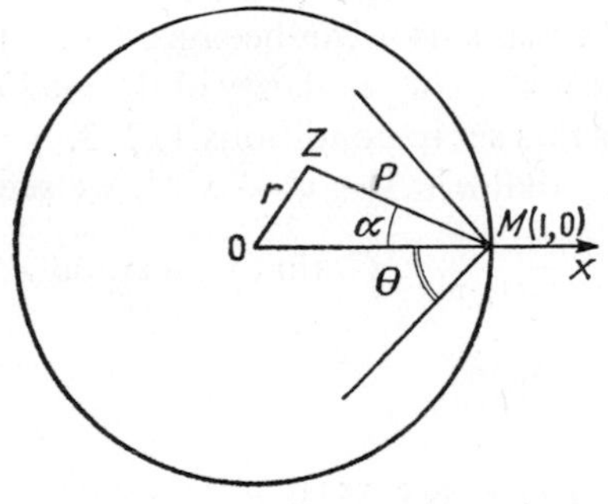


FIG. 2

$x$, $0 \leqslant x < 1$, tending to 1, we consider complex numbers. We will say that $z \to 1$ *along a path which is non-tangential to the circumference*, if the point $z$ whilst tending towards the point $M$ (1,0) does not go outside a certain angle of magnitude $2\theta$ ($\theta < \pi/2$) with vertex at $M$ and with its bisector coinciding with $Ox$. From geometrical considerations (see Fig. 2) it is clear that this condition can be described in the form

$$|1-z| < C(1-|z|), \tag{7.7}$$

where $C$ is some constant. In fact,

$$\left.\begin{aligned} |1-z| = \varrho,\quad 1-|z| &= 1-r,\\ r^2 &= 1+\varrho^2-2\varrho\cos\alpha,\\ 2\varrho\cos\alpha-\varrho^2 &= 1-r^2 = (1-r)(1+r),\\ \frac{\varrho}{1-r} = \frac{1+r}{2\cos\alpha-\varrho} &< \frac{1+r}{2\cos\alpha\theta-\varrho}. \end{aligned}\right\} \tag{7.8}$$

As $z \to 1$ we have $\varrho \to 0$, the denominator on the right-hand side is bounded below and the numerator does not exceed 2, which signifies that $\varrho/(1-r) < C$.

We will now give a definition.

DEFINITION. A series $\sum u_n$ is said to be *summable to S by the method A** (or briefly to be summable $A^*$ to $S$), if

$$\lim_{z\to 1} \sum_{n=0}^{\infty} u_n z^n = S,$$

when $z \to 1$ along any non-tangential path (in other words, if $z \to 1$, then

$$\left| \frac{1 - z}{1 - |z|} \right| < C,$$

where $C$ is a constant).

It is clear that if a series is summable $A^*$, then it is also summable $A$.

We will now demonstrate that *method A** is also *regular*. In order to prove this we note that when we use the method of summation described in § 7, the functions figuring in this method can also be considered to be functions of a complex variable. Instead of $x \to 1$ along the real axis it can be considered that $x \to 1$ for some set for which the point (1,0) is the limit. The regularity of the method continues to hold if it is considered that $x \to 1$ for this set in conditions 1, 2, 3.

In particular, supposing that $a_k(x) = x^k - x^{k+1}$, we see that all the conditions of regularity are fulfilled, if $\frac{|1 - x|}{1 - |x|} < C$, that is, method $A^*$ is regular.

# III. INEQUALITIES FOR NUMBERS, SERIES AND INTEGRALS

## § 8. Numerical inequalities

1. For any two numbers $a$ and $b$ and for any $p \geqslant 1$ we have

$$|a + b|^p \leqslant 2^p(|a|^p + |b|^p). \tag{8.1}$$

In fact if

$$|a| > |b|,$$

then

$$|a + b| \leqslant 2\,|a|$$

and

$$|a + b|^p \leqslant 2^p\,|a|^p \leqslant (|a|^p + |b|^p)\cdot 2^p.$$

If

$$|a| \leqslant |b|,$$

then

$$|a + b| \leqslant 2\,|b|$$

and

$$|a + b|^p \leqslant 2^p\,|b|^p \leqslant 2^p(|a|^p + |b|^p).$$

2. For any two numbers $a$ and $b$ and $0 \leqslant p < 1$ we have

$$|a + b|^p \leqslant |a|^p + |b|^p. \tag{8.2}$$

Let us suppose that

$$t = \left| \frac{b}{a} \right|.$$

The inequality will be verified if we prove that

$$(1 + t)^p \leqslant 1 + t^p \quad \text{for} \quad 0 \leqslant p < 1. \tag{8.3}$$

But inequality (8.3) is true since the function $(1 + t)^p - (1 + t^p)$ becomes zero at $t = 0$ and decreases with increase of $t$, which indicates that it is everywhere non-positive.

3. If $a$ and $b$ are any positive numbers and $p$ and $q$ are such that $p > 1, q > 1$ and

$$\frac{1}{p} + \frac{1}{q} = 1,$$

then

$$ab \leqslant \frac{a^p}{p} + \frac{b^p}{q}. \tag{8.4}$$

Let us suppose that $p = 1 + \alpha, \alpha > 0$ and draw the graph of the function $y = x^\alpha$ (Fig. 3). Since this function is increasing, then the inverse function $x = y^{1/\alpha}$ is defined uniquely. Since

$$S_1 = \frac{a^p}{p} = \int_0^a x^\alpha \, dx$$

and

$$S_2 = \frac{b^q}{q} = \int_0^b y^{1/\alpha} \, dy$$

(because $1 + 1/\alpha = 1 + 1/(p - 1) = p/(p - 1) = q$), then the required inequality follows from the fact that the area of the rectangle with sides $a$ and $b$ does not exceed the sums of the areas $S_1$ and $S_2$.

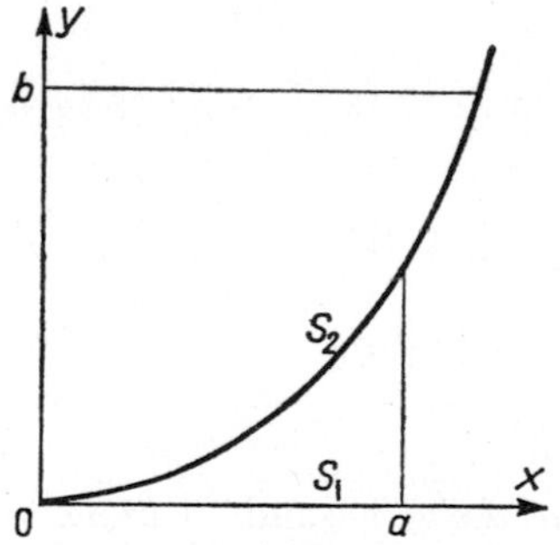


FIG. 3

In the case when $b = a^\alpha$ and only in this case the inequality changes into an equality.

It can thus be proved completely that if $\varphi(u)$ is continuous at $u \geqslant 0, \varphi(0) = 0, \varphi(u)$ increases and $\varphi(u) \to \infty$, also its inverse function $\psi(u) \to \infty$, then supposing that

$$\Phi(x) = \int_0^x \varphi(u) \, du, \quad \Psi(y) = \int_0^y \psi(v) \, dv,$$

we have

$$ab \leqslant \Phi(a) + \Psi(b) \tag{8.5}$$

for any positive $a$ and $b$.

These functions $\Phi$ and $\Psi$ are sometimes called mutually complementary. (In the preceding example $\varphi(u) = u^{\alpha}$, where $\alpha = p - 1$, $\psi(v) = v^{1/\alpha}$). The inequality (8.5) is known as *Young's inequality.*

## § 9. Hölder's inequality

Let

$$f(x) \in L^p[\alpha, \beta], \ \varphi(x) \in L^q[\alpha, \beta],$$

where

$$\frac{1}{p} + \frac{1}{q} = 1. \tag{9.1}$$

We will prove the truth of the inequality

$$\left| \int_{\alpha}^{\beta} f(x)\, \varphi(x)\, dx \right| \leqslant \left( \int_{\alpha}^{\beta} |f(x)|^p\, dx \right)^{1/p} \left( \int_{\alpha}^{\beta} |\varphi(x)|^q\, dx \right)^{1/q} \tag{9.2}$$

or briefly

$$\left| \int_{\alpha}^{\beta} f(x)\, \varphi(x)\, dx \right| \leqslant \|f\|_p\, \|\varphi\|_q \tag{9.3}$$

(see Notation for definition of norm).

In fact, supposing for brevity's sake

$$a = \frac{|f(x)|}{\|f\|_p}, \qquad b = \frac{|\varphi(x)|}{\|\varphi\|_q},$$

we have by virtue of (8.4)

$$|f(x)\, \varphi(x)| = \|f\|_p\, \|\varphi\|_q\, ab \leqslant \|f\|_p\, \|\varphi\|_q \left( \frac{a^p}{p} + \frac{b^q}{q} \right). \tag{9.4}$$

But

$$a^p = \frac{|f(x)|^p}{\int_{\alpha}^{\beta} |f|^p\, dx}, \ b^q = \frac{|\varphi(x)|^q}{\int_{\alpha}^{\beta} |\varphi|^q dx}.$$

$$\int_{\alpha}^{\beta} a^p\, dx = 1 \quad \text{and} \quad \int_{\alpha}^{\beta} b^q\, dx = 1$$

and in conjunction with (9.1) and (9.4) this gives

$$\int_{\alpha}^{\beta} |f(x)\, \varphi(x)|\, dx \leqslant \|f\|_p\, \|\varphi\|_q,$$

and this is (9.3).

*Note 1.* Supposing $p = q = 2$, we obtain the well-known Bunyakovskii's inequality

$$\left|\int_\alpha^\beta f(x)\,\varphi(x)\,dx\right| \leqslant \left(\int_\alpha^\beta |f|^2\,dx\right)^{1/2}\left(\int_\alpha^\beta |\varphi|^2\,dx\right)^{1/2} \tag{9.5}$$

or

$$\left|\int_\alpha^\beta f(x)\,\varphi(x)\,dx\right| \leqslant \|f\|_2\,\|\varphi\|_2.$$

If $\{a_n\}$ and $\{b_n\}$ are two sequences of numbers, whilst the series

$$\sum_1^\infty |a_n|^p \quad\text{and}\quad \sum_1^\infty |b_n|^q$$

converge, then we have

$$\sum_1^\infty |a_n b_n| \leqslant \left(\sum_1^\infty |a_n|^p\right)^{1/p}\left(\sum_1^\infty |b_n|^q\right)^{1/q} \tag{9.6}$$

at

$$\frac{1}{p} + \frac{1}{q} = 1.$$

*Note 2.* Inequality (9.3) holds at $p = 1$ and $q = \infty$ if it is considered that

$$\|\varphi\|_\infty = \lim_{q\to\infty} \|\varphi\|_q. \tag{9.7}$$

We will show that the limit on the right-hand side of (9.7) exists, if the function is essentially bounded, and it equals its essential upper bound. In this case a number $M$ is taken to be the essential upper bound such that almost everywhere in $(\alpha, \beta)$, we have

$$|\varphi(x)| \leqslant M \tag{9.8}$$

and, on the other hand, for any $M' < M$, there is found a set $E$ such that $mE > 0$, where $|\varphi(x)| > M'$.

Indeed, if (9.8) is fulfilled almost everywhere, then

$$\|\varphi\|_q = \left\{\int_\alpha^\beta |\varphi(x)|^q\,dx\right\}^{1/q} \leqslant M(\beta - \alpha)^{1/q},$$

and therefore

$$\overline{\lim_{q\to\infty}}\, \|\varphi\|_q \leqslant M.$$

On the other hand, if $M' < M$ and $|\varphi(x)| > M'$ in $E$, then

$$\|\varphi\|_q \geqslant M'(mE)^{1/q},$$

and therefore

$$\lim_{q\to\infty} \|\varphi\|_q \geqslant M',$$

and since $M'$ is any number provided that $M' < M$, then

$$\lim_{q\to\infty} \|\varphi\|_q \geqslant M,$$

whence it follows that

$$M = \lim_{q\to\infty} \|\varphi\|_q = \|\varphi\|_\infty. \tag{9.9}$$

Now we see that if $B$ is a class of essentially bounded functions, then for $f \in L$ and $\varphi \in B$ the inequality (9.3) is true if it is understood that $\|\varphi\|_\infty$ is the essential upper bound for $\varphi$, definable by formula (9.9).

From Hölder's inequality we derive one corollary which will be extremely useful later.

Let $g(t)$ be bounded, periodic with a period $2\pi$, and non-negative such that

$$\int_{-\pi}^{\pi} g(t)\,dt = 1. \tag{9.10}$$

Let $f(x) \in L^p$. If

$$\sigma(x) = \int_{-\pi}^{\pi} f(t)\,g(t-x)\,dt,$$

then

$$\|\sigma(x)\|_p \leqslant \|f(x)\|_p. \tag{9.11}$$

Indeed, by virtue of Hölder's inequality

$$|\sigma(x)|^p \leqslant \left\{\int_{-\pi}^{\pi} |f|\,g(t-x)\,dt\right\}^p$$

$$= \left\{\int_{-\pi}^{\pi} |f(t)|\,\{g(t-x)\}^{1/p}\,\{g(t-x)\}^{1/q}\,dt\right\}^p$$

$$\leqslant \int_{-\pi}^{\pi} |f(t)|^p\,g(t-x)\,dt\left\{\int_{-\pi}^{\pi} g(t-x)\,dt\right\}^{p/q}$$

$$= \int_{-\pi}^{\pi} |f(t)|^p\,g(t-x)\,dt,$$

whence

$$\int_{-\pi}^{\pi} |\sigma(x)|^p\,dx \int_{-\pi}^{\pi}\left\{\int_{-\pi}^{\pi} |f(t)|^p\,g(t-x)\,dt\right\}dx$$

and changing the order of the integration

$$\int_{-\pi}^{\pi} |\sigma(x)|^p\,dx \leqslant \int_{-\pi}^{\pi} |f(t)|^p\left\{\int_{-\pi}^{\pi} g(t-x)\,dx\right\}dt. \tag{9.12}$$

Because of the period icity of $g(t)$ we obtain from (9.10) and (9.12)

$$\int_{-\pi}^{+\pi} |\sigma(x)|^p\,dx \leqslant \int_{-\pi}^{+\pi} |f(t)|^p\,dt$$

and raising to the power $1/p$ we have the desired inequality.

## § 10. Minkowski's inequality

Let $f(x) \in L^p\ [a, b]$ and $\varphi(x) \in L^p\ [a, b]$ for $p > 1$. We will prove that then

$$\left(\int_a^b |f(x) + \varphi(x)|^p\, dx\right)^{1/p} \leqslant \left(\int_a^b |f(x)|^p\, dx\right)^{1/p} + \left(\int_a^b |\varphi(x)|^p\, dx\right)^{1/p}, \quad (10.1)$$

that is,

$$\|f + \varphi\|_p \leqslant \|f\|_p + \|\varphi\|_p. \quad (10.2)$$

We notice particularly that if $\Psi(x) \in L^p$, then $|\Psi(x)|^{p-1} \in L^q$. In fact

$$(|\Psi(x)|^{p-1})^q = |\Psi(x)|^{(p-1)\frac{p}{p-1}} = |\Psi(x)|^p.$$

Therefore, applying Hölder's inequality, we obtain

$$\int_a^b |f(x) + \varphi(x)|^p\, dx$$

$$\leqslant \int_a^b |f(x) + \varphi(x)|^{p-1} |f(x)|\, dx + \int_a^b |f(x) + \varphi(x)|^{p-1}\, |\varphi(x)|\, dx$$

$$\leqslant \left(\int_a^b |f(x) + \varphi(x)|^{(p-1)q}\, dx\right)^{1/q} \left(\int_a^b |f(x)|^p\, dx\right)^{1/p}$$

$$+ \left(\int_a^b |f(x) + \varphi(x)|^{(p-1)q}\, dx\right)^{1/q} \left(\int_a^b |\varphi(x)|^p\, dx\right)^{1/p}$$

$$= \left(\int_a^b |f(x) + \varphi(x)|^p\, dx\right)^{1/q} \left[\left(\int_a^b |f(x)|^p\, dx\right)^{1/p} + \left(\int_a^b |\varphi(x)|^p\, dx\right)^{1/p}\right].$$

If both sides of the inequality obtained are divided by $\left(\int_a^b |f + \varphi|^p\, dx\right)^{1/q}$, then we find

$$\left(\int_a^b |f + \varphi|^p\, dx\right)^{1-1/q} \leqslant \left(\int_a^b |f|^p\, dx\right)^{1/p} + \left(\int_a^b |\varphi|^p\, dx\right)^{1/p}$$

and since $1 - 1/q = 1/p$, this concludes the proof.

It can also be proved completely that at $1/p + 1/q = 1$

$$\left(\sum_{n=1}^{\infty} |a_n + b_n|^p\right)^{1/p} \leqslant (\sum |a_n|^p)^{1/p} + (\sum |b_n|^p)^{1/p}. \quad (10.3)$$

In Minkowski's inequality the integral is estimated from the power of the sum of two functions, when this power $p \geqslant 1$. If $p < 1$, then this inequality loses its validity. But instead the following inequality holds

$$\int_a^b |f(x) + \varphi(x)|^p\, dx \leqslant \int_a^b |f(x)|^p\, dx + \int_a^b |\varphi(x)|^p\, dx \quad (0 \leqslant p < 1). \quad (10.4)$$

This follows immediately from (8.2).

In a completely analogous manner we obtain for the series

$$\sum_{n=1}^{\infty} |a_n + b_n|^p = \sum_{n=1}^{\infty} (|a_n|^p + |b_n|^p) \quad \text{for} \quad 0 \leqslant p < 1. \tag{10.5}$$

## § 11. *O*- and *o*-relationships for series and integrals

Using the notation now accepted in mathematical literature we write

$$u_n = o(v_n)$$

if $v_n > 0$ $(n = 0, 1, 2, \ldots)$ and $u_n/v_n \to 0$ at $n \to \infty$.

If $u_n/v_n$ is bounded, we write

$$u_n = O(v_n).$$

If two positive constants $A$ and $B$ exist for which at sufficiently large $n$

$$A \leqslant \frac{u_n}{v_n} \leqslant B,$$

then we can write

$$u_n \sim v_n,$$

and finally

$$u_n \approx v_n,$$

will signify

$$\lim_{n\to\infty} \frac{u_n}{v_n} = 1$$

(in this case it is usually said that $u_n$ and $v_n$ are asymptotically equal).

We will prove that

(1) from $u_n = O(v_n)$ it follows that $\sum_{k=0}^{n} u_k = O\left(\sum_{k=0}^{n} v_k\right)$,

(2) from $u_n \sim v_n$ it follows that $\sum_{k=0}^{n} u_k \sim \sum_{k=0}^{n} v_k$.

Indeed case (1) follows from the inequality

$$\left| \frac{\sum_{k=0}^{n} u_n}{\sum_{k=0}^{n} v_k} \right| \leqslant \frac{\sum_{k=0}^{n} |u_k|}{\sum_{k=0}^{n} v_k} \leqslant M,$$

and case (2) from the inequality

$$A \leqslant \frac{\sum_{k=0}^{n} u_k}{\sum_{k=0}^{n} v_k} \leqslant B.$$

For the case $u_n = o(v_n)$ and $u_n \approx v_n$ analogous relationships do not in general occur but, however

(3) if $\quad \sum_{k=0}^{n} v_k \to \infty \quad$ and $\quad u_n = o(v_n), \quad$ then $\quad \sum_{k=0}^{n} u_k = o\left(\sum_{k=0}^{n} v_k\right);$

(4) if $\quad \sum_{k=0}^{n} v_k \to \infty \quad$ and $\quad u_n \approx v_n, \quad$ then $\quad \sum_{k=0}^{n} u_k \approx \sum_{k=0}^{n} v_k.$

To prove (3) if it is given that $\varepsilon > 0$, then we will find $N$ such that

$$|u_n| \leqslant \varepsilon v_n \quad \text{for} \quad n \geqslant N.$$

We have

$$\left|\sum_{k=0}^{u} u_k\right| \leqslant \left|\sum_{k=0}^{N} u_k\right| + \left|\sum_{N+1}^{n} u_k\right| \leqslant \left|\sum_{k=0}^{N} u_k\right| + \varepsilon \sum_{N+1}^{n} v_k,$$

whence

$$\left|\frac{\sum_{k=0}^{n} u_k}{\sum_{k=0}^{n} v_k}\right| \leqslant \frac{\sum_{k=0}^{N} u_k}{\sum_{k=0}^{n} v_k} + \varepsilon. \tag{11.1}$$

But the denominator on the right-hand side of (11.1) tends to infinity as $n \to \infty$, and the numerator is constant, which indicates that the whole right-hand side can be made less than $2\varepsilon$, if $n$ is sufficiently large, and since $\varepsilon$ is arbitrary, the left-hand side is as small as we please, which was to be proved.

Case (4) can be proved in a similar manner. We must choose $N$ such that

$$(1 - \varepsilon)\, v_n \leqslant u_n \leqslant (1 + \varepsilon)\, v_n \quad \text{for} \quad n \geqslant N$$

and pay attention to

$$\frac{\sum_{k=0}^{N} v_k}{\sum_{k=0}^{n} v_k} \to 0 \text{ as } n \to \infty.$$

It is evident also that

(5) if $v_n > 0$, $\sum v_n < +\infty$ and $u_n = o(v_n)$, then the series $\sum u_n$ converges and

$$\sum_{n+1}^{\infty} u_k = o\left(\sum_{n+1}^{\infty} v_k\right).$$

In fact, for any $\varepsilon < 0$, if $n$ is sufficiently large, then $|u_k| < \varepsilon_k$, whence

$$\left|\sum_{n+1}^{\infty} u_k\right| < \varepsilon\left(\sum_{n+1}^{\infty} v_k\right).$$

In an entirely analogous manner, instead of comparing terms of two sequences, a comparison can be made of two functions $f(x)$ and $\varphi(x)$ of which one is positive, for example, $\varphi(x) > 0$.

We write

$$f(x) = o(\varphi(x)), \quad \text{if} \quad \frac{f(x)}{\varphi(x)} \to 0, \tag{11.2}$$

$$f(x) = O(\varphi(x)), \quad \text{if} \quad \frac{f(x)}{\varphi(x)} \text{ is bounded} \tag{11.3}$$

$$f(x) \sim \varphi(x), \quad \text{if} \quad A < \frac{f(x)}{\varphi(x)} < B, \tag{11.4}$$

where $A$ and $B$ are positive and

$$f(x) \approx \varphi(x), \quad \text{if} \quad \frac{f(x)}{\varphi(x)} \to 1.$$

Here in the relationships (11.2), (11.3) and (11.4) we can consider both the case when $x \to +\infty$ (or $x \to -\infty$) and the case $x \to x_0$, where $x_0$ is some fixed number.

An analogous statement to the preceding can be made, namely:

LEMMA. 1. *If*

$$F(x) = \int_a^x f(t)\,dt, \quad \Phi(x) = \int_a^x \varphi(t)\,dt,$$

*then from*

$$f(x) = O(\varphi(x)) \quad in \quad a \leqslant x \leqslant b$$

*it follows that*

$$F(x) = O[\Phi(x)] \quad in \quad a \leqslant x \leqslant b.$$

In fact

$$|F(x)| = \left|\int_a^x f(t)\,dt\right| \leqslant M \int_a^x \varphi(t)\,dt = M\Phi(x),$$

where $M$ is a constant.

Such a statement replacing $O$ by $o$ is in general untrue, but it becomes true if $\Phi(x) \to \infty$ at $x \to b$; the following statement would be more exact.

LEMMA 2. *Let $\varphi(x) > 0$, $f(x)$ and $\varphi(x)$ be defined in $a \leqslant x < b$ and summable in $a \leqslant x \leqslant b - \varepsilon$ for any $\varepsilon > O$. Then if*

$$f(x) = o(\varphi(x)) \quad as \quad x \to b$$

*and*

$$\Phi(x) \to \infty \quad as \quad x \to b,$$

*then*

$$F(x) = o[\Phi(x)] \quad as \quad x \to b.$$

Let it be given that $\varepsilon > 0$. Then it is possible to find $x_0$ such that

$$|f(x)| < \varepsilon\,\varphi(x) \quad \text{for} \quad a < x_0 \leqslant x < b.$$

Then

$$|F(x)| \leqslant \int_a^{x_0} |f(t)|\,dt + \int_{x_0}^x |f(t)|\,dt \leqslant \int_a^{x_0} |f(t)|\,dt + \varepsilon\Phi(x),$$

whence

$$\left|\frac{F(x)}{\Phi(x)}\right| < \frac{\int\limits_a^{x_0} |f(t)|\, dt}{\Phi(x)} + \varepsilon.$$

Since $\Phi(x) \to \infty$ as $x \to b$, then the first term of the right-hand side becomes less than $\varepsilon$, only as $x$ becomes sufficiently close to $b$, and then therefore

$$|F(x)| < 2\varepsilon\Phi(x)$$

and because of the arbitrariness of $\varepsilon$, our lemma is proved.

*Note.* Of course, the validity of the statement can be completely established, if $f(x) = o(\varphi(x))$ as $x \to a$.

# IV. THEORY OF SETS AND THEORY OF FUNCTIONS

## § 12. On the upper limit of a sequence of sets

LEMMA. *If for the sequence of sets $E_n$ we have*

$$\sum_{n=1}^{\infty} mE_n < +\infty, \quad \textit{then} \quad m\overline{\lim}\, E_n = 0.$$

In fact,

$$\overline{\lim}\, E_n = (E_1 + E_2 + \cdots)(E_2 + \cdots) \ldots (E_n + \cdots) \ldots$$

Therefore

$$m\,\overline{\lim}\, E_n = \lim_{n\to\infty} m(E_n + \cdots).$$

But

$$m(E_n + \cdots) \leqslant mE_n + mE_{n+1} + \cdots$$

and since $\sum mE_n < +\infty$, then the right-hand side tends to zero as $n \to \infty$, which signifies that $m\,\overline{\lim}\, E_n = 0$.

## § 13. Convergence in measure

Let $\{f_n(x)\}$ be a sequence of functions, measurable and finite almost everywhere in $[a, b]$. Let $f(x)$ also be measurable and finite almost everywhere in $[a, b]$.

Following F. Riesz's definition, we say that *the sequence $f_n(x)$ converges in measure to $f(x)$ if for any $\sigma > 0$ we have*

$$\lim_{n\to\infty} mE(|f - f_n| \geqslant \sigma) = 0.$$

Lebesgue showed that if the sequence $f(x)$ converges to $f(x)$ almost everywhere in $[a, b]$, then it also converges in measure to $f(x)$. This theorem is irreversible (see Natanson, ref. A23, pp. 106–108).

## § 14. Passage to the limit under Lebesgue's integral sign

1. THEOREM 1 (Lebesgue's theorem). *If $f_1(x), \ldots, f_n(x), \ldots$ is a sequence of measurable functions, all bounded in the set $E$, that is,*

$$|f_n(x)| \leqslant M \quad \text{in} \quad E \quad (n = 1, 2, \ldots),$$

*and if*

$$\lim_{n\to\infty} f_n(x) = f(x) \quad \textit{almost everywhere in} \quad E,$$

*then*

$$\lim_{n\to\infty} \int_E f_n(x)\, dx = \int_E f(x)\, dx. \tag{14.1}$$

(see Natanson, ref. A23, p. 139†).

2. THEOREM 2. *The same relationship* (14.1) *is true if instead of the functions $f_n(x)$ being all bounded it is supposed that*

$$|f_n(x)| \leqslant \Phi(x) \textit{ almost everywhere in } E,$$

*where $\Phi(x)$ is a positive function summable in $E$.*

(See Natanson, ref. A23, p. 166†).

3. THEOREM 3 (Fatou's lemma). *If a sequence of measurable and non-negative functions $f_1(x), f_2(x), \ldots, f_n(x), \ldots$ converges to the function $F(x)$ almost everywhere in $E$, then*

$$\int_E F(x)\, dx \leqslant \inf \left\{\int_E f_n(x)\, dx\right\} \tag{14.2}$$

(see Natanson, ref. A23, p. 155).

THEOREM 4. *If $f_1(x), f_2(x), \ldots, f_n(x), \ldots$ is a sequence of non-negative functions such that*

$$f_1(x) \leqslant f_2(x) \leqslant \cdots \leqslant f_n(x) \leqslant \cdots$$

*and*

$$f(x) = \lim_{n\to\infty} f_n(x),$$

*then*

$$\lim_{n\to\infty} \int_E f_n(x)\, dx = \int_E f(x)\, dx, \tag{14.1}$$

*whilst if $f(x)$ is not summable in $E$, then the relationship* (14.1) *holds in the sense that both terms of the equality become equal to $+\infty$.*

Indeed, if $f(x)$ is summable, then this assertion immediately follows from Theorem 2. Even if $f(x)$ is not summable, then, supposing $(f)_N = f(x)$ at $f(x) \leqslant N$ and $(f)_N = N$ at $f(x) > N$, we see that $\int_E (f)_N\, dx \to \infty$ as $N \to \infty$. If a function $(f_n)_N$ is defined

† The theorem was proved here on the assumption that $f_n(x)$ converges in measure to $f(x)$, but since any kind of sequence which converges almost everywhere also converges in measure (see § 13), then our statement is all the more accurate.

for every $f_n$ in the same way as $(f)_N$ in the case of $f$, then $(f_n)_N \leqslant N (n = 1, 2, \ldots,)$ and $(f_n)_N \to (f)_N$ as $n \to \infty$ and therefore from Theorem 1

$$\int_E (f_n)_N \, dx \to \int_E (f)_N \, dx \quad \text{as} \quad n \to \infty .$$

This signifies that $\int_E (f_n)_N \, dx$ can be made as large as we please for a sufficiently large $N$ and therefore this is all the more true for $\int_E f_n(x) \, dx$, whence it follows that the left-hand side of (14.1) equals $+ \infty$.

As a corollary of this theorem we obtain

4. THEOREM 5. *If $u_1(x), u_2(x), \ldots, u_n(x)$ is a sequence of non-negative functions summable in E and if*

$$\sum_{n=0}^{\infty} \int_E u_n(x) \, dx \leqslant + \infty, \tag{14.3}$$

*then the series $\sum u_n(x)$ converges almost everywhere in E to the non-negative summable function $f(x)$.*

In fact, supposing that $S_n(x) = \sum_{k=0}^{n} u_k(x)$, we see that $S_1(x) \leqslant S_2(x) \leqslant \cdots \leqslant S_n(x) \leqslant \cdots$. Supposing that $f(x) = \lim_{n \to \infty} S_n(x)$ where $f(x)$ is finite or infinite, we have from Theorem 4

$$\lim_{n \to \infty} \int_E S_n(x) \, dx = \int_E f(x) \, dx .$$

But since

$$\lim_{n \to \infty} \int_E S_n(x) \, dx = \lim \sum_{k=0}^{n} \int_E u_k(x) \, dx < + \infty ,$$

it follows that $\int_E f(x) \, dx < + \infty$ and then $f(x)$ is summable.

## § 15. Lebesgue points

We will define the point $x$ as a *Lebesgue point* for a summable function $f(x)$ if

$$\lim_{n \to \infty} \frac{1}{h} \int_x^{x+h} |f(t) - f(x)| \, dt = 0. \tag{15.1}$$

It is clear that any point where $f(x)$ is continuous is a Lebesgue point; in fact, if there exists any $\varepsilon > 0$ and the function $f(x)$ is continuous at the point $x$, there can be found $\delta$ such that $|f(t) - f(x)| < \varepsilon$ for $|h| \leqslant \delta$ and then for all such values of $x$

$$\frac{1}{h} \int_x^{x+h} |f(t) - f(x)| \, dt \leqslant \varepsilon ,$$

which provides the necessary proof.

However, in a summable function there need not be a single point of continuity. The following theorem is no less true.

LEBESGUE'S THEOREM. *If $f(x)$ is summable in $[a, b]$, then almost all the points of this interval are Lebesgue points for $f(x)$.*

In order to prove this, we will first consider any number $r$ and let

$$F(u) = \int_0^u |f(t) - r|\, dt.$$

Then for almost all $x \in [a, b]$ we have (from the theorem concerning the derivative of an indefinite Lebesgue integral)

$$F'(x) = |f(x) - r|,$$

that is,

$$\lim_{h\to 0} \frac{F(x+h) - F(x)}{h} = \lim_{h\to 0} \frac{1}{h} \int_x^{x+h} |f(t) - r|\, dt = |f(x) - r|. \tag{15.2}$$

Let $r$ be rational and $E_r$ a set of $x$ in the interval $[a, b]$ where the relationship (15.2) is violated; consequently, $mE_r = 0$. Let $E = \sum E_{r_n}$, where $r_n$ runs through all the rational numbers; then $mE = 0$. We will prove that any point, not belonging to $E$, at which $f(x)$ is finite, is a Lebesgue point for $f(x)$.

In fact, let $x_0$ be such a point and it is given that $\varepsilon > 0$. A rational $r_n$ can be found such that

$$|f(x_0) - r_n| < \varepsilon. \tag{15.3}$$

Then

$$\frac{1}{h} \int_{x_0}^{x_0+h} |f(t) - f(x_0)|\, dt \leqslant \frac{1}{h} \int_{x_0}^{x_0+h} |f(t) - r_n|\, dt + \frac{1}{h} \int_{x_0}^{x_0+h} |r_n - f(x_0)|\, dt$$

$$\leqslant \frac{1}{h} \int_{x_0}^{x_0+h} |f(t) - r_n|\, dt + \varepsilon. \tag{15.4}$$

But since $x_0 \bar{\in} E$, then $x_0 \bar{\in} E_{r_n}$, which means that

$$\lim_{h\to 0} \frac{1}{h} \int_{x_0}^{x_0+h} |f(t) - r_n|\, dt = |f(x_0) - r_n|,$$

therefore

$$\left| \frac{1}{h} \int_{x_0}^{x_0+h} |f(t) - r_n|\, dt - |f(x_0) - r_n| \right| < \varepsilon, \tag{15.5}$$

if $|h|$ is sufficiently small.

Combining (15.3), (15.4) and (15.5) we see that

$$\frac{1}{h}\int_{x_0}^{x_0+h} |f(t) - f(x_0)|\, dt \leqslant 3\varepsilon,$$

whence the proof of the theorem follows.

COROLLARY. Supposing $t = x + u$ or $t = x - u$, we see that for any Lebesgue point

$$\lim_{h\to 0} \frac{1}{h}\int^{h} |f(x \pm u) - f(x)|\, du = 0,$$

that is,

$$\int_0^h |f(x \pm u) - f(x)|\, du = o\,(h).$$

Let us suppose

$$\Phi_x(h) = \int_0^h |f(x + 2u) + f(x - 2u) - 2f(x)|\, du. \tag{15.6}$$

Then from Lebesgue's theorem it follows that

$$\Phi_x(h) = o(h) \tag{15.7}$$

almost everywhere.

*Note.* If $x$ is a Lebesgue point, then at this point $f(x)$ is a derivative of its indefinite integral.

Indeed, if

$$F(x) = C_0 + \int_a^x f(t)\, dt,$$

then

$$\frac{F(x + h) - F(x)}{h} = \frac{1}{h}\int_x^{x+h} f(t)\, dt,$$

and therefore for $h \neq 0$

$$\left|\frac{F(x + h) - F(x)}{h} - f(x)\right| \leqslant \frac{1}{|h|}\left|\int_x^{x+h} |f(t) - f(x)|\, dt\right| = o\,(1).$$

The converse hypothesis does not occur.

## § 16. Riemann–Stieltjes integral

Let $f(x)$ and $g(x)$ be defined and finite in $[a, b]$. Le us subdivide the interval $[a, b]$ by the points

$$x_0 = a < x_1 < x_2 < \cdots < x_n = b.$$

Let $\xi_i$ be any point in $[x_i, x_{i+1}]$. We will set up the sum

$$\sigma = \sum_{k=0}^{n-1} f(\xi_k)\,[g(x_{k+1}) - g(x_k)]. \tag{16.1}$$

If $\sigma$ tends to a limit as $\max(x_{k+1} - x_k) \to 0$ and this limit does not depend on either the method of dividing the interval or on the choice of the points $\xi_k$, then this limit is denoted by

$$\int_a^b f(x)\, dg(x)$$

*and is called the Riemann–Stieltjes integral of $f(x)$ with respect to $g(x)$.*

It is shown that

*if $f(x)$ is continuous in $[a, b]$ and $g(x)$ is of bounded variation in it, then the integral has meaning* (see Natanson, ref. A23, p. 251). *If $f(x)$ is continuous and $g(x)$ is absolutely continuous in $[a, b]$, then*

$$\int_a^b f(x)\, dg = (L) \int_a^b f(x)\, g'(x)\, dx, \tag{16.2}$$

*where the integral on the right is a Lebesgue integral.*

(See Natanson, ref. A23, p. 290).

The following theorem holds: –

THEOREM. *Let $f_n(x)$ $(n = 1, 2, \ldots)$ be a sequence of continuous functions converging uniformly in $[a, b]$. Then*

$$\lim_{n\to\infty} \int_a^b f_n(x)\, dg = \int_a^b f(x)\, dg. \tag{16.3}$$

In fact, for any $\varepsilon$ we can find $N$ such that

$$|f(x) - f_n(x)| < \varepsilon \quad \text{for} \quad n \geqslant N \quad \text{and} \quad a \leqslant x \leqslant b.$$

Therefore

$$\left| \int_a^b [f(x) - f_n(x)]\, dg \right| \leqslant \varepsilon \operatorname*{var}_{[a,b]} g \quad \text{for} \quad n \geqslant N,$$

and the theorem is proved.

## § 17. Helly's two theorems

HELLY'S FIRST THEOREM. *Let $\{f(x)\}$ be some family of functions of bounded variation in $[a, b]$. If these functions themselves and their complete variations are all bounded*† *in $[a, b]$, that is*

$$|f(x)| < M$$

*and* $\qquad (a \leqslant x \leqslant b),$

$$V_a^b(f) < M$$

*then from the family $\{f(x)\}$ it is possible to extract the sequence $f_n(x)$, converging at every point of $[a, b]$ to some function $\varphi(x)$, also of bounded variation in $[a, b]$.*

(See Natanson, ref. A23, p. 242).

---

† The phrase "all bounded" is used instead of the literal translation of "bounded in totality" or "bounded in combination" and is defined as follows:— Functions $f(x, y, z \ldots)$ are all bounded if they are bounded for all combinations of values of $x, y, z, \ldots$

HELLY'S SECOND THEOREM. *Let $f(x)$ be continuous in $[a, b]$ and the sequence $g_n(x)$ $(n = 1, 2, \ldots)$ consist of functions of bounded variation in $[a, b]$, whilst*

$$V_a^b(g_n) < M < +\infty .$$

*If* $\lim_{n\to\infty} g_n(x) = g(x)$ *where* $g(x)$ *is finite everywhere in* $[a, b]$, *then*

$$\lim_{n\to\infty} \int_a^b f(x)\, dg_n(x) = \int_a^b f(x)\, dg(x). \tag{17.1}$$

(See Natanson, ref. A23, p. 254).

## § 18. Fubini's theorem

*If $f(x, y)$ is summable in the rectangle $R[a \leqslant x \leqslant b,\ c \leqslant y \leqslant d]$, then for nearly all $x \in [a, b]$ the function $f(x, y)$ is summable with respect to $y$ in $[c, d]$, and for nearly all $y$ the function $f(x, y)$ is summable with respect to $x$ in $[a, b]$; the following formula holds,*

$$\iint_R f(x, y)\, dx\, dy = \int_a^b dx \int_c^d f(x, y)\, dy = \int_c^d dy \int_a^b f(x, y)\, dx. \tag{18.1}$$

(See Natanson, ref. A23, p. 279 and p. 385).

We note that both the repeated integrals occurring on the right-hand side of (18.1) can exist and be equal without the double integral on the left-hand side of (18.1) existing at all (see Natanson, ref. A23, p. 385), but the case is also possible when each of these integrals exists but they are unequal, that is, changing the order of integration is invalid (see Natanson, ref. A23, p. 386).

However, for functions maintaining sign this case is not possible, namely:

*If $f(x, y) \geqslant 0$ and $f(x, y)$ is measurable in $R$, then the finiteness of one of the repeated integrals implies the summability of $f(x, y)$ in $R$, in the same way as the finiteness of the second repeated integral implies the equality* (18.1).

(See Natanson, ref. A23, p. 387).

We will note one of the important particular cases of Fubini's theorem.

*If $E$ is a plane set of zero measure, then almost all its straight sections, parallel to the co-ordinate axes, are linear sets of zero measure.*

(See Natanson, ref. A23, p. 371).

# V. FUNCTIONAL ANALYSIS

## § 19. Linear functionals in $C$

In connection with any function $f \in C\,[a, b]$ let some quantity be defined which we will denote as $U(f)$, such that

(1) $U(f_1 + f_2) = U(f_1) + U(f_2)$,

(2) there exists a constant $M$ such that

$$|U(f)| \leqslant M \|f\|_{C[a,b]}. \tag{19.1}$$

Then we say that $U(f)$ is a *linear functional* in $C[a, b]$.

Then we have

RIESZ'S THEOREM. *Any linear functional in $C[a, b]$ has the form*

$$U(f) = \int_a^b f(t)\, dg, \tag{19.2}$$

*where $g(t)$ is some function of bounded variation in $[a, b]$.*

(See Natanson, ref. A23, p. 258).

*The norm of a linear functional* is the smallest value of $M$, for which the inequality (19.1) holds.

Let us now note the hypothesis that we will have to use later.

*If $U(f)$ has the form* (19.2) *then*

$$\sup_{\|f\|_c \leqslant 1} |U(f)| = \operatorname*{var}_{[a,b]} g = V_a^b g \tag{19.3}$$

(in other words, if the functional has the form (19.2), then its norm is $V_a^b g$).

(See Lyusternik and Sobolev, ref. A18, p. 167).

## § 20. Linear functionals in $L^p (p > 1)$

Let $f(x) \in L^p [a, b]$, $p > 1$. If connected with each such function a quantity $U(f)$ is set up satisfying the conditions:

(1) $U(f_1 + f_2) = U(f_1) + U(f_2)$,

(2) there exists an $M$ such that

$$|U(f)| \leqslant M \|f\|_{L^p[a,b]}, \tag{20.1}$$

then $U(f)$ is a *linear functional* in $L^p [a, b]$.

*The norm of the functional* is the least $M$ for which (20.1) holds.

We have

THEOREM. *If $q$ is defined by the equation*

$$\frac{1}{p} + \frac{1}{q} = 1,$$

*then any linear functional in $L^p [a, b]$ has the form*

$$U(f) = \int_a^b f(x) g(x) dx, \tag{20.2}$$

*where $g(x) \in L^q [a, b]$.*

(See Lyusternik and Sobolev, ref. A18, p. 170).

This theorem is not necessary to us, but we do have to prove that

$$\sup_{\|f\|_p \leqslant 1} |U(f)| = \|g\|_{L^q[a,b]}, \tag{20.3}$$

where $U(f)$ is defined by formula (20.2).

This last statement is proved very easily. First, by Hölder's inequality we have

$$|U(f)| \leqslant \|f\|_{L^p} \|g\|_{L^q} \leqslant \|g\|_{L^q}, \tag{20.4}$$

if $\|f\|_{L^p} \leqslant 1$.

Now we will prove that there exists $f$ such that for $\|f\|_{L^p[a,b]} = 1$ and the inequality (20.4) becomes an equality.

In fact, let us suppose

$$f(x) = \frac{[g(x)]^{q-1} \operatorname{sign} g(x)}{\|g\|_{L^q}^{q-1}}.$$

Since $p(q-1) = q$, we immediately derive

$$|f(x)|^p = \frac{|g(x)|^q}{\|g\|_{L^q}^q},$$

and then integrating over $[a, b]$ we at once obtain

$$\int_a^b |f(x)|^p dx = 1,$$

that is

$$\|f\|_{L^p} = 1.$$

Now we note that

$$U(f) = \int_a^b f(x)g(x)dx = \frac{\int_a^b |g|^q dx}{\left(\int_a^b |g|^q dx\right)^{\frac{q-1}{q}}} = \left(\int_a^b |g|^q dx\right)^{\frac{1}{q}} = \|g\|_{L^q},$$

and the theorem is proved.

## § 21. Convergence in norm in the spaces $L^p$

We will recall a number of properties of functions belonging to $L^p\,[a, b]$ at $p \geqslant 1$.

(1) *In order for the sequence of functions* $f_n(x) \in L^p\,[a, b]$ *to converge to function* $f(x) \in L^p\,[a, b]$ *in norm, that is,*

$$\lim_{n\to\infty} \|f_n - f\|_{L^p[a,b]} = 0,$$

*it is necessary and sufficient that for any* $\varepsilon > 0$ *a value* $N$ *must be found such that*

$$\|f_n - f_m\|_{L^p[a,b]} \leqslant \varepsilon \quad \textit{for} \quad n \geqslant N,\ m \geqslant N. \tag{21.1}$$

(2) *From any sequence* $f_n(x)$ *converging in norm in* $L^p$ *to* $f(x)$, *it is possible to isolate a sub-sequence which converges almost everywhere to* $f(x)$.

(3) *Let* $p > 1$. *If* $g(x) \in L^q$, *where* $1/p + 1/q = 1$, *then it follows from* $\| f_n - f \|_{L^p} \to 0$ *that*

$$\lim_{n\to\infty} \int_a^b f_n(x) g(x) dx = \int_a^b f(x) g(x) dx.$$

Proofs of all these statements can be found in Natanson's book, ref. A23, Chapter VII, § 2 and § 6.

The class of functions $\{f(x)\}$ belonging to $L^p$ forms an *everywhere dense set* in $L^p$, $p \geqslant 1$, if for any $\varepsilon > 0$ and for any $\varphi \in L^p$ a function $f$ can be found such that $\| f - \varphi \|_{L^p} < \varepsilon$.

It may be proved that:

(1) *the class of all measurable bounded functions,*

(2) *the class of all continuous functions,*

(3) *the class of all polynomials,*

(4) *the class of all step-functions*

*are everywhere dense in* $L^p$.

When the class $L^p$ $[a, b]$ is concerned, it is similarly necessary to consider the function $\varphi$ only in $[a, b]$.

For the proof, see Natanson, ref. A23, pp. 188 and 218.

The fact that the class of trigonometric polynomials is everywhere dense in $L^p$ $[-\pi, \pi]$ will be proved in Chapter I, § 28.

# VI. THEORY OF APPROXIMATION OF FUNCTIONS BY TRIGONOMETRIC POLYNOMIALS

## § 22. Elementary properties of trigonometric polynomials

*Trigonometric polynomial* is the name given to an expression of the form

$$T(x) = \alpha_0 + \sum_{k=1}^{n} (\alpha_k \cos kx + \beta_k \sin kx),$$

whilst, if $|\alpha_n| + |\beta_n| > 0$, then the number $n$ is known as the *order of the polynomial.*

We refer to the following simple properties of trigonometric polynomials.

1. The product of two trigonometric polynomials is itself a trigonometric polynomial (see Natanson, ref. A22, p. 32) and consequently $[T(x)]^k$ is also a trigonometric polynomial for any integer $k$.

(2) A trigonometric polynomial of order $n$ cannot possess more than $2n$ real roots in $[0, 2\pi)$, even if each multiple root is counted the number of times it occurs. (See Natanson, ref. A22, p. 85).

WEIERSTRASS'S THEOREM. *If $f(x)$ is continuous on the entire infinite axis and $f(x+2\pi) = f(x)$ for any $x$, then for any $\varepsilon > 0$ a trigonometric polynomial $T(x)$ is found such that*

$$|f(x) - T(x)| < \varepsilon, \quad -\infty < x < +\infty.$$

We shall prove this theorem in Chapter I, § 27. We refer to it now because it is impossible to prove later theorems without it.

## § 23. Bernstein's inequality

The following fundamental theorem derived by S. N. Bernstein[1] holds for trigonometric polynomials:

BERNSTEIN'S THEOREM. *If $T_n(x)$ is a trigonometric polynomial of order not higher than $n$ and*

$$|T_n(x)| \leqslant M \quad \text{in} \quad [0 \leqslant x \leqslant 2\pi],$$

*then*

$$|T_n'(x)| \leqslant nM \quad \text{in} \quad [0 \leqslant x \leqslant 2\pi].$$

Very many different proofs of this theorem exist. We will give S. B. Stechkin's[1] proof here which seems to be very simple. First of all, we establish the validity of a lemma.

LEMMA. *If* $\max |T_n(x)| = M$ *and* $T_n(x_0) = M$, *then*

$$T_n(x_0 + t) \geqslant M \cos nt \quad \text{for} \quad -\frac{\pi}{n} \leqslant t \leqslant \frac{\pi}{n}$$

Let us suppose that

$$\psi_n(t) = T_n(x_0 + t) - M \cos nt$$

and assume that the lemma is untrue. Then $t_0$ can be found, $-\pi/n < t_0 < \pi/n$, such that

$$\psi_n(t_0) < 0. \tag{23.1}$$

We suppose that $0 < t_0 < \pi/n$ (in the case when $-\pi/n < t < 0$, the reasoning must be carried out not for $[0, 2\pi]$ but for $[-2\pi, 0]$; otherwise everything is exactly the same).

Since $\psi_n(t)$ is a trigonometric polynomial of order not higher than $n$, then it should possess not more than $2n$ roots in $[0, 2\pi]$ [or it will be identically equal to zero, which contradicts (23.1)].

Meanwhile, we will show that it has not less than $2n + 1$ roots. Indeed, we have for any $k$

$$\psi_n\left(\frac{k\pi}{n}\right) = T_n\left(x_0 + \frac{k\pi}{n}\right) - (-1)^k M,$$

and since $|T_n(x)| \leqslant M$, then $\psi_n(k\pi/n)$ has the sign $(-1)^{k+1}$ or $= 0$. In particular, $\psi_n(\pi/n) \geqslant 0$ and therefore in the interval $[t_0, \pi/n]$ the function $\psi_n(t)$ has a root. Moreover, it should also have a root in each of the intervals $[k\pi/n, (k+1)\pi/n]$, $(k = 1, 2, \ldots 2n - 2)$, lying in $(0, 2\pi)$, since at the ends of the interval it has different signs (or it becomes zero).† Thus in $\psi_n(t)$ we have found not less than $2n-1$ roots. However, it also possesses a double root at $t=0$, for

$$\psi_n(0) = T_n(x_0) - M = 0$$

and from

$$\psi_n'(t) = T_n'(x_0+t) + nM\sin nt$$

it follows that

$$\psi_n'(0) = 0,$$

since $x_0$ is the maximum point for $T_n(x_0)$.

Thus the trigonometric polynomial $\psi_n(t)$ possesses $2n+1$ roots and we have already seen that this leads to a contradiction. The lemma is thus proved.

Let us return to proving the theorem.

Let $|T_n(x)| \leqslant M$. We will denote $\max|T_n'(x)| = \mu$. Let $x_0$ be a point such that

$$T_n'(x_0) = \mu$$

(if $-T_n'(x_0) = \mu$, then it is sufficient to discuss $-T_n(x)$). Then according to the preceding lemma

$$T_n'(x_0+t) \geqslant \mu\cos nt, \quad -\frac{\pi}{n} \leqslant t \leqslant \frac{\pi}{n},$$

whence

$$\int_{-\frac{\pi}{2n}}^{\frac{\pi}{2n}} T_n'(x_0+t)dt = T_n\left(x_0+\frac{\pi}{2n}\right) - T_n\left(x_0-\frac{\pi}{2n}\right) \geqslant \mu\int_{-\frac{\pi}{2n}}^{\frac{\pi}{2n}} \cos nt dt = 2\frac{\mu}{n}.$$

Thus

$$\mu \leqslant \frac{n}{2}\left[T_n\left(x_0+\frac{\pi}{2n}\right) - T_n\left(x_0-\frac{\pi}{2n}\right)\right].$$

But $|T_n(x)| \leqslant M$, whence $\mu \leqslant nM$, that is, $|T_n'(x)| \leqslant nM$, which gives the required proof.

*Note.* Bernstein's inequality cannot be strengthened, since supposing that

$$T_n(x)M = \cos nx,$$

we see that

$$\max|T_n(x)| = M, \quad \text{and} \quad \max|T_n'(x)| = nM.$$

## § 24. Trigonometric polynomial of best approximation

Let $f(x)$ be a continuous function with period $2\pi$. We will denote by $T_n(x)$ any trigonometric polynomial of order not higher than $n$. Let

$$\Delta(T_n) = \max_{0\leqslant x\leqslant 2\pi}|f(x) - T_n(x)|. \tag{24.1}$$

† We note that if $\psi_n(t)$ has the same root in two neighbouring intervals, then this root is multiple.

Let us consider the lower bound of the values $\Delta(T_n)$ where $T_n$ refers to all the trigonometric polynomials $T_n(x)$ in turn. We define

$$E_n(f) = \inf \Delta(T_n) \tag{24.2}$$

and call this magnitude *the best approximation* of $f(x)$ by trigonometric polynomials of order not higher than $n$.

BOREL'S THEOREM. *For any continuous periodic function with period $2\pi$ and for any n there exists a trigonometric polynomial of order not higher than n for which*

$$\max_{0 \leqslant x \leqslant 2\pi} |f(x) - T_n(x)| = E_n(f) \tag{24.3}$$

(*that is, the lower bound is reached*).

This polynomial is known as the *polynomial of best approximation.*

A proof of the theorem can be found, for example, in Natanson's book, ref. A22, p. 94.

It is easily proved that

$$E_1 \geqslant E_2 \geqslant \cdots \geqslant E_n \geqslant \cdots. \tag{24.4}$$

Moreover, it immediately follows from Weierstrass's theorem (see § 22) that

$$\lim_{n\to\infty} E_n = 0.$$

If we suppose that

$$\Delta^{(p)}(T_n) = \|f(x) - T_n(x)\|_{L^p[0,2\pi]} \tag{24.5}$$

and define

$$E_n^{(p)}(f) = \inf \Delta^{(p)}(T_n),$$

where again the lower bound refers to all the trigonometric polynomials of order not higher than $n$, then $E^{[p]}(f)$ is called *the best approximation of $f(x)$ in the space $L^p$.*

Later for an arbitrary $p > 1$ we will use this definition only and not the existence of a polynomial for which $\Delta^p(T_n) = E_n^{[p]}(f)$. In the case $p = 2$ such existence is proved very easily; we will discuss this in § 13, Chapter I.

Finally, we note that it is expedient to consider the best approximation not in $[0, 2\pi]$ but in any interval $[a, b] \subset [0, 2\pi]$. In this case

$$E_n(f, a, b) = \inf_{T_n} \max_{a \leqslant x \leqslant b} |f(x) - T(x)|. \tag{24.7}$$

and similarly we define

$$E_n^{(p)}(f, a, b) = \inf_{T_n} \|f(x) - T_n(x)\|_{L^p[a,b]}. \tag{24.8}$$

## § 25. Modulus of continuity, modulus of smoothness, and integral modulus of continuity

*Modulus of continuity.* Let the function $f(x)$ be defined in the interval $[a, b]$. Let any $\delta > 0$ be given. We will consider for any two points $x_1$ and $x_2$ of the interval $[a, b]$, provided $|x_1 - x_2| \leqslant \delta$, the difference $|f(x_1) - f(x_2)|$ and let

$$\omega(\delta, a, b, f) = \sup_{|x_1 - x_2| \leqslant \delta} |f(x_1) - f(x_2)| \begin{matrix} x_1 \in [a, b] \\ \\ x_2 \in [a, b] \end{matrix}. \tag{25.1}$$

If the same interval is under discussion the whole time, then we write briefly $\omega(\delta, f)$. This quantity is called *the modulus of continuity of $f(x)$ in $[a \ b]$*.

If no restrictions are put on $f(x)$, then $\omega(\delta)$ can turn out to be infinite. But if $f(x)$ is continuous in $[a, b]$, then it is evident that $\omega(\delta, f)$ is finite for any $\delta$ and

$$\lim_{\delta \to 0} \omega(\delta, f) = 0. \tag{25.2}$$

It is seen from the definition that

$$\omega(\delta, f_1 + f_2) \leqslant \omega(\delta, f_1) + \omega(\delta, f_2), \tag{25.3}$$

if the function is considered in one and the same interval.

Let us note a number of virtually obvious properties of the modulus of continuity (for brevity, the symbol $f$ is omitted and we write simply $\omega(\delta)$):

(1) $\omega(\delta)$ monotonically increases,
(2) if $n$ is an integer, then

$$\omega(n\delta) \leqslant n\omega(\delta), \tag{25.4}$$

and if $\lambda$ is any positive number then

$$\omega(\lambda\delta) \leqslant (\lambda + 1)\omega(\delta), \tag{25.5}$$

(3) if $f(x) \in \mathrm{Lip}\,\alpha$ (see Notation), then

$$\omega(\delta) = O(\delta^\alpha) \tag{25.6}$$

and vice versa.

(See Natanson, ref. A22, p. 107–109).

If $f(x)$ is defined in a certain interval $[\alpha, \beta]$ containing $[a, b]$, then a modulus of continuity can be defined thus

$$\omega(\delta, a, b, f) = \sup_{0 \leqslant |h| \leqslant \delta} |f(x + h) - f(x)| \quad x \in [a, b] \tag{25.7}$$

under the condition $\delta \leqslant \min[a - \alpha, \beta - b]$, that is, so that the point $x \pm h$ for $x \in [a, b]$ does not lie outside the interval $[\alpha, \beta]$. In particular, if $f(x)$ is periodic with period $2\pi$ and defined in an interval of length $2\pi$, then we can define $\omega(\delta, f)$ briefly as

$$\omega(\delta, f) = \sup_{0 \leqslant h \leqslant \delta} |f(x + h) - f(x)|, \tag{25.8}$$

where $x$ is any number.

*Modulus of smoothness*. If instead of the first difference $f(x + h) - f(x)$ we consider the second symmetrical difference, that is $f(x + h) + f(x - h) - 2f(x)$, then we obtain the definition of the modulus of smoothness in a similar manner.

$$\omega_2(\delta, f) = \sup_{0 \leqslant h \leqslant \delta} |f(x + h) + f(x - h) - 2f(x)|. \tag{25.9}$$

It is clear that the following properties hold here:

(1) $\omega_2(\delta)$ does not monotonically decrease,
(2) for any positive $\lambda$

$$\omega_2(\lambda\delta) \leqslant (\lambda + 1)\omega_2(\delta). \tag{25.10}$$

It is useful to note that if for any monotonically increasing $g(x)$ the relationship is proved

$$\omega\left(\frac{1}{n}, f\right) = O\left(g\left(\frac{1}{n}\right)\right), \quad n \to \infty,$$

then it is also true to say

$$\omega(\delta, f) = O[g(\delta)] \quad \text{at} \quad \delta \to 0.$$

In fact, if $\delta$ is given, then $n$ is defined such that

$$\frac{1}{n+1} \leqslant \delta < \frac{1}{n}.$$

Then

$$\omega(\delta, f) \leqslant \omega\left(\frac{1}{n}, f\right) \leqslant \omega\left(\frac{2}{n+1}, f\right) \leqslant 2\omega\left(\frac{1}{n+1}, f\right)$$

$$\leqslant Cg\left(\frac{1}{n+1}\right) \leqslant Cg(\delta),$$

where $C$ is a constant, which gives the required proof.

A similar assertion is true for the modulus of smoothness.

For the connection between the modulus of continuity of a function and its best approximation by trigonometrical polynomials, see Appendix, § 7.

*Integral modulus of continuity*. If $f(x) \in L[\alpha, \beta]$ and $[a, b]$ lies inside $[\alpha, \beta]$, then *the integral modulus of continuity of $f(x)$ in $[a, b]$* is usually the name given to the expression

$$\omega^{(1)}(\delta, a, b, f) = \sup_{0 \leqslant |k| \leqslant \delta} \int_a^b |f(x+h) - f(x)|\, dx,$$

where again $\delta$ is taken such that for $x \in [a, b]$ and $0 \leqslant |h| \leqslant \delta$ we have $x \pm h \in [\alpha, \beta]$.

For a periodic function with period $2\pi$ we will write briefly

$$\omega^{(1)}(\delta, f) = \sup_{0 \leqslant |h| \leqslant \delta} \int_{-\pi}^{\pi} |f(x+h) - f(x)|\, dx \tag{25.11}$$

(here $\delta$ can be any positive number).

For the integral modulus of continuity the following holds:

LEBESGUE'S THEOREM. *For any $f(x) \in L[-\pi, \pi]$ we have*

$$\lim_{\delta \to 0} \omega^{(1)}(\delta, f) = 0.$$

It is sufficient to prove the theorem for non-negative functions, since each summable function can be represented as the difference of non-negative summable functions. Moreover, for any $\varepsilon > 0$ a bounded function $\varphi(x)$ can be chosen for which

$$\int_{-\pi}^{\pi} |f(x) - \varphi(x)|\, dx < \varepsilon.$$

Therefore

$$\int_{-\pi}^{\pi} |f(x+h) - f(x)|\, dx \leqslant \int_{-\pi}^{\pi} |\varphi(x+h) - \varphi(x)|\, dx + 2\varepsilon \tag{25.12}$$

and it remains to prove our assertion for the bounded $\varphi(x)$.

Let $|\varphi(x)| \leqslant M$. Because of the $C$-property it is possible to find a continuous $\psi(x)$ corresponding to $\varphi(x)$ in the perfect set $P \subset [-\pi, \pi]$, $mP > 2\pi - 2\pi \cdot \varepsilon/M$. We can choose $\psi(x)$ so that $\psi(-\pi) = \psi(\pi)$ and so that $|\psi(x)| \leqslant M$ in $[-\pi, \pi]$. Therefore it must be expanded periodically with period $2\pi$. It is clear that

$$\int_{-\pi}^{\pi} |\varphi(x+h) - \varphi(x)|\, dx \leqslant \int_{-\pi}^{\pi} |\psi(x+h) - \psi(x)|\, dx + 2\int_{-\pi}^{\pi} |\varphi(x) - \psi(x)|\, dx$$

$$\leqslant \int_{-\pi}^{\pi} |\psi(x+h) - \psi(x)|\, dx + 4\varepsilon. \tag{25.13}$$

Finally, we have

$$\int_{-\pi}^{\pi} |\psi(x+h) - \psi(x)|\, dx \leqslant \omega(\delta, \psi)\, 2 \cdot \pi$$

for $0 \leqslant |h| \leqslant \delta$, whence by virtue of (25.12) and (25.13)

$$\int_{-\pi}^{\pi} |f(x+h) - f(x)|\, dx \leqslant 6\varepsilon + 2\pi\omega(\delta, \psi) \quad \text{at} \quad 0 \leqslant |h| \leqslant \delta. \tag{25.14}$$

Because $\delta$ is arbitrary and $\psi(x)$ is continuous, that is, $\omega(\delta, \psi) \to 0$ as $\delta \to 0$, we see from (25.11) and (25.14) that

$$\omega^{(1)}(\delta, f) \to 0 \quad \text{at} \quad \delta \to 0,$$

which was required to be proved.

*Note.* Later the following will be required.

THEOREM. *If $f(x)$ is of bounded variation in* $[0, 2\pi]$, *then*

$$\omega^{(1)}(\delta, f) = O(\delta). \tag{25.15}$$

In fact, expressing $f(x)$ as the difference between two monotonic functions $f(x) = f_1(x) - f_2(x)$ and noting that

$$\omega^{(1)}(\delta, f) \leqslant \omega^{(1)}(\delta, f_1) + \omega^{(1)}(\delta, f_2),$$

we see that it is sufficient to establish the validity of relationship (25.15) for non-decreasing $f(x)$. But if this is so, then for $h > 0$ the function $f(x+h) - f(x)$ is non-negative in $[0, 2\pi - h]$. Therefore

$$\int_{0}^{2\pi} |f(x+h) - f(x)|\, dx = \int_{0}^{2\pi-h} [f(x+h) - f(x)]\, dx + \int_{2\pi-h}^{2\pi} |f(x+h) - f(x)|\, dx$$

$$\leqslant 2Mh + \int_{0}^{2\pi-h} [f(x+h) - f(x)]\, dx,$$

where $M$ is the upper bound of $f(x)$; moreover

$$\int_0^{2\pi-h} [f(x+h) - f(x)]\,dx = \int_h^{2\pi} f(x)\,dx - \int_0^{2\pi-h} f(x)\,dx = \int_{2\pi-h}^{2\pi} f(x)\,dx - \int_0^{h} f(x)\,dx.$$

The modulus of each of the last two integrals does not exceed $Mh$. Therefore

$$\int_0^{2\pi} |f(x+h) - f(x)|\,dx \leqslant 4Mh$$

and

$$\omega^{(1)}(\delta, f) \leqslant \sup_{0 \leqslant h \leqslant \delta} 4M|h| = 4M\delta = O(\delta).$$

CHAPTER I

# BASIC CONCEPTS AND THEOREMS IN THE THEORY OF TRIGONOMETRIC SERIES

## § 1. The concept of a trigonometric series; conjugate series

A *trigonometric series* is the name given to an expression of the form

$$\frac{a_0}{2} + \sum_{n=1}^{\infty} (a_n \cos nx + b_n \sin nx), \tag{1.1}$$

where $a_n$ and $b_n$ are constants ($n = 0, 1, 2 \ldots$), known as *the coefficients of the series.*†

If such a series converges for all $x$ in $-\infty < x < +\infty$, then it represents a function possessing a period of $2\pi$. Therefore, if a function is to be represented by a trigonometric series, either periodic functions with period $2\pi$ are considered or a function is taken which is given in an interval of length $2\pi$ and is then expanded periodically, that is, it is required that $f(x + 2\pi) = f(x)$ for any $x$.

Trigonometric series play a prominent role not only in mathematics itself but also in very many of its applications. But before we discuss this role, we will mention first the connection between trigonometric and power series. If we consider the series

$$\sum_{n=0}^{\infty} c_n z^n, \tag{1.2}$$

where $c_n = a_n - ib_n$, $c_0 = a_0/2$ and we suppose that $z = re^{ix}$, then the series (1.1) is no different from the real part of series (1.2) on the unit circle; the purely imaginary part of the series (1.2) for $z = e^{ix}$ is the series

$$\sum_{n=1}^{\infty} (- b_n \cos nx + a_n \sin nx), \tag{1.3}$$

which is usually called *the series conjugate to series* (1.1).

If it is assumed that the constants $c_n$ are bounded then the series (1.2) represents an analytic function inside a unit circle, that is, for $z = re^{ix}$, where $0 \leqslant r < 1$ and $0 \leqslant x \leqslant 2\pi$; therefore its real and imaginary parts

$$u(r, x) = \frac{a_0}{2} + \sum_{n=1}^{\infty} (a_n \cos nx + b_n \sin nx) r^n$$

† The reason why the free term is written as $a_0/2$ will become clear later (see § 4).

and

$$v(r, x) = \sum_{n=1}^{\infty}(-b_n \cos nx + a_n \sin nx)r^n$$

are conjugate harmonic functions; whence is derived the name "conjugate series". The study of the behaviour of conjugate series is no different from an investigation of the behaviour of conjugate harmonic functions on the circle $|z| = 1$.

## § 2. The complex form of a trigonometric series

It is often more convenient to give the trigonometric series

$$\frac{a_0}{2} + \sum_{n=1}^{\infty}(a_n \cos nx + b_n \sin nx) \tag{2.1}$$

a different form. Thus, from the well-known Euler's identity

$$e^{ix} = \cos x + i \sin x$$

it follows that

$$\cos x = \frac{e^{ix} + e^{-ix}}{2}; \quad \sin x = \frac{e^{ix} - e^{-ix}}{2i},$$

so that we can write series (2.1) in the form

$$\frac{a_0}{2} + \sum_{n=1}^{\infty}\left(a_n \frac{e^{inx} + e^{-inx}}{2} + ib_n \frac{e^{-inx} - e^{inx}}{2}\right),$$

whence, supposing that

$$c_0 = \frac{a_0}{2}, \quad c_n = \frac{a_n - ib_n}{2}, \quad c_{-n} = \frac{a_n + ib_n}{2}, \tag{2.2}$$

we see that the series (2.1) takes the form

$$\sum_{n=-\infty}^{n=+\infty} c_n e^{inx}. \tag{2.3}$$

This is the so-called *complex form of the trigonometric series.* The partial sum of series (2.1), that is,

$$S_n(x) = \frac{a_0}{2} + \sum_{k=1}^{n}(a_k \cos kx + b_k \sin kx),$$

now takes the form

$$S_n(x) = \sum_{k=-n}^{k=+n} c_k e^{ikx}, \tag{2.4}$$

that is, the convergence of series (2.3) must be understood as the tending to the limit of sums of the form (2.4).

Some problems are concerned with trigonometric series of the form (2.3), the coefficients of which are any complex numbers. If it is assumed that the numbers $a_n$

and $b_n$ in series (2.1) are all real, then from formula (2.2) it is seen that the numbers $c_n$ and $c_{-n}$ are conjugate complex numbers, that is, $c_{-n} = \overline{c_n}$ (the symbol $\bar{a}$ always indicates the number conjugate to $a$).

## § 3. A brief historical synopsis

The possibility of representing a function by a trigonometric series was first considered by Euler in 1753 in connection with the work by Daniel Bernoulli on "Vibrating Strings" which had appeared at that time.

If a string, fixed at both ends, is disturbed from its state of equilibrium and is allowed to vibrate freely without being given any initial velocity, then Bernoulli affirmed that the position of the string at time $t$ is determined by the formula

$$y = \sum_{p=1}^{\infty} \alpha_p \sin p \frac{\pi x}{l} \cos pkt,$$

where $l$ is the length of the string and $k$ is some coefficient which depends on the density and tension of the string. The coefficients $\alpha_p$ are arbitrary constants and it is possible to choose them so that the initial condition is satisfied, namely, the requirement that initially the string occupies a certain given position.

Euler noticed that this assertion by Bernoulli leads to a paradoxical result, according to the views of mathematicians of that time. Indeed, if $y = f(x)$ is the initial position of the string, then assuming $t = 0$, we should obtain

$$f(x) = \sum_{p=1}^{\infty} \alpha_p \sin p \frac{\pi x}{l},$$

that is, the "arbitrary" function $f(x)$ can be expanded as a sine series. However, Euler and his contemporaries divided the curves into two classes: those that they called "continuous" and the others "geometrical". In contrast to the terminology adopted today, a curve was named "continuous" if $y$ and $x$ were connected by some formula: on the other hand, a geometrical curve was the name given to any curve which could be drawn "free-hand". It is evident from all this that if the curve is given by a formula, then being determinable in some small interval, it is automatically determinable everywhere else†. Therefore they did not doubt that the second category of curves was wider than the first, since they could not consider, for example, a broken line to be "continuous", but merely composed of sections of continuous lines.

If an "arbitrary" function could be expanded as a sine series, i.e. represented by a formula, this would signify that any kind of "geometrical" curve is a "continuous" curve which appeared to be incredible. In particular, D'Alembert noticed that the most natural method of disturbing a string from its state of equilibrium is to take hold of some point on it and pull it upwards, so that it takes up a position represented by two straight lines forming an angle between them. D'Alembert considered that a curve of this nature could not be the sum of a sine series††.

† This property is inherent in analytic functions.

†† For the result of the argument between Euler and D'Alembert concerning the definition of an "arbitrary function", which arose in connection with the solution of the problem of the vibrating string, see the extremely interesting report on "Functions" by N. N. Lusin[4] (it should also appear in Vol. III of the Collected Works of N. N. Lusin).

The problem of what functions can be represented by trigonometric series arose again considerably later in Fourier's researches. In connection with the study of the problem of heat transfer he was confronted with the following problem: let the given function be

$$f(x) = \begin{cases} -1 & \text{in} \quad -\pi < x < 0, \\ 1 & \text{in} \quad 0 < x < \pi. \end{cases}$$

It is required to represent it in the form

$$\sum_{n=1}^{\infty} \alpha_n \sin nx. \tag{3.1}$$

Fourier indicated formulae with the help of which $\alpha_n$ can be determined so that series (3.1) can have $f(x)$ for its sum. In this way, it is a series of form

$$\frac{4}{\pi}\left[\frac{\sin x}{1} + \frac{\sin 3x}{3} + \cdots + \frac{\sin(2n+1)x}{2n+1} + \cdots\right].$$

Fourier did not prove that the series is bound to converge to the function $f(x)$, but this question was answered in the affirmative by later investigations. In any case it is important that Fourier first solved the problem of how to determine the coefficients of a trigonometric series for it to be able to possess a given function as its sum. It is an entirely different question whether this series does indeed converge and does really possess this function as its sum.

## § 4. Fourier formulae

Let us assume that the function $f(x)$ is not only the sum of a trigonometric series but also that this series converges uniformly in $-\pi \leqslant x \leqslant \pi$; then its coefficients can be determined very easily. This follows simply by multiplying

$$f(x) = \frac{a_0}{2} + \sum_{n=1}^{\infty} (a_n \cos nx + b_n \sin nx)$$

by $\cos kx$ or by $\sin kx$, by integrating it between the limits $-\pi$ to $+\pi$ (which is valid) and noting that

$$\left.\begin{aligned} &\int_{-\pi}^{\pi} \cos mx \cos nx \, dx = 0, \quad m \neq n, \\ &\int_{-\pi}^{\pi} \sin mx \sin nx \, dx = 0, \quad m \neq n, \\ &\int_{-\pi}^{\pi} \cos mx \sin nx \, dx = 0, \quad m \neq n \quad \text{and} \quad m = n, \\ &\int_{-\pi}^{\pi} \cos^2 mx \, dx = \int_{-\pi}^{\pi} \sin^2 mx \, dx = \pi. \end{aligned}\right\} \tag{4.1}$$

As a result we obtain†

$$a_n = \frac{1}{\pi}\int_{-\pi}^{\pi} f(x)\cos nx\,dx; \quad b_n = \frac{1}{\pi}\int_{-\pi}^{\pi} f(x)\sin nx\,dx. \tag{4.2}$$

Formulae (4.2) are called *Fourier formulae,*†† the numbers $a_n$ and $b_n$ are Fourier coefficients and finally the series, the coefficients of which are determined by Fourier formulae derived from the function $f(x)$, is named *the Fourier series* of the function $f(x)$. We will denote it by $\sigma(f)$.

## § 5. The complex form of a Fourier series

If the series representing $f(x)$ is given in a complex form (see § 2)†††, i.e., if we suppose that

$$f(x) = \sum_{n=-\infty}^{n=+\infty} c_n e^{inx}, \tag{5.1}$$

then the coefficients $c_n$ are determined by the formulae

$$c_n = \frac{1}{2\pi}\int_{-\pi}^{\pi} f(t)e^{-int}\,dt \quad (n = 0, \pm 1, \ldots), \tag{5.2}$$

which can be obtained either by starting from equalities (2.2) and substituting the values for $a_n$ and $b_n$ from the Fourier formulae or in a similar manner to that by which the Fourier formulae themselves were produced. Namely, by supposing that

$$f(x) = \sum_{k=-\infty}^{k=+\infty} c_k e^{ikx}. \tag{5.3}$$

where the convergence is uniform, multiplying both sides of equality (5.3) by $e^{-inx}$ and integrating term by term, we find that

$$\int_{-\pi}^{\pi} f(x)e^{-inx}dx = \sum_{k=-\infty}^{k=+\infty} c_k \int_{-\pi}^{\pi} e^{i(k-n)x}dx.$$

But

$$\int_{-\pi}^{\pi} e^{i(k-n)x}dx = \begin{cases} 0, & \text{if } k \neq n, \\ 2\pi, & \text{if } k = n. \end{cases} \tag{5.4}$$

---

† The free term of the series must be written in the form $a_0/2$ for $a_0$ to be obtained from $a_n$ when $n = 0$.

†† Strictly speaking, these formulae were already known to Euler, but Fourier began to use them systematically; therefore they are traditionally called Fourier formulae and the corresponding series Fourier series.

††† For references to the text or formulae from the same chapter, the number of the chapter is omitted.

whence

$$\int_{-\pi}^{\pi} f(x) e^{-inx} dx = 2\pi c_n,$$

which proves the validity of formula (5.2).

The numbers $c_n$ are called *the complex Fourier coefficients of the function* $f(x)$.

## § 6. Problems in the theory of Fourier series; Fourier–Lebesgue series

In §§ 4 and 5 we have solved only the problem of how the coefficients of a trigonometric series should be determined if we know that it converges uniformly to some function $f(x)$. It was shown that in this case the series possesses coefficients determinable by Fourier formulae, that is, it is a Fourier series of $f(x)$.

However, for the function to be the sum of an uniformly convergent series of continuous functions, it is necessary that it be continuous. Therefore, it could appear that if it is desired to represent a function by a Fourier series, we must confine ourselves to the case when it is continuous. We will see that in fact the theory of Fourier series embraces a very much wider class of functions. But first of all we must define more exactly what we understand by Fourier series.

Integrals figure in Fourier formulae. We know that the concept of an integral, starting with Cauchy, has widened, so that an increasingly large class of integrable functions has developed. In this book we will always understand by the class of "integrable functions" those integrable according to Lebesgue. These functions, as is known, are called summable; the series set up for them are named the Fourier–Lebesgue series. For brevity's sake we shall simply say "Fourier series" but at the same time realise that the series being considered are always summable.

Let $f(x)$ be summable in $[-\pi, \pi]$. Then it is always possible to determine for it the numbers $a_n$ and $b_n$ from Fourier formulae and to set up a series which we will name the Fourier series for this function and write

$$f(x) \sim \frac{a_0}{2} + \sum_{n=1}^{\infty} (a_n \cos nx + b_n \sin nx) \tag{6.1}$$

or

$$\sigma(f) = \frac{a_0}{2} + \sum_{n=1}^{\infty} (a_n \cos nx + b_n \sin nx). \tag{6.2}$$

The sign $\sim$ indicates that we established this series in a purely formal manner, starting from $f(x)$ and using Fourier formulae, but we know nothing of the convergence of this series. A whole succession of problems arises: should the Fourier series converge (in the whole interval $[-\pi, \pi]$ or at a given point or in a certain set) and if so, does it converge to the function $f(x)$ or not? In which cases will the convergence be absolute, when will it be uniform? What can be said of divergent Fourier series (is it possible to use them in any way for assessing functions?). These and many other problems will be discussed in later chapters of this book.

It should also be mentioned that there are cases when the trigonometric series is given by its coefficients but we do not know whether it is a Fourier series of a certain function or not. This is one of the very interesting but difficult problems of the theory of trigonometric series.

## § 7. Expansion into a trigonometric series of a function with period $2l$

Up until now we have considered the expansion into a trigonometric series of a function with period $2\pi$. If the function $f(x)$ has a period $2l$, where $l$ is some real number, then performing a change of variable,

$$x = \frac{lt}{\pi},$$

we obtain the function

$$\varphi(t) = f\left(\frac{lt}{\pi}\right),$$

which will also possess a period $2\pi$.

If we find its Fourier series

$$\varphi(t) \sim \frac{a_0}{2} + \sum (a_n \cos nt + b_n \sin nt),$$

where

$$a_n = \frac{1}{\pi}\int_{-\pi}^{\pi} \varphi(t) \cos nt\, dt; \quad b_n = \frac{1}{\pi}\int_{-\pi}^{\pi} \varphi(t) \sin nt\, dt,$$

then, reverting again to the variable $x$, we obtain

$$\left.\begin{aligned} a_n &= \frac{1}{\pi}\int_{-\pi}^{\pi} f\left(\frac{lt}{\pi}\right) \cos nt\, dt = \frac{1}{l}\int_{-l}^{l} f(x) \cos n\frac{\pi}{l}x\, dx, \quad n = 0, 1, \ldots, \\ b_n &= \frac{1}{\pi}\int_{-\pi}^{\pi} f\left(\frac{lt}{\pi}\right) \sin nt\, dt = \frac{1}{l}\int_{-l}^{l} f(x) \sin n\frac{\pi}{l}x\, dx, \quad n = 1, 2, \ldots, \end{aligned}\right\} \tag{7.1}$$

and therefore the function $f(x)$ will correspond to the series

$$f(x) \sim \frac{a_0}{2} + \sum_{n=1}^{\infty}\left(a_n \cos n\frac{\pi}{l}x + b_n \sin n\frac{\pi}{l}x\right), \tag{7.2}$$

where the numbers $a_n$ and $b_n$ are determined by the formulae (7.1).

Everything that will be said later concerning the convergence of normal trigonometric series is completely applicable to series of the form (7.2).

Finally we consider the case when the function $f(x)$ is not periodic. If it is defined in a certain interval $[a, b]$ where $-\pi < a < b < \pi$ (Fig. 4) and is summable in it, then it is possible to expand it into a trigonometric series thus: construct a function $\varphi(x)$ coinciding with $f(x)$ in $[a, b]$ and defined in $(-\pi, a)$ and $(b, \pi)$ as desired, provided that it is summable. Then assuming that $\varphi(x + 2\pi) = \varphi(x)$ we expand $\varphi(x)$ into a Fourier series. We assume that this series converges to $\varphi(x)$ at a certain point $x$, $a < x < b$; this means that its sum at this point will equal $f(x)$.

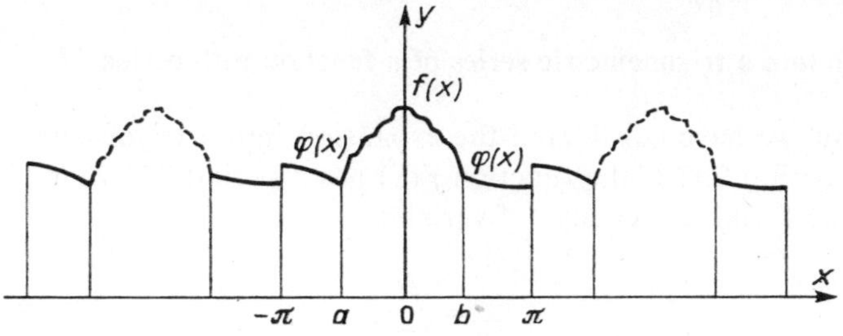


FIG. 4

It is clear that on extending $f(x)$ by various means outside the limits $(a, b)$, we will obtain various functions $\varphi(x)$. However, it will be proved subsequently (see § 33) that the Fourier series of all these functions will behave identically, that is, if one of them converges to $f(x)$ at a given point, then all the others will also converge likewise.

## § 8. Fourier series for even and odd functions

If $f(x)$ is even, i.e. $f(-x) = f(x)$ and $g(x)$ is odd, i.e. $g(-x) = -g(x)$, then $f(x)\,g(x)$ is evidently odd; on the other hand, if $f(x)$ and $g(x)$ are both even or both odd, then $f(x)\,g(x)$ is even.

It can be concluded immediately from this simple statement that for any even function the Fourier series contains cosines alone and for any odd function sines alone. Indeed, for any odd function $\varphi(x)$ and for any $a > 0$ we have

$$\int_{-a}^{a} \varphi(x)\,dx = 0,$$

and therefore for even $f(x)$ we have

$$b_n = \frac{1}{\pi} \int_{-\pi}^{\pi} f(x) \sin nx \, dx = 0 \quad (n = 1, 2, 3, \ldots),$$

and for odd $f(x)$ we have

$$a_n = \frac{1}{\pi} \int_{-\pi}^{\pi} f(x) \cos nx \, dx = 0, \quad (n = 0, 1, \ldots).$$

Moreover, for any even $\varphi(x)$ and for any $a > 0$ we have

$$\int_{-a}^{a} \varphi(x)\,dx = 2 \int_{0}^{a} \varphi(x)\,dx.$$

Therefore, in conclusion: if $f(x)$ is even, then

$$\sigma(f) = \frac{a_0}{2} + \sum_{n=1}^{\infty} a_n \cos nx,$$

where

$$a_n = \frac{2}{\pi} \int_0^{\pi} f(x) \cos nx \, dx;$$

if $f(x)$ is odd, then

$$\sigma(f) = \sum_{n=1}^{\infty} b_n \sin nx,$$

where

$$b_n = \frac{2}{\pi} \int_0^{\pi} f(x) \sin nx \, dx.$$

## § 9. Fourier series with respect to the orthogonal system

When we set ourselves the task of defining the coefficients of a trigonometric series so that it converges to a given function $f(x)$ we only considered a particular case of an extremely general problem. In order to formulate this problem we introduce the concept of an orthogonal system.

A system of functions $\varphi_n(x) \in L^2(a, b)$ $(n = 1, 2, \ldots)$ is said to be *orthogonal* in the interval $[a, b]$, if

$$\left.\begin{aligned} &\int_a^b \varphi_m(x)\varphi_n(x)\,dx = 0 \quad m \neq n; \quad m = 1, 2, \ldots; \quad n = 1, 2, \ldots, \\ &\int_a^b \varphi_n^2(x)\,dx \neq 0 \qquad n = 1, 2, \ldots. \end{aligned}\right\} \tag{9.1}$$

The relationships (4.1) are simply proof of the orthogonality of the trigonometric system

$$1, \cos x, \sin x, \ldots, \cos nx, \sin nx, \ldots$$

in the interval $[-\pi, \pi]$.

The orthogonal system is said to be *normal*, if

$$\int_a^b \varphi_n^2(x)\,dx = 1 \quad (n = 1, 2, \ldots).$$

*Rademacher's system*[1] can serve as an example of a normal orthogonal system; it is set up thus: the interval [0,1] is divided into $2^n$ equal intervals and the function $r_n(x)$ is assumed to equal $+1$ in the first, third, ..., $(2^n - 1)$th interval and to equal $-1$ in the second, fourth, ..., $2^n$ th interval (i.e. it assumes alternately the values $+1$ and $-1$) and at the end points of the intervals it is considered to equal zero. This holds for all values of $n$ $(n = 1, 2, \ldots)$. The orthogonality of the system $\{r_n(x)\}$ obtained in the interval [0,1] follows from the fact that if $m \neq n$ (let $m < n$), then the function $r_n(x)$ in every interval when $r_m(x)$ is constant takes the value $+1$ just as many times as the value $-1$ and the lengths of the intervals in which it is constant are all equal. Thus we are satisfied that

$$\int_0^1 r_m(x) r_n(x)\,dx = 0 \quad (m \neq n).$$

Since for any $n$ we have $r_n^2(x) = 1$ everywhere, apart from a finite number of points, then the system $\{r_n(x)\}$ is normal†.

Later whilst studying the properties of trigonometric series Rademacher's system will prove very useful.

A trigonometric system is not normal but can be made normal, if the first function is multiplied by $1/\sqrt{2\pi}$ and all the other functions by $1/\sqrt{\pi}$, that is, the system

$$\frac{1}{\sqrt{2\pi}}, \quad \frac{\cos x}{\sqrt{\pi}}, \quad \frac{\sin x}{\sqrt{\pi}}, \ldots, \quad \frac{\cos nx}{\sqrt{\pi}}, \quad \frac{\sin nx}{\sqrt{\pi}}, \quad \ldots$$

is already a normal orthogonal system.

We will not consider the question why the study of orthogonal systems is extremely interesting and important. Specialized books are devoted to this question. Here we shall merely show that a whole series of theorems concerning the theory of trigonometric series can be obtained extremely easily, starting from very general results relating to the so-called orthogonal series.

A series of the form

$$\sum_{n=1}^{\infty} c_n \varphi_n(x), \tag{9.2}$$

where $c_n$ are constant coefficients and $\{\varphi_n(x)\}$ is a given orthogonal system of functions, is called *a series with respect to the orthogonal system* $\{\varphi_n(x)\}$ or briefly, *an orthogonal series.*

In the same way as we described how to find the coefficients of a trigonometric series if we know that it converges to a certain function $f(x)$, we can discuss how to determine the coefficients $c_n$, if we know that

$$f(x) = \sum_{n=1}^{\infty} c_n \varphi_n(x). \tag{9.3}$$

We again assume that the series converges uniformly. We suppose that the system $\{\varphi_n(x)\}$ is orthogonal and normal in $(a, b)$. Then multiplying both sides of equality (9.3) by $\varphi_m(x)$ and integrating between the limits from $a$ to $b$ we find††

$$\int_a^b f(x)\varphi_m(x)\,dx = c_m \int_a^b \varphi_m^2(x)\,dx = c_m,$$

† The reader can find more detail of the properties of Rademacher's system in Kaczmarz and Steinhaus's book, ref. A 12.

†† Here the functions $\varphi_n(x)$ and $f(x)$ are supposed to be such that the integrals (9.4) have meaning.

i.e.

$$c_m = \int_a^b f(x)\varphi_m(x)dx \quad (m = 1, 2, \ldots). \tag{9.4}$$

These formulae are also called *Fourier formulae* and if for some functions $f(x)$ the numbers $c_n$ are found from the formulae (9.4) and the series (9.2) is formed from them, then it is named the *Fourier series for the function $f(x)$ with respect to the orthogonal system $\{\varphi_n(x)\}$*.

Here, as in the case of the trigonometric system, the hypothesis of uniform convergence of the system was extremely limiting. We can consider a Fourier series for the function $f(x)$ with the single assumption that the integrals (9.4) have meaning and then write

$$f(x) \sim \sum_{n=1}^{\infty} c_n\varphi_n(x).$$

Just as in the theory of trigonometric series, the question arises of the convergence of the Fourier series and to what extent it characterizes the function $f(x)$.

It is, above all, clear that for the Fourier series to be able to define to any extent the properties of a function, it is necessary that there should not be identical Fourier series for two different functions. To explain the problem when this does occur, we must first study the concept of the completeness of an orthogonal system. The problem will be discussed in § 10. Here we shall just describe what we understand by an orthogonal system in the case when the functions $\varphi_n(x)$ are complex.

If the functions $\varphi_n(x)$ are complex functions of the real variable $x$, then they are said to be *orthogonal* when

$$\int_a^b \varphi_m(x)\bar{\varphi}_n(x)dx = 0 \quad (m \neq n) \tag{9.5}$$

and

$$\int_a^b |\varphi_n(x)|^2 dx \neq 0, \quad (n = 1, 2, \ldots). \tag{9.6}$$

The system is *normal* if

$$\int_a^b |\varphi_n(x)|^2 dx = 1 \quad (n = 1, 2, \ldots).$$

In the case of complex functions the Fourier formulae take the form

$$c_n = \int_a^b f(x)\bar{\varphi}_n(x)dx \tag{9.7}$$

for normal systems and

$$c_n = \frac{\int_a^b f(x)\bar{\varphi}_n(x)dx}{\int_a^b |\varphi_n(x)|^2 dx}$$

for non-normal systems.

An important example of an orthogonal system of complex functions is the system $\{e^{inx}\}$ $(n = 0, \pm 1, \pm 2, \ldots)$; it is orthogonal over any interval of length $2\pi$ (see § 5). If the multiplier $1/\sqrt{2\pi}$ is introduced, i.e., if the system

$$\left\{\frac{1}{\sqrt{2\pi}}\, e^{inx}\right\} \quad (n = 0, \pm 1, \ldots),$$

is considered, then it is also normal.

## § 10. Completeness of an orthogonal system

We now introduce the following important definition.†

DEFINITION. The system of functions $\{\varphi_n(x)\}$, defined in some interval $[a, b]$, is said to be complete in $L^p\,[a, b]$ $(p \geqslant 1)$ (or in $C\,[a, b]$) if there does not exist a single function $f(x) \in L^p\,[a, b]$ (or $f(x) \in C\,[a, b]$), which is orthogonal to all the functions of this system, unless $f(x) = 0$ almost everywhere in $[a, b]$ (for the case of the space $C$, everywhere in $[a, b]$).

In other words, for a complete system of the equalities

$$\int_a^b f(x)\varphi_n(x)\,dx = 0 \quad (n = 1, 2, \ldots) \tag{10.1}$$

and for $f(x) \in L^p\,[a, b]$ it should follow that $f(x) = 0$ almost everywhere in $[a, b]$ (similarly for space $C$, but the word "everywhere" should be substituted for the words "almost everywhere").

For the integrals occurring in (10.1) to have meaning for any $f(x) \in L\,[a, b]$, it is necessary and sufficient for all $\varphi_n(x)$ to be bounded in $[a, b]$; if $f(x) \in L^p\,[a, b]$, then it is necessary and sufficient for $\varphi_n(x) \in L^q\,[a, b]$ $(n = 1, 2, \ldots)$ where $1/p + 1/q = 1$ (see Introductory Material, § 9 and Appendix, § 3), finally for $f(x) \in C$ from the functions $\varphi_n(x)$ only summability is required.

The concept of completeness is introduced without assuming the orthogonality of the system $\{\varphi_n(x)\}$ but we will be interested in the case when it is orthogonal.

If the functions $\varphi_n(x)$ are complex, then the definition holds, only instead of equations (10.1) we must write

$$\int_a^b f(x)\bar{\varphi}_n(x)\,dx = 0 \quad (n = 1, 2, \ldots).$$

If the two functions $f(x) \in L^p\,[a, b]$ and $g(x) \in L^p\,[a, b]$ are different in a set of measure greater than zero, then they cannot possess identical Fourier series with respect to a system of functions $\{\varphi_n(x)\}$ complete in $L^p\,[a, b]$ (at $p \geqslant 1$). Indeed, if this were the case, then the difference $\psi(x) = f(x) - g(x)$ would be functions belonging to $L^p\,[a, b]$ and orthogonal to all $\{\varphi_n(x)\}$, whilst the condition $\psi(x) = 0$ almost everywhere in $[a, b]$ is not fulfilled and this contradicts the definition of completeness of the system.

---

† For all the notation used here reference should be made to the Notation (p. xxiii).

## § 11. Completeness of the trigonometric system in the space $L$

We shall prove that the trigonometrical system is complete in the space $L(-\pi, \pi)$, i.e., we shall demonstrate that two summable functions possess identical trigonometrical Fourier series only in the case when they coincide almost everywhere in $(-\pi, \pi)$.

For this we prove first of all that if the completeness of the trigonometric system is already known in $C$, then we can immediately obtain from it its completeness in $L$.

In fact, we assume that $f(x) \in L$ and

$$\left.\begin{aligned} \int_{-\pi}^{\pi} f(x) \cos nx\, dx &= 0 \quad (n = 0, 1, \ldots), \\ \int_{-\pi}^{\pi} f(x) \sin nx\, dx &= 0 \quad (n = 1, 2, \ldots). \end{aligned}\right\} \tag{11.1}$$

Then denoting the Fourier coefficients of $f(x)$ by $a_n$ and $b_n$ we have

$$a_n = 0 \quad (n = 0, 1, \ldots),$$
$$b_n = 0 \quad (n = 1, 2, \ldots).$$

Let us consider the function

$$F(x) = \int_{-\pi}^{x} f(t)\, dt$$

in

$$-\pi \leqslant x \leqslant \pi$$

and

$$F(x + 2\pi) = F(x).$$

It is clear that $F(\pi) = \pi a_0 = 0$ and $F(-\pi) = 0$, consequently $F(x)$ is continuous not only in $[-\pi, \pi]$ but also along the whole straight line $-\infty < x < +\infty$. We find its Fourier coefficients $A_n$ and $B_n$ by integrating by parts, so that

$$A_n = \frac{1}{\pi} \int_{-\pi}^{\pi} F(x) \cos nx\, dx = \frac{1}{n\pi} \int_{-\pi}^{\pi} f(x) \sin nx\, dx = 0.$$

(due to (11.1)) and similarly

$$B_n = \frac{1}{\pi} \int_{-\pi}^{\pi} F(x) \sin nx\, dx = \frac{1}{n\pi} \int_{-\pi}^{\pi} f(x) \cos nx\, dx = 0 \quad (n = 1, 2, \ldots).$$

Thus, all the Fourier coefficients for $F(x)$ apart from $A_0$ should be equal to zero. Since $F(x)$ is continuous, then supposing $\Phi(x) = F(x) - A_0/2$, we see that $\Phi(x)$ is continuous and all its Fourier coefficients equal zero, i.e., it is orthogonal to all the functions of the trigonometric system. But we have already assumed that the trigonometric system is complete in $C$. This means that $\Phi(x) \equiv 0$ and therefore $F(x) = A_0/2$

= const. But since $F'(x) = f(x)$ almost everywhere, then $f(x) = 0$ almost everywhere and this is what was required to be proved.

We will now prove the completeness of the system in $C$.

We have defined (Introductory Material, § 22) a trigonometric polynomial as any expression of the form

$$T_n(x) = \alpha_0 + \sum_{k=1}^{n} (\alpha_k \cos kx + \beta_k \sin kx). \tag{11.2}$$

It is clear that if $f(x)$ is orthogonal to all the functions of the trigonometric system, then it is orthogonal also to any trigonometric polynomial, i.e. for any $T_n(x)$

$$\int_{-\pi}^{\pi} f(x) T_n(x) dx = 0. \tag{11.3}$$

We will show that if $f(x)$ is continuous but not identically equal to zero, then a trigonometric polynomial $T_n(x)$ can be chosen such that the integral on the left-hand side of equation (11.3) is positive; then it becomes clear that it is only possible to avoid the contradiction if it is assumed that $f(x) \equiv 0$.

Thus, let $f(x) \not\equiv 0$; then a point $\xi$ can be found such that $f(\xi) = c \neq 0$. It can be assumed that $c > 0$, without altering the whole argument (since in the opposite case, it would be sufficient to show that $-f(x) \equiv 0$). It can also be assumed that $\xi = 0$, since if we are able for the functions $\varphi(x)$, of which $\varphi(0) > 0$, to find a polynomial $T_n^*(x)$ for which

$$\int_{-\pi}^{\pi} \varphi(x) T_n(x) dx > 0,$$

then, supposing $\varphi(x) = f(\xi + x)$ and $T_n(x) = T_n^*(x - \xi)$, we see that

$$\int_{-\pi}^{\pi} f(t) T_n(t) dt = \int_{-\pi}^{\pi} f(\xi + x) T_n(\xi + x) dt = \int_{-\pi}^{\pi} \varphi(x) T_n^*(x) dx > 0.$$

Thus, it remains to prove that if $f(0) = c > 0$, it is possible to find a polynomial $T_n(x)$ for which

$$\int_{-\pi}^{\pi} f(x) T_n(x) dx > 0. \tag{11.4}$$

But if $f(0) = c > 0$, then because of the continuity of $f(x)$ it is possible to find an interval $(-\delta, +\delta)$ where $f(x) \geqslant c/2$. We have

$$\int_{-\pi}^{\pi} f(x) T_n(x) dx = \int_{-\delta}^{\delta} f(x) T_n(x) dx + \int_{-\pi}^{-\delta} f(x) T_n(x) dx + \int_{\delta}^{\pi} f(x) T_n(x) dx.$$

Since $f(x)$ is continuous, then it is bounded, i.e.

$$|f(x)| \leqslant M \quad -\pi \leqslant x \leqslant \pi, \tag{11.5}$$

where $M$ is a constant.

Let $A > 0$ be given. We will assume that $T_n(x)$ can be chosen such that the following conditions are satisfied

$$T_n(x) \geqslant 1 \quad \text{in} \quad (-\delta, \delta), \tag{11.6}$$

$$\int_{-\pi}^{\pi} T_n(x)\,dx > A \tag{11.7}$$

and

$$|T_n(x)| \leqslant 1 \quad \text{in} \quad (-\pi, \delta) \quad \text{and} \quad (\delta, \pi). \tag{11.8}$$

Let us take $A > 4M\pi/c$, where $M$ is given by condition (11.5). Then

$$\int_{-\pi}^{\pi} f(x)T_n(x)\,dx > \frac{cA}{2} - M \cdot 2\pi > 0$$

and this signifies that (11.4) occurs and now the proof will be concluded.

So, it remains to choose a trigonometric polynomial $T_n(x)$ such that the conditions (11.6), (11.7) and (11.8) are satisfied.

To find this polynomial we note that if

$$T(x) = 1 + \cos x - \cos\delta,$$

then $T(x) \geqslant 1$ in $(-\delta, \delta)$ and $|T(x)| \leqslant 1$ outside $(-\delta, \delta)$, and therefore for

$$T_n(x) = [T(x)]^n$$

we also have

$$|T_n(x)| \leqslant 1 \quad \text{outside} \quad (-\delta, \delta) \quad \text{and} \quad T_n(x) \geqslant 1 \quad \text{in} \quad (-\delta, \delta).$$

Moreover, in $(-\delta/2, \delta/2)$ we have

$$T(x) > 1 + \cos\frac{\delta}{2} - \cos\delta = q > 1,$$

and therefore

$$\int_{-\delta}^{\delta} T_n(x)\,dx > \int_{-\delta/2}^{\delta/2} T_n(x)\,dx > q^n\delta \to \infty$$

as $n \to \infty$, which means that for any $A$, by choosing $n$ sufficiently large, the inequality (11.7) can be fulfilled.

It remains to prove that $T_n(x)$ is a trigonometric polynomial. But since $T(x) = \cos x + c$, where $c$ is a constant, then $[T(x)]^n$ is a trigonometric polynomial for any $n$ (see Introductory Material, § 22).

Thus, our theorem is completely proved. From the very definition of completeness of the system in the space $L^p$ it follows that if $p' > p$, then the completeness in $L^p$ implies completeness in $L^{p'}$. In particular, the trigonometric system which is complete in $L$ (§ 11) will be complete also in $L^p$ for any $p > 1$.

## § 12. Uniformly convergent Fourier series

From the completeness of the trigonometric system in $C$, the following simple but important conclusion can be drawn:

THEOREM. *If the Fourier series for a continuous function $f(x)$ converges uniformly, then the sum of this series coincides with $f(x)$.*

Indeed, let

$$f(x) \sim \frac{a_0}{2} + \sum_{n=1}^{\infty} (a_n \cos nx + b_n \sin nx),$$

where $f(x)$ is continuous, and the series on the right-hand side converges uniformly in $[-\pi, \pi]$. We will denote its sum by $S(x)$. It is clear that $S(x)$ is continuous. But we have seen (see § 4) that if $S(x)$ is the sum of an uniformly convergent trigonometric series, then its coefficients $a_n$ and $b_n$ are obtained from $S(x)$ by means of the Fourier formulae. On the other hand, it is conditional that $a_n$ and $b_n$ are obtained from $f(x)$ by means of the Fourier formulae. Thence it follows that $S(x)$ and $f(x)$ possess identical Fourier coefficients. Therefore, because of the completeness of the trigonometric system in $C$, they should coincide identically.

Later (see § 48) we will show that in this theorem the requirement of uniform convergence can be discarded and it can be affirmed that if $f(x)$ is continuous, then at any point where its Fourier series converges, it converges to $f(x)$.

At the present moment, as we are referring to uniformly convergent series, it is appropriate to prove one lemma, which will be used frequently later.

LEMMA. *Let the trigonometric series $a_0/2 + \sum_{n=1}^{\infty} (a_n \cos nx + b_n \sin nx)$ possess a sub-sequence of partial sums, converging uniformly to some function $f(x)$. Then this series is its Fourier series* (in particular, this statement is more accurate, when the series itself converges uniformly to $f(x)$).

Indeed, let $S_{n_k}(x)$ $(k = 1, 2, \dots)$ converge uniformly to $f(x)$. Then, the more so

$$\int_{-\pi}^{\pi} |f(x) - S_{n_k}(x)|\, dx \to 0 \quad \text{as} \quad k \to \infty.$$

Hence for any $m$ we have

$$\int_{-\pi}^{\pi} [f(x) - S_{n_k}(x)] \cos mx\, dx \to 0 \quad \text{as} \quad k \to \infty,$$

$$\int_{-\pi}^{\pi} [f(x) - S_{n_k}(x)] \sin mx\, dx \to 0 \quad \text{as} \quad k \to \infty,$$

i.e.

$$\lim_{k \to \infty} \int_{-\pi}^{\pi} S_{n_k}(x) \cos mx\, dx = \int_{-\pi}^{\pi} f(x) \cos mx\, dx$$

and similarly for $\sin mx$. But because of the orthogonality of the trigonometric system, if $n_k \geqslant m$, then we have

$$\int_{-\pi}^{\pi} S_{n_k}(x) \cos mx\, dx = a_m \int_{-\pi}^{\pi} \cos^2 mx\, dx = \pi a_m,$$

and therefore

$$\lim_{k\to\infty} \int_{-\pi}^{\pi} S_{n_k}(x) \cos mx \, dx = \pi a_m$$

which means

$$a_m = \frac{1}{\pi} \int_{-\pi}^{\pi} f(x) \cos mx \, dx$$

and similarly for $b_m$. Thus the lemma is proved.

## § 13. The minimum property of the partial sums of a Fourier series; Bessel's inequality

Let us now return to the general case, i.e., to considering the Fourier series with respect to any orthogonal system. We will refer to orthogonal systems complete in $L^2$, since they possess a number of important properties which we will proceed to study.

Let $\{\varphi_n(x)\}$ be complete in $L^2$ $[a, b]$ and orthogonal and normal in this interval. We set ourselves the following problem: given a function $f(x) \in L^2$, we take $n$ functions of the system $\{\varphi_n(x)\}$ and consider all possible expressions of the form $\sum_{k=1}^{n} \alpha_k \varphi_k(x)$, which are known as polynomials of the $n$th order with respect to the system $\{\varphi_n(x)\}$. We want to know how to choose the constants $\alpha_1, \alpha_2, \ldots, \alpha_n$ so that the polynomial $\sum_{k=1}^{n} \alpha_k \varphi_k(x)$ gives the best approximation for $f(x)$ in the metric space $L^2$, i.e. for the norm of the difference

$$\| f(x) - \sum_{k=1}^{n} \alpha_k \varphi_k(x) \| L^2$$

to be a minimum. We will prove a theorem.

THEOREM. *Of all the polynomials of the n-th order with respect to a normal orthogonal system $\{\varphi_n(x)\}$, the best approximation in the metric space $L^2$ for $f(x) \in L^2$ is given by the n-th partial sum of its Fourier series with respect to this system.*

In order to verify this theorem which we will prove generally by assuming that $\varphi_n(x)$ is complex, we write, using the identity $|A^2| = A \cdot \bar{A}$:

$$\left\| f(x) - \sum_{k=1}^{n} \alpha_k \varphi_k(x) \right\|_{L^2}^2 = \int_a^b \left| f(x) - \sum_{k=1}^{n} \alpha_k \varphi_k(x) \right|^2 dx$$

$$= \int_a^b \left[ f(x) - \sum_{k=1}^{n} \alpha_k \varphi_k(x) \right] \left[ \bar{f}(x) - \sum_{k=1}^{n} \bar{\alpha}_k \bar{\varphi}_k(x) \right] dx$$

$$= \int_a^b |f(x)|^2 dx - \sum_{k=1}^{n} \alpha_k \int_a^b \bar{f}(x) \varphi_k(x) dx - \sum_{k=1}^{n} \bar{\alpha}_k \int_a^b f(x) \bar{\varphi}_k(x) dx$$

$$+ \sum_{k=1}^{n} \sum_{j=1}^{n} \alpha_k \bar{\alpha}_j \int_a^b \varphi_k(x) \bar{\varphi}_j(x) dx;$$

and since

$$\int_a^b \varphi_k(x)\bar{\varphi}_j(x)\,dx = 0 \quad \text{for} \quad k \neq j,$$

$$\int_a^b |\varphi_k(x)|^2\,dx = 1 \quad \text{for} \quad k = 1, 2, \ldots,$$

then

$$\int_a^b |f(x) - \sum_{k=1}^n \alpha_k\varphi_k(x)|^2\,dx = \int_a^b |f(x)|^2\,dx - \sum_{k=1}^n \alpha_k\bar{c}_k - \sum_{k=1}^n \bar{\alpha}_k c_k + \sum_{k=1}^n |\alpha_k|^2,$$

where $c_k$ are the Fourier coefficients of the function $f(x)$.

In other words $\left(\text{adding and subtracting} \sum_{k=1}^n |c_k|^2\right)$,

$$\left\| f(x) - \sum_{k=1}^n \alpha_k\varphi_k(x) \right\|_{L^2}^2 = \|f\|_{L^2}^2 + \sum_{k=1}^n |c_k - \alpha_k|^2 - \sum_{k=1}^n |c_k|^2. \tag{13.1}$$

It is clear that the right-hand side of (13.1) will be a minimum when and only when

$$\alpha_k = c_k \quad (k = 1, 2, \ldots, n),$$

and the theorem is proved.

Substituting the numbers $c_k$ in (13.1) instead of $\alpha_k$, we obtain as a result

$$\left\| f(x) - \sum_{k=1}^n c_k\varphi_k(x) \right\|_{L^2}^2 = \|f\|_{L^2}^2 - \sum_{k=1}^n |c_k|^2. \tag{13.2}$$

Since the left-hand side of equation (13.2) is non-negative, then the right-hand side is also non-negative and therefore

$$\sum_{k=1}^n |c_k|^2 \leqslant \|f\|_{L^2}^2.$$

This inequality is true for any $n$ and therefore the series $\sum_{k=1}^\infty |c_k|^2$ converges and

$$\sum_{k=1}^\infty |c_k|^2 \leqslant \|f\|_{L^2}^2. \tag{13.3}$$

The inequality (13.3) is called *Bessel's inequality*. It holds for any normal orthogonal system and for any $f(x) \in L^2$.

## § 14. Convergence of a Fourier series in the metric space $L^2$

An important theorem can be obtained easily from Bessel's inequality.

THEOREM. *For any function with an integrable square, the Fourier series with respect to any normal orthogonal system converges in the metric space $L^2$.*

In order to prove this assertion, we recall (see Introductory Material, § 21) that for convergence of the sequence $f_n(x)$ in the metric space $L^2$ it is necessary and sufficient that for any $\varepsilon$ it is possible to find $N$ such that

$$\|f_n(x) - f_m(x)\|_{L^2} < \varepsilon \quad \text{for} \quad n \geqslant N \quad \text{and} \quad m \geqslant N.$$

We will show that this criterion is fulfilled if the partial sums $S_n(x)$ of the Fourier series for $f(x) \in L^2$ play the role of the functions $f_n(x)$.

We have for any integer $n$ and $p \geqslant 1$

$$\| S_{n+p}(x) - S_n(x) \|_{L^2}^2 = \left\| \sum_{k=n+1}^{n+p} c_k \varphi_k(x) \right\|_{L^2}^2$$

$$= \int_a^b \left| \sum_{k=n+1}^{n+p} c_k \varphi_k(x) \right|^2 dx = \sum_{k=n+1}^{n+p} |c_k|^2,$$

since the system $\{\varphi_n(x)\}$ is orthogonal and normal. But by virtue of Bessel's inequality we know that if $f(x) \in L^2$, then $\sum_{k=1}^{\infty} |c_k|^2 < +\infty$, and therefore for any $\varepsilon > 0$, it is possible to find $N$ such that $\sum_{n+1}^{n+p} |c_k|^2 < \varepsilon$ for $n \geqslant N$ and then

$$\| S_{n+p}(x) - S_n(x) \|_{L^2} < \varepsilon,$$

which concludes the proof of the convergence of the Fourier series for $f(x) \in L^2$.

However, it should be noted that only the convergence of the Fourier series in the metric space $L^2$ was proved. It is not evident from this that the sum in the sense of the metric space $L^2$ of this series should be equal to the function $f(x)$. This in fact is not always the case. The question whether the Fourier series in the metric space $L^2$ does converge to a given function is linked with the question of the so-called closure of the orthogonal system in the metric space $L^2$. We will now start discussing this question.

## § 15. Concept of the closure of the system. Relationship between closure and completeness

It is said that the system of functions $\{\varphi_n(x)\}$ is *closed in the space* $C$ in $[a, b]$ or in $L^p(p \geqslant 1)$ in $[a, b]$, if it is possible to represent any function $f(x) \in C$ (or $f(x) \in L^p$) in this space to a given degree of accuracy in the form of a polynomial with respect to the system $\{\varphi_n(x)\}$.

Re-stating this more precisely, the system $\{\varphi_n(x)\}$ is closed in $C$ (or in $L^p$) if for any $f(x) \in C$ (or $f(x) \in L^p$) and for any $\varepsilon > 0$ it is possible to choose the numbers $\alpha_1$, $\alpha_2, \ldots, \alpha_n$, so that

$$\left| f(x) - \sum_{k=1}^{n} \alpha_k \varphi_k(x) \right| < \varepsilon \quad \text{at} \quad a \leqslant x \leqslant b$$

or

$$\left\| f(x) - \sum_{k=1}^{n} \alpha_k \varphi_k(x) \right\|_{L^p} < \varepsilon.$$

We will now formulate without proof two theorems referring to the connection between closed and complete systems, namely: if $1/p + 1/q = 1$, then every system closed in $L^p(p > 1)$ (or in $C$) is complete in $L^q$ (or in $L$). Conversely, every system complete in $L^p(p > 1)$ is closed in $L^q$.†

† The proof of these theorems can be found, for example, in Kaczmarz and Steinhaus's book, ref. A 12.

We will consider in more detail only the most important case, when $p = 2$. In this case $q = 2$ and the formulation of our theorem leads to:

THEOREM. *In the space $L^2$ the completeness and closure of a system are equivalent, i.e. every complete system is closed and vice versa.*

This statement can be proved for any systems consisting of functions occurring in $L^2$. But we shall confine ourselves to a consideration of the case when the given system is orthogonal. Moreover, since neither the closure nor the completeness of a system can disappear or appear, if we multiply all the functions of the system by any constants, then the system can be assumed to be normal.

Thus, let $\{\varphi_n(x)\}$ be a normal orthogonal system in the interval $[a, b]$. We have seen in § 14 that for any $f(x) \in L^2\,[a, b]$ its Fourier series with respect to the system $\{\varphi_n(x)\}$ converges in the metric space $L^2$. We will denote its sum by $F(x)$, then

$$F(x) = \sum_{k=1}^{\infty} c_k \varphi_k(x), \tag{15.1}$$

where the equal sign is understood to mean convergence in the metric $L^2$.

We will prove that the numbers $c_n$ are the Fourier coefficients of the functions $F(x)$. In fact, multiplying both sides of equality (15.1) by $\bar{\varphi}_n(x)$ and integrating (this is valid according to Riesz's theorem, see Introductory Material, § 21), we have

$$\int_a^b F(x)\bar{\varphi}_n(x)\,dx = \sum_{k=1}^{\infty} c_k \int_a^b \varphi_k(x)\bar{\varphi}_n(x)\,dx. \tag{15.2}$$

Because of the orthogonality and normality of $\{\varphi_n(x)\}$, we find that

$$c_n = \int_a^b F(x)\bar{\varphi}_n(x)\,dx.$$

Hence we conclude that all the Fourier coefficients of the functions $f(x)$ and $F(x)$ are identical. If it is assumed that the system $\{\varphi_n(x)\}$ is complete, then this is possible only in the case when $f(x) = F(x)$ almost everywhere and therefore we obtain

$$f(x) = \sum_{k=1}^{n} c_k \varphi_k(x).$$

Here the equality sign is again understood in the sense of convergence in $L^2$. Therefore

$$\left\| f(x) - \sum_{k=1}^{n} c_k \varphi_k(x) \right\|_{L^2} \to 0$$

as $n \to \infty$, i.e. for any $\varepsilon > 0$ it is possible to find $N$ such that

$$\left\| f(x) - \sum_{k=1}^{n} c_k \varphi_k(x) \right\|_{L^2} < \varepsilon.$$

But $f(x)$ was any function of $L^2$. Therefore, in agreement with the definition of closure, we see that $\{\varphi_n(x)\}$ is closed in $L^2$.

Thus, we have proved that the completeness of a system in $L^2$ implies its closure in $L^2$. The converse is very easily proved.

Let $\{\varphi_n(x)\}$ be a closed system in $L^2$ and $f(x)$ any function of $L^2$. Then for any $\varepsilon > 0$ it is possible to choose numbers $\alpha_1, \alpha_2, \ldots, \alpha_n$ such that

$$\left\| f(x) - \sum_{k=1}^{n} \alpha_k \varphi_k(x) \right\| < \varepsilon.$$

But it was proved (see § 13) that of all the polynomials of order $n$ with respect to the system $\{\varphi_n(x)\}$ the best approximation to $f(x)$ in the metric $L^2$ is given by the polynomial $\sum_{k=1}^{n} c_k \varphi_k(x)$, the coefficients of which are the Fourier coefficients of $f(x)$. Therefore

$$\left\| f(x) - \sum_{k=1}^{n} c_k \varphi_k(x) \right\| \leqslant \left\| f(x) - \sum_{k=1}^{n} \alpha_k \varphi_k(x) \right\| < \varepsilon.$$

But since we know (see (13.2)) that

$$\left\| f(x) - \sum_{k=1}^{n} c_k \varphi_k(x) \right\|^2 = \| f \|^2 - \sum_{k=1}^{n} |c_k|^2,$$

then

$$0 \leqslant \| f \|^2 - \sum_{k=1}^{n} |c_k|^2 < \varepsilon^2,$$

whence it follows that

$$\sum_{k=1}^{\infty} |c_k|^2 = \| f \|^2. \tag{15.3}$$

We have seen earlier (§ 13) that for any normal orthogonal system Bessel's inequality (13.3) holds

$$\sum_{k=1}^{\infty} |c_k|^2 \leqslant \| f \|^2.$$

We now see that in the case of a closed system this inequality changes to the equality (15.3); it is usually known as *Parseval's equality*.

Thus, *if a system is closed, then for any $f(x) \in L^2$ Parseval's equality holds.*

But from this the completeness of the system $\{\varphi_n(x)\}$ in $L^2$ follows immediately, since if the function $f(x) \in L^2$ is orthogonal to all functions of the system $\{\varphi_n(x)\}$, then

$$c_n = \int_a^b f(x) \overline{\varphi}_n(x) dx = 0 \quad (n = 1, 2, \ldots),$$

i.e. all its Fourier coefficients equal zero; but then $\|f\|^2 = 0$ due to (15.3), i.e.

$$\int_a^b |f|^2 dx = 0,$$

and this is possible only if $f(x) = 0$ almost everywhere.

Thus, the closure of a system in $L^2$ implies its completeness in $L^2$; and the proof is concluded.

## § 16. The Riesz–Fischer theorem

We have seen in § 13 that for any function $f(x) \in L^2$ the series $\sum_{n=1}^{\infty} |c_n|^2$, comprising the squares of the moduli of its Fourier coefficients, converges for any orthogonal system. Moreover, in the case when the system under consideration, is complete, then (see 15.3)

$$\|f\|^2 = \sum_{n=1}^{\infty} |c_n|^2.$$

But the following considerably deeper theorem also holds:

THE RIESZ–FISCHER THEOREM. *Let $c_n$ $(n = 1, 2, \ldots)$ be any sequence of numbers for which $\sum_{n=1}^{\infty} |c_n|^2 < +\infty$ and $\{\varphi_n(x)\}$ be any normal orthogonal system. Then there exists an $f(x) \in L^2$ such that the numbers $c_n$ are its Fourier coefficients with respect to this system; if the system is complete, then there exists only one such $f(x)$.*

To prove this we note that if a series $\sum_{n=1}^{\infty} c_n \varphi_n(x)$ is set up, then it should converge in the metric $L^2$; indeed since $\sum_{n=1}^{\infty} |c_n|^2 < +\infty$, then for any $\varepsilon > 0$, $N$ can be chosen sufficiently large for $\sum_{N+1}^{\infty} |c_n|^2 < \varepsilon$. But then

$$\|S_{n+p}(x) - S_n(x)\|^2 = \sum_{n+1}^{n+p} |c_k|^2 < \varepsilon \quad (n \geqslant N,\ p > 0)$$

(we have already carried out a similar argument in § 14); therefore, the sequence $S_n(x)$ converges in the metric $L^2$. Thus, an $f(x)$ is found such that $\|f(x) - S_n(x)\|_{L_2} \to 0$ as $n \to \infty$. Repeating the argument of § 15 we see that the series $\sum_{n=1}^{\infty} c_n \varphi_n(x)$ is the Fourier series for $f(x)$, whilst if the system is complete, this $f(x)$ is the only one.

## § 17. The Riesz–Fischer theorem and Parseval's equality for a trigonometric system

Both the Riesz–Fischer theorem and Parseval's equality have been proved for normal systems of functions. Therefore they hold for the system

$$\frac{1}{\sqrt{2\pi}}, \frac{\cos x}{\sqrt{\pi}}, \frac{\sin x}{\sqrt{\pi}}, \ldots, \frac{\cos nx}{\sqrt{\pi}}, \frac{\sin nx}{\sqrt{\pi}}, \ldots$$

Therefore, if $a_0$, $a_n$, $b_n$ are a sequence of numbers for which

$$\frac{a_0^2}{2} + \sum_{n=1}^{\infty} (a_n^2 + b_n^2) < +\infty, \tag{17.1}$$

then it is possible to find $F(x)$ such that

$$\frac{a_0}{\sqrt{2}} = \int_{-\pi}^{\pi} \frac{1}{\sqrt{2\pi}} F(x)\,dx; \quad a_n = \int_{-\pi}^{\pi} F(x) \frac{\cos nx}{\sqrt{\pi}}\,dx; \quad b_n = \int_{-\pi}^{\pi} F(x) \frac{\sin nx}{\sqrt{\pi}}\,dx.$$

Hence, supposing $f(x) = \sqrt{\pi}\, F(x)$, we see that

$$a_0 = \frac{1}{\pi}\int_{-\pi}^{\pi} f(x)dx; \quad a_n = \frac{1}{\pi}\int_{-\pi}^{\pi} f(x)\cos nx\, dx; \quad b_n = \frac{1}{\pi}\int_{-\pi}^{\pi} f(x)\sin nx\, dx.$$

Thus, if the series (17.1) converges, then there exists $f(x) \in L^2$, such that the series with coefficients $a_n$, $b_n$ is a Fourier series.

Parseval's equality for a trigonometric system takes the form

$$\frac{1}{\pi}\int_{-\pi}^{\pi} f^2(x)\, dx = \frac{a_0^2}{2} + \sum_{n=1}^{\infty} (a_n^2 + b_n^2). \tag{17.2}$$

We will also note that by virtue of the minimum property of partial sums of a Fourier series (see § 13), we can state particularly for the case of a trigonometric series, that of all the trigonometric polynomials of order not higher than $n$, the best approximation in the metric $L^2$ for any $f(x) \in L^2$ is given by the $n$th partial sum of the series $\sigma(f)$.

In Introductory Material, § 24, we denoted by $E_n^{(p)}(f)$ the best approximation of $f(x) \in L^p$ in the metric $L^p$ by trigonometric polynomials of order not higher than $n$; this means

$$E_n^{(2)}(f) = \left\{\int_{-\pi}^{\pi} |f(x) - s_n(x)|^2 dx\right\}^{\frac{1}{2}}. \tag{17.3}$$

This formula will be useful later.

## § 18. Parseval's equality for the product of two functions

In this section we will only consider functions which assume real values.

We note yet another useful equality, easily derived from Parseval's equality.

*If $f(x) \in L^2$ and $g(x) \in L^2$, and the system $\{\varphi_n(x)\}$ is orthogonal, normal and complete in $(a, b)$, whilst $c_n$ are Fourier coefficients for $f(x)$ and $d_n$ are Fourier coefficients for $g(x)$, then we have the formula*

$$\int_a^b f(x)g(x)dx = \sum_{n=1}^{\infty} c_n d_n. \tag{18.1}$$

Indeed, if $f \in L^2$ and $g \in L^2$, then this is just as true for their sums and applying Parseval's equality to $f(x)$, $g(x)$ and $f(x) + g(x)$, we have

$$\int_a^b f^2(x)dx = \sum_{n=1}^{\infty} c_n^2, \quad \int_a^b g^2(x)\, dx = \sum_{n=1}^{\infty} d_n^2, \tag{18.2}$$

$$\int_a^b [f(x) + g(x)]^2 dx = \sum_{n=1}^{\infty} (c_n + d_n)^2. \tag{18.3}$$

Removing the brackets on the left-hand side of (18.3) we obtain

$$\int_a^b [f(x) + g(x)]^2 dx = \int_a^b f^2(x) dx + 2 \int_a^b f(x) g(x) dx + \int_a^b g^2(x) dx$$

$$= \sum_{n=1}^{\infty} c_n^2 + 2 \sum_{n=1}^{\infty} c_n d_n + \sum_{n=1}^{\infty} d_n^2.$$

Subtracting equation (18.2) from (18.3) and dividing by 2, we obtain the desired formula (18.1).

For the case of the trigonometric system, formula (18.1) takes the form

$$\frac{1}{\pi} \int_{-\pi}^{\pi} f(x) g(x) dx = \frac{a_0 \alpha_0}{2} + \sum_{n=1}^{\infty} (a_n \alpha_n + b_n \beta_n),$$

where $a_n$, $b_n$ are the coefficients for $f(x)$ and $\alpha_n$, $\beta_n$ are the coefficients for $g(x)$.

## § 19. The tending to zero of Fourier coefficients

We have seen that if $f(x) \in L^2$, then $\sum_{n=1}^{\infty} |c_n|^2 < +\infty$, whence it immediately follows that $|c_n| \to 0$ as $n \to \infty$. This holds for any orthogonal system. Moreover, the Riesz–Fischer theorem proves that if for some $c_n$ we have $\sum c_n^2 < +\infty$, then these $c_n$ are certainly Fourier coefficients of some function $f(x) \in L^2$.

Matters become considerably more complicated if $f(x) \in L$ but $f^2(x)$ is non-summable. Then we can say very little about the Fourier coefficients of $f(x)$. It would be true to say that given a sequence of numbers $c_n$ for which $\sum c_n^2 = +\infty$, then we do not even know whether there exists a function that possesses these numbers for its Fourier coefficients.

We will state here a few simple facts which will permit us to judge Fourier coefficients to a certain extent.

MERCER'S THEOREM. *If for an orthogonal normal system*† $\{\varphi_n(x)\}$ *the functions are all bounded, i.e.*

$$|\varphi_n(x)| \leqslant M \quad a \leqslant x \leqslant b \quad (n = 1, 2, \ldots),$$

*then the Fourier coefficients of any summable function with respect this system tend to zero.*

Let $f(x)$ be summable and $\varepsilon > 0$ be given; we will first find a function $F(x)$, for which $\int_a^b |f(x) - F(x)| \, dx < \varepsilon$, whilst $F(x)$ is bounded. This is always possible from the very definition of a Lebesgue integral.

† Here we are concerned only with functions which assume real values.

Since any bounded function is known to belong to $L^2$, then its Fourier coefficients tend to zero, which means that for a sufficiently large $N$ we will have

$$\left|\int_a^b F(x)\varphi_n(x)\,dx\right| < \varepsilon \quad \text{at} \quad n > N.$$

Moreover

$$\left|\int_a^b [f(x) - F(x)]\varphi_n(x)\,dx\right| \leqslant M\varepsilon.$$

and then

$$\left|\int_a^b f(x)\varphi_n(x)\,dx\right| < \varepsilon(1 + M) \quad \text{for} \quad n > N,$$

and therefore

$$\int_a^b f(x)\varphi_n(x)\,dx \to 0 \quad \text{as} \quad n \to \infty,$$

and the theorem is proved.

Since a trigonometric system consists of functions which are all bounded, it follows in particular that

THEOREM. *For any summable function its Fourier coefficients with respect to the trigonometric system tend to zero.*

This fact has very great significance since later (see § 62) we will see that the trigonometric series, the coefficients of which do not tend to zero, can converge only in a set of measure zero. However, the tending to zero of the coefficients of a trigonometric series alone is not sufficient for it to converge (see § 63); moreover, we will later see (Chapter V, § 20) that a Fourier series can also diverge at every point. Thus, the problem of convergence of trigonometric series requires serious investigation.

## § 20. Fejér's lemma

The theorem of § 19 on the tending to zero of the Fourier coefficients is a particular case of the following general result, due to Fejér[1].

FEJÉR'S LEMMA.† *If $f(x) \in L$ has a period $2\pi$ and $g(x)$ has a period $2\pi$ and is bounded then*

$$\lim_{n \to \infty} \int_{-\pi}^{\pi} f(x)g(nx)\,dx = \frac{1}{2\pi} \int_{-\pi}^{\pi} f(x)\,dx \cdot \int_{-\pi}^{\pi} g(x)\,dx. \tag{20.1}$$

Here $n \to \infty$, assuming any values, not only integers (supposing $g(x) = \cos x$ or $g(x) = \sin x$, we immediately see that the assertion concerning Fourier coefficients is true).

† This lemma can be omitted on a first reading. It is only used in Chapter XIII.

For the proof of Fejér's lemma, let us note first that if for any $\varepsilon > 0$ it is possible to find $\varphi(x)$ such that

$$\int_{-\pi}^{\pi} |f(x) - \varphi(x)|\, dx < \varepsilon \tag{20.2}$$

and if for $\varphi(x)$ equality (20.1) has already been proved, then it is also true for $f(x)$.

In fact, we have for any $n$

$$\left| \int_{-\pi}^{\pi} f(x) g(nx) dx - \int_{-\pi}^{\pi} \varphi(x) g(nx) dx \right| < M\varepsilon, \tag{20.3}$$

where $M$ is the upper bound of $f(x)$ in $[-\pi, \pi]$. Moreover, if (20.1) is true for $\varphi(x)$, then $N$ is found such that

$$\left| \int_{-\pi}^{\pi} \varphi(x) g(nx) dx - \frac{1}{2\pi} \int_{-\pi}^{\pi} \varphi(x) dx \int_{-\pi}^{\pi} g(x) dx \right| < \varepsilon \quad \text{for} \quad n > N. \tag{20.4}$$

Finally, it follows from (20.2) that

$$\left| \frac{1}{2\pi} \int_{-\pi}^{\pi} f(x) dx \int_{-\pi}^{\pi} g(x)\, dx - \frac{1}{2\pi} \int_{-\pi}^{\pi} \varphi(x) dx \int_{-\pi}^{\pi} g(x) dx \right|$$

$$< \frac{\varepsilon}{2\pi} \left| \int_{-\pi}^{\pi} g(x) dx \right| < \varepsilon M. \tag{20.5}$$

Therefore, from (20.3), (20.4) and (20.5)

$$\left| \int_{-\pi}^{\pi} f(x) g(nx) dx - \frac{1}{2\pi} \int_{-\pi}^{\pi} f(x) dx \int_{-\pi}^{\pi} g(x) dx \right| < (2M + 1)\varepsilon \tag{20.6}$$

for any $n > N$. Since $\varepsilon$ can be as small as desired, (20.1) follows from (20.6).

Since the class of step-functions is everywhere dense in the class of functions $f \in L$ (see Introductory Material, § 21), then on the basis only of what has already been proved we see that it is sufficient to prove equality (20.1) for step-functions. But this is also easily proved for them, since the interval $[-\pi, \pi]$ is divided into a finite number of intervals in each of which $f(x)$ is constant; then if $\delta_j$ is such an interval $f(x) = c_j$ in it and $k$ is the number of intervals $\delta_j$, equality (20.1) takes the form

$$\lim_{n \to \infty} \sum_{j=1}^{k} c_j \int_{\delta_j} g(nx) dx = \sum_{j=1}^{k} c_j \delta_j \frac{1}{2\pi} \int_{-\pi}^{\pi} g(x) dx \tag{20.7}$$

it will be proved if we will satisfy ourselves that for any interval $\delta$

$$\lim_{n \to \infty} \int_{\delta} g(nx) dx = \frac{\delta}{2\pi} \int_{-\pi}^{\pi} g(x) dx. \tag{20.8}$$

Let $\delta = (a, b)$. We have $-\pi \leqslant a < b \leqslant \pi$. It must be proved that

$$\lim_{n\to\infty} \frac{1}{b-a} \int_a^b g(nx)dx = \frac{1}{2\pi} \int_{-\pi}^{\pi} g(x)dx, \tag{20.9}$$

taking into account that $|g(x)| < M$ and $g(x)$ is periodic with period $2\pi$.

For this purpose we will note first of all that

$$\frac{1}{b-a} \int_a^b g(nx)dx = \frac{1}{n(b-a)} \int_{na}^{nb} g(t)dt. \tag{20.10}$$

Let $m_1$ and $m_2$ be integers (each of them can be positive, negative or equal to zero) such that

$$\left.\begin{aligned} m_1 \cdot 2\pi \leqslant na < (m_1 + 1)\, 2\pi, \\ m_2 \cdot 2\pi \leqslant nb < (m_2 + 1)\, 2\pi. \end{aligned}\right\} \tag{20.11}$$

Since

$$\int_{na}^{nb} g(t)dt = \int_{m_1 \cdot 2\pi}^{m_2 \cdot 2\pi} g(t)dt + \int_{m_2 \cdot 2\pi}^{nb} g(t)dt - \int_{m_1 \cdot 2\pi}^{na} g(t)dt \tag{20.12}$$

and the range of integration of the last two integrals for formula (20.12) does not exceed $2\pi$, then

$$\left| \int_{na}^{nb} g(t)dt - \int_{2\pi m_1}^{2\pi m_2} g(t)dt \right| < 4M\pi, \tag{20.13}$$

Moreover

$$\int_{2\pi m_1}^{2\pi m_2} g(t)dt = (m_2 - m_1) \int_{-\pi}^{\pi} g(t)dt \tag{20.14}$$

because of the periodicity of $g(t)$. From (20.13) and (20.14) this means that

$$\left| \int_{na}^{nb} g(t)dt - (m_2 - m_1) \int_{-\pi}^{\pi} g(t)dt \right| < 4M\pi. \tag{20.15}$$

But from (20.11)

$$(m_2 - m_1 - 1)\, 2\pi < n(b-a) < (m_2 - m_1 + 1)\, 2\pi,$$

and therefore

$$n(b-a) = (m_2 - m_1 + \theta)\, 2\pi, \quad \text{where} \quad |\theta| < 1.$$

In other words,

$$m_2 - m_1 = \frac{n(b-a)}{2\pi} - \theta, \tag{20.16}$$

and therefore from (20.15) and (20.16)

$$\left| \frac{1}{n(b-a)} \int_{na}^{nb} g(t)dt - \frac{1}{2\pi} \int_{-\pi}^{\pi} g(t)dt + \frac{\theta}{n(b-a)} \int_{-\pi}^{\pi} g(t)dt \right| < \frac{4M\pi}{n(b-a)}.$$

Hence it follows that

$$\lim_{n\to\infty} \frac{1}{n(b-a)} \int_{nb}^{na} g(t)\,dt = \frac{1}{2\pi} \int_{-\pi}^{\pi} g(t)\,dt$$

and taking into account (20.10) we see that (20.9) is proved and thus the proof of the lemma is concluded.

## § 21. Estimate of Fourier coefficients in terms of the integral modulus of continuity of the function

We have seen in § 19 that for any summable function $f(x)$ the Fourier coefficients $a_n$, $b_n$ tend to zero as $n \to \infty$. However, sometimes the knowledge of this one fact is insufficient and the rate at which it tends to zero should be estimated.

Let us recall that in Introductory Material, § 25 we defined the concept of the integral modulus of continuity $\omega_1(\delta, f)$ for $f(x)$ and we proved that for any $f \in L$ we have $\omega_1(\delta, f) \to 0$ as $\delta \to 0$.

Let $c_n$ be complex Fourier coefficients of the function $f(x)$, i.e.

$$c_n = \frac{1}{2\pi} \int_0^{2\pi} f(x) e^{-inx}\,dx \quad (n = 0, \pm 1, \pm 2, \ldots). \tag{21.1}$$

By substituting $x + \pi/n$ for $x$ we can write

$$c_n = -\frac{1}{2\pi} \int_0^{2\pi} f\left(x + \frac{\pi}{n}\right) e^{-inx}\,dx. \tag{21.2}$$

Adding (21.2) and (21.2) and dividing by two, we obtain

$$c_n = \frac{1}{4\pi} \int_0^{2\pi} \left[ f(x) - f\left(x + \frac{\pi}{n}\right) \right] e^{-inx}\,dx,$$

whence

$$|c_n| \leqslant \frac{1}{4\pi} \int_0^{2\pi} \left| f\left(x + \frac{\pi}{n}\right) - f(x) \right| dx \leqslant \frac{1}{4\pi} \omega_1\left(\frac{\pi}{n}, f\right).$$

Thus for complex Fourier coefficients of the function $f(x)$ we have

$$|c_n| \leqslant \frac{1}{4\pi} \omega_1\left(\frac{\pi}{n}, f\right) \quad (n = \pm 1, \pm 2, \ldots). \tag{21.3}$$

In the case of real Fourier coefficients, arguing in just the same way we have

$$\left.\begin{aligned} |a_n| &\leqslant \frac{1}{2\pi} \omega_1\left(\frac{\pi}{n}, f\right), \\ |b_n| &\leqslant \frac{1}{2\pi} \omega_1\left(\frac{\pi}{n}, f\right), \end{aligned}\right\} \quad (n = 1, 2, \ldots). \tag{21.4}$$

Formulae (21.4) give new evidence of the fact that the Fourier coefficients of any $f(x) \in L$ tend to zero but they also permit the rate of this tendency to be judged in terms of the properties of the function, since, roughly speaking, the "better" the function is, the more rapidly its integral modulus of continuity tends to zero.

If $f(x)$ is periodic and continuous in $[-\pi, \pi]$, then from the definition of the modulus of continuity (see Introductory Material, § 25) we immediately conclude that

$$\omega_1(\delta, f) \leqslant \omega(\delta, f) \cdot 2\pi,$$

and therefore for continuous $f(x)$ we have

$$\left.\begin{aligned} |a_n| &\leqslant \omega\left(\frac{\pi}{n}, f\right), \\ & \qquad\qquad (n = 1, 2, \ldots). \\ |b_n| &\leqslant \omega\left(\frac{\pi}{n}, f\right), \end{aligned}\right\} \tag{21.5}$$

## § 22. Fourier coefficients for functions of bounded variation

Let $f(x)$ be a function of bounded variation in $[0, 2\pi]$. If $V$ is its complete variation in $[0, 2\pi]$, then we have

$$\sum_{k=1}^{2n} \left| f\left(x + k\frac{\pi}{n}\right) - f\left(x + (k-1)\frac{\pi}{n}\right) \right| \leqslant V. \tag{22.1}$$

But by arguing as in § 21 we have

$$|a_n| \leqslant \frac{1}{2\pi} \int_0^{2\pi} \left| f\left(x + \frac{n}{\pi}\right) - f(x) \right| dx,$$

$$|b_n| \leqslant \frac{1}{2\pi} \int_0^{2\pi} \left| f\left(x + \frac{\pi}{n}\right) - f(x) \right| dx,$$

and since, because of the periodicity of $f(x)$, we have for any $k$

$$\int_0^{2\pi} \left| f\left(x + k\frac{\pi}{n}\right) - f\left(x + (k-1)\frac{\pi}{n}\right) \right| dx = \int_0^{2\pi} \left| f\left(x + \frac{\pi}{n}\right) - f(x) \right| dx,$$

then it is also possible to write

$$|a_n| \leqslant \frac{1}{2\pi} \int_0^{2\pi} \left| f\left(x + k\frac{\pi}{n}\right) - f\left(x + (k-1)\frac{\pi}{n}\right) \right| dx.$$

Adding all such inequalities for $k = 1, 2, \ldots, 2n$ and then dividing by $2n$ and taking into account (22.1) we find

$$|a_n| \leqslant \frac{1}{4\pi n} \cdot \int_0^{2\pi} V\, dx = \frac{V}{2n} \tag{22.2}$$

and similarly

$$|b_n| \leqslant \frac{V}{2n}. \tag{22.3}$$

Hence we conclude: *for any function of bounded variation*

$$a_n = O\left(\frac{1}{n}\right), \quad b_n = O\left(\frac{1}{n}\right) \tag{22.4}$$

(for the notation $O(1/n)$ see Introductory Material, § 11).

If it is required that apart from being of bounded variation $f(x)$ is also continuous, then the question arises whether it is not possible to better this estimate? We will prove that this is not so in Chapter II, § 2).

## § 23. Formal operations on Fourier series

We have seen (see § 11) that the trigonometric system is complete in $L$, i.e. two summable functions can possess identical Fourier series only if they are equal almost everywhere. Thus a Fourier series, even if it is not convergent, is nevertheless closely connected with only one function. We will now demonstrate that it is possible to carry out just the same operations on divergent Fourier series as on series convergent to those functions of which they are the Fourier series.

(1) *Addition and subtraction of Fourier series.* If we have to construct the Fourier series of the sum or difference of two functions, then it is sufficient to add (or subtract) the Fourier series of these functions. Indeed, if

$$f(x) \sim \sum_{n=-\infty}^{n=+\infty} c_n e^{inx}$$

and

$$g(x) \sim \sum_{n=-\infty}^{n=+\infty} \gamma_n e^{inx},$$

then

$$f(x) \pm g(x) \sim \sum_{n=-\infty}^{n=+\infty} (c_n \pm \gamma_n) e^{inx},$$

since

$$\frac{1}{2\pi}\int_{-\pi}^{\pi} [f(x) \pm g(x)]e^{-inx}\,dx$$

$$= \frac{1}{2\pi}\int_{-\pi}^{\pi} f(x)e^{-inx}\,dx \pm \frac{1}{2\pi}\int_{-\pi}^{\pi} g(x)e^{-inx}\,dx = c_n \pm \gamma_n.$$

Thus if the Fourier series were written in a real form, we should be satisfied that if $a_n$ and $b_n$ are the Fourier coefficients for $f(x)$ and $c_n$ and $d_n$ are the Fourier coefficients for $g(x)$, then for $f(x) \pm g(x)$ the coefficients have the form $a_n \pm c_n$ and $b_n \pm d_n$.

(2) *Multiplication by a constant.* It is immediately evident that if

$$f(x) \sim \sum_{n=-\infty}^{n=+\infty} c_n e^{inx},$$

then

$$kf(x) \sim \sum_{n=-\infty}^{n=+\infty} k c_n e^{inx},$$

where $k$ is any constant. The proof is carried out just as in the preceding case.

(3) *Fourier series for $f(x+\alpha)$.* If $\alpha$ is any constant, then from

$$f(x) \sim \sum c_n e^{inx}$$

it follows that

$$f(x+\alpha) \sim \sum (c_n e^{in\alpha}) e^{inx} \sim \sum c_n e^{in(x+\alpha)}.$$

Indeed

$$\frac{1}{2\pi}\int_{-\pi}^{\pi} f(x+\alpha) e^{-inx}\, dx = \frac{1}{2\pi}\int_{-\pi}^{\pi} f(t) e^{-in(t-\alpha)}\, dt = e^{in\alpha}\frac{1}{2\pi}\int_{-\pi}^{\pi} f(t) e^{-int}\, dt.$$

Therefore the Fourier series for $f(x+\alpha)$ has just the same form as if we substituted $x+\alpha$ for $x$ in the Fourier series for $f(x)$.

The reader can easily satisfy himself that this is the result if the Fourier series is given in a real form.

(4) *Fourier series for $f(x)\, e^{imx}$ where $m$ is an integer.* We have

$$f(x) e^{imx} \sim \sum_{n=-\infty}^{n=+\infty} c_{n-m} e^{inx},$$

since

$$\frac{1}{2\pi}\int_{-\pi}^{\pi} f(x) e^{imx} e^{-inx}\, dx = \frac{1}{2\pi}\int_{-\pi}^{\pi} f(x) e^{-i(n-m)x}\, dx.$$

Hence it again follows that the Fourier coefficients are determined just as if we had operated directly with the series as with a convergent one; in this case we would have

$$f(x) e^{imx} = \sum_{n=-\infty}^{n=+\infty} c_n e^{inx} e^{imx} = \sum_{n=-\infty}^{n=+\infty} c_n e^{i(n+m)x} = \sum_{k=-\infty}^{k=+\infty} c_{k-m} e^{ikx}$$

(5) *Fourier series for $\bar{f}(x)$.* If

$$f(x) \sim \sum c_n e^{inx},$$

then

$$\bar{f}(x) = \sum \bar{c}_n e^{inx},$$

which is verified directly from the Fourier formulae.

(6) *Fourier series for a "convolution".* It is given that $f(x)$ and $g(x)$ are two periodic functions,

$$f(x) \in L[-\pi, \pi] \quad \text{and} \quad g(x) \in L[-\pi, \pi].$$

Let us consider the product $f(x+t)\,g(t)$. If no additional limitations are put on $f(x)$ and $g(x)$, then it might appear to be a non-summable function of the variable $t$. But we will prove, following Young[3], that this product for almost all $x$ is a summable function of $t$ in $[-\pi, \pi]$, and supposing

$$Q(x) = \frac{1}{2\pi} \int_{-\pi}^{\pi} f(x+t)g(t)\,dt, \tag{23.1}$$

we have $Q(x) \in L\,[0, 2\pi]$. This function $Q(x)$ is known as the *convolution* for $f(x)$ and $g(x)$.

It is sufficient to consider the case when $f(x) \geqslant 0$ and $g(x) \geqslant 0$.

We assume

$$F(x) = \int_{-\pi}^{x} f(t)\,dt.$$

Then the function

$$\int_{-\pi}^{\pi} [F(x+t) - F(t-\pi)]g(t)\,dt = \int_{-\pi}^{\pi} dt \left[\int_{-\pi}^{x} f(t+u)g(t)\,du\right]$$

exists and is finite for any $x$. We will suppose that

$$f(t, u, M) = \begin{cases} f(t+u)g(t), & \text{if } f(t+u)g(t) \leqslant M, \\ M, & \text{if } f(t+u)g(t) > M. \end{cases}$$

We have

$$\int_{-\pi}^{\pi} dt \int_{-\pi}^{x} f(t+u)g(t)\,du = \int_{-\pi}^{\pi} dt \lim_{M\to\infty} \int_{-\pi}^{x} f(t, u, M)\,du$$

$$= \lim_{M\to\infty} \int_{-\pi}^{\pi} dt \int_{-\pi}^{x} f(t, u, M)\,du = \lim_{M\to\infty} \int_{-\pi}^{x} du \int_{-\pi}^{\pi} f(t, u, M)\,dt$$

$$= \int_{-\pi}^{x} du \lim_{M\to\infty} \int_{-\pi}^{\pi} f(t, u, M)\,dt. \tag{23.2}$$

The limit $\lim\limits_{M\to\infty} \int_{-\pi}^{\pi} f(t, u, M)\,dt$ might seem to be equal to $+\infty$, but because of the equality (23.2) this can occur only for points of some set of measure zero. At those points, where it is finite, it equals $\int_{-\pi}^{\pi} f(t+u)\,g(t)\,dt$.

Thus we have proved that the convolution $Q(x)$ is almost everywhere defined and summable. Now we will express the coefficients of its Fourier series in terms of the coefficients of the series for $f(x)$ and $g(x)$.

If

$$f(x) \sim \sum c_n e^{inx},$$

$$g(x) \sim \sum d_n e^{inx},$$

then the Fourier coefficients $\mu_n$ for $Q(x)$ have the form

$$\mu_n = c_n d_{-n}. \tag{23.3}$$

Indeed

$$\mu_n = \frac{1}{2\pi}\int_{-\pi}^{\pi} Q(x)e^{-inx}dx = \frac{1}{2\pi}\int_{-\pi}^{\pi}\left\{\frac{1}{2\pi}\int_{-\pi}^{\pi} f(x+t)g(t)dt\right\}e^{-inx}dx.$$

Changing the order of the integration, we obtain

$$\mu_n = \frac{1}{2\pi}\int_{-\pi}^{\pi} g(t)\left\{\frac{1}{2\pi}\int_{-\pi}^{\pi} f(x+t)e^{-inx}dx\right\}dt$$

$$= \frac{1}{2\pi}\int_{-\pi}^{\pi} g(t)\left\{\frac{1}{2\pi}\int_{-\pi}^{\pi} f(z)e^{-in(z-t)}\,dz\right\}dt = \frac{1}{2\pi}\int_{-\pi}^{\pi} g(t)e^{int}c_n dt = c_n d_{-n}.$$

(Changing the order of integration is valid here, since according to Fubini's theorem (see Introductory Material, § 18) such a change can always be carried out for non-negative summable functions, but $e^{-inx} = \cos nx - i\sin nx$, and $\cos nx$ and $\sin nx$ change sign only a finite number of times in $[-\pi, \pi]$, therefore the integrals under consideration reduce to those for which the rearrangement of the order is valid.)

Thus

$$Q(x) \sim \sum c_n d_{-n} e^{inx}. \tag{23.4}$$

It is appropriate to note here that if $f(x) \in L^2$ and $g(x) \in L^2$, then $\sum |c_n|^2 < +\infty$ and $\sum |d_n|^2 < +\infty$, and therefore $\sum |c_n d_{-n}| < +\infty$. Now we will show that under the given conditions $Q(x)$ is continuous. For this we first partition $g(t)$ into two terms, $g(t) = g_1(t) + g_2(t)$ so that $g_1(t)$ is bounded and $\int_{-\pi}^{\pi} g_2^2(t)\,dt < \varepsilon^2$, where $\varepsilon > 0$ is given. We have

$$Q(x+h) - Q(x) = \frac{1}{2\pi}\int_{-\pi}^{\pi}[f(x+t+h) - f(x+t)]g_1(t)dt$$

$$+ \frac{1}{2\pi}\int_{-\pi}^{\pi}[f(x+t+h) - f(x+t)]g_2(t)dt = I_1 + I_2.$$

If $|g_1(t)| \leqslant M$ $(0 \leqslant t \leqslant 2\pi)$, then

$$|I_1| \leqslant \frac{M}{2\pi}\int_{-\pi}^{\pi}|f(x+t+h) - f(x+t)|\,dt$$

$$= \frac{M}{2\pi}\int_{-\pi}^{\pi}|f(t+h) - f(t)|\,dt \leqslant \frac{M}{2\pi}\,\omega_1(\delta, f)$$

for $0 \leqslant |h| \leqslant \delta$, where $\omega_1(\delta, f)$ is the integral modulus of continuity of the function $f(x)$ and signifies that $I_1$ can be made as small as desired, if $\delta$ is sufficiently small.

For $I_2$ we find that

$$|I_2| \leqslant \frac{1}{2\pi}\sqrt{\int_{-\pi}^{\pi}[f(x+t+h)-f(x+t)]^2\,dt}\sqrt{\int_{-\pi}^{\pi}g_2^2(t)\,dt} \leqslant \frac{\varepsilon}{\pi}\sqrt{\int_{-\pi}^{\pi}f^2(t)\,dt}.$$

Thus, $|Q(x+h)-Q(x)|$ can be made as small as desired, if $h$ is sufficiently small.

We will now remark that since $Q(x)$ is continuous and the series (23.4) converges absolutely and uniformly, then this series by virtue of the theorem in § 12 converges to $Q(x)$ at every point. In particular, we derive from this, by supposing $x = 0$,

$$Q(0) = \frac{1}{2\pi}\int_{-\pi}^{\pi} f(t)g(t)\,dt = \sum_{n=-\infty}^{n=+\infty} c_n d_{-n}. \tag{23.5}$$

(7) *Fourier series for a product.* Let

$$f(x) \sim \sum_{n=-\infty}^{n=+\infty} c_n e^{inx}, \quad g(x) \sim \sum_{n=-\infty}^{n=+\infty} d_n e^{inx}.$$

We assume that $f(x) \in L^2$ and $g(x) \in L^2$. Then $f(x)\,g(x) \in L$.

Supposing

$$f(x)g(x) \sim \sum_{n=-\infty}^{n=+\infty} \gamma_n e^{inx},$$

we will show that

$$\gamma_n = \sum_{k=-\infty}^{k=+\infty} c_k d_{n-k}. \tag{23.5'}$$

In order to succeed in doing this, we note that

$$\gamma_n = \frac{1}{2\pi}\int_{-\pi}^{\pi} f(x)g(x)e^{-inx}\,dx,$$

and therefore, supposing

$$h(x) = g(x)e^{-inx}, \tag{23.6}$$

we have

$$\gamma_n = \frac{1}{2\pi}\int_{-\pi}^{\pi} f(x)h(x)\,dx.$$

If we denote the Fourier coefficients of $h(x)$ by $\mu_n$, then according to formula (23.4)

$$\gamma_n = \sum_{k=-\infty}^{k=+\infty} c_k \mu_{-k}. \tag{23.7}$$

But since on the basis of item (4) of this section it follows from (23.6) that

$$\mu_k = d_{k+n},$$

then

$$\gamma_n = \sum_{k=-\infty}^{k=+\infty} c_k d_{n-k},$$

and this is formula (23.5′) which we wanted to prove.

*Note.* We will recall that for numerical series the following theorem is valid: if $u_0 + u_1 + \cdots + u_n + \cdots$ absolutely converges and its sum equals $u$, and $v_0 + v_1 + \cdots + v_n + \cdots$ absolutely converges and its sum equals $v$, then the series

$$u_0 v_0 + (u_0 v_1 + v_0 u_1) + \cdots + (u_0 v_n + u_1 v_{n-1} + \cdots + u_n v_0) + \cdots$$

absolutely converges and its sum is $uv$.

It is not difficult to prove that if we established a series for the product $f(x)\, g(x)$ using this formula for the multiplication of the series, then the coefficients of this series would be expressed by the formula (23.7), i.e. we see that Fourier series can be treated here in the same way as if they converged absolutely.

*Conclusion.* If we have $\sum |c_n| < +\infty$ and $\sum |d_n| < +\infty$, then $\sum |\gamma_n| < +\infty$, since it is known that the product of two absolutely convergent series converge absolutely; moreover, $\sum |\gamma_n| \leqslant \sum |c_n| \sum |d_n|$, since in an absolutely convergent series it is possible to rearrange its terms, without altering its sum.

Later (see § 61) we will see that absolute convergence of a trigonometric series in $[-\pi, \pi]$ occurs when and only when the series of the absolute values of its coefficients converges. Therefore we have

THEOREM. *If $f(x)$ and $g(x)$ expand into absolutely convergent series, then their product also possesses this property.*

(8) *Integration of Fourier series.* Let $f(x)$ be a periodic summable function, and $F(x)$ its indefinite Lebesgue integral

$$F(x) = C + \int_0^x f(t)\,dt.$$

We set ourselves the task of expanding $F(x)$ into a Fourier series, if the series for $f(x)$ has already been obtained:

$$f(x) \sim \sum_{n=-\infty}^{n=+\infty} c_n e^{inx}.$$

We note above all that

$$F(2\pi) - F(0) = \int_0^{2\pi} f(t)\,dt = 2\pi c_0,$$

and therefore if $c_0 \neq 0$, then $F(x)$ will not be periodic. Therefore, we shall consider the auxiliary function

$$\Phi(x) = F(x) - c_0 x. \tag{23.8}$$

Since

$$\Phi(x + 2\pi) = F(x + 2\pi) - c_0(x + 2\pi) = C + \int_0^{2\pi+x} f(t)\,dt - c_0 x - c_0 2\pi$$

$$= C + \int_0^x f(t)\,dt - c_0 x = \Phi(x),$$

then $\Phi(x)$ is already periodic. It is absolutely continuous as is also $F(x)$ and

$$\Phi'(x) = F'(x) - c_0 = f(x) - c_0$$

almost everywhere.

Let us find the Fourier coefficients for $\Phi(x)$; we have for $n \neq 0$

$$C_n = \frac{1}{2\pi}\int_0^{2\pi} \Phi(x)e^{-inx}dx$$

$$= \frac{1}{2\pi}\left\{\frac{\Phi(x)e^{-inx}}{-in}\right\}\Bigg|_0^{2\pi} + \frac{1}{2\pi in}\int_0^{2\pi} f(x)e^{-inx}\,dx - \frac{c_0}{2\pi in}\int_0^{2\pi} e^{-inx}dx \quad (23.9)$$

(integration by parts is valid because of the absolute continuity of $\Phi(x)$). Since $\Phi(2\pi) = \Phi(0)$, then we obtain immediately

$$C_n = \frac{c_n}{in}, \quad (n = \pm 1, \pm 2, \ldots). \quad (23.10)$$

We can now write

$$\Phi(x) \sim C_0 + \sum{}' \frac{c_n}{in}\, e^{inx}, \quad (23.11)$$

where the symbol $\sum'$ denotes that the term with $n = 0$ is omitted.

From (23.8) and (23.11) we conclude that

$$F(x) - c_0 x \sim C_0 + \sum{}' \frac{c_n}{in}\, e^{inx}. \quad (23.12)$$

It is clear that if we were to integrate completely formally the series $\sigma(f)$, then we would obtain this same series (23.12) for $F(x)$.

If the series for $f(x)$ were written in the real form

$$f(x) \sim \frac{a_0}{2} + \sum (a_n \cos nx + b_n \sin nx),$$

then we would obtain

$$F(x) - \frac{a_0}{2}\, x \sim C + \sum \frac{-b_n \cos nx + a_n \sin nx}{n}.$$

(9) *Differentiation of Fourier series. Fourier–Stieltjes series.* Let $F(x)$ be absolutely continuous in $[0, 2\pi]$ and have a period $2\pi$. If

$$F(x) \sim \sum c_n e^{inx},$$

then for its derivative we have

$$F'(x) \sim \sum in c_n e^{inx}. \quad (23.13)$$

Indeed, it is sufficient to apply formula (23.10), assuming that $f(x) = F'(x)$.

Thus the Fourier series for the derivative of $F(x)$ is obtained in the same way as if we differentiated the Fourier series for $F(x)$.

Similarly, if

$$F(x) \sim \frac{a_0}{2} + \sum (a_n \cos nx + b_n \sin nx),$$

then

$$F'(x) \sim \sum n(b_n \cos nx - a_n \sin nx).$$

We note, however, that these formulae are valid only if $F(x)$ is absolutely continuous, otherwise it is not an indefinite Lebesgue integral of its derivative, even if this derivative exists and is summable.

In the case when $F(x)$ is a function of bounded variation, then, supposing

$$c_n = \frac{1}{2\pi}\int_0^{2\pi} e^{-inx}\,dF \quad (n = 0, \pm 1, \ldots), \tag{23.14}$$

where the integral in formula (23.14) is a Riemann–Stieltjes integral (see Introductory Material, § 16), we write

$$dF \sim \sum c_n e^{inx} \tag{23.15}$$

and this series (23.15) is known as *the Fourier–Stieltjes series for dF*.

If we assume

$$\Phi(x) = F(x) - c_0 x,$$

then $\Phi(x)$ is also of bounded variation and is periodic too. Let $C_n$ be the Fourier coefficients for $\Phi(x)$; then for $n \neq 0$, integrating by parts, we find

$$C_n = \frac{1}{2\pi}\int_0^{2\pi} \Phi(x)\, e^{-inx}\,dx = \frac{1}{2\pi\, in}\int_0^{2\pi} e^{-inx}\,d\Phi = \frac{c_n}{in},$$

since $d\Phi = dF - c_0\,dx$. Therefore, if

$$\Phi(x) \sim C_0 + \sum{}' C_n\, e^{inx},$$

where the symbol $\sum{}'$ indicates that the term at $n = 0$ is omitted, then

$$\Phi(x) \sim C_0 + \sum{}' \frac{c_n}{in}\, e^{inx}$$

and

$$F(x) - C_0 x \sim C_0 + \sum{}' \frac{c_n}{in}\, e^{inx}. \tag{23.16}$$

From formulae (23.15) and (23.16) it follows that *the Fourier–Stieltjes series for dF agrees accurately as regards the constants with the result of differentiating the Fourier series for* $F(x) - c_0 x$.

## § 24. Fourier series for repeatedly differentiated functions

Let us assume that $k \geqslant 2$, the function $f(x)$ has derivatives up to the order $k-1$ inclusive and the derivative of the $(k-1)$th order is absolutely continuous; then the $k$th derivative is summable. Denoting the Fourier coefficients for $f^{(k)}(x)$ by $c_n^{(k)}$, we find from formula (23.10) that

$$c_n^{(k-1)} = \frac{c_n^{(k)}}{in}; \quad c_n^{(k-2)} = \frac{c_n^{(k-1)}}{in} = \frac{c_n^{(k)}}{(in)^2},$$

etc., and finally

$$c_n = \frac{c_n^{(k)}}{(in)^k}.$$

Hence it is immediately clear that the higher the derivative of the function is, then the more rapidly do its Fourier coefficients tend to zero.

In particular, if $f^{(k)}(x)$ is defined and summable almost everywhere, then $c_n^{(k)}$ tends to zero as $n \to \pm\infty$, just as the Fourier coefficients of a summable function and then

$$c_n = o\left(\frac{1}{|n|^k}\right). \tag{24.1}$$

Such an estimate does of course occur if the Fourier series has a real form, i.e.

$$a_n = o\left(\frac{1}{n^k}\right) \quad \text{and} \quad b_n = o\left(\frac{1}{n^k}\right). \tag{24.2}$$

## § 25. On Fourier coefficients for analytic functions

Let $f(x)$ be a function of a real variable, analytic in the interval $[-\pi, \pi]$ and periodic with period $2\pi$. Let us estimate its Fourier coefficients. We will show that they decrease at the rate of a geometric progression; more exactly, it is possible to find $\theta$, $0 < \theta < 1$, and a constant $A$ such that

$$|c_n| \leqslant A\,\theta^{|n|} \quad (n = 0, \pm 1, \pm 2, \ldots) \tag{25.1}$$

or in a real form

$$|a_n| \leqslant A\,\theta^n \quad \text{and} \quad |b_n| \leqslant A\,\theta^n \quad (n = 0, 1, 2, \ldots). \tag{25.2}$$

The numbers $\theta$ and $A$ vary, generally speaking, with the function $f(x)$ being considered.

In order to prove this, we note first of all that because of the conditions imposed on $f(x)$, we have

$$f(-\pi) = f(\pi) \quad \text{and} \quad f^{(k)}(-\pi) = f^{(k)}(\pi) \quad (k = 1, 2, \ldots).$$

In estimating the Fourier coefficients for functions possessing $k$ derivatives, we have seen (see § 24) that

$$|c_n| = \frac{1}{|n|^k}\,|c_n^{(k)}|,$$

where $c_n^{(k)}$ are the Fourier coefficients of $f^{(k)}(x)$. But

$$c_n^{(k)} = \frac{1}{2\pi}\int_{-\pi}^{\pi} f^{(k)}(x)\,e^{-inx}\,dx.$$

Therefore, if the maximum modulus of $f^{(k)}(x)$ is denoted by $M_k$, then

$$|c_n| \leqslant \frac{M_k}{|n|^k}.$$

But for the numbers $M_k$, this inequality holds

$$M_k < B^k k! \quad (k = 1, 2, \ldots),$$

where $B$ is a constant.† Therefore

$$|c_n| \leqslant \frac{B^k k!}{|n|^k} \leqslant \left(\frac{Bk}{|n|}\right)^k \quad (n = \pm 1, \pm 2, \ldots) \tag{25.3}$$

Let us choose $p$ such that

$$\frac{B}{p} < 1, \tag{25.4}$$

and suppose that

$$\theta_1 = \frac{B}{p}. \tag{25.5}$$

The number $k$ in formula (25.3) is at our disposal, since the function $f(x)$ possesses derivatives of all orders. Therefore, for given $n$ and $p$ we can find an integer $k$ from the condition

$$k \leqslant \frac{|n|}{p} < k + 1.$$

If this is so, then $|n| \geqslant pk$ and taking into account (25.3) and (25.5)

$$|c_n| \leqslant \left(\frac{B}{p}\right)^k = \theta_1^k = \frac{\theta_1^{k+1}}{\theta_1} < \frac{\theta_1^{|n|/p}}{\theta_1}, \tag{25.6}$$

whilst by virtue of (25.4) and (25.5) we have $\theta_1 < 1$; denoting by $\theta$ the number which satisfies the condition

$$\theta_1^{1/p} < \theta < 1, \tag{25.7}$$

and supposing

$$A = \frac{1}{\theta_1},$$

we have from (25.6) and (25.7)

$$|c_n| < A\theta^{|n|} \quad (n = 0, 1, 2, \ldots),$$

and this is what was required to be proved (see (25.1)).

---

† Indeed, from the assumptions made regarding $f(x)$, it follows that it is possible to expand it analytically in some plane region containing the interval $[-\pi, \pi]$. If we denote by $C$ an arbitrary rectifiable contour enclosing the interval $[-\pi, \pi]$ and lying in the region where $f(z)$ is analytic, then according to Cauchy's formula

$$f^{[k]}(x) = \frac{k!}{2\pi i} \int_C \frac{f(z)}{(z-x)^{k+1}} dz.$$

If the length of the contour $C$ is $l$, $\max_C |f(z)| = M$ and the minimum distance of the points $z$ on $C$ from the points $x$ in $[-\pi, \pi]$ equals $\delta$, then

$$|f^{(k)}(x)| \leqslant Ml \frac{1}{2\pi} k! \frac{1}{\delta^{k+1}} < B^k k!,$$

if $B$ is chosen so that $B > 1/\delta$ and $B > Ml/8\pi\delta^2$.

If we take a Fourier series in its real form, then the inequality takes the form

$$|a_n| \leqslant A\,\theta^n \quad \text{and} \quad |b_n| \leqslant A\,\theta^n \quad (n = 0, 1, 2, \ldots).$$

The reverse statement is also true, namely: if for a function $f(x)$ the Fourier coefficients satisfy the inequality (25.1) where $A$ is a constant and $0 < \theta < 1$, then $f(x)$ is an analytic function in the interval $[-\pi, \pi]$.

Indeed, the series $\sum |c_n| < +\infty$ and we then have

$$f(x) = \sum_{n=-\infty}^{n=+\infty} c_n\, e^{inx}.$$

Differentiating this equality $k$ times, where $k$ is any number, we obtain

$$f^{(k)}(x) = \sum_{n=-\infty}^{n=+\infty} c_n (i)^k\, n^k\, e^{inx}.$$

The differentiation term-by-term is valid, since the series obtained converges absolutely and uniformly because

$$|c_n (i)^k\, n^k| \leqslant A\,\theta^{|n|}\, |n|^k,$$

and since $k$ is a constant, then the convergence of the series $\sum \theta^{(n)}\, |n^k|$ follows if only from the application of Cauchy's test to it.

Thus, $f(x)$ possesses derivatives of all orders. But, moreover,

$$M_k = \max |f^{(k)}(x)| \leqslant 2A \sum_{n=1}^{\infty} \theta^n\, n^k.$$

Hence it is possible to deduce the validity of the inequality

$$M_k < B^k\, k!$$

for some $B$. Indeed

$$\int_0^\infty \theta^x x^k\, dx = -\frac{k}{\ln\theta}\int_0^\infty \theta^x x^{k-1}\, dx = \frac{k(k-1)}{\ln^2\theta}\int_0^\infty \theta^x\, x^{k-2}\, dx = \cdots = (-1)^k\, \frac{k!}{\ln^k\theta},$$

which gives the desired inequality.

Now let $x_0$ be any point in $[-\pi, \pi]$. Let $x$ be any other point for which

$$|x - x_0| < \frac{1}{B}.$$

Using Taylor's formula with a remainder in a Lagrange form

$$f(x) = \sum_{k=0}^{n-1} \frac{f^{(k)}(x_0)}{k!}(x - x_0)^k + \frac{f^{(n)}(x_0 + \theta'(x - x_0))}{n!}(x - x_0)^n,$$

where $0 < \theta' < k$. But

$$\left|\frac{f^{(n)}(x_0 + \theta'(x - x_0))}{n!}(x - x_0)^n\right| \leqslant \frac{B^n n!}{n!}(x - x_0)^n = (B\,|x - x_0|)^n.$$

Because $|x - x_0| < 1/B$ the right-hand side tends to zero as $n \to \infty$ and this means that

$$f(x) = \sum_{k=0}^{\infty} \frac{f^{(k)}(x_0)}{k!} (x - x_0)^k,$$

i.e. $f(x)$ expands into a Taylor series in the neighbourhood of the point $x_0$; but $x_0$ is any point of $[-\pi, \pi]$, which means that $f(x)$ is an analytic function in $[-\pi, \pi]$.

## § 26. The simplest cases of absolute and uniform convergence of Fourier series

We will start with the following simple observations. Let us consider a trigonometric series

$$\frac{a_0}{2} + \sum_{n=1}^{\infty} (a_n \cos nx + b_n \sin nx). \tag{26.1}$$

If

$$\sum (|a_n| + |b_n|) < +\infty, \tag{26.2}$$

then it converges absolutely (and uniformly) in $[-\pi, \pi]$.

It is useful to note (we have already referred to this in § 23) that the convergence of series (26.2) is not only sufficient but necessary† for the series (26.1) to converge absolutely in $[-\pi, \pi]$.

It now remains to consider some concrete cases when the Fourier series converges absolutely and uniformly. If this occurs, then this series has as its sum the function $f(x)$ for which it serves as Fourier series (see § 12). In particular, it follows that

*If $f(x)$ possesses a summable derivative of the second order, then its Fourier series converges uniformly to $f(x)$.*

Indeed (see § 24) in this case

$$a_n = O\left(\frac{1}{n^2}\right), \quad b_n = O\left(\frac{1}{n^2}\right).$$

Later we will see that the requirements imposed on $f(x)$ are too limiting and we can obtain uniform convergence for considerably more general assumptions, but it is expedient to mention this theorem, since even in this form it can be useful.

We will mention here yet another simple but important case, where the absolute and uniform convergence of a Fourier series is readily detected, namely:

THEOREM. *If $F(x)$ is absolutely continuous and its derivative $F'(x) = f(x)$ is a function with an integrable square, then the Fourier series of $F(x)$ converges absolutely and uniformly.*

Indeed, in this case, if the Fourier coefficients for $f(x)$ are denoted by $a_n$, $b_n$, then $\sum (a_n^2 + b_n^2) < +\infty$ (see § 13) and according to formula (23.10), denoting the Fourier coefficients for $F(x)$ by $A_n$ and $B_n$, we have

$$|A_n| = \left|\frac{b_n}{n}\right| \text{ and } |B_n| = \left|\frac{a_n}{n}\right|,$$

† In § 61 it will be shown that for the convergence of (26.2) the absolute convergence of (16.1) is sufficient not in the whole interval $[-\pi, \pi]$, but only in a set of positive measure.

and therefore

$$|A_n| \leqslant \frac{1}{2}|b_n|^2 + \frac{1}{2}\frac{1}{n^2} \quad \text{and} \quad |B_n| \leqslant \frac{1}{2}a_n^2 + \frac{1}{2}\frac{1}{n^2}.$$

Consequently

$$\sum_{n=1}^{\infty}(|A_n| + |B_n|) < +\infty,$$

and the theorem is proved.

In § 3 of Chapter IX, this theorem is generalized, so that instead of the hypothesis $f'(x) \subset L^2$ we consider the case $f'(x) \subset L^p (p > 1)$ and we show that the result still holds. A number of considerably stronger theorems on the absolute convergence of Fourier series will also be given there.

A very particular case of the given theorem is given by the following example; if $F(x)$ is represented by a continuous broken line, then its Fourier series converges absolutely and uniformly.

In fact, in this case $F'(x)$ is a function which possesses a derivative everywhere except for a finite number of points and this derivative $f(x)$ consists of a finite number of steps, and is therefore bounded, and consequently $f^2(x)$ is moreover summable.

## § 27. Weierstrass's theorem on the approximation of a continuous function by trigonometric polynomials

Let $f(x)$ be a continuous function in the interval $[-\pi, \pi]$ and $f(-\pi) = f(\pi)$. If we expand it periodically with period $2\pi$, it will be continuous along the whole axis $Ox$. We define a function with period $2\pi$ as a continuous periodic function when and only when it remains continuous after its periodic expansion; if $f(x)$ is continuous only in a certain interval of length $2\pi$, but at its end points assumes different values and therefore becomes discontinuous if it is expanded periodically (see Fig. 4 on page 50), then we will not call it a continuous periodic function.

After this definition we can express a theorem.

WEIERSTRASS'S THEOREM. *For any continuous periodic function $f(x)$ and for any $\varepsilon > 0$ a trigonometric polynomial $T(x)$ can be found such that*

$$|f(x) - T(x)| < \varepsilon \quad (-\infty < x < +\infty). \tag{27.1}$$

A large number of proofs of this important theorem exist. We will refer here to one of them.

Because of the continuity of $f(x)$ in $[-\pi, \pi]$ it is possible to find a $\delta$ such that

$$|f(x') - f(x'')| < \frac{\varepsilon}{2} \quad \text{for} \quad |x' - x''| \leqslant \delta, \tag{27.2}$$

where $x'$ and $x''$ are any two points in $[-\pi, \pi]$.

Let us divide the interval $[-\pi, \pi]$ into $m$ equal parts, choosing $m$ so that $2\pi/m < \delta$. We will denote by $\psi(x)$ the broken line coinciding with $f(x)$ at the points $k\pi/m$, where $k = 0, \pm 1, \ldots, \pm m$, and will assume that $\psi(x + 2\pi) = \psi(x)$ for any $x(-\infty < x < +\infty)$. From (27.2) it is clear that

$$|f(x) - \psi(x)| < \frac{\varepsilon}{2} \quad \text{for} \quad |x' - x''| \leqslant \delta$$

and because of the periodicity of the two functions this is also true for any $x$, $-\infty < x < +\infty$.

Since $\psi(x)$ is a broken line, then according to the proof at the end of § 26 its Fourier series converges absolutely to it. Therefore denoting the sum of the first $n$ terms of its Fourier series by $S_n(x)$, it is possible to choose $n$ sufficiently large for

$$|\psi(x) - S_n(x)| < \frac{\varepsilon}{2} \quad \text{for} \quad -\infty < x < +\infty.$$

It is clear that $S_n(x)$ is a trigonometric polynomial and denoting it by $T(x)$ we see that the theorem is proved.

## § 28. The density of a class of trigonometric polynomials in the spaces $L^p$ $(p \geqslant 1)$

Weierstrass's theorem which has just been proved can be considered as evidence of the fact that the class of trigonometric polynomials is everywhere dense in the space $C$ of continuous periodic functions.

It follows from this that this class is everywhere dense in any space $L^p (p \geqslant 1)$.

Indeed, if $f(x) \in L^p$, then for any $\varepsilon$ (see Introductory Material, § 21) it is possible to find a continuous $\varphi(x)$ such that

$$\|f - \varphi\|_{L^p} \leqslant \varepsilon,$$

and on the other hand it is possible to find a trigonometric polynomial $T(x)$ such that

$$|\varphi(x) - T(x)| < \frac{\varepsilon}{2\pi}, \quad 0 \leqslant x \leqslant 2\pi,$$

and therefore

$$\|\varphi - T\|_{L^p} < \varepsilon$$

(it is assumed that the norm is calculated in an interval of length $2\pi$). Therefore, according to Minkowski's inequality (see Introductory Material, § 10)

$$\|f - T\|_{L^p} < 2\varepsilon,$$

and the theorem is proved.

## § 29. Dirichlet's kernel and its conjugate kernel

An important role in the study of the convergence of trigonometric series is played by the functions

$$D_n(x) = \frac{1}{2} + \cos x + \cdots + \cos nx \tag{29.1}$$

and

$$\bar{D}_n(x) = \sin x + \cdots + \sin nx. \tag{29.2}$$

The function $D_n(x)$ can be written thus:

$$D_n(x) = \frac{\sin\left(n + \frac{1}{2}\right) x}{2 \sin \frac{x}{2}}. \tag{29.3}$$

Indeed

$$\begin{aligned} 2 \sin \frac{x}{2}\, D_n(x) &= \sin \frac{x}{2} + \sum_{k=1}^{n} 2 \sin \frac{x}{2} \cos kx \\ &= \sin \frac{x}{2} + \sum_{k=1}^{n} \left[\sin\left(k + \frac{1}{2}\right) x - \sin\left(k - \frac{1}{2}\right) x\right] \\ &= \sin\left(n + \frac{1}{2}\right) x, \end{aligned}$$

whence after dividing by $2 \sin(x/2)$, formula (29.3) is obtained.

Expression (29.3) is called *the Dirichlet kernel*, since Dirichlet first used it in the study of the convergence of Fourier series (see § 31).

Similarly $\bar{D}_n(x)$ is called *the kernel conjugate to the Dirichlet kernel*; it takes the form

$$\bar{D}_n(x) = \frac{\cos \frac{x}{2} - \cos\left(n + \frac{1}{2}\right) x}{2 \sin \frac{x}{2}}, \tag{29.4}$$

which can also be easily verified directly.

From formulae (29.3) and (29.4) it is immediately evident that if $x \not\equiv 0 \pmod{2\pi}$, then

$$| D_n(x) | \leqslant \frac{1}{2 \left[\sin \frac{x}{2}\right]} \tag{29.5}$$

and

$$| \bar{D}_n(x) | \leqslant \frac{1}{\left[\sin \frac{x}{2}\right]}. \tag{29.6}$$

We now note that the function $(\sin x)/x$ decreases in the interval $(0, \pi/2)$ (which it is possible to prove by simple differentiation) and therefore

$$\frac{\sin x}{x} \geqslant \frac{\sin \frac{\pi}{2}}{\left(\frac{\pi}{2}\right)} = \frac{2}{\pi}$$

This means

$$\frac{\sin x}{x} \geqslant \frac{2}{\pi} \quad \text{for} \quad 0 \leqslant x \leqslant \frac{\pi}{2}. \tag{29.7}$$

Using (29.5) and (29.6) we obtain

$$|D_n(x)| \leqslant \frac{\pi}{2x} \quad \text{for} \quad 0 < |x| \leqslant \pi \tag{29.8}$$

and

$$|\bar{D}_n(x)| \leqslant \frac{\pi}{x} \quad \text{for} \quad 0 < |x| \leqslant \pi. \tag{29.9}$$

We will use these formulae frequently later. Most often it will be sufficient to estimate

$$D_n(x) = O\left(\frac{1}{x}\right) \quad \text{and} \quad \bar{D}_n(x) = O\left(\frac{1}{x}\right) \text{ as } x \to 0; \tag{29.10}$$

sometimes it will be important that if $\delta \leqslant |x| \leqslant \pi$, then

$$|D_n(x)| \leqslant \frac{\pi}{2\delta} \quad \text{and} \quad |\bar{D}_n(x)| \leqslant \frac{\pi}{\delta}. \tag{29.11}$$

Because of the periodicity of $D_n(x)$ and $\bar{D}_n(x)$ it is also possible to say that (29.11) holds if $\delta \leqslant x \leqslant 2\pi - \delta$.

## § 30. Sine or cosine series with monotonically decreasing coefficients

Before turning to a study of the cases when the problem of convergence of the trigonometric series requires close examination, we will consider some cases where it is very easy to judge the convergence.

Let us begin with series of the form

$$\frac{a_0}{2} + \sum_{n=1}^{\infty} a_n \cos nx \tag{30.1}$$

and

$$\sum_{n=1}^{\infty} b_n \sin nx, \tag{30.2}$$

i.e., series consisting of either cosines only or sines only. We will consider firstly the important case when these series possess monotonically decreasing coefficients tending to zero, which can be denoted thus:

$$a_n \downarrow 0 \quad \text{and} \quad b_n \downarrow 0.$$

In studying these series we will use the estimates of $D_n(x)$ and $\bar{D}_n(x)$ given in § 29 and Abel's lemma (see Introductory Material, § 1). This permits us to prove the theorem.

THEOREM 1. *If $a_n \downarrow 0$, then the series*

$$\frac{a_0}{2} + \sum a_n \cos nx$$

*converges everywhere apart, perhaps, from the points $x \equiv 0 \pmod{2\pi}$; at any $\delta > 0$ it converges uniformly in $\delta \leqslant x \leqslant 2\pi - \delta$.*

*If $b_n \downarrow 0$, then the series*

$$\sum b_n \sin nx$$

*converges everywhere; at any $\delta > 0$ it converges uniformly in $\delta \leqslant x \leqslant 2\pi - \delta$.*

Indeed, supposing in Abel's lemma that

$$u_n = a_n, \quad v_0 = \frac{1}{2} \quad \text{and} \quad v_n(x) = \cos nx \quad (n = 1, 2, \ldots),$$

we have

$$V_n(x) = D_n(x),$$

and since the uniform boundedness of the functions $D_n(x)$ in $\delta \leqslant x \leqslant 2\pi - \delta$ follows from formula (29.11), then the series converges uniformly in this interval. If $0 < x < 2\pi$, then it is always possible to take $\delta$ so small that $\delta \leqslant x \leqslant 2\pi - \delta$, which indicates that the series (30.1) converges at the point $x$.

At $x = 0$, the series (30.1) converges when and only when $\sum a_n < +\infty$.

For the series (30.2), the proof is similar; it is only necessary to substitute $u_n = b_n$ and $v_n(x) = \sin nx$ in Abel's lemma; then $V_n(x) = \bar{D}_n(x)$ and again the application of the inequality (29.11) gives evidence of the uniform convergence of series (30.2) in $\delta \leqslant x \leqslant 2\pi - \delta$, and therefore its convergence at every point, apart from the points $x \equiv 0 \pmod{2\pi}$. But at the latter it also converges because all the terms of the series equal zero.

The theorem is completely proved.

*Note.* By the generalization of Abel's Lemma (see Introductory Material, § 1) the series (30.1) and (30.2) converge uniformly in $\delta \leqslant x \leqslant 2\pi - \delta$ (this indicates that it also converges in $0 < x < 2\pi$) and when instead of $a_n \downarrow 0$ or $b_n \downarrow 0$ we assume only that $\{a_n\}$ or $\{b_n\}$ is a sequence of bounded variation, $a_n \to 0$ and $b_n \to 0$, moreover.

Let us return to the case of the monotonically decreasing coefficients. It is clear that if

$$a_n \downarrow 0 \quad \text{and} \quad \sum a_n < +\infty,$$

then the series $a_0/2 + \sum a_n \cos nx$ converges absolutely and uniformly in the whole interval $0 \leqslant x \leqslant 2\pi$ (and even for $-\infty < x < +\infty$). On the other hand if the condition $\sum a_n < +\infty$ is not fulfilled, then not only uniform but also simple convergence along the whole axis is not possible, since at the points $x \equiv 0 \pmod{2\pi}$ the series (30.1) diverges.

The question of the uniform convergence of the series $\sum b_n \sin nx$ is decided in another manner. Here we have.

THEOREM 2. *If $b_n \downarrow 0$, then for uniform convergence of the series $\sum b_n \sin nx$ in $[0, 2\pi]$ it is necessary and sufficient that $nb_n \to 0$.*

*Necessity condition.* If the series (30.2) converges uniformly in $[0, 2\pi]$, then for any $\varepsilon > 0$ it is possible to find $m$ such that

$$\left| \sum_{m+1}^{2m} b_n \sin nx \right| < \varepsilon, \quad 0 \leqslant x \leqslant 2\pi.$$

We will let $x = \pi/4m$; then for $(m+1) \leqslant n \leqslant 2m$ we have $\pi/4 \leqslant nx \leqslant \pi/2$ and therefore $\sin nx \geqslant \sin \pi/4 = 1/\sqrt{2}$. Consequently,

$$\frac{1}{\sqrt{2}} \sum_{m+1}^{2m} b_n < \varepsilon,$$

and since $b_n$ decrease monotonically, $(1/\sqrt{2})mb_{2m} < \varepsilon$, i.e., $mb_{2m} < \sqrt{2}\varepsilon$, which means that $mb_m \to 0$ as $m \to \infty$. The necessity is thus proved.

*Sufficiency condition.* We already know that series (30.2) converges uniformly in $\delta \leqslant x \leqslant 2\pi - \delta$ for any $\delta$ (for the single condition $b_n \downarrow 0$). This means that if we prove that the addition of the condition $nb_n \to 0$ implies uniform convergence in $(-a, a)$, where $a$ is any number $> 0$, then everything will be proved. Moreover, because of the oddness of $\sin nx$ it is sufficient to take $0 \leqslant x \leqslant a$. We will prove uniform convergence of the series in $0 \leqslant x \leqslant \pi/4$.

Let $\varepsilon_n = \max\limits_{k \geqslant n} kb_k$. It is known that series (30.2) converges for any $x$; let us define

$$r_n(x) = \sum_{k=n}^{\infty} b_k \sin kx.$$

We will prove that $|r_n(x)| \leqslant K\varepsilon_n$ in $0 \leqslant x \leqslant \pi/4$, where $K$ is a constant whence the uniform convergence of the series (30.2) in $[0, 2\pi]$ follows.

Above all, $r_n(0) = 0$, if $x \neq 0$, then it is always possible to find an integer $N$ such that $1/N < x \leqslant 1/(N-1)$. If $N > n$, then we write

$$r_n(x) = \sum_{k=n}^{N-1} b_k \sin kx + \sum_{k=N}^{\infty} b_k \sin kx = r_n^{(1)}(x) + r_n^{(2)}(x).$$

If $N \leqslant n$, then let $r_n^{(1)}(x) = 0$ and $r_n^{(2)}(x) = r_n(x)$. Let us estimate $r_n^{(1)}(x)$ and $r_n^{(2)}(x)$ separately.

We have, since $|\sin kx| \leqslant k|x|$,

$$|r_n^{(1)}(x)| \leqslant \sum_{k=n}^{N-1} kb_k x \leqslant x\varepsilon_n(N-n) \leqslant \frac{N-n}{N-1}\varepsilon_n \leqslant \varepsilon_n.$$

In order to estimate $r_n^{(2)}(x)$ we consider two separate cases:

(1) If $n < N$, then using Abel's transformation (see Introductory Material, § 1) we find

$$|r_n^{(2)}(x)| \leqslant \sum_{k=N}^{\infty} (b_k - b_{k+1})\,|\bar{D}_k(x)| + b_N\,|\bar{D}_{N-1}(x)|.$$

But since (see (29.9))

$$|\bar{D}_k(x)| \leqslant \frac{\pi}{x} \quad \text{for} \quad 0 < |x| \leqslant \pi,$$

then

$$|r_n^{(2)}(x)| \leqslant \frac{2\pi}{x} b_N \leqslant 2\pi N b_N \leqslant 2\pi\varepsilon_n$$

because $n < N$ and because of the definition of $\varepsilon_n$.

(2) If $N \leqslant n$, then $r_n^{(2)}(x) = r_n(x)$ and then calculation shows that

$$|r_n(x)| = |r_n^{(2)}(x)| \leqslant 2\pi\varepsilon_n.$$

Therefore

$$|r_n(x)| \leqslant |r_n^{(1)}(x)| + |r_n^{(2)}(x)| \leqslant (2\pi + 1)\,\varepsilon_n,$$

which means that the desired inequality has been proved.

*Note.* From the theorem just proved the following conclusion can be deduced immediately:

*There exist trigonometric series that converge uniformly in* $[-\pi, \pi]$ *without converging absolutely in this interval.*

In fact let us consider, for example, the series

$$\sum_{n=2}^{\infty} \frac{\sin nx}{n \ln n}. \tag{30.3}$$

Since $b_n = 1/(n \ln n)$, then $nb_n \to 0$ as $n \to \infty$ and moreover $b_n \downarrow 0$. This means that the given series converges uniformly in $[-\pi, \pi]$, but it does not converge absolutely in $[-\pi, \pi]$, since otherwise the series $\sum 1/(n \ln n)$ should converge and this series does actually diverge.†

We make this brief comment because very frequently in proving the uniform convergence of functional series Weierstrass's criterion (the comparison of the terms of a given series with the terms of a convergent numerical series) is used and in this case both absolute and uniform convergence is directly obtained.

In particular, for the trigonometric series $\sum b_n \sin nx$, where $\sum |b_n| < +\infty$, both absolute and uniform convergence occurs in $[-\pi, \pi]$, but in the example considered this is not so.

It is even possible to construct a trigonometric series which converges uniformly in $[-\pi, \pi]$ but which does not possess a single point of absolute convergence in this interval (see Chapter IX, § 3).

In connection with series of the type (30.2), where $b_n \downarrow 0$, it is useful to note yet another theorem:

THEOREM 3. *If* $b_n \downarrow 0$ *and the numbers* $nb_n$ *are bounded, then the partial sums of the series*

$$\sum_{n=1}^{\infty} b_n \sin nx$$

*are all bounded in* $-\infty < x < +\infty$.

---

† From the Lusin–Denjoy theorem which will be proved in § 61, it follows that the series (30.3) can converge absolutely only in a set of measure zero $\left(\text{because } \sum_{n=2}^{\infty} 1/(n \ln n) \text{ diverges}\right)$. Moreover, it is easily proved that the series (30.3) is not absolutely convergent at any $x \not\equiv 0 \pmod{\pi}$. Indeed, if for such $x$ we had

$$\sum_{n=2}^{\infty} \frac{|\sin nx|}{n \ln n} < +\infty,$$

then

$$\sum_{n=2}^{\infty} \frac{\sin^2 nx}{n \ln n} < +\infty.$$

therefore

$$\sum_{n=2}^{\infty} \frac{(1 - \cos 2nx)}{n \ln n} < +\infty,$$

and since $\sum_{n=2}^{\infty} \frac{\cos 2nx}{n \ln n}$ converges, if $x \not\equiv 0 \pmod{\pi}$ then the convergence of $\sum_{n=2}^{\infty} \frac{1}{n \ln n}$ would follow and we would arrive at a contradiction.

Because of the periodicity and oddness of all the terms of the series it is sufficient to consider the interval $[0, \pi]$ and since at $x = 0$ and $x = \pi$ all the terms become zero, then we can confine ourselves to the case $0 < x < \pi$.

We have the condition

$$|kb_k| < M \quad (k = 1, 2, \dots), \tag{30.4}$$

where $M$ is a constant. Let us suppose

$$\nu = \left[\frac{\pi}{x}\right]. \tag{30.5}$$

If $n \leqslant \nu$, then

$$|S_n(x)| \leqslant \left|\sum_{k=1}^{n} b_k \sin kx\right| \leqslant \sum_{k=1}^{n} |kb_k|\, x \leqslant M x\nu \leqslant M\pi.$$

If $n > \nu$, then

$$S_n(x) = \sum_{k=1}^{\nu} b_k \sin kx + \sum_{\nu+1}^{n} b_k \sin kx = S_n^{(1)}(x) + S_n^{(2)}(x),$$

where $S_n^{(1)}(x)$ is estimated as in the preceding case, i.e.

$$|S_n^{(1)}(x)| \leqslant M\pi, \tag{30.6}$$

and to $S_n^{(2)}(x)$ we apply the corollary of Abel's transformation (see Introductory Material, § 1). Remembering (29.9)

$$|\bar{D}_n(x)| \leqslant \frac{\pi}{x} \quad \text{for} \quad 0 < |x| \leqslant \pi,$$

we find from (30.4) and (30.5)

$$|S_n^{(2)}(x)| \leqslant 2b_{\nu+1}\frac{\pi}{x} \leqslant 2M\frac{\pi}{x(\nu+1)} \leqslant 2M. \tag{30.7}$$

From (30.6) and (30.7) it follows that

$$|S_n(x)| \leqslant M\pi + 2M = M(\pi + 2),$$

and Theorem 3 is proved.

COROLLARY. *We have for any $n$ and $x$*

$$\left|\sum_{k=1}^{n} \frac{\sin kx}{k}\right| < C, \tag{30.8}$$

*where $C$ is an absolute constant.*

Indeed, here we are concerned with the partial sums of the series

$$\sum_{n=1}^{\infty} \frac{\sin nx}{n}, \tag{30.9}$$

in which $b_n = 1/n$, i.e. $b_n \downarrow 0$ and $nb_n = 1$.

Series (30.9) plays an important rôle in the many problems of the theory of trigonometric series; in § 41, in particular, we will investigate its behaviour in the neighbourhood of the point $x = 0$, since it permits us to obtain certain data on the behaviour of Fourier series for functions of bounded variation at those points where they are discontinuous.

In this paragraph we have considered only a few problems concerning sine and cosine series with monotonic coefficients. Chapter X will be devoted to a detailed investigation of this class of series. Here instead of referring the reader to Chapter X, we prove yet another important theorem concerning these series.

THEOREM 4. *If $a_n \downarrow 0$ and the sequence $\{a_n\}$ is convex, then the series*

$$\frac{a_0}{2} + \sum_{j=1}^{\infty} a_j \cos jx \tag{30.1}$$

*converges everywhere, apart from, perhaps, $x \equiv 0 \pmod{2\pi}$, to a non-negative summable function $f(x)$ and is the Fourier series for this function.*

To prove, this, we consider

$$S_n(x) = \frac{a_0}{2} + \sum_{j=1}^{n} a_j \cos jx$$

and apply Abel's transformation; this gives

$$S_n(x) = \sum_{j=0}^{n-1} (a_j - a_{j+1}) D_j(x) + a_n D_n(x) = \sum_{j=0}^{n-1} \Delta a_j D_j(x) + a_n D_n(x), \tag{30.10}$$

where $\Delta a_j = a_j - a_{j+1}$. Supposing $\Delta^2 a_j = \Delta a_j - \Delta a_{j+1}$ and again using Abel's transformation, we find

$$S_n(x) = \sum_{j=0}^{n-2} \Delta^2 a_j \sum_{p=0}^{j} D_p(x) + \Delta a_{n-1} \sum_{p=0}^{n-1} D_p(x) + a_n D_n(x). \tag{30.11}$$

An expression of the form

$$K_j(x) = \frac{1}{j+1} \sum_{p=0}^{j} D_p(x) \tag{30.12}$$

is usually called *a Fejér kernel of order j*. We will study it in more detail in § 47. Here we shall refer to the fact that $K_j(x) \geqslant 0$ for all $x$ (see (47.5)). From (30.11) and (30.12) it immediately follows that

$$S_n(x) = \sum_{j=0}^{n-2} (j+1) \Delta^2 a_j K_j(x) + n \Delta a_{n-1} K_{n-1}(x) + a_n D_n(x). \tag{30.13}$$

If $x \not\equiv 0 \pmod{2\pi}$, then since $a_n \to 0$ the last term of the right-hand side of (30.13) tends to zero as $n \to \infty$. Moreover, at $x \not\equiv 0 \pmod{2\pi}$ from (30.12) and (29.3) we note that $K_n(x)$ always remains finite as $n \to \infty$ and $n \Delta a_{n-1} \to 0$ for the convex sequences $\{a_n\}$ (see Introductory Material, § 3) and therefore $n \Delta a_{n-1} K_{n-1}(x) \to 0$ as $n \to \infty$. Hence for $x \not\equiv 0 \pmod{2\pi}$

$$f(x) = \lim_{n \to \infty} S_n(x) = \sum_{j=1}^{\infty} (j+1) \Delta^2 a_j K_j(x). \tag{30.14}$$

It is not necessary for us to prove the very existence of the limit, since the convergence of series (30.1) for all $x$, apart from $x \equiv 0 \pmod{2\pi}$, was established for $a_n \downarrow 0$, without the hypothesis of the convexity of $\{a_n\}$, in Theorem 1 of this section.

Thus, from (30.14) we conclude that the sum $f(x)$ of series (30.14) is a non-negative function, because all $\Delta^2 a_j \geqslant 0$ and $K_j(x) \geqslant 0$ for all $x$.

It remains for us to prove that the series (30.1) is a Fourier series of $f(x)$. For this purpose we note that because

$$f(x) = \frac{a_0}{2} + \sum_{n=1}^{\infty} a_n \cos nx \tag{30.15}$$

and because $a_n \downarrow 0$ the series on the right-hand side of (30.15) converges uniformly in $(\varepsilon, \pi)$ for any $\varepsilon > 0$, then

$$\int_0^{\pi} f(x)\,dx = \frac{a_0}{2}\int_{\varepsilon}^{\pi} dx + \sum_{n=1}^{\infty} a_n \int_{\varepsilon}^{\pi} \cos nx\,dx = \frac{a_0}{2}(\pi - \varepsilon) - \sum_{n=1}^{\infty} a_n \frac{\sin n\varepsilon}{n}. \tag{30.16}$$

From $a_n \downarrow 0$ due to Theorem 2, it follows that the series $\sum (a_n \sin nx)/n$ converges uniformly in $[0, 2\pi]$, which means that its sum is continuous in this interval, and therefore the series on the right-hand side of (30.16) has a sum which tends to zero as $\varepsilon \to 0$. Hence it follows that

$$\lim_{\varepsilon \to 0} \int_{\varepsilon}^{\pi} f(x)\,dx = \frac{a_0}{2}\pi. \tag{30.17}$$

But since $f(x) \geqslant 0$, then from the existence of the limit on the left-hand side of (30.17) the summability of $f(x)$ in $[0, \pi]$ follows, and because $f(x)$ is even, this gives

$$\int_{-\pi}^{\pi} f(x)\,dx = 2\int_0^{\pi} f(x)\,dx = a_0\pi,$$

whence

$$a_0 = \frac{1}{\pi}\int_{-\pi}^{\pi} f(x)\,dx.$$

We will now prove that at any $k = 1, 2, \ldots$ we have

$$a_k = \frac{1}{\pi}\int_{-\pi}^{\pi} f(x)\cos kx\,dx.$$

For this purpose, multiplying both sides of (30.15) by $\cos kx$ and integrating in the interval $[\varepsilon, \pi]$, we find

$$\int_{\varepsilon}^{\pi} f(x)\cos kx\,dx = \frac{a_0}{2}\int_{\varepsilon}^{\pi}\cos kx\,dx + \sum_{n=1}^{k-1} a_n \int_{\varepsilon}^{\pi}\cos kx \cos nx\,dx$$

$$+ a_k \int_{\varepsilon}^{\pi}\cos^2 kx\,dx + \sum_{n=k+1}^{\infty} a_n \int_{\varepsilon}^{\pi}\cos kx\cos nx\,dx. \tag{30.18}$$

As $\varepsilon \to 0$ each of the integrals $\int_\varepsilon^\pi \cos kx\,dx$ and $\int_\varepsilon^\pi \cos kx \cos nx\,dx$ $(n = 1, 2, \ldots k-1)$ tend to zero. Then

$$\lim_{\varepsilon\to 0} \int_\varepsilon^\pi \cos^2 kx\,dx = \int_0^\pi \cos^2 kx\,dx = \frac{\pi}{2}.$$

Finally

$$\sum_{n=k+1}^{\infty} a_n \int_\varepsilon^\pi \cos kx \cos nx\,dx = \sum_{n=k+1}^{\infty} a_n \int_\varepsilon^\pi \frac{\cos(k+n)\,x + \cos(n-k)\,x}{2}\,dx$$

$$= \sum_{n=k+1}^{\infty} a_n \left[\frac{\sin(k+n)\,\varepsilon}{2(k+n)} + \frac{\sin(n-k)\,\varepsilon}{2(n-k)}\right] \tag{30.19}$$

and arguing as previously, we see that as $\varepsilon \to 0$ the right-hand side of (30.19) tends to zero.

Thus, from (30.18) we obtain as $\varepsilon \to 0$

$$\int_0^\pi f(x) \cos kx\,dx = a_k \frac{\pi}{2}$$

and taking into account the evenness of $f(x)$

$$a_k = \frac{1}{\pi} \int_{-\pi}^{\pi} f(x) \cos kx\,dx.$$

Thus, series (30.1) is a Fourier series of $f(x)$ and the proof, therefore, is concluded.

COROLLARY. Since the sequence $1/\ln n$ $(n = 2, 3, \ldots)$ is convex, then from the given theorem it follows in particular that: *the series*

$$\sum_{n=2}^{\infty} \frac{\cos nx}{\ln n} \tag{30.20}$$

*is a Fourier series.*

It is also known that $\sum_{n=2}^{\infty} (\sin nx)/\ln n$ is not a Fourier series (see § 40), therefore we see that a series conjugate to a Fourier series is not necessarily itself a Fourier series.

*Note.* It will be useful to us later to know that *the partial sums of series* (30.20) *satisfy the condition*

$$\int_0^{2\pi} |S_n(x)|\,dx < C, \tag{30.21}$$

*where C is an absolute constant.*

Indeed from formula (30.13) we obtain

$$\int_0^{2\pi} |S_n(x)|\,dx$$

$$\leqslant \sum_{j=0}^{n-2} (j+1)\,\Delta^2 a_j \int_0^{2\pi} K_j(x)\,dx + n\,\Delta a_{n-1} \int_0^{2\pi} K_{n-1}(x)\,dx + a_n \int_0^{2\pi} |D_n(x)|\,dx.$$

But since $\int_0^{2\pi} |D_n(x)|\,dx < A \ln n$, where $A$ is a constant (see § 35) and

$$\int_0^{2\pi} K_j(x)dx = \frac{1}{j+1} \sum_{p=0}^{j} \int_0^{2\pi} D_p(x)\,dx = \pi,$$

then

$$\int_0^{2\pi} |S_n(x)|\,dx \leqslant \pi \left[ \sum_{j=0}^{n-2} (j+1)\Delta^2 a_j + n\Delta a_{n-1} \right] + A a_n \ln n.$$

This formula is true for any $a_n \downarrow 0$ forming a convex sequence. Therefore, taking into account that for such sequences $\sum_{j=0}^{\infty} (j+1)\Delta^2 a_j < +\infty$ (see Introductory Material, § 3) we have

$$\int_0^{2\pi} |S_n(x)|\,dx < A a_n \ln n + B,$$

where $A$ and $B$ are constants. For the case we are considering when $a_n = 1/\ln n$, supposing that $A + B = C$, we see therefore that (30.21) is valid, i.e.

$$\int_0^{2\pi} \left| \sum_{k-1}^{n} \frac{\cos kx}{\ln k} \right| dx \leqslant C \quad (n = 1, 2, \ldots). \tag{30.22}$$

## § 31. Integral expressions for the partial sums of a Fourier series and its conjugate series

In order to study the question of the convergence of a Fourier series in the whole interval $[-\pi, \pi]$ or at any point of it, it seems very convenient to represent the partial sum of the series in the form given it by Dirichlet.

Let

$$\sigma(f) = \frac{a_0}{2} + \sum_{k=1}^{\infty} (a_k \cos kx + b_k \sin kx) \tag{31.1}$$

and

$$S_n(x) = \frac{a_0}{2} + \sum_{k=1}^{\infty} (a_k \cos kx + b_k \sin kx). \tag{31.2}$$

Substituting in (31.2) the expressions for $a_k$ and $b_k$ from the Fourier formulae, we find

$$S_n(x) = \frac{1}{2\pi} \int_{-\pi}^{\pi} f(t)\,dt + \sum_{k=1}^{n} \left[ \left( \frac{1}{\pi} \int_{-\pi}^{\pi} f(t) \cos kt\,dt \right) \cos kx \right.$$
$$\left. + \left( \frac{1}{\pi} \int_{-\pi}^{\pi} f(t) \sin kt\,dt \right) \sin kx \right]$$

$$= \frac{1}{\pi}\int_{-\pi}^{\pi} f(t)\left[\frac{1}{2} + \sum_{k=1}^{n}(\cos kt \cos kx + \sin kt \sin kx)\right] dt$$

$$= \frac{1}{\pi}\int_{-\pi}^{\pi} f(t)\left[\frac{1}{2} + \sum_{k=1}^{n}\cos k(t-x)\right] dt = \frac{1}{\pi}\int_{-\pi}^{\pi} f(t)\, D_n(t-x)\, dt, \quad (31.3)$$

where $D_n(u)$ is a Dirichlet kernel (see § 29) and therefore

$$D_n(u) = \frac{\sin\left(n + \frac{1}{2}\right)u}{2\sin\frac{u}{2}}. \quad (31.4)$$

Supposing $t - x = u$, we obtain from (31.3) and (31.4)

$$S_n(x) = \frac{1}{\pi}\int_{-\pi}^{\pi} f(u+x)\, D_n(u)\, du = \frac{1}{\pi}\int_{-\pi}^{\pi} f(u+x)\frac{\sin\left(n+\frac{1}{2}\right)u}{2\sin\frac{u}{2}}\, du. \quad (31.5)$$

If we have to consider simultaneously the Fourier series of several functions, for example, $f, g, \psi$, we will write $S_n(x,f)$, $S_n(x,g)$, $S_n(x,\psi)$ in order to distinguish between their partial sums. Using this notation, we note immediately that it follows directly from (31.5) that

$$\left.\begin{aligned} S_n(x, f_1 + f_2) &= S_n(x, f_1) + S_n(x, f_2), \\ S_n(x, Cf) &= C S_n(x, f), \end{aligned}\right\} \quad (31.6)$$

and if $f(x) = \sum_{k=1}^{\infty} f_k(x)$, where the series converges uniformly, then

$$S_n(x, f) = \sum_{k=1}^{\infty} S_n(x, f_k) \quad (31.7)$$

(because uniformly convergent series can be integrated term-by-term).

We will also note that since

$$|D_n(x)| \leqslant n + \frac{1}{2}$$

for any $x$, then in every case

$$|S_n(x, f)| \leqslant \left(n + \frac{1}{2}\right)\int_{0}^{2\pi} |f(t)|\, dt, \quad (31.8)$$

and although this estimate in the majority of cases is rough, it is, however, sometimes sufficient.

In investigating the problems of the convergence of formula (31.5), the series is usually transformed, but before going into this question, we will remark here that the partial sum of the series conjugate to (31.1) can be written in a similar manner, i.e.

$$\sum_{k=1}^{\infty} (-b_n \cos nx + a_n \sin nx).$$

Thus, supposing

$$\bar{S}_n(x) = \sum_{k=1}^{n} (-b_k \cos kx + a_k \sin kx),$$

we find following a similar argument

$$\bar{S}_n(x) = -\frac{1}{\pi}\int_0^{2\pi} f(t)\,\bar{D}_n(t-x)\,dt, \tag{31.9}$$

where

$$D_n(u) = \sum_{k=1}^{n} \sin ku.$$

The kernel $\bar{D}_n(u)$, conjugate to the Dirichlet kernel, as we have seen (see § 29), has the form

$$\bar{D}_n(x) = \frac{\cos\dfrac{u}{2} - \cos\left(n+\dfrac{1}{2}\right)u}{2\sin\dfrac{u}{2}}, \tag{31.10}$$

therefore

$$\bar{S}_n(x) = -\frac{1}{\pi}\int_{-\pi}^{\pi} f(t)\,\frac{\cos\dfrac{t-x}{2} - \cos\left(n+\dfrac{1}{2}\right)(t-x)}{2\sin\dfrac{t-x}{2}}\,dt \tag{31.11}$$

or

$$\bar{S}_n(x) = -\frac{1}{\pi}\int_{-\pi}^{\pi} f(u+x)\,\frac{\cos\dfrac{u}{2} - \cos\left(n+\dfrac{1}{2}\right)u}{2\sin\dfrac{u}{2}}\,du. \tag{31.12}$$

Now for the transformation of formulae (31.5) and (31.12) to more suitable forms, we will prove an important lemma.

LEMMA. *If $f(x)$ is summable, $g(x)$ bounded and both possess a period $2\pi$, then the integrals*

$$\int_{-\pi}^{\pi} f(x+t)\,g(t)\cos nt\,dt \quad \textit{and} \quad \int_{-\pi}^{\pi} f(x+t)\,g(t)\sin nt\,dt \tag{31.13}$$

*tend to zero uniformly as $n \to \infty$.*

*Proof.* Let

$$\psi_x(t) = f(x+t)\,g(t).$$

If $x$ is fixed, then $\psi_x(t)$ is a summable function of the variable $t$ and therefore it is clear that the integrals being considered only differ by a constant multiplier $1/\pi$ from the Fourier coefficients of this function. Thus for every $x$ the integrals (31.13) tend to zero as $n \to \infty$. But the significance of the lemma is to prove how uniformly they tend to zero.

Following the argument of § 21, we have

$$\left| \int_{-\pi}^{\pi} \psi_x(t) \cos nt\, dt \right| \leqslant \int_{-\pi}^{\pi} \left| \psi_x\left(t + \frac{\pi}{n}\right) - \psi_x(t) \right| dt$$

and similarly for $\sin nt$. Therefore it is sufficient to prove that

$$\int_{-\pi}^{\pi} \left| \psi_x\left(t + \frac{\pi}{n}\right) - \psi_x(t) \right| dt \tag{31.14}$$

tends to zero uniformly with respect to $x$ as $n \to \infty$. But

$$\int_{-\pi}^{\pi} \left| \psi_x\left(t + \frac{\pi}{n}\right) - \psi_x(t) \right| dt = \int_{-\pi}^{\pi} \left| f\left(x + t + \frac{\pi}{n}\right) g\left(t + \frac{\pi}{n}\right) - f(x+t)\, g(t) \right| dt$$

$$\leqslant \int_{-\pi}^{\pi} \left| f\left(x + t + \frac{\pi}{n}\right) - f(x+t) \right| \left| g\left(t + \frac{\pi}{n}\right) \right| dt$$

$$+ \int_{-\pi}^{\pi} \left| f(x+t) \right| \left| g\left(t + \frac{\pi}{n}\right) - g(t) \right| dt. \tag{31.15}$$

Noting that $g(t)$ is bounded and has a period of $2\pi$, then $|g(t)| \leqslant M$ for any $t$, and also remembering that $f(t)$ also has period $2\pi$, we find for the first of the integrals on the right-hand side of (31.15)

$$\int_{-\pi}^{\pi} \left| f\left(x + t + \frac{\pi}{n}\right) - f(x+t) \right| \left| g\left(t + \frac{\pi}{n}\right) \right| dt$$

$$\leqslant M \int_{-\pi}^{\pi} \left| f\left(x + t + \frac{\pi}{n}\right) - f(x+t) \right| dt \leqslant M \int_{-\pi}^{\pi} \left| f\left(t + \frac{\pi}{n}\right) - f(t) \right| dt$$

$$\leqslant M \omega_1\left(\frac{\pi}{n}, f\right), \tag{31.16}$$

where $\omega_1(\delta, f)$ is the integral modulus of continuity of $f(x)$ (see Introductory Material, § 25); we already know that $\omega_1(\delta, f)$ tends to zero as $\delta \to 0$ for any summable $f(x)$. Since $x$ no longer figures on the right-hand side of the inequality (31.16), we obtain

$$\int_{-\pi}^{\pi} \left| f\left(x + t + \frac{\pi}{n}\right) - f(x+t) \right| \left| g\left(t + \frac{\pi}{n}\right) \right| dt \to 0$$

uniformly relative to $x$ as $n \to \infty$.

For the estimate of the second integral of formula (31.15), we take any $\varepsilon > 0$ and resolve $f(x)$ into the sum of two functions $f_1(x)$ and $f_2(x)$, of which the first is bounded, for example, $|f_1(x)| \leqslant K$ and for the second

$$\int_{-\pi}^{\pi} |f_2(t)|\,dt < \varepsilon.$$

Then

$$\int_{-\pi}^{\pi} \left| f(x+t) \right| \left| g\left(t + \frac{\pi}{n}\right) - g(t) \right| dt$$

$$\leqslant K \int_{-\pi}^{\pi} \left| g\left(t + \frac{\pi}{n}\right) - g(t) \right| dt + \int_{-\pi}^{\pi} \left| f_2(x+t) \right| \left| g\left(t + \frac{\pi}{n}\right) - g(t) \right| dt$$

$$\leqslant K\omega_1\left(\frac{\pi}{n}, g\right) + 2M \int_{-\pi}^{\pi} \left| f_2(x+t) \right| dt \leqslant K\omega_1\left(\frac{\pi}{n}, g\right) + 2M\varepsilon. \tag{31.17}$$

Since $\omega_1(\pi/n, g) \to 0$, the number $\varepsilon$ is arbitrary and $x$ does not enter into the right-hand side of (31.17), then the left-hand side of (31.17) tends to zero uniformly and the proof is concluded.

*Note 1.* Our lemma holds if instead of the integrals of (31.13) we consider the integrals

$$\int_a^b f(x+t) g(t) \cos nt\,dt \quad \text{and} \quad \int_a^b f(x+t) g(t) \sin nt\,dt,$$

where $a$ and $b$ are any two points in $[-\pi, \pi]$. Indeed, it is sufficient to assume that

$$g_1(t) = \begin{cases} g(t) & \text{in} \quad [a, b], \\ 0 & \text{outside } [a, b], \end{cases}$$

which would reduce this case to the preceding one.

*Note 2.* In carrying out the proof we never made use of the fact that $n$ is an integer. Therefore the lemma holds if $n \to \infty$ passing through all real values.

*Note 3.* It will be useful later to know that our lemma holds if instead of $g(t)$ we consider the function $g_x(t)$ for which the following conditions are fulfilled

(a) $|g_x(t)| \leqslant M$ for $\begin{array}{l} -\pi \leqslant x \leqslant \pi, \\ -\pi \leqslant t \leqslant \pi \end{array}$

and moreover as $h \to 0$

(b) $\int_{-\pi}^{\pi} |g_x(t+h) - g_x(t)|\,dt \to 0$

uniformly relative to $x$ in $[-\pi, \pi]$.

Indeed in this case the proof of the lemma is exactly the same.

*Note 4*. If $f(x)$ is a continuous function, then from the given proof we obtain

$$\left| \int_{-\pi}^{\pi} f(x+t)g(t)\cos nt\, dt \right| \leqslant A\omega\left(\frac{\pi}{n}, f\right) + B\omega_1\left(\frac{\pi}{n}, g\right),$$

$$\left| \int_{-\pi}^{\pi} f(x+t)g(t)\sin nt\, dt \right| \leqslant A\omega\left(\frac{\pi}{n}, f\right) + B\omega_1\left(\frac{\pi}{n}, g\right),$$

where $\omega(\delta, f)$ is the modulus of continuity of $f(x)$ and $A$ and $B$ are constants.

In fact, in formula (31.16) when $f(x)$ is continuous, $2\pi\omega(\pi/n, f)$ can be substituted for $\omega_1(\pi/n, f)$, and as $f(x)$ is bounded, the second integral of formula (31.15) does not exceed $B\omega_1(\pi/n, g)$ where $B$ is a constant.

## § 32. Simplification of expressions for $S_n(x)$ and $\bar{S}_n(x)$

We will now use the lemma proved in § 31 to simplify the expressions for $S_n(x)$ and $\bar{S}_n(x)$ (see (31.5) and (31.11)).

We will first note that

$$\frac{\sin\left(n+\frac{1}{2}\right)u}{2\sin\frac{u}{2}} = \frac{\sin nu \cos\frac{u}{2} + \cos nu \sin\frac{u}{2}}{2\sin\frac{u}{2}} = \frac{\sin nu}{2\,\mathrm{tg}\,\frac{u}{2}} + \frac{1}{2}\cos nu. \quad (32.1)†$$

We will also note that the function

$$g(u) = \frac{1}{2\,\mathrm{tg}\,\frac{u}{2}} - \frac{1}{u} \quad (32.2)$$

is continuous in $[-\pi, \pi]$. The only uncertainty could be caused by the point $u = 0$; but, using L'Hôpital's rule, it is easily seen that $\lim\limits_{u\to 0} g(u) = 0$. We still require that $g(u+2\pi) = g(u)$; then $g(u)$ is bounded in $(-\infty, +\infty)$.

From (32.1) and (32.2) we obtain

$$\frac{\sin\left(n+\frac{1}{2}\right)u}{2\sin\frac{u}{2}} = \frac{\sin nu}{u} + g(u)\sin nu + \frac{1}{2}\cos nu. \quad (32.3)$$

† The Continental abbreviation "tg" is used for "tangent" throughout this work (Translator).

Therefore from (31.5) we obtain

$$S_n(x) = \frac{1}{\pi}\int_{-\pi}^{\pi} f(u+x)\frac{\sin nu}{u}\,du + \frac{1}{\pi}\int_{-\pi}^{\pi} f(u+x)g(u)\sin nu\,du$$

$$+ \frac{1}{2\pi}\int_{-\pi}^{\pi} f(u+x)\cos nu\,du. \tag{32.4}$$

The last two integrals of formula (32.4) tend to zero uniformly as $n \to \infty$ due to the lemma of § 31 and since $g(u)$ is bounded. Therefore

$$S_n(x) = \frac{1}{\pi}\int_{-\pi}^{\pi} f(u+x)\frac{\sin nu}{u}\,du + o(1), \tag{32.5}$$

where $o(1)$ is a magnitude which tends to zero uniformly. We will frequently use this fact.

*Note.* It is sometimes important to estimate the magnitude $o(1)$ more exactly; therefore we will now show that if $f(x)$ is continuous, then from Note 4 made at the end of § 31, the modulus of each of the last two integrals in (32.4) does not exceed

$$A\omega\left(\frac{\pi}{n}, f\right) + B\omega_1\left(\frac{\pi}{n}, g\right), \tag{32.6}$$

where $A$ and $B$ are constants. But since $g(u)$ is a function of bounded variation and for such functions the integral modulus of continuity $\omega_1(\delta)$ has the order $O(\delta)$ (see Introductory Material, § 25), then (32.6) is a magnitude of order

$$O\left[\omega\left(\frac{\pi}{n}, f\right)\right] + O\left(\frac{1}{n}\right). \tag{32.7}$$

Finally, having noted that for any continuous function $f(x)$ the modulus of continuity $\omega(\delta, f)$ does not exceed $O(\delta)$, we conclude that in (32.7) the second term is either of the same order as the first or is infinitely small of a higher order. Therefore finally, supposing that

$$\tilde{S}_n(x, f) = \frac{1}{\pi}\int_{-\pi}^{\pi} f(u+x)\frac{\sin nu}{u}\,du, \tag{32.8}$$

we find from (32.5) for continuous $f(x)$

$$S_n(x, f) = \tilde{S}_n(x, f) + O\left[\omega\left(\frac{\pi}{n}, f\right)\right]. \tag{32.9}$$

When $f(x)$ is any summable function, it is sometimes useful to estimate

$$|S_n(x, f) - \tilde{S}_n(x, f)| \leqslant C\int_0^{2\pi} |f(x)|\,dx, \tag{32.10}$$

where $C$ is an absolute constant. This estimate is obtained directly from (32.4) and (32.8) if it is remembered that the function $g(u)$ is bounded.

After this remark which will be useful later, let us return to the simplification of formulae for partial sums. We wish to simplify the expression for $\bar{S}_n(x)$. For this purpose we note that (see (31.10))

$$\bar{D}_n(u) = \frac{\cos\frac{u}{2} - \cos\left(n+\frac{1}{2}\right)u}{2\sin\frac{u}{2}} = \frac{\cos\frac{u}{2} - \cos\frac{u}{2}\cos nu}{2\sin\frac{u}{2}} + \frac{\sin nu}{2}$$

$$= \frac{1-\cos nu}{2\operatorname{tg}\frac{u}{2}} + \frac{\sin nu}{2}. \tag{32.11}$$

Hence if the lemma of § 31 is used, we immediately obtain

$$\bar{S}_n(x) = -\frac{1}{\pi}\int_{-\pi}^{\pi} f(u+x)\frac{1-\cos nu}{2\operatorname{tg}\frac{u}{2}}\,du + o(1).$$

If the function $g(u)$ is used again, then another expression can be obtained for $\bar{S}_n(x)$. Namely, if we write

$$\bar{D}_n(u) = \frac{1-\cos nu}{u} + g(u)(1-\cos nu) + \frac{\sin nu}{2},$$

then, again using the lemma of § 31 we obtain

$$\bar{S}_n(x) = -\frac{1}{\pi}\int_{-\pi}^{\pi} f(u+x)\frac{1-\cos nu}{u}\,du - \frac{1}{\pi}\int_{-\pi}^{\pi} f(u+x)g(u)\,du + o(1),$$

and since the second integral is $O(1)$, then

$$\bar{S}_n(x) = -\frac{1}{\pi}\int_{-\pi}^{\pi} f(u+x)\frac{1-\cos nu}{u}\,du + O(1) \tag{32.12}$$

or

$$\bar{S}_n(x) = -\frac{1}{\pi}\int_{0}^{\pi} [f(x+u) - f(x-u)]\frac{1-\cos nu}{u}\,du + O(1). \tag{32.13}$$

For future reference it will also be useful to note that, if $\delta > 0$ is arbitrary, and $f(x)$ is bounded, then it is possible to rewrite (32.13) in the form

$$\bar{S}_n(x) = -\frac{1}{\pi}\int_{0}^{\delta} [f(x+u) - f(x-u)]\frac{1-\cos nu}{u}\,du + O(1), \tag{32.14}$$

since the discarded integral $\int_{\delta}^{\pi}$ is $O(1)$.

## § 33. Riemann's principle of localization

In § 32 we found a suitable expression for the partial sum of the Fourier series, from which an important corollary can easily be drawn. First, taking any $\delta > 0$ and denoting by $g(u)$ a function, defined thus

$$g(u) = \begin{cases} 0 & \text{in } (-\delta, \delta), \\ \dfrac{1}{u} & \text{in } (-\pi, -\delta) \text{ and } (\delta, \pi), \end{cases}$$

$$g(u + 2\pi) = g(u),$$

on the basis of (32.5) we can write

$$S_n(x) = \frac{1}{\pi} \int_{-\delta}^{\delta} f(u + x) \frac{\sin nu}{u} \, du + \frac{1}{\pi} \int_{-\pi}^{\pi} f(u + x) g(u) \sin nu \, du + o(1),$$

and since $g(u)$ is bounded and periodic, it follows that

$$S_n(x) = \frac{1}{\pi} \int_{-\delta}^{\delta} f(u + x) \frac{\sin nu}{u} \, du + o(1), \qquad (33.1)$$

where again $o(1)$ tends to zero.† This formula allows the following extremely important theorem, known as *Riemann's principle of localization*, to be expressed.

RIEMANN'S THEOREM. *The convergence or divergence of a Fourier series at a point $x$ depends only on the behaviour of the function $f(x)$ in the neighbourhood of the point $x$.*

In fact, the value of the function $f(x)$ outside the interval $(x - \delta, x + \delta)$ does not figure at all in formula (33.1), and therefore the question whether $S_n(x)$ tends to a limit as $n \to \infty$ depends only on the behaviour of $f(x)$ in this interval. Moreover, since in formula (33.1), as has already been proved, $o(1)$ tends uniformly to zero, it is possible to judge the uniform convergence of $S_n(x)$ in any interval by whether the integral on the right-hand side of (33.1) tends uniformly to a limit.

This result is appropriately expressed in the form:

THEOREM. *If two functions $f_1(x)$ and $f_2(x)$ coincide in some interval $[a, b]$, then in any interval $[a + \varepsilon, b - \varepsilon]$ where $\varepsilon > 0$, their Fourier series are uniformly equiconvergent, i.e. the difference of these series converges uniformly to zero.*

Indeed, let

$$f(x) = f_1(x) - f_2(x).$$

---

† We draw the reader's attention to the work by Hille and Klein[1] where it is proved that

$$\left| S_n(x,f) - \frac{1}{\pi} \int_{-\delta}^{\delta} f(x + t) \frac{\sin nt}{t} \, dt \right| \leqslant \frac{K}{\delta} \left[ \int_0^{2\pi} |f(x)| \, dx + 1 \right] \omega_1 \left( \frac{1}{n}, f \right).$$

Here $\omega_1(\delta, f)$ is the integral modulus of continuity of $f(x)$ and $K$ is an absolute constant.

Then $f(x) = 0$ in $[a, b]$. Let a number $\delta > 0$ be chosen such that $\delta \leqslant \varepsilon$ and $x$ is any point of the interval $[a + \varepsilon, b - \varepsilon]$. Then $u + x \in [a, b]$ for $-\delta \leqslant u \leqslant \delta$ and therefore $f(u + x) = 0$; from formula (33.1):

$$S_n(x) = o(1) \quad \text{in} \quad [a + \varepsilon, b - \varepsilon],$$

where $o(1)$ tends uniformly to zero in $[0, 2\pi]$. This means that the Fourier series of $f(x)$ converges uniformly to zero in $[a + \varepsilon, b - \varepsilon]$.

## § 34. Steinhaus's theorem

A useful corollary can be derived from the preceding results. It is due to Steinhaus[3] and can be expressed in the following form:

*If $\lambda(x)$ is a periodic function, satisfying Lipschitz' condition of order 1, then the series $\sigma(\lambda f)$ and $\lambda(x)\,\sigma(f)$ are uniformly convergent in $[-\pi, \pi]$.*

In fact, we have

$$S_n(\lambda f) = \frac{1}{\pi} \int_{-\pi}^{\pi} f(x + t)\,\lambda(x + t)\,\frac{\sin nt}{t}\,dt + o(1),$$

$$\lambda(x) S_n(f) = \frac{1}{\pi} \int_{-\pi}^{\pi} f(x + t)\,\lambda(x)\,\frac{\sin nt}{t}\,dt + o(1).$$

Therefore, supposing

$$g_x(t) = \frac{\lambda(x + t) - \lambda(x)}{t},$$

we have

$$S_n(\lambda f) - \lambda(x) S_n(f) = \frac{1}{\pi} \int_{-\pi}^{\pi} f(x + t) g_x(t) \sin nt\,dt + o(1). \tag{34.1}$$

In order to prove that the right-hand side of (34.1) tends uniformly to zero, it is sufficient to apply to it the first part of Note 3 of the lemma in § 31, providing only that the limitations imposed there on $g_x(t)$ are fulfilled. But the condition

$$|g_x(t)| \leqslant M$$

uniformly with respect to $x$ and $t$ is the result of the fact that $g_x(t)$ satisfies the Lipschitz condition of order 1; it remains to prove that

$$\int_{-\pi}^{\pi} |g_x(t + h) - g_x(t)|\,dt = o(1)$$

uniformly relative to $x$ as $h \to 0$.

To do so, taking $\varepsilon > 0$, we will consider an interval of length $(-\varepsilon, \varepsilon)$; in it we have

$$\int_{-\varepsilon}^{\varepsilon} |g_x(t + h) - g_x(t)|\,dt \leqslant 4M\varepsilon.$$

If $t \in (-\pi, -\varepsilon)$ or $t \in (\varepsilon, \pi)$, then for any $\eta$ it is possible to find $h$ such that the expression under the integral sign for all $t$ in the considered interval will be less than $\eta$, and therefore the corresponding integral less than $\pi\eta$. This concludes the proof of the theorem.

## § 35. Integral $\int_0^\infty \frac{\sin x}{x}\, dx$. Lebesgue constants

Before continuing with the study of the convergence of a Fourier series, we should mention certain properties of the expression

$$D_n^*(t) = \frac{\sin nt}{t}, \tag{35.1}$$

which we will call *a simplified Dirichlet kernel.* Let us note first that from formula (33.1), taking into account the evenness of the simplified Dirichlet kernel, we immediately find that

$$S_n(x) = \frac{1}{\pi} \int_0^\delta [f(x+u) + f(x-u)] \frac{\sin nu}{u}\, du + o(1). \tag{35.2}$$

If we consider the case $f(x) \equiv 1$, then $S_n(x) \equiv 1$ for any $n$, and therefore

$$1 = \frac{2}{\pi} \int_0^\delta \frac{\sin nu}{u}\, du + o(1). \tag{35.3}$$

Supposing $nu = t$, we then find that

$$1 = \frac{2}{\pi} \int_0^{n\delta} \frac{\sin t}{t}\, dt + o(1),$$

and therefore

$$\lim_{n\to\infty} \int_0^{n\delta} \frac{\sin t}{t}\, dt = \frac{\pi}{2}.$$

Hence it immediately follows that

$$\int_0^\infty \frac{\sin t}{t}\, dt = \frac{\pi}{2}, \tag{35.4}$$

i.e. this improper integral has meaning and we even know its magnitude.

From the existence of this integral it follows that: if $\delta > 0$ and $\delta' > 0$, then

$$\lim_{n\to\infty} \int_\delta^{\delta'} \frac{\sin nt}{t}\, dt = \lim_{n\to\infty} \int_{n\delta}^{n\delta'} \frac{\sin t}{t}\, dt = 0. \tag{35.5}$$

This formula will be necessary later.

We note that it is necessary to understand the existence of the integral (35.4) geometrically; therefore we will dwell somewhat on this problem, although it should be known to the reader from courses on analysis.

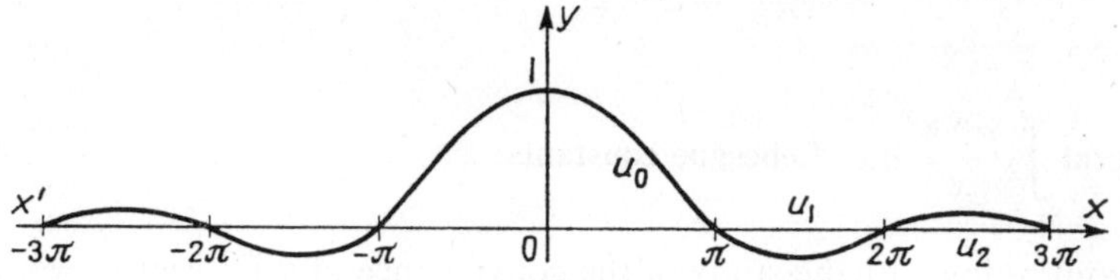


FIG. 5

The convergence of the integral $\int_0^\infty [(\sin t)/t]\, dt$ could also be proved in another way. Supposing (Fig. 5)

$$u_k = \int_{k\pi}^{(k+1)\pi} \frac{\sin t}{t}\, dt \quad (k = 0, 1, 2, \ldots),$$

we see that

$$u_k = \int_0^\pi \frac{\sin(t + k\pi)}{t + k\pi}\, dt = (-1)^k \int_0^\pi \frac{\sin t}{t + k\pi}\, dt,$$

whence it follows that the series $\sum_{k=0}^{\infty} u_k$ alternates its signs, whilst its terms monotonically decrease in their absolute value and tend to zero, since

$$|u_k| = \int_0^\pi \frac{\sin t}{t + k\pi}\, dt < \frac{1}{k\pi}\pi = \frac{1}{k} \quad (k = 1, 2, \ldots).$$

But according to Leibniz' well-known theorem this type of series should converge. On the other hand it is clear that when the sum $\sum u_k$ has meaning, then it is the integral (35.4). Thus,

$$\sum_{k=0}^{\infty} u_k = \int_0^\infty \frac{\sin u}{u}\, du = \frac{\pi}{2}.$$

We now note that

$$\sum_{k=0}^{\infty} u_k < u_0,$$

whence

$$\frac{\pi}{2} < u_0 = \int_0^\pi \frac{\sin u}{u}\, du < \pi. \tag{35.6}$$

Thus from the monotonic nature of $u_n$ and the alternating of their signs, we see that if $A$ and $B$ are any two numbers such that $0 \leqslant A < B$, then

$$\left| \int_A^B \frac{\sin t}{t}\, dt \right| < \pi. \tag{35.7}$$

Because of the evenness of $(\sin t)/t$, this is also true if $A < B \leqslant 0$.

Finally, if $A$ and $B$ are of different signs, then dividing the integral by two, namely from $A$ to 0 and from 0 to $B$, we find that

$$\left| \int_A^B \frac{\sin t}{t}\, dt \right| < 2\pi.$$

This simple statement will be very important to us later, since it follows from it that for any $a$ and $b$ we have

$$\left| \int_a^b \frac{\sin nt}{t}\, dt \right| < 2\pi, \tag{35.8}$$

because

$$\left| \int_a^b \frac{\sin nt}{t}\, dt \right| = \left| \int_{na}^{nb} \frac{\sin t}{t}\, dt \right| < 2\pi \tag{35.9}$$

by virtue of (35.7).

Now the fact that the integral of (35.8) is bounded is solely due to the interference of the positive and negative sinusoidal waves. If the modulus of the expression under the integral sign were taken, then the result would be completely different. We will prove that

$$\int_0^\pi \left| \frac{\sin nt}{t} \right| dt$$

increases without bound on increase of $n$ and we will even estimate the order of its growth exactly. This will be very important later.

Let

$$I_n = \int_0^\pi \left| \frac{\sin nt}{t} \right| dt = \int_0^\pi \left| \frac{\sin u}{u} \right| du. \tag{35.10}$$

Then it is clear that

$$I_{n+1} - I_n = \int_{n\pi}^{(n+1)\pi} \left| \frac{\sin u}{u} \right| du = \int_0^\pi \frac{\sin v}{v + n\pi}\, dv$$

and since at $0 \leqslant v \leqslant \pi$, we have

$$\frac{1}{(n+1)\pi} \leqslant \frac{1}{v + n\pi} \leqslant \frac{1}{n\pi} \quad (n = 1, 2, \ldots),$$

and

$$\int_0^\pi \sin v\, dv = 2,$$

then

$$\frac{2}{\pi(n+1)} \leqslant I_{n+1} - I_n \leqslant \frac{2}{n\pi}. \tag{35.11}$$

Letting $n$ run through the values $1, 2, \ldots, m-1$ and summing the inequalities (35.11) we find

$$\frac{2}{\pi}\sum_{n=1}^{m-1}\frac{1}{n+1} \leqslant \sum_{n=1}^{m-1}(I_{n+1}-I_n) \leqslant \frac{2}{\pi}\sum_{n=1}^{m-1}\frac{1}{n}$$

or

$$I_1 + \frac{2}{\pi}\sum_{n=2}^{m}\frac{1}{n} \leqslant I_m \leqslant I_1 + \frac{2}{\pi}\sum_{n=1}^{m-1}\frac{1}{n}.$$

But taking into account that

$$1 + \frac{1}{2} + \cdots + \frac{1}{m} \approx \ln m,$$

where $\approx$ denotes an asymptotic equality (see Introductory Material, § 11), we find $I_m \approx \ln m$. Thus, we find

$$\int_0^{n\pi}\frac{|\sin u|}{u}\,du = I_n \approx \frac{2}{\pi}\ln n. \tag{35.12}$$

Thus, $I_n$ increases infinitely with increase of $n$, and we also see the exact order of this increase.

It immediately follows from (35.12) that

$$\lim_{n\to\infty}\int_0^{n\pi}\left|\frac{\sin u}{u}\right| du = +\infty,$$

i.e. the integral

$$\int_0^{\infty}\left|\frac{\sin x}{x}\right| dx = \infty, \tag{35.13}$$

which means that the integral (35.4) is known to converge only conditionally, not absolutely.

From formula (35.12) we will derive a corollary, which will play an important role later.

*A Lebesgue constant* is defined by the expression

$$L_n = \frac{1}{\pi}\int_{-\pi}^{\pi}|D_n(t)|\,dt, \tag{35.14}$$

where $D_n(t)$ is a Dirichlet kernel.

Since $D_n(t)$ is an even function,

$$L_n = \frac{2}{\pi}\int_0^{\pi}|D_n(t)|\,dt.$$

But we know (see § 32) that

$$D_n(t) = \frac{\sin nt}{t} + O(1),$$

and therefore

$$L_n = \frac{2}{\pi} \int_0^\pi \left| \frac{\sin nt}{t} \right| dt + O(1),$$

whence

$$L_n = \frac{2}{\pi} I_n + O(1)$$

and due to (35.12)

$$L_n \approx \frac{4}{\pi^2} \ln n.$$

Thus

$$L_n = \frac{1}{\pi} \int_{-\pi}^{\pi} |D_n(t)|\, dt \approx \frac{4}{\pi^2} \ln n. \tag{35.15}$$

It can be proved similarly that for a kernel conjugate to a Dirichlet kernel the integral of the modulus has the same order of increase, i.e. it increases as $\ln n$.

To prove this, we will consider an auxiliary integral, namely

$$J_n = \int_0^{\pi/2} \frac{\sin^2 nt}{\sin t}\, dt. \tag{35.16}$$

Since

$$\frac{\sin^2 nt}{\sin t} = \sum_{k=1}^{n} \sin(2k-1)t$$

(which is proved directly by multiplying both sides by $\sin t$ and changing the product of sines to the difference of cosines), then

$$J_n = \sum_{k=1}^{n} \int_0^{\pi/2} \sin(2k-1)t\, dt = \sum_{k=1}^{n} \frac{1}{2k-1} \sim \ln n \tag{35.17}$$

(here and later, we will not calculate the constant exactly but will simply write $u_n \sim v_n$, if $A < u_n/v_n < B$, where $A$ and $B$ are positive constants).

Let us now consider

$$\varrho_n = \frac{1}{\pi} \int_{-\pi}^{\pi} |\bar{D}_n(t)|\, dt = \frac{2}{\pi} \int_0^{\pi} |\bar{D}_n(t)|\, dt.$$

Since (see (32.11))

$$\bar{D}_n(t) = \frac{1 - \cos nt}{2 \operatorname{tg} \frac{t}{2}} + \frac{\sin nt}{2},$$

then we have

$$\bar{D}_n(t) = \frac{1 - \cos nt}{2 \sin \frac{t}{2}} + O(1) = \frac{\sin^2 \frac{n}{2} t}{\sin \frac{t}{2}} + O(1)$$

(because
$$\frac{1}{2\operatorname{tg}\frac{t}{2}} - \frac{1}{2\sin\frac{t}{2}} = \frac{1}{2\sin\frac{t}{2}}\left[\cos\frac{t}{2} - 1\right] = -\frac{1}{2}\operatorname{tg}\frac{t}{4}\Big).$$

Therefore
$$\varrho_n = \frac{2}{\pi}\int_0^\pi \frac{\sin^2 n\frac{t}{2}}{\sin\frac{t}{2}}\,dt + O(1) = \frac{4}{\pi}\int_0^{\pi/2}\frac{\sin^2 nu}{\sin u}\,du + O(1) = \frac{4}{\pi}J_n + O(1),$$

and therefore
$$\varrho_n \sim \ln n.$$

Thus,
$$\frac{1}{\pi}\int_{-\pi}^{\pi}\left|\bar{D}_n(t)\right|dt \sim \ln n, \tag{35.18}$$

and this is what we wanted to prove.

## § 36. Estimate of the partial sums of a Fourier series of a bounded function

From the results of the preceding section we immediately obtain the following theorem:

LEBESGUE'S THEOREM. *If $f(x)$ is a bounded function*
$$|f(x)| \leqslant M,$$
*then for* $n = 2, 3, \ldots$
$$|S_n(x)| \leqslant CM\ln n, \quad 0 \leqslant x \leqslant 2\pi \tag{36.1}$$
*and*
$$\left|\bar{S}_n(x)\right| \leqslant CM\ln n, \quad 0 \leqslant x \leqslant 2\pi, \tag{36.2}$$
*where C is an absolute constant.*

Indeed (see (31.3) and (35.15)),
$$|S_n(x)| = \left|\frac{1}{\pi}\int_{-\pi}^{\pi} f(t)D_n(t-x)\,dt\right| \leqslant M\frac{1}{\pi}\int_{-\pi}^{\pi}|D_n(t-x)|\,dt = ML_n < CM\ln n$$

and similarly (see (31.9) and (35.18))
$$|\bar{S}_n(x)| < CM\ln n.$$

The theorem is proved.

*Note 1.* It could be thought that formula (36.1) is extremely rough; in fact, it can be proved that for a bounded function the partial sums of a Fourier series should be bounded. However, this is untrue even for continuous functions. If the Fourier series of a continuous function converged uniformly towards it, then such a bound should occur; but we will see later that for continuous functions Fourier series can converge non-uniformly, and can also diverge and even have unbounded partial sums in an infinite set of points.

*Note 2.* If $f(x) \in L[0, 2\pi]$ and $|f(x)| \leqslant M$ in some $[a, b] \subset [0, 2\pi]$, then in any $[a', b']$, $a < a' < b' < b$, we have

$$|S_n(x)| \leqslant AM \ln n + \frac{1}{\delta} \int_{-\pi}^{\pi} |f(t)|\, dt \quad (n = 2, 3, \ldots), \tag{36.3}$$

where $A$ is an absolute constant and $\delta = \min(a' - a, b - b')$.

Indeed, since

$$S_n(x) = \frac{1}{\pi} \int_{-\pi}^{\pi} f(t + x) D_n(t)\, dt$$

$$= \frac{1}{\pi} \int_{-\delta}^{\delta} f(t + x) D_n(t)\, dt + \frac{1}{\pi} \int_{[-\pi,\pi]-(-\delta,\delta)} f(x + t) D_n(t)\, dt, \tag{36.4}$$

then by choosing $\delta$ so that $\delta = \min(a' - a,\ b - b')$, we see that at $x \in [a', b']$ the argument $t + x$ in the first integral does not go outside $[a, b]$ which means that

$$\left| \frac{1}{\pi} \int_{-\delta}^{\delta} f(t + x) D_n(t)\, dt \right| \leqslant M \frac{1}{\pi} \int_{-\pi}^{\pi} |D_n(t)|\, dt \leqslant AM \ln n, \tag{36.5}$$

where $A$ is an absolute constant.

But since outside $(-\delta, \delta)$ we have $|D_n(t)| \leqslant \pi/\delta$ then for the second integral in (36.4) we find

$$\left| \frac{1}{\pi} \int_{[-\pi,\pi]-(-\delta,\delta)} f(x + t) D_n(t)\, dt \right| \leqslant \frac{1}{\delta} \int_{-\pi}^{\pi} |f(t)|\, dt. \tag{36.6}$$

Combining (36.4), (36.5) and (36.6), we obtain (36.3). Instead of (36.3) we can also write

$$|S_n(x)| \leqslant CM \ln n \quad \text{as} \quad n \geqslant N,$$

where $N$ varies with $M$, $\delta$ and $\int_{-\pi}^{\pi} |f(t)|\, dt$, since if $N$ is sufficiently large, then at $n \geqslant N$ the second term of formula (36.3) becomes less than the first.

## § 37. Criterion of convergence of a Fourier series

Let us return to the problem of the convergence of Fourier series. We want to find the conditions under which $\sigma(f)$ converges at some point $x$ to some value $S$.

For this purpose we first remark that it follows from (33.1) that

$$S_n(x) = \frac{1}{\pi} \int_0^{\delta} [f(x + t) + f(x - t)] \frac{\sin nt}{t}\, dt + o(1), \tag{37.1}$$

where $o(1)$ signifies a magnitude tending uniformly to zero in $[-\pi, \pi]$. Moreover, multiplying both sides of equality (35.3) by $S$ we have

$$S = \frac{2}{\pi} \int_0^\delta S \frac{\sin nu}{u} du + o(1). \tag{37.2}$$

From (37.1) and (37.2) we now find that

$$S_n(x) - S = \frac{1}{\pi} \int_0^\delta [f(x+u) + f(x-u) - 2S] \frac{\sin nu}{u} du + o(1). \tag{37.3}$$

It is clear from this that for the convergence of $\sigma(f)$ to the value $S$ at the point $x$ it is necessary and sufficient that

$$\lim_{n\to\infty} \int_0^\delta [f(x+u) + f(x-u) - 2S] \frac{\sin nu}{u} du = 0. \tag{37.4}$$

If we wish the series $\sigma(f)$ to have a "natural sum" at the point $x$, i.e. a sum equal to $f(x)$, then it is necessary and sufficient that

$$\lim_{n\to\infty} \int_0^\delta [f(x+u) + f(x-u) - 2f(x)] \frac{\sin nu}{u} du = 0. \tag{37.5}$$

Supposing

$$\varphi_x(u) = f(x+u) + f(x-u) - 2f(x), \tag{37.6}$$

we can therefore formulate this statement:

*For the series $\sigma(f)$ to converge to $f(x)$ at some point $x$, it is necessary and sufficient that*

$$\lim_{n\to\infty} \int_0^\delta \varphi_x(u) \frac{\sin nu}{u} du = 0, \tag{37.7}$$

*where $\delta > 0$ and $\varphi_x(u)$ is defined by formula* (37.6).

If the function $f(x)$ is continuous in some interval $(a, b)$, then it is possible to raise the question of the uniform convergence of the series $\sigma(f)$ to $f(x)$.

Given any $\varepsilon > 0$. From the continuity of $f(x)$ in the interval $(a, b)$, it follows that it is continuous and therefore bounded in the interval $[a+\varepsilon, b-\varepsilon]$. Therefore, if (35.3) is multiplied by $f(x)$, we have

$$f(x) = \frac{2}{\pi} \int_0^\delta f(x) \frac{\sin nt}{t} dt + o(1), \tag{37.8}$$

where $o(1)$ tends uniformly to zero in $[a+\varepsilon, b-\varepsilon]$. From (37.1) and (37.8) we then derive

$$S_n(x) - f(x) = \frac{1}{\pi} \int_0^\delta [f(x+u) + f(x-u) - 2f(x)] \frac{\sin nu}{u} du + o(1). \tag{37.9}$$

Here $\delta$ can be taken as any number. Therefore if we take $\delta < \varepsilon$, then for $x \in [a + \varepsilon, b - \varepsilon]$ and $|u| \leqslant \delta$ we will have $u + x \in (a, b)$ and $u - x \in (a, b)$, and then $\varphi_x(u)$, defined by formula (37.6), will be still more continuous in $(a, b)$. Hence, using (37.9), we can conclude:

*If $f(x)$ is continuous in $(a, b)$ and given any $\varepsilon > 0$, then for uniform convergence of the series $\sigma(f)$ in $[a + \varepsilon, b - \varepsilon]$, it is necessary and sufficient that*

$$\lim_{n\to\infty} \int_0^\delta \varphi_x(u) \frac{\sin nu}{u} du = 0$$

*uniformly in $[a, b]$; here $\delta$ is any number satisfying the inequality $0 < \delta < \varepsilon$, and $\varphi_x(u)$ is a function defined by the equality* (37.6) *and continuous for*

$$a + \varepsilon \leqslant x \leqslant b - \varepsilon, \quad |u| \leqslant \delta.$$

## § 38. Dini's test

The conditions that have been obtained for convergence (and for uniform convergence), even though they are necessary and sufficient, are very difficult to apply. Therefore we derive from them a series of tests which will be sufficient only for convergence (or for uniform convergence) but are frequently found to be very useful in simple and important cases.

Before deriving these tests, we will give a definition.

DEFINITION. Following Lebesgue, we say that the point $x_0$ is *regular*, if $f(x_0 - 0)$ and $f(x_0 + 0)$ exist and if

$$f(x_0) = \frac{f(x_0 + 0) + f(x_0 - 0)}{2}.$$

It is clear that any point of continuity is regular; also the points of discontinuity of the first kind will be regular, that is, those in which the magnitude of the function is the arithmetic mean of its limits left and right.

Let us prove the following theorem:

*Dini's test. The series $\sigma(f)$ converges to $f(x)$ at every regular point $x$, where the integral*

$$\int_0^\delta |f(x + u) + f(x - u) - 2f(x)| \frac{du}{u}$$

*has meaning.*

Indeed, if this integral has meaning, then it is possible for any $\varepsilon > 0$ to choose $\eta$ so small that

$$\int_0^\eta |f(x + u) + f(x - u) - 2f(x)| \frac{du}{u} < \varepsilon.$$

Then for any $n$, since $|\sin nu| \leqslant 1$, we have

$$\left| \int_0^\eta [f(x + u) + f(x - u) - 2f(x)] \frac{\sin nu}{u} du \right| < \varepsilon.$$

But by virtue of Note 1 of the lemma in § 31

$$\int_{\eta}^{\delta}\left[\frac{f(x+u)+f(x-u)-2f(x)}{u}\right]\sin nu\,du \to 0 \quad \text{as} \quad n\to\infty.$$

From this, it follows that

$$\lim_{n\to\infty}\int_0^{\delta}[f(x+u)+f(x-u)-2f(x)]\frac{\sin nu}{u}\,du = 0$$

and from (37.9) it follows that the convergence is proved.

In particular, if it is supposed that

$$\varphi_x(u) = f(x+u)+f(x-u)-2f(x).$$

then Dini's test gives: if the function $f(x)$ is continuous at the point $x$ and

$$\int_0^{\delta}\frac{|\varphi_x(t)|}{t}\,dt \tag{38.1}$$

has meaning, then $\sigma(f)$ converges to $f(x)$ at the point $x$.

A number of corollaries can be derived from this. For example, if $f(x)$ in the neighbourhood of the point $x$ satisfies the Lipschitz condition of order $\alpha > 0$, i.e. if

$$|f(x+u)-f(x)| \leqslant K|u|^{\alpha}$$

for $|u| \leqslant \delta$, then the integral (38.1) has meaning, which signifies that $\sigma(f)$ converges to $f(x)$. If the function $f(x)$ has a finite derivative at the point $x$, then in the neighbourhood of this point it satisfies the Lipschitz condition of order $\alpha = 1$ and therefore:

*At the point $x$, where $f(x)$ possesses a finite derivative, its Fourier series converges to it.*

In particular, *if $f(x)$ is differentiable everywhere in $(-\pi, \pi)$, then its Fourier series converges everywhere in this interval.*

## § 39. Jordan's test

As is known, any function of bounded variation is the difference of two non-decreasing bounded functions. If the function is monotonic, then it only has a discontinuity of the first kind. Moreover, if a function of bounded variation is continuous, then it is possible to represent it as the difference of two continuous non-decreasing functions.

We use the facts to prove the following theorem:

JORDAN'S THEOREM. *If $f(x)$ is of bounded variation in some interval $(a, b)$, then its Fourier series converges at every point of this interval. Its sum is $f(x)$ at a point of continuity and $[f(x+0)+f(x-0)]/2$ at a point of discontinuity. Finally, if $(a', b')$*

*lies entirely inside the interval* $(a, b)$, *where* $f(x)$ *is continuous, then the Fourier series converges uniformly in* $(a', b')$.

From remarks made earlier, it is clear that it is sufficient to prove the theorem for the case of non-decreasing $f(x)$. In this case, supposing

$$S = \frac{f(x+0) + f(x-0)}{2},$$

we see from

$$f(x+u) + f(x-u) - 2S = [f(x+u) - f(x+0)] + [f(x-u) - f(x-0)],$$

that at a fixed $x$, each function in brackets is a monotonic function of $u$. We will now estimate

$$\int_0^\delta [f(x+u) - f(x+0)] \frac{\sin nu}{u}\, du. \tag{39.1}$$

Here $\delta$ is chosen so that $x \pm \delta \in (a, b)$. But whatever $\varepsilon > 0$, it is possible to take $\delta_1 < \delta$ so small that

$$|f(x+u) - f(x+0)| < \varepsilon \quad 0 \leqslant u \leqslant \delta_1.$$

Since $f(x+u) - f(x+0)$ does not decrease and is non-negative, then applying the second mean value theorem we see that

$$\int_0^{\delta_1} [f(x+u) - f(x+0)] \frac{\sin nu}{u}\, du$$

$$= [f(x+\delta_1) - f(x+0)] \int_{\delta_2}^{\delta_1} \frac{\sin nu}{u}\, du, \tag{39.2}$$

where $0 < \delta_2 < \delta_1$. But since (see (35.7))

$$\left| \int_{\delta_2}^{\delta_1} \frac{\sin nu}{u}\, du \right| < \pi$$

for any positive $\delta_1$ and $\delta_2$, then the modulus of integral (39.2) does not exceed $\pi\varepsilon$.

On the basis of the lemma of § 31

$$\left| \int_0^\delta [f(x+u) - f(x+0)] \frac{\sin nu}{u}\, du \right| < 2\pi\varepsilon,$$

if $n$ is sufficiently large.

In the same way,

$$\int_0^\delta [f(x-u) - f(x-0)] \frac{\sin nu}{u}\, du.$$

is estimated.

Therefore, for sufficiently large $n$

$$\left| \int_0^\delta [f(x+u)+f(x-u)-2S] \frac{\sin nu}{u} du \right| \leqslant 4\pi\varepsilon.$$

where $\varepsilon$ is as small as desired, and then on the basis of the convergence test of § 37 we see that the series converges at the point $x$ to the value $S$.

Now let $f(x)$ be continuous in some interval $[a, b]$, and $[a', b']$ be any interval lying completely within $(a, b)$.

It is possible to choose $\delta_1$ so small that

$$|f(x+u)-f(x)| < \varepsilon \quad \text{and} \quad |f(x-u)-f(x)| < \varepsilon,$$

if $a' \leqslant x \leqslant b'$ and $0 \leqslant u \leqslant \delta_1$. If this is so, then in the preceding estimates of the integrals, $x$ can be taken anywhere in $(a', b')$ and therefore

$$\left| \int_0^\delta [f(x+u)+f(x-u)-2f(x)] \frac{\sin nu}{u} du \right| \leqslant 4\pi\varepsilon$$

for $a' \leqslant x \leqslant b'$, because of the test in § 37, which means that the series converges uniformly in $(a', b')$.

Jordan's theorem has been proved.

From the given theorem, it follows in particular that *if $f(x)$ is of bounded variation in the whole interval $[-\pi, \pi]$ and continuous in it, whilst $f(-\pi) = f(\pi)$, then its Fourier series converges uniformly in $-\infty < x < +\infty$.*

Therefore: *the Fourier series for any periodic absolutely continuous function converges uniformly to it in $-\infty < x < +\infty$.*

*Note.* An important particular case of the given theorem was considered by Dirichlet. He investigated the case when the function $f(x)$ is bounded and has only a finite number of maxima and minima and no more than a finite number of points of discontinuity. For these functions he proved the convergence of the Fourier series at every point. It is clear that these functions are all of bounded variation.

## § 40. Integration of Fourier series

Let $f(x)$ be summable and

$$f(x) \sim \frac{a_0}{2} + \sum_{n=1}^{\infty} (a_n \cos nx + b_n \sin nx).$$

Let us denote the primitive of $f(x)$ by $F(x)$. Then

$$F(x) = \frac{a_0}{2} x + C + \sum \frac{-b_n \cos nx + a_n \sin nx}{n}, \tag{40.1}$$

whilst the series on the right-hand side converges uniformly.

This theorem is due to Lebesgue. In order to prove it, it is sufficient to note that $F(x) - (a_0/2)x$ is the primitive of $f(x) - a_0/2$, it is absolutely continuous and has a period $2\pi$ (see § 23, No. 8).

Therefore, the Fourier series for $F(x) - (a_0/2)x$ converges uniformly to it. But it has the form (see § 23, No. 8)

$$\sum \frac{-b_n \cos nx + a_n \sin nx}{n}.$$

This concludes the proof.

As a corollary, we obtain for any $a$ and $b$

$$\int_a^b f(x)\,dx = \frac{a_0 x}{2}\Big|_a^b + \sum_{n=1}^{\infty} \frac{-b_n \cos nx + a_n \sin nx}{n}\Big|_a^b,$$

i.e. *Fourier series (even divergent) can be integrated term by term in any interval.*

*Corollary.* In formula (40.1) the series converges for all $x$; in particular, at $x = 0$; but this indicates the convergence of the series

$$\sum_{n=1}^{\infty} \frac{b_n}{n}.$$

Thus: *for any Fourier–Lebesgue series, the series* $\sum_{n=1}^{\infty} b_n/n$ *converges.*

This theorem makes it possible in some cases to establish immediately that the given series is not a Fourier–Lebesgue series. Thus, for example, the series

$$\sum_{n=2}^{\infty} \frac{\sin nx}{\ln n}$$

is not a Fourier–Lebesgue series, although from Theorem 1 § 30 it converges at every point.

On the other hand, the series $\sum_{n=1}^{\infty} a_n/n$ can also diverge; in particular, the series

$$\sum_{n=2}^{\infty} \frac{\cos nx}{\ln n},$$

for which the series $\sum a_n/n = \sum 1/(n \ln n)$ diverges, is nevertheless a Fourier–Lebesgue series (this was proved in § 30).

## § 41. Gibbs's phenomenon

We have proved in § 39 that for a function of bounded variation the Fourier series converges at every point, particularly, at points of discontinuity. We want to study in more detail the behaviour of the partial sums of the series $\sigma(f)$ at those points where $f(x)$ is discontinuous. Let us start with an investigation of a special case and then transfer to a general case.

Let $f(x) = x$ in $(-\pi, \pi)$ and $f(x)$ have a period $2\pi$. Since $f(x)$ is odd, then its Fourier series consists of sines only and (see § 8)

$$b_n = \frac{2}{\pi}\int_0^\pi f(x)\sin nx\, dx = \frac{2}{\pi}\int_0^\pi x\sin nx\, dx.$$

Integrating by parts, we find that

$$b_n = \frac{2}{\pi}\cdot\frac{-x\cos nx}{n}\Bigg|_0^\pi + \frac{2}{n\pi}\int_0^\pi \cos nx\, dx = 2(-1)^{n-1}\frac{1}{n}.$$

Thus

$$f(x) \sim 2\left[\frac{\sin x}{1} - \frac{\sin 2x}{2} + \frac{\sin 3x}{3} - \cdots + (-1)^{n-1}\frac{\sin nx}{n} + \cdots\right].$$

Since $f(x)$ is of bounded variation, then its Fourier series converges everywhere to $f(x)$ at its points of continuity and to $[f(x+0) + f(x-0)]/2$ at the points of discontinuity of the first kind. Therefore we have for $x \neq \pm\pi$

$$x = 2\left[\frac{\sin x}{1} - \frac{\sin 2x}{2} + \frac{\sin 3x}{3} + \cdots \pm \frac{\sin nx}{n} \mp \cdots\right],$$

if $x = \pm\pi$, then the series converges to 0 (which is evident immediately, as all its terms then equal zero).

If we make the change in variable $x = \pi - t$, then when $x$ passes through the interval $[-\pi, \pi]$, the variable $t$ will pass through the interval $[0, 2\pi]$, whence it follows that

$$\frac{\pi - t}{2} = \frac{\sin(\pi - t)}{1} - \frac{\sin 2(\pi - t)}{2} + \frac{\sin 3(\pi - t)}{3} - \cdots \pm \frac{\sin n(\pi - t)}{n} \pm \cdots$$

$$= \frac{\sin t}{1} + \frac{\sin 2t}{2} + \frac{\sin 3t}{3} + \cdots + \frac{\sin nt}{n} + \cdots, \tag{41.1}$$

if $t \neq 0$ and $t \neq 2\pi$. At these points the series on the right-hand side of (41.1) converges to zero.

We have already said in § 30 that this series will play an important role in many problems of the theory of trigonometric series. In § 30 it was proved the partial sums of series (41.1) are all bounded, i.e. there exists a constant $C$ such that

$$\left|\sum_{k=1}^{n}\frac{\sin kx}{k}\right| \leqslant C, \qquad \begin{array}{l} -\infty < x < +\infty, \\ n = 1, 2, \ldots. \end{array}$$

However, later it will be necessary for us to study in more detail the behaviour of these partial sums in the neighbourhood of the point $x = 0$.

We have

$$S_n(x) = \sum_{k=1}^{n}\frac{\sin kx}{k} = \int_0^x \left(\sum_{k=1}^{n}\cos kt\right) dt = \int_0^x \left[D_n(t) - \frac{1}{2}\right] dt,$$

where, as always, $D_n(t)$ is a Dirichlet kernel. Therefore

$$S_n(x) = \int_0^x D_n(t)\,dt - \frac{x}{2}. \tag{41.2}$$

But we know that (see (32.3))

$$D_n(t) = \frac{\sin nt}{t} + g(t)\sin nt + \frac{1}{2}\cos nt,$$

where $g(t)$ is bounded.

Supposing

$$\psi_x(t) = \begin{cases} g(t) & \text{for } 0 \leqslant t \leqslant x, \\ 0 & \text{for } x < t \leqslant 2\pi, \end{cases}$$

$$\psi_x(t + 2\pi) = \psi_x(t)$$

and using Note 3 of the lemma in § 31, we conclude that

$$\int_0^x D_n(t)\,dt = \int_0^x \frac{\sin nt}{t}\,dt + o(1) \tag{41.3}$$

uniformly in $0 \leqslant x \leqslant 2\pi$; therefore from (41.2) and (41.3)

$$S_n(x) = -\frac{x}{2} + \int_0^x \frac{\sin nt}{t}\,dt + o(1)$$

or

$$S_n(x) = -\frac{x}{2} + \int_0^{nx} \frac{\sin t}{t}\,dt + o(1). \tag{41.4}$$

If

$$\psi(x) = \frac{\pi - x}{2} \quad \text{in} \quad 0 < x < 2\pi, \tag{41.5}$$

$$\psi(x + 2\pi) = \psi(x),$$

then the function $\psi(x)$ has the form given in Fig. 6. We have already seen that the series (41.1) is $\sigma(\psi)$ and it converges everywhere to $\psi(x)$, apart from the points $x = 0$ and $x = 2\pi$, where it converges to zero.

Allowing $x$ to take the values

$$x = \frac{\pi}{n}, \quad x = \frac{2\pi}{n}, \quad \ldots, \quad x = \pi,$$

we see from (41.4) that

$$\left.\begin{aligned} S_n\left(\frac{\pi}{n}\right) + \frac{\pi}{2n} &= \int_0^{\pi} \frac{\sin t}{t}\,dt + o(1),\\ S_n\left(\frac{2\pi}{n}\right) + \frac{\pi}{n} &= \int_0^{2\pi} \frac{\sin t}{t}\,dt + o(1),\\ &\cdots\cdots\cdots\cdots\\ S_n\left(\frac{k\pi}{n}\right) + \frac{k\pi}{2n} &= \int_0^{k\pi} \frac{\sin t}{t}\,dt + o(1). \end{aligned}\right\} \qquad (41.6)$$

Taking into account what was said in § 35 concerning the behaviour of the curve $y = (\sin x)/x$, it is immediately seen that the curves $y = S_n(x)$ pass through the origin

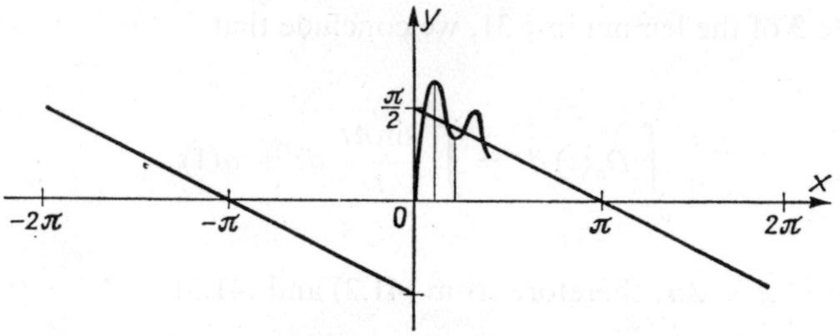


FIG. 6

of the co-ordinates, fluctuate around the straight line $y = \psi(x)$ and although for any $x$, $0 < x < \pi$, we have

$$\lim_{n\to\infty} S_n(x) = \psi(x),$$

however, from (41.6) it is evident that the curves $y = S_n(x)$ to the right of the point $x = 0$ concentrate round the interval $(0, l)$ where

$$l = \int_0^{\pi} \frac{\sin t}{t}\,dt.$$

This type of picture is also obtained on the left of $x = 0$, since all $S_n(x)$ are odd functions. Therefore, around the point $x = 0$ the curves oscillate not between $-\pi/2$ and $\pi/2$, as would be expected, but are concentrated round the interval $[-l, l]$. But calculation shows that $l = 1{\cdot}8519\ldots$, and since $\pi/2 = 1{\cdot}57\ldots$, then the length of the interval $[-l, l]$ exceeds the length of $[-\pi/2, \pi/2]$.

This circumstance was first noticed by Gibbs[1], which is why it is known as *Gibbs's phenomenon*, and the ratio $l$ to $\pi/2$ is *Gibbs's constant*; this constant equals $1{\cdot}17$.

We will show that Gibbs's phenomenon holds for any function of bounded variation about its points of discontinuity, as long as they are isolated. Indeed, in a function of bounded variation the points of discontinuity are only of the first kind.

Let $f(x)$ be such a function and $x_0$ be an isolated point of discontinuity. If $f(x_0 + 0) - f(x_0 - 0) = d$, then the function

$$\varrho(x) = f(x) - \frac{d}{\pi}\psi(x - x_0)$$

is continuous in a sufficiently small neighbourhood of the point $x_0$, since $\varrho(x_0 \pm 0) = f(x_0 \pm 0) - (d/\pi)\,\psi(\pm 0)$ and therefore

$$\varrho(x_0 + 0) - \varrho(x_0 - 0) = d - \frac{d}{\pi}[\psi(+0) - \psi(-0)] = 0.$$

Since there are no other points of discontinuity for $f(x)$ in the neighbourhood being considered, if this neighbourhood were chosen to be sufficiently small, then $\varrho(x)$ is continuous in this neighbourhood and is of bounded variation in $[0, 2\pi]$. This means that its Fourier series converges uniformly in a sufficiently small neighbourhood of $x_0$; therefore the behaviour of the partial sums of the Fourier series for $f(x)$ around $x_0$ will be just the same as for $(d/\pi)\,\psi(x - x_0)$, i.e. as for $(d/\pi)\,\psi(x)$ around $x = 0$; therefore, Gibbs's phenomenon should also occur here.

From Riemann's principle of localization (see § 33) this is true if $f(x) \in L[-\pi, \pi]$ is of bounded variation in $[a, b]$ and $x_0$ is an isolated point of discontinuity of $f(x)$ in $[a, b]$.

## § 42. Determination of the magnitude of the discontinuity of a function from its Fourier series

Let us assume that at some point $x$ the function $f(x)$ has a discontinuity of the first kind, whilst

$$f(x + 0) - f(x - 0) = d. \tag{42.1}$$

The magnitude of this discontinuity can be determined from the following formula (see Lukács[11]):

$$\lim_{n\to\infty} \frac{\overline{S}_n(x)}{\ln n} = -\frac{d}{\pi}. \tag{42.2}$$

In fact, we have

$$f(x + t) - f(x - t) = d + \varepsilon(t), \quad \text{where} \quad \varepsilon(t) \to 0 \quad \text{as} \quad t \to 0.$$

But from formula (31.9) due to the oddness of $\overline{D}_n(t)$ we have

$$\overline{S}_n(x) = -\frac{1}{\pi}\int_0^{\pi} [f(x + t) - f(x - t)]\,\overline{D}_n(t)\,dt,$$

therefore

$$\overline{S}_n(x) = -\frac{d}{\pi}\int_0^\pi \overline{D}_n(t)\,dt - \frac{1}{\pi}\int_0^\pi \varepsilon(t)\overline{D}_n(t)\,dt. \tag{42.3}$$

We will prove first that

$$\lim_{n\to\infty}\frac{1}{\ln n}\int_0^\pi \overline{D}_n(t)\,dt = 1. \tag{42.4}$$

Indeed, supposing that $\nu = (n-1)/2$, we have

$$\int_0^\pi \overline{D}_n(t)\,dt = -\sum_{k=1}^{n}\frac{\cos kt}{k}\Big|_0^\pi = 2\left(1+\frac{1}{3}+\cdots+\frac{1}{2\nu+1}\right)$$

$$= 2\left[\left(1+\frac{1}{2}+\frac{1}{3}+\cdots+\frac{1}{2\nu}+\frac{1}{2\nu+1}\right)-\frac{1}{2}\left(1+\frac{1}{2}+\cdots+\frac{1}{\nu}\right)\right]$$

$$\approx 2\left[\ln\nu - \frac{1}{2}\ln\nu\right] = \ln\nu \approx \ln n. \tag{42.5}$$

Thus, formula (42.4) is proved.
We will prove now that

$$\lim_{n\to\infty}\frac{1}{\ln n}\int_0^\pi \varepsilon(t)\overline{D}_n(t)\,dt = 0. \tag{42.6}$$

For this we will take any $\eta > 0$ and choose $\delta$ such that

$$|\varepsilon(t)| < \eta \quad \text{at} \quad 0 \leqslant t \leqslant \delta.$$

Then

$$\left|\int_0^\delta \varepsilon(t)\overline{D}_n(t)\,dt\right| < \eta\int_0^\delta \left|\overline{D}_n(t)\right| dt < C\eta\ln n \tag{42.7}$$

(from (35.18)) where $C$ is a constant. Moreover, since

$$\left|\overline{D}_n(t)\right| \leqslant \frac{\pi}{\delta} \quad \text{at} \quad \delta \leqslant t \leqslant \pi \tag{42.8}$$

from (29.11) it follows that

$$\int_\delta^\pi \varepsilon(t)\overline{D}_n(t)\,dt = O(1),$$

and therefore, (42.6) follows from (42.7) and (42.8). From (42.3), (42.4) and (42.6), the truth of formula (42.2) now follows.

COROLLARY 1. *At any point of discontinuity of the first kind, the series conjugate to the Fourier series for $f(x)$ diverges.*

Indeed, at this point

$$\overline{S}_n(x,f) = -\frac{d}{\pi}\ln n + \varepsilon_n \ln n,$$

where $\varepsilon_n \to 0$.

COROLLARY 2. *If $f(x)$ is continuous at the point $x$, then $\overline{S}_n(f, x) = o(\ln n)$; if $\overline{S}_n(x,f) = o(\ln n)$, then the point $x$ cannot be a point of discontinuity of the first kind.*

COROLLARY 3. *If for the function $f(x)$, the Fourier coefficients are of order $o(1/n)$, then there can be no points of discontinuity of the first kind in it.*

Indeed, then

$$\overline{S}_n(f, x) = o\left(1 + \frac{1}{2} + \cdots + \frac{1}{n}\right) = o(\ln n)$$

(see Introductory Material, § 11).

From this we conclude in particular that:

*If $f(x)$ is of bounded variation and the Fourier coefficients are of order $o(1/n)$, then it is continuous.*

Indeed, in a function $f(x)$ of bounded variation, points of discontinuity can only be of the first kind; but from Corollary 3 it follows that such points cannot exist and therefore $f(x)$ is continuous.

However, it must be stated that if $f(x)$ is continuous and of bounded variation, then its Fourier coefficients are of order $o(1/n)$. We will prove this in Chapter II, § 2.

## § 43. Singularities of Fourier series of continuous functions. Fejér polynomials

We want to show that if no limitations are imposed on the function $f(x)$ except continuity, then its Fourier series can also diverge at some point and converge non-uniformly about some point, although it converges everywhere. The first examples of this kind were given by du Bois-Reymond[1] and Lebesgue, therefore it is customary to refer to these facts as *du Bois-Reymond's singularity* (for the case of divergence) and *Lebesgue's singularity* (for the case of non-uniform convergence).

Here, following Fejér[2], we will establish some trigonometric polynomials, from which functions will be constructed possessing either one or other of these singularities. Subsequently (in Chapter IV) these Fejér polynomials will help in the construction of considerably more complicated examples, namely: continuous functions, in which the Fourier series diverges in an everywhere dense set, or in a set of the power of the continuum and also continuous functions in which the series converges everywhere but non-uniformly in any interval $\delta$, lying in $[-\pi, \pi]$.

*Constructional elements.* Let us consider two trigonometric polynomials

$$Q(x, n) = \frac{\cos nx}{n} + \frac{\cos(n+1)x}{n-1} + \cdots + \frac{\cos(2n-1)x}{1} - \left[\frac{\cos(2n+1)x}{1} + \frac{\cos(2n+2)x}{2} + \cdots + \frac{\cos 3nx}{n}\right], \tag{43.1}$$

$$\overline{Q}(x, n) = \frac{\sin nx}{n} + \frac{\sin(n+1)x}{n-1} + \cdots + \frac{\sin(2n-1)x}{1} - \left[\frac{\sin(2n+1)x}{1} + \frac{\sin(2n+2)x}{2} + \cdots + \frac{\sin 3nx}{n}\right]. \tag{43.2}$$

Let us note their properties as follows:

(a) There exists a constant $C$ such that

$$|Q(x, n)| \leqslant C \quad \text{and} \quad |\bar{Q}(x, n)| \leqslant C \tag{43.3}$$

for any $x$ and $n$.

In fact

$$Q(x, n) = \sum_{k=1}^{n} \frac{\cos(2n-k)x - \cos(2n+k)x}{k} = 2\sin 2nx \sum_{k=1}^{n} \frac{\sin kx}{k},$$

$$\bar{Q}(x, n) = \sum_{k=1}^{n} \frac{\sin(2n-k)x - \sin(2n+k)x}{k} = -2\cos 2nx \sum_{k=1}^{n} \frac{\sin kx}{k}.$$

But, as is known (see (30.8)) we have

$$\left| \sum_{k=1}^{n} \frac{\sin kx}{k} \right| \leqslant M \quad (-\infty < x < +\infty,\ n = 1, 2, \ldots).$$

Therefore, supposing $C = 2M$, we see that property (a) is proved.

(b) If we denote by $\varphi(x, Q)$ or $\varphi(x, \bar{Q})$ any partial sum of the polynomial $Q(x)$ or $\bar{Q}(x)$, (i.e. the sum of any number of the first terms in the polynomial), then

$$\left.\begin{aligned} &|\varphi(x, Q)| \leqslant 2(1 + \ln n) \\ \text{and} \quad &|\varphi(x, \bar{Q})| \leqslant 2(1 + \ln n), \end{aligned}\right\} \tag{43.4}$$

because

$$1 + \frac{1}{2} + \cdots + \frac{1}{n} < 1 + \ln n.$$

(c) If $\delta \leqslant x \leqslant \pi$, then

$$|\varphi(x, Q)| \leqslant M_\delta \quad \text{and} \quad |\varphi(x, \bar{Q})| \leqslant M_\delta, \tag{43.5}$$

where $M_\delta$ is a constant depending only on $\delta$.

Indeed, every sum $\varphi(x, Q)$ has either the form

$$\sum_{k=0}^{p} \frac{\cos(n+k)x}{n-k} \quad \text{for} \quad p \leqslant n-1,$$

or the form

$$\sum_{k=0}^{n-1} \frac{\cos(n+k)x}{n-k} - \sum_{k=1}^{p} \frac{\cos(2n+k)x}{k} \quad \text{for} \quad p \leqslant n.$$

This means that each of the sums in the expression $\varphi(x, Q)$ has the form $\sum \alpha_k \cos(n+k)x$, where the numbers $\alpha_k$ are positive, decrease or increase monotonically and do not exceed 1; therefore, using the corollary of Abel's transformation (see Introductory Material, § 1), we see that each such sum does not exceed the constants depending only on $\delta$. The same argument holds for $\varphi(x, \bar{Q})$, since there everything is the same except that sines are substituted for cosines.

(d) Finally, we assume

$$P(x, n) = \frac{\cos nx}{n} + \frac{\cos(n+1)x}{n-1} + \cdots + \frac{\cos(2n-1)x}{1}, \tag{43.6}$$

$$\bar{P}(x, n) = \frac{\sin nx}{n} + \frac{\sin(n+1)x}{n-1} + \cdots + \frac{\sin(2n-1)x}{1}, \tag{43.7}$$

i.e. $P(x, n)$ is the sum of the first $n$ terms of $Q(x, n)$ and $\bar{P}(x, n)$ is the sum of the first $n$ terms of $\bar{Q}(x, n)$. Then we have

$$P(0, n) = 1 + \frac{1}{2} + \cdots + \frac{1}{n} > \ln n, \tag{43.8}$$

$$\bar{P}\left(\frac{\pi}{4n}, n\right) = \frac{\sin n \dfrac{\pi}{4n}}{n} + \cdots + \frac{\sin(2n-1)\dfrac{\pi}{4n}}{1}$$

$$> \left(1 + \frac{1}{2} + \cdots + \frac{1}{n}\right) \sin\frac{\pi}{4} > \frac{1}{\sqrt{2}} \ln n,$$

Therefore,

$$\bar{P}\left(\frac{\pi}{4n}, n\right) > \frac{\ln n}{\sqrt{2}}. \tag{43.9}$$

We will use these facts for establishing the examples required.

## § 44. A continuous function with a Fourier series which converges everywhere but not uniformly

Let $a > 1$ be an integer, which we will select later. Let us suppose that

$$n_k = a^{k^2} \tag{44.1}$$

and define

$$\bar{Q}_k(x) = \bar{Q}(x, n_k), \tag{44.2}$$

where $\bar{Q}(x, n)$ is a trigonometric polynomial, defined by formula (43.2).

Let us assume

$$g(x) = \sum_{k=2}^{\infty} \frac{1}{k^2} \bar{Q}_k(x) \tag{44.3}$$

and prove if $a$ is chosen suitably that $g(x)$ is a function with the properties given in the title of this section.

Indeed, from (43.3) for all $x$ and $k$

$$|\bar{Q}_k(x)| < C, \tag{44.4}$$

and therefore series (44.3) converges absolutely and uniformly, which means $g(x)$ is continuous. Since for any $a > 1$ and for $k \geqslant 2$ we have

$$a^{k^2} > 3a^{(k-1)^2},$$

i.e. (see (44.1))

$$n_k > 3n_{k-1},$$

then from (44.2) it follows that no term containing $\sin nx$ appears simultaneously for any $n$ in two different $\overline{Q}_k(x)$, therefore in the series (44.3) all the sines, as in a normal trigonometric series, are arranged in ascending order of the multiplier $n$ for $x$.

On the basis of the lemma of § 12, series (44.3) is the Fourier series of $g(x)$, because its partial sums with indices $3n_k$ converge uniformly to $g(x)$.

We will prove that the partial sums $S_n(x, g)$ of the Fourier series for $g(x)$ are all bounded.

Indeed, each such sum has the form

$$S_n(x, g) = \sum_{k=1}^{m} \frac{1}{k^2} \overline{Q}_k(x) + \frac{1}{(m+1)^2} \varphi(x, \overline{Q}_{m+1}) \tag{44.5}$$

(in particular cases the second term of the sum (44.5) can disappear). But then on the basis of (44.2) and (43.3) we have

$$\left| \sum_{k=2}^{m} \frac{1}{k^2} \overline{Q}_k(x) \right| \leqslant C \sum_{k=2}^{m} \frac{1}{k^2} < A, \tag{44.6}$$

where $A$ is an absolute constant. Moreover, on the basis of (44.2), (43.2) and (43.4) we have

$$\left| \frac{1}{(m+1)^2} \varphi(x, \overline{Q}_{m+1}) \right| \leqslant \frac{1}{(m+1)^2} 2\,(1 + \ln a^{(m+1)^2}) < 2(1 + \ln a) \tag{44.7}$$

and, therefore, from (44.5), (44.6) and (44.7)

$$|S_n(x, g)| \leqslant B \quad (n = 0, 1, \ldots; \; 0 \leqslant x \leqslant 2\pi), \tag{44.8}$$

where $B$ is an absolute constant.

We will note in passing (this will be necessary in Chapter IV) that, supposing

$$S_n(x, g) - g(x) = R_n(x, g),$$

we have

$$|R_n(x, g)| \leqslant K \quad (n = 1, 2, \ldots; \; -\pi \leqslant x \leqslant \pi), \tag{44.9}$$

where $K$ is an absolute constant, which follows from the fact that $g(x)$ is bounded and from (44.8).

Let us turn to a study of the convergence of series $\sigma(g)$.

We will first remark that for any $\delta > 0$ in the interval $\delta \leqslant x \leqslant \pi$ (which also means $-\pi \leqslant x \leqslant -\delta$) the Fourier series for $g(x)$ converges uniformly.

Indeed, from formula (44.5) it is evident that

$$R_n(x, g) = \frac{1}{(m+1)^2} \varphi(x, \overline{Q}_{m+1}) - \sum_{m+1}^{\infty} \frac{1}{k^2} \overline{Q}_k(x),$$

and then from (43.3) and (43.5) it follows that

$$|R_n(x, g)| \leqslant C \sum_{m+1}^{\infty} \frac{1}{k^2} + \frac{M_\delta}{(m+1)^2} < \varepsilon,$$

if $n$ and therefore $m$ is sufficiently large.

Thus we see that the Fourier series for $g(x)$ converges for any $x \not\equiv 0 \pmod{2\pi}$. But for $x \equiv 0 \pmod{2\pi}$ it should also converge, since it consists only of sines.

It remains for us to prove that the series $\sigma(g)$ converges non-uniformly near $x = 0$. For this purpose we consider its partial sums with indices

$$\nu_m = 2n_m - 1.$$

Every such sum has the form

$$S_{\nu_m}(x) = \sum_{k=1}^{m-1} \frac{1}{k^2} \bar{Q}_k(x) + \frac{1}{m^2} \bar{P}(x, n_m),$$

therefore

$$R_{\nu_m}(x) = S_{\nu_m}(x) - g(x) = \frac{1}{m^2} \bar{P}(x, n_m) - \sum_{m}^{\infty} \frac{1}{k^2} \bar{Q}_k(x).$$

Supposing

$$x_m = \frac{\pi}{4n_m},$$

we find from (43.3) and (43.9)

$$R_{\nu_m}(x_m) > \frac{1}{m^2} \bar{P}\left(\frac{\pi}{4n_m}, n_m\right) - C\sum_{m}^{\infty} \frac{1}{k^2} > \frac{1}{m^2} \frac{1}{\sqrt{2}} \ln a^{m^2} - \frac{C}{m} = \frac{\ln a}{\sqrt{2}} - C > 1,$$

provided we choose $a$ so that

$$\ln a > \sqrt{2}\,(1 + C).$$

Thus

$$R_{\nu_m}(x_m) > 1 \quad (m = 1, 2, \ldots) \tag{44.10}$$

for some sequence of points $x_m$ tending to 0, which means that the Fourier series for $g(x)$ converges non-uniformly near $x = 0$.

The theorem is proved.

## § 45. Continuous function with a Fourier series divergent at one point (Fejér's example)

We shall consider Fejér's polynomials $Q(x, n)$, described in § 43, and by using them establish the Fourier series of continuous functions divergent at $x = 0$; in this case, series will be obtained as desired possessing either bounded or unbounded partial sums. These and other examples will be used later (in Chapter IV) for constructions of more complex character.

We assume first as in the preceding section

$$n_k = a^{k^2},$$

where $a$ is an integer and $a \geqslant 2$; let us suppose

$$Q_k(x) = Q(x, n_k), \tag{45.1}$$

and let

$$f(x) = \sum_{k=1}^{\infty} \frac{1}{k^2} Q_k(x). \tag{45.2}$$

We will again see as in the preceding section that $f(x)$ is continuous and the series (45.2), if every term of any polynomial $Q_k(x)$ in it is considered separately (but not grouped in sums), is its Fourier series.

We see, just as in the proof of (44.8), that

$$|S_n(x, f)| \leqslant B \tag{45.3}$$

for any $n$ and $x$ and that the series $\sigma(f)$ converges uniformly in $(-\pi \leqslant x \leqslant -\delta)$ and $(\delta \leqslant x \leqslant \pi)$, i.e. it converges for any $x \not\equiv 0 \pmod{2\pi}$. But at $x = 0$ it diverges, since supposing that

$$\nu_m = 2n_m - 1, \quad \mu_m = 3n_{m-1},$$

we have

$$S_{\nu_m}(0) - S_{\mu_m}(0) = \frac{P(0, n_m)}{m^2} > \frac{\ln n_m}{m^2} = \frac{m^2 \ln a}{m^2} = \ln a > 0, \quad m = 1, 2, \ldots$$

Consequently, Cauchy's test of convergence is not fulfilled.

Thus, $\sigma(f)$ diverges at $x = 0$, although its partial sums are all bounded by virtue of (45.3).

If instead of $n_k = a^{k^2}$ we supposed

$$n_k = a^{k^3} \quad (a > 2),$$

then we would obtain

$$S_{\nu_m}(0) - S_{\mu_m}(0) = \frac{P(0, n_m)}{m^2} > \frac{m^3 \ln a}{m^2} = m \ln a,$$

i.e. the series would not only diverge at the point $x = 0$, but would have unbounded partial sums at this point.

## § 46. Divergence at one point (Lebesgue's example)

The preceding examples of Fejér (see § 45) although suitable for use in further constructions possess one disadvantage; since the corresponding functions were established purely analytically with the help of formulae, it is not possible to represent them by curves and understand geometrically why the divergence of the Fourier series occurs.

Therefore, we will describe Lebesgue's example (only slightly modified in order to shorten the proof), where it is possible to represent the function graphically though only approximately.

Let $n_1, n_2, \ldots, n_k, \ldots$ be a sequence of integers which we shall define later. Let us suppose

$$a_0 = 1, \quad a_k = n_1 n_2 \ldots n_k \quad (k = 1, 2, \ldots).$$

and define

$$I_k = \left(\frac{\pi}{a_k}, \frac{\pi}{a_{k-1}}\right) \quad (k = 1, 2, \ldots).$$

We shall later define a sequence of numbers $c_k$, whilst now we only assume that $c_k \downarrow 0$.

Let

$$f(x) = c_k \sin a_k x \quad \text{in} \quad I_k,$$

$$f(0) = 0,$$

$$f(-x) = f(x).$$

It is clear that $f(x)$ is defined everywhere in $[-\pi, \pi]$, it is continuous in each $I_k$ and reverts to 0 at its end points, i.e. it has no discontinuities at finite points; finally, $f(x) \to 0$ as $x \to 0$ (Fig. 7) since $c_k \downarrow 0$, which means that $f(x)$ is continuous everywhere.

We shall prove that its Fourier series converges everywhere in $[-\pi, \pi]$ apart from $x = 0$. Since $f(x)$ has only a finite number of maxima and minima in $[\delta, \pi]$ it is of

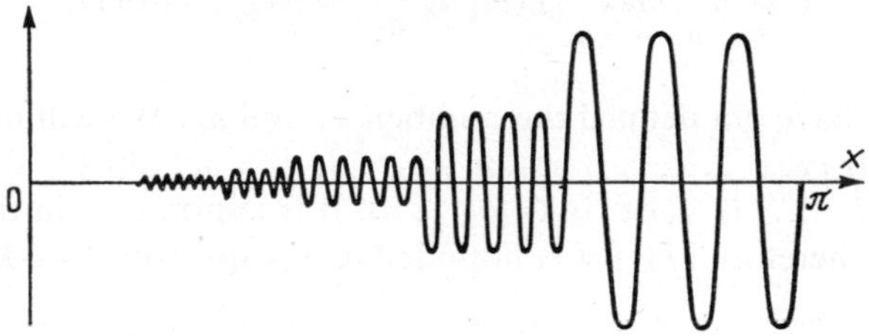


FIG. 7

bounded variation in this interval (and also in $[-\pi, -\delta]$). This means that its Fourier series converges at each point $[-\pi, \pi]$, apart from $x = 0$.

We will show that with a proper choice of the numbers $c_k$ and $n_k$ the series $\sigma(f)$ diverges at $x = 0$.

As is known, for any $f(x)$ we have

$$S_n(x, f) = \frac{1}{\pi} \int_{-\pi}^{\pi} f(x + t) \frac{\sin nt}{t} dt + o(1),$$

which means that at $x = 0$

$$S_n(0, f) = \frac{1}{\pi} \int_{-\pi}^{\pi} f(t) \frac{\sin nt}{t} dt + o(1).$$

Our $f(x)$ is even, therefore

$$S_n(0, f) = \frac{2}{\pi} \int_{0}^{\pi} f(t) \frac{\sin nt}{t} dt + o(1). \tag{46.1}$$

We will show that by a suitable choice of $c_k$ and $n_k$, we have

$$J_k = \int_0^{\pi} f(t) \frac{\sin a_k t}{t} dt \to \infty \quad \text{as} \quad k \to \infty. \tag{46.2}$$

If this is so, then $S_{a_k}(0, f) \to +\infty$ as $k \to \infty$ (as is evident from (46.1)) and then the series $\sigma(f)$ diverges at $x = 0$.

In order to evaluate $J_k$, we will divide it into three terms

$$J_k = \int_0^{\pi/a_k} f(t) \frac{\sin a_k t}{t} dt + \int_{\pi/a_k}^{\pi/a_{k-1}} f(t) \frac{\sin a_k t}{t} dt + \int_{\pi/a_{k-1}}^{\pi} f(t) \frac{\sin a_k t}{t} dt$$

$$= J_k' + J_k'' + J_k'''. \tag{46.3}$$

We have

$$\left| \frac{\sin a_k t}{t} \right| \leqslant a_k.$$

This means that

$$(J_k') \leqslant \max_{0 \leqslant t \leqslant \pi/a_k} |f(t)| \, a_k \frac{\pi}{a_k} = \pi c_{k+1} = o(1), \tag{46.4}$$

since $c_k \downarrow 0$.

Up to now we have not defined the numbers $c_k$ and $n_k$. We will now suppose that $n_1 = 2$, $c_1 = 1$. If $c_1, c_2, \ldots, c_{k-1}$ and $n_1, n_2, \ldots, n_{k-1}$ are already defined, then $f(t)$ is defined in $I_1, I_2, \ldots, I_{k-1}$, i.e. in $(\pi/a_{k-1}, \pi)$. It is continuous in this semi-interval and $t \geqslant \pi/a_{k-1}$, therefore $[f(t)]/t$ is bounded. Consequently, if $n$ is sufficiently large, then

$$\int_{\pi/a_{k-1}}^{\pi} \frac{f(t)}{t} \sin nt \, dt$$

can be made as small as desired (see § 19).

Since $a_k = n_1 n_2 \ldots n_k$, then if $n_1, \ldots, n_{k-1}$ are already fixed, $n_k$ is still at our disposal, which means that by increasing it we can make $a_k$ as large as desired, in particular such that

$$|J_k'''| \leqslant \left| \int_{\pi/a_{k-1}}^{\pi} f(t) \frac{\sin a_k t}{t} dt \right| < \frac{1}{k}, \tag{46.5}$$

whence it follows that $J_k''' = o(1)$ as $k \to \infty$.

It remains to estimate $J_k''$. We have

$$J_k'' = \int_{\pi/a_k}^{\pi/a_{k-1}} c_k \sin a_k t \, \frac{\sin a_k t}{t} dt = \frac{c_k}{2} \int_{\pi/a_k}^{\pi/a_{k-1}} \frac{1 - \cos 2a_k t}{t} dt$$

$$= \frac{c_k}{2} \ln n_k - \frac{c_k}{2} \int_{\pi/a_k}^{\pi/a_{k-1}} \frac{\cos 2a_k t}{t} dt.$$

But according to the second mean value theorem, taking into account that $1/t$ is positive and decreases monotically in the range of integration, we find

$$\left|\int_{\pi/a_k}^{\pi/a_{k-1}} \frac{\cos 2a_k t}{t}\,dt\right| \leqslant \frac{a_k}{\pi}\left|\int_{\pi/a_k}^{\xi} \cos 2a_k t\,dt\right| \leqslant \frac{a_k}{\pi}\,\frac{2}{2a_k} = \frac{1}{\pi}.$$

Therefore from $c_k \to 0$ it follows that

$$J_k'' = \frac{1}{2}c_k \ln n_k + o(1),$$

whence from (46.4) and (46.5)

$$J_k = \frac{1}{2}c_k \ln n_k + o(1).$$

We can now assume, provided $c_k = 1/\sqrt{\ln n_k}$, that $c_k \downarrow 0$ and

$$J_k = \frac{1}{2}\sqrt{\ln n_k} + o(1) \quad \text{as} \quad k \to \infty.$$

Thus, the proof is concluded.

From Fig. 7 it is evident that the function $f(x)$, as $x$ approaches zero, performs more and more frequent oscillations; thus, it is found graphically that the divergence of the series $\sigma(f)$ at $x = 0$ is produced by the fact that $f(x)$ is of unbounded variation in the neighbourhood of this point.

*Note.* Later (in Chapter V, § 22) we will need the example of a continuous function, for which the Fourier series converges to zero everywhere in $[0, 2\pi]$ external to some interval $[a, b]$, converges at every point of $(a, b)$ and diverges either only at $a$ or only at $b$ or at both end points of the interval $(a, b)$, and possesses unbounded partial sums at points of divergence (we say briefly: it diverges without bound). All such examples are easily obtained, following the method of establishing Lebesgue's example.

Indeed, if we suppose

$$\varphi(x) = \begin{cases} 0 & \text{in} \quad [-\pi, 0], \\ f(x) & \text{in} \quad [0, \pi], \end{cases}$$

then

$$S_n(0, \varphi) = \frac{1}{2}S_n(0, f),$$

and therefore $\sigma(\varphi)$ diverges without bound at $x = 0$; moreover, $\sigma(\varphi)$ converges in $0 < x \leqslant \pi$ and converges to zero in $(-\pi, 0)$, which follows from the principle of localization (see § 33). If we suppose

$$\varphi_a(x) = \varphi(x - a),$$

then we obtain a function for which $\sigma(\varphi_a)$ diverges at $x = a$, converges to zero in $[a - \pi, a]$ and converges in $(a, a + \pi]$.

The function $\Psi(x) = \varphi(-x)$ has a Fourier series which converges everywhere except at $x = 0$, where it diverges without bound, and moreover this series converges to zero at $0 < x \leqslant \pi$.

Therefore

$$\Psi_b(x) = \Psi(x - b)$$

has a series which converges everywhere except at $x = b$, where it diverges without bound, whilst it converges to zero in $(b, b + \pi)$.

Now let $0 < a < b < 2\pi$. Let us construct $\lambda(x)$ in the following way. We choose the points $\alpha$ and $\gamma$ such that $0 < \alpha < a < \gamma < b$ and let

$$\lambda(x) = \begin{cases} 1 & \text{in } (a, \gamma), \\ 0 & \text{outside } (\alpha, b), \end{cases}$$

$\lambda(x)$ is interpolated linearly by $(\alpha, a)$ and $(\gamma, b)$ (Fig. 8).

According to Steinhaus' theorem (§ 34) the series $\sigma(\lambda\varphi_a)$ is equiconvergent with $\lambda(x)\sigma(\varphi_a)$ and therefore it converges everywhere, apart from $x = a$, where it diverges without bound, whilst outside $[a, b)$ it converges everywhere to zero (either because $\lambda(x) = 0$ or because $\varphi_a(x) = 0$).

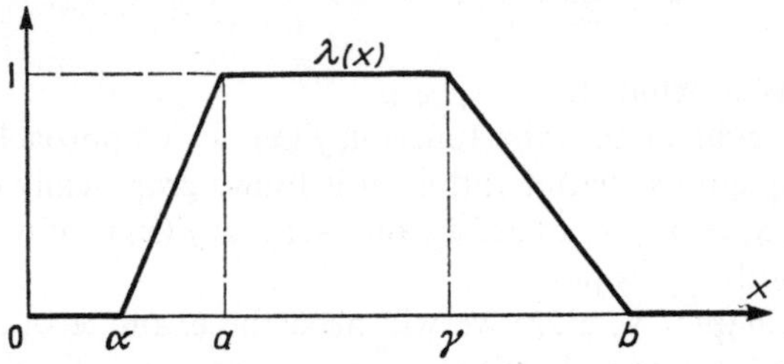


FIG. 8

In just the same way, if we denote by $\lambda^*(x)$ a function which is equal to 1 in $(\gamma, b)$, to 0 outside $(a, \beta)$ and can be interpolated linearly in $(a, \gamma)$ and $(b, \beta)$, where

$$0 < a < \gamma < b < \beta < 2\pi,$$

then we see that $\sigma(\lambda^*\Psi_b)$ is equiconvergent with $\lambda^*(x)\sigma(\Psi_b(x))$ and therefore it diverges without bound at $x = b$, converges everywhere apart from $x = b$ and converges to zero outside $(a, b]$.

Finally, supposing

$$F(x) = \lambda\varphi_a(x) + \lambda^*\Psi_b(x),$$

we see that $F(x)$ is continuous and $\sigma(f)$ diverges without bound at $x = a$ and $x = b$, but converges at all the other points, and moreover converges to zero everywhere outside $[a, b]$.

*Note.* The Fourier coefficients for those series which we established in §§ 45 and 46 tend to zero according to a rather complicated law. In connection with the solution of some problems in the theory of integral equations, the question arose: is it possible to find some continuous even function $f(x)$ for which

$$\sigma(f) = \sum_{n=1}^{\infty} a_n \cos nx, \quad \text{where} \quad |a_n| \downarrow 0$$

and moreover $\sigma(f)$ diverges at $x = 0$? Salem[14] gave an affirmative answer to this question. We will not give the proof here, since it is based on the study of some theoretical numerical inequalities, which would digress too far from the subject matter of this book.

## § 47. Summation of a Fourier series by Fejér's method

We have seen that even Fourier series of continuous functions have points of divergence (§§ 45 and 46). The question arises as to what extent the Fourier series can then be used for calculating the values of the function $f(x)$? Here, as is always the case with divergent series, it is natural to resort to one or other method of summation.

Let us recall (see Introductory Material, § 6) that the functional series is said to be *summable by the method* (C, 1), if there exists a limit

$$\lim_{n\to\infty} \sigma_n(x),$$

where

$$\sigma_n(x) = \frac{1}{n+1}\sum_{k=0}^{n} S_k(x), \tag{47.1}$$

and $S_n(x)$ are the partial sums of the series.

The application of this method to Fourier series is usually known as *summation by Fejér's method*, since Fejér first drew attention to the usefulness of Cesàro sums in this case and proved the fundamental theorem. Later it was generalized by Lebesgue.

We know (see (31.3)) that the partial sum $S_n(x)$ of the Fourier series of the function $f(x)$ is expressed by the formula

$$S_n(x) = \frac{1}{\pi}\int_{-\pi}^{\pi} f(t) D_n(t - x)\, dt,$$

where $D_n(u)$ is a Dirichlet kernel. Therefore a Cesàro sum, defined by (47.1), should have the form

$$\sigma_n(x) = \frac{1}{\pi}\int_{-\pi}^{\pi} f(t)\frac{1}{n+1}\sum_{k=0}^{n} D_k(t-x)\, dt = \frac{1}{\pi}\int_{-\pi}^{\pi} f(t) K_n(t-x)\, dt, \tag{47.2}$$

where

$$K_n(u) = \frac{1}{n+1}\sum_{k=0}^{n} D_k(u). \tag{47.3}$$

Consequently

$$\sigma_n(x) = \frac{1}{\pi}\int_{-\pi}^{\pi} f(x+u) K_n(u)\, du. \tag{47.4}$$

The function $K_n(u)$ is known as a *Fejér kernel*; we will now find an appropriate expression for it.

Since

$$D_n(u) = \frac{\sin\left(n + \frac{1}{2}\right)u}{2\sin\frac{u}{2}} = \frac{\cos nu - \cos(n+1)u}{4\sin^2\frac{u}{2}},$$

then

$$K_n(u) = \frac{1}{n+1}\sum_{k=0}^{n} \frac{\cos ku - \cos(k+1)u}{4\sin^2\frac{u}{2}} = \frac{1-\cos(n+1)u}{(n+1)4\sin^2\frac{u}{2}}$$

$$= \frac{1}{2(n+1)}\left(\frac{\sin(n+1)\frac{u}{2}}{\sin\frac{u}{2}}\right)^2.$$

Thus

$$K_n(u) = \frac{1}{2(n+1)}\left(\frac{\sin(n+1)\frac{u}{2}}{\sin\frac{u}{2}}\right)^2. \tag{47.5}$$

From this expression we immediately derive a number of properties of the kernel.

(1) $K_n(u) \geqslant 0$.

This property will play an essential role later.

(2) We have

$$K_n(u) \leqslant \frac{1}{2(n+1)\sin^2\frac{u}{2}} \leqslant \frac{\pi^2}{2(n+1)u^2} \quad \text{for} \quad 0 < |u| \leqslant \pi, \tag{47.6}$$

and therefore

$$K_n(u) = O\left(\frac{1}{nu^2}\right) \quad \text{for} \quad 0 < |u| \leqslant \pi \tag{47.7}$$

and

$$K_n(u) \leqslant \frac{\pi^2}{2(n+1)\delta^2} \quad \text{for} \quad 0 < \delta \leqslant |u| \leqslant \pi, \tag{47.8}$$

whence for any $\delta > 0$, supposing

$$M_n(\delta) = \max_{\delta \leqslant u \leqslant \pi} K_n(u),$$

we have

$$\lim_{n\to\infty} M_n(\delta) = 0. \tag{47.9}$$

(3) We have

$$\frac{1}{\pi}\int_{-\pi}^{\pi} K_n(u)\,du = 1. \tag{47.10}$$

This follows from (47.3) and from

$$\frac{1}{\pi}\int_{-\pi}^{\pi} D_k(u)\,du = 1 \quad (k = 0, 1, 2, \ldots).$$

(4) If $\delta > 0$, then

$$\lim_{n\to\infty} \frac{1}{\pi}\int_{-\delta}^{\delta} K_n(u)\,du = 1. \tag{47.11}$$

This immediately follows from (47.9) and (47.10).

Starting from these properties, we can prove the following theorem, concerning the summation of Fourier series by Fejér's method.

FEJÉR'S THEOREM. *If $x$ is a point of continuity of the function $f(x)$ or a point of discontinuity of the first kind, then at this point $\sigma(f)$ is summable by Fejér's method to $f(x)$ or to $[f(x+0)+f(x-0)]/2$, respectively; if $(a, b)$ is an interval where $f(x)$ is continuous, then $\sigma(f)$ is uniformly summable by Fejer's method to $f(x)$ in any interval $[\alpha, \beta]$ lying within the interval $(a, b)$.*

*Finally, if $f(x)$ is everywhere continuous, then its Fourier series is uniformly summable by Fejér's method in $[-\pi, \pi]$, i.e. $\sigma_n(x)$ uniformly converges to $f(x)$ in this interval.*

In order to prove this theorem we will turn to a lemma which is also useful in other circumstances.

LEMMA. *Let*

$$f_n(x) = \frac{1}{\pi}\int_{-\pi}^{\pi} f(x+t)\Psi_n(t)\,dt, \tag{47.12}$$

*where the function $\Psi_n(t)$ possesses the following properties:*

(1) *$\Psi_n(t)$ is an even function.*

(2) $\int_{-\pi}^{\pi} |\Psi_n(t)|\,dt \leqslant C$ *$(n = 1, 2, \ldots)$ where $C$ is a constant.*

(3) *Supposing for $\delta > 0$*

$$M_n(\delta) = \sup_{\delta\leqslant|t|\leqslant\pi} |\Psi_n(t)|,$$

*we have*

$$\lim_{n\to\infty} M_n(\delta) = 0;$$

(4) $\frac{1}{\pi}\int_{-\pi}^{\pi} \Psi_n(t)\,dt = 1.$

*Then: if $x$ is a point of discontinuity of the first kind for $f(x)$, then*

$$f_n(x) \to \frac{f(x+0)+f(x-0)}{2} \quad \textit{as} \quad n\to\infty,$$

*$f_n(x) \to f(x)$ at each point of continuity of $f(x)$.*

*If $f(x)$ is continuous in $(a, b)$, then $f_n(x) \to f(x)$ uniformly in $(\alpha, \beta)$ for any $[\alpha, \beta] \subset (a, b)$.*

To prove this lemma we will note first that from property (4) of the function $\Psi_n(t)$ we have

$$\frac{f(x+0)+f(x-0)}{2} = \frac{1}{\pi}\int_{-\pi}^{\pi} \frac{f(x+0)+f(x-0)}{2}\Psi_n(t)\,dt$$

$$= \frac{1}{\pi}\int_{0}^{\pi} [f(x+0)+f(x-0)]\Psi_n(t)\,dt \qquad (47.13)$$

because of the evenness of $\Psi_n(t)$. From (47.12) and the evenness of $\Psi_n(t)$ we conclude that

$$f_n(x) = \frac{1}{\pi}\int_{-\pi}^{\pi} [f(x+t)+f(x-t)]\Psi_n(t)\,dt. \qquad (47.14)$$

Therefore from (47.13) and (47.14)

$$f_n(x) - \frac{f(x+0)+f(x-0)}{2}$$
$$= \frac{1}{\pi}\int_{0}^{\pi} [f(x+t)+f(x-t)-f(x+0)-f(x-0)]\Psi_n(t)\,dt. \qquad (47.15)$$

We will show that the integral on the right-hand side of (47.15) tends to zero as $n \to \infty$ and moreover if $f(x)$ is continuous in $(a, b)$, then it tends to zero uniformly in $[\alpha, \beta]$, where $a < \alpha < \beta < b$. For this purpose we will choose a number $\delta$ such that

$$\left.\begin{aligned} |f(x+t)-f(x+0)| &< \varepsilon, \\ |f(x-t)-f(x-0)| &< \varepsilon \end{aligned}\right. \quad \text{at} \quad 0 \leqslant x \leqslant \delta. \qquad (47.16)$$

This is possible for any fixed $x$; if $f(x)$ is continuous in $(a, b)$ (in this case $f(x+0) = f(x-0) = f(x)$), then it is possible to choose $\delta$ so that it is independent of $x$, $\alpha \leqslant x \leqslant \beta$ and the inequalities (47.16) hold. Having chosen $\delta$ in this way, we divide the integral of formula (47.15) into two: integral $I_1$ in the interval $(0, \delta)$ and integral $I_2$ in the interval $(\delta, \pi)$. We have on the basis of (47.16)

$$|I_1| < 2\varepsilon \int_0^{\pi} |\Psi_n(t)|\,dt < 2\varepsilon C$$

from property (2) of the function $\Psi_n(t)$.

For $I_2$ we find

$$|I_2| \leqslant M_n(\delta) \int_{\delta}^{\pi} \{|f(x+t)| + |f(x+0)| + |f(x-t)| + |f(x-0)|\}dt. \qquad (47.17)$$

For constant $x$ the integral in (47.17) is finite and the factor in front of it tends to zero because of property (3) of the function $\Psi_n(t)$, which means that $I_2 \to 0$. Moreover, if $x \in [\alpha, \beta] \subset (a, b)$, then the integral in (47.17) for any $x$ does not exceed

$$\int_{-\pi}^{\pi} |f(t)|\, dt + 2\pi\, |f(x)|,$$

and since $f(x)$ is continuous in $(a, b)$ and is therefore bounded in $[\alpha, \beta]$, then $I_2 \to 0$ uniformly. The lemma is completely proved.

In order to derive Fejér's theorem formulated above from the above lemma, it is sufficient to prove that the Fejér kernel satisfies the properties given in the lemma; then, supposing $f_n(x) = \sigma_n(x)$, we arrive at the required result.

But property (1) for a Fejér kernel has been fulfilled; (3) and (4) have already been proved by us and (2) follows from the fact that for a Fejér kernel

$$\int_{-\pi}^{\pi} |K_n(t)|\, dt = \int_{-\pi}^{\pi} K_n(t)\, dt = \pi$$

since $K_n(t) \geqslant 0$ and from property (3). Thus Fejér's theorem is completely proved.

## § 48. Corollaries of Fejér's theorem

From Fejér's theorem, it is possible to deduce a number of interesting corollaries. First, it gives a new proof of Weierstrass's classic theorem on the approximation of a continuous function by means of a trigonometric polynomial (see § 27).

Indeed, since we have proved that for a continuous $f(x)$ the function $\sigma_n(x)$ tends uniformly to $f(x)$, then having chosen $n$ sufficiently large, it can be stated that

$$|f(x) - \sigma_n(x)| < \varepsilon, \quad -\infty < x < +\infty.$$

But $\sigma_n(x)$ is evidently a trigonometric polynomial and therefore the theorem is proved.

We will also note that method $(C, 1)$ is regular (see Introductory Material, § 6) i.e. the convergence of a series to a value $S$ implies its summability by method $(C, 1)$ to the same value $S$. From this, it immediately follows that:

*If $\sigma(f)$ converges at a point of continuity of the function $f(x)$, then it converges to $f(x)$; similarly, at a point of discontinuity of the first kind, if $\sigma(f)$ converges, then it certainly tends to $[f(x+0) + f(x-0)]/2$.*

Finally, Fejér sums make it possible in some cases to pass judgment on the normal partial sums of the Fourier series. Thus, for example, it is possible to prove the theorem:

*For the function $f(x)$ of bounded variation, the partial sums of the series $\sigma(f)$ are all bounded.*

In order to prove this, we will note first that if

$$m \leqslant f(x) \leqslant M, \quad -\pi \leqslant x \leqslant \pi, \tag{48.1}$$

then for Fejér sums we also have

$$m \leqslant \sigma_n(x) \leqslant M, \quad -\pi \leqslant x \leqslant \pi. \tag{48.2}$$

Indeed, taking into account that the Fejér kernel is positive, we immediately derive from (47.4) and (48.1) that

$$m\frac{1}{\pi}\int_{-\pi}^{\pi} K_n(t)\,dt \leqslant \sigma_n(x) \leqslant M\frac{1}{\pi}\int_{-\pi}^{\pi} K_n(t)\,dt,$$

and then formula (47.10) immediately shows the truth of our statement.

Having noted this, we will now compare $\sigma_n(x)$ and $S_n(x)$. We have (see Introductory Material, § 6)

$$S_n(x) - \sigma_n(x) = \frac{1}{n+1}\sum_{k=1}^{n} k(a_k \cos kx + b_k \sin kx). \tag{48.3}$$

Hence it follows that

$$|S_n(x) - \sigma_n(x)| \leqslant \frac{1}{n+1}\sum_{k=1}^{n} k(|a_k| + |b_k|).$$

But if $f(x)$ is of bounded variation, then as we know (§ 22)

$$|a_k| \leqslant \frac{V}{K} \quad \text{and} \quad |b_k| \leqslant \frac{V}{K},$$

where $V$ is the complete variation of $f(x)$; therefore

$$|S_n(x) - \sigma_n(x)| \leqslant 2V,$$

whence

$$2V - M \leqslant S_n(x) \leqslant 2V + M. \tag{48.4}$$

Formula (48.4) not only proves that the partial sums of the Fourier series for functions of bounded variation are all bounded, but it also gives the bounds within which they are contained in terms of the bounds of this function and its complete variation.

*Note.* We have seen (see (48.1) and (48.2)) that if $f(x)$ is contained between $m$ and $M$ in an interval of length $2\pi$, then $\sigma_n(x)$ $(n = 1, 2, \ldots)$ are also contained in this interval between $m$ and $M$. Later we will find it useful to estimate $\sigma_n(x)$, knowing only the bounds of $f(x)$ in some interval $[a, b]$. We will prove that:

*If*

$$m \leqslant f(x) \leqslant M \quad \textit{in} \quad a \leqslant x \leqslant b,$$

*then for any* $\delta > 0$, $N_0$ *(dependent on* $\delta$*) is found such that*

$$m - \delta \leqslant \sigma_n(x) \leqslant M + \delta \quad \text{at} \quad n \geqslant N_0(\delta), \quad a + \delta \leqslant x \leqslant b - \delta. \tag{48.5}$$

Indeed, from (47.4) we find that

$$\sigma_n(x) = \frac{1}{\pi}\int_{-\pi}^{-\delta} f(x+u)K_n(u)\,du + \frac{1}{\pi}\int_{-\delta}^{\delta} f(x+u)\,K_n(u)\,du$$

$$+ \frac{1}{\pi}\int_{\delta}^{\pi} f(x+u)K_n(u)\,du = I_n' + I_n'' + I_n'''. \tag{48.6}$$

From (47.7), it follows that

$$I_n' = O\left(\frac{1}{n}\right) \int_{-\pi}^{-\delta} |f(x+u)|\, du = O\left(\frac{1}{n}\right) \int_{-\pi}^{\pi} |f(u)|\, du = o(1) \qquad (48.7)$$

and a similar result holds for $I_n'''$.

To estimate $I_n''$ we note that if $a + \delta \leqslant x \leqslant b - \delta$ and $|u| \leqslant \delta$, then $x + u \in [a, b]$ and then

$$m \frac{1}{\pi} \int_{-\delta}^{\delta} K_n(u)\, du \leqslant I_n'' \leqslant M \frac{1}{\pi} \int_{-\delta}^{\delta} K_n(u)\, du.$$

But we know from (47.11) that

$$\lim_{n\to\infty} \frac{1}{\pi} \int_{-\delta}^{\delta} K_n(u)\, du = 1.$$

This means that it is possible to choose $N_0$ (dependent on $\delta$) so large that, for example, we have

$$m - \frac{\delta}{3} \leqslant I_n'' \leqslant M + \frac{\delta}{3}, \quad n \geqslant N_0,$$

and moreover (see (48.7))

$$|I_n'| \leqslant \frac{\delta}{3} \quad \text{and} \quad |I_n'''| < \frac{\delta}{3},$$

whence we see from (48.6) that (48.5) is proved.

## § 49. Fejér–Lebesgue theorem

Fejér's theorem, proved in § 47, makes it possible to judge the summability of the series $\sigma(f)$ only at those points where $f(x)$ is either continuous or possesses a discontinuity of the first kind. However, an arbitrary summable function cannot possess a point of the given type. Lebesgue generalized Fejér's result and proved the following theorem.

FEJÉR–LEBESGUE THEOREM. *For any summable function $f(x)$, the series $\sigma(f)$ is summable almost everywhere by Fejér's method to $f(x)$.*

To prove this theorem, let us assume

$$\varphi_x(t) = f(x+t) + f(x-t) - 2f(x) \qquad (49.1)$$

and

$$\Phi_x(t) = \int_0^t |\varphi_x(u)|\, du. \qquad (49.2)$$

We will prove that the series $\sigma(f)$ is summable by Fejér's method to $f(x)$ at any point $x$ where

$$\Phi_x(t) = o(t). \qquad (49.3)$$

For this we note (see § 47) that

$$\sigma_n(x) - f(x) = \frac{1}{\pi}\int_0^{\pi} [f(x+t) + f(x-t) - 2f(x)]K_n(t)\,dt$$

$$= \frac{1}{\pi}\int_0^{\pi} \varphi_x(t)K_n(t)\,dt \tag{49.4}$$

and we will prove that when (49.3) is fulfilled the integral on the right-hand side of (49.4) tends to zero. For this purpose we note that

$$|K_n(t)| \leqslant 2n \quad (n \geqslant 1), \tag{49.5}$$

since

$$|D_k(t)| \leqslant k + \frac{1}{2} < 2n \quad \text{for any} \quad k \leqslant n,$$

and

$$K_n(t) = \frac{1}{n+1}\sum_{k=0}^{n} D_k(t).$$

Therefore

$$\left|\frac{1}{\pi}\int_0^{1/n} \varphi_x(t)K_n(t)\,dt\right| \leqslant \frac{2n}{\pi}\int_0^{1/n} |\varphi_x(t)|\,dt = \frac{2n}{\pi}\Phi_x\left(\frac{1}{n}\right) = o(1) \tag{49.6}$$

due to (49.3).

Also, because of (47.6)

$$\left|\frac{1}{\pi}\int_{1/n}^{\pi} \varphi_x(t)K_n(t)\,dt\right| \leqslant \frac{\pi}{2n}\int_{1/n}^{\pi} |\varphi_x(t)|\,\frac{dt}{t^2}. \tag{49.7}$$

For the integral on the right-hand side of (49.7) we will carry out integration by parts; we obtain, again operating on (49.3) (see Introductory Material, § 11)

$$\frac{\pi}{2n}\int_{1/n}^{\pi} |\varphi_x(t)|\,\frac{dt}{t^2} = \frac{\pi}{2n}\left[\frac{\Phi_x(\pi)}{\pi^2} - \frac{\Phi_x\left(\frac{1}{n}\right)}{\left(\frac{1}{n}\right)^2}\right] + \frac{2\pi}{2n}\int_{1/n}^{\pi} \Phi_x(t)\,\frac{dt}{t^3}$$

$$= o(1) + \frac{1}{n}\,o\left(\int_{1/n}^{\pi} \frac{dt}{t^2}\right) = o(1). \tag{49.8}$$

From (49.6) and (49.8), it follows because of (49.4) that

$$\sigma_n(x) - f(x) = o(1)$$

at every point, where (49.3) is fulfilled.

It remains for us to prove that the condition (49.3) holds almost everywhere. But in § 15 of the Introductory Material it was remarked that this relationship is fulfilled at any Lebesgue point and consequently almost everywhere.

The Fejér–Lebesgue theorem is proved.

As a corollary, we obtain the following important theorem.

*If $\sigma(f)$ converges in some set $E$, $mE > 0$, then its sum equals $f(x)$ almost everywhere in $E$.*

Indeed, we know that method $(C, 1)$ is regular. Therefore at the point where $\sigma(f)$ possesses a certain sum $S$, it should be summable to this value $S$ by Fejér's method. But since by Fejér's method it is summable to $f(x)$ almost everywhere, then the set of points of $E$, where the sum of the series $\sigma(f)$ differs from $f(x)$, is of measure zero.

*Note.* We have seen that the series $\sigma(f)$ is summable by Fejér's method at any Lebesgue point. It is known that a these points $f(x)$ is the derivative of its indefinite integral. The question can be raised whether the series $\sigma(f)$ is summable by Fejér's method at a point, where the latter condition is fulfilled. Lebesgue[1] proved that this should not, however, occur, though here we have summability $(C, 2)$.

## § 50. Estimate of the partial sums of a Fourier series

In § 49 we have proved that at the points where the following condition is fulfilled,

$$\Phi_x(h) = \int_0^h |f(x+u) + f(x-u) - 2f(x)|\, du = o(h), \tag{50.1}$$

the series $\sigma(f)$ is summable by Fejér's method. It was also remarked that condition (50.1) is fulfilled almost everywhere. Now we want to estimate the increase of the partial sums $S_n(x)$ at these points.

We will prove that at any point $x$, where (50.1) is fulfilled, we have

$$S_n(x) = o(\ln n). \tag{50.2}$$

Consequently, estimate (50.2) also holds almost everywhere.

We have seen (see (37.9)) that

$$S_n(x) - f(x) = \frac{1}{\pi}\int_0^\delta [f(x+u) + f(x-u) - 2f(x)]\frac{\sin nu}{u}\, du + o(1), \tag{50.3}$$

where $o(1)$ tends to zero and $\delta$ is any positive given number. Supposing $\varphi(u) = f(x+u) + f(x-u) - 2f(x)$, we have

$$\int_0^\delta |\varphi(x)| \left|\frac{\sin nu}{u}\right| du = \int_0^{1/n} |\varphi(u)| \frac{\sin nu}{u}\, du + \int_{1/n}^\delta |\varphi(u)| \left|\frac{\sin nu}{u}\right| du$$

$$\leqslant n\int_0^{1/n} |\varphi(u)|\, du + \int_{1/n}^\delta |\varphi(u)| \frac{1}{u}\, du. \tag{50.4}$$

Then from (50.1)

$$\Phi_x(h) = \int_0^h |\varphi(u)|\, du, \tag{50.5}$$

therefore (for brevity's sake, we will dispense with the index $x$)

$$\int_0^{1/n} |\varphi(u)|\, du = \Phi\left(\frac{1}{n}\right) = o\left(\frac{1}{n}\right) \tag{50.6}$$

and

$$\int_{1/n}^{\delta} |\varphi(u)|\, \frac{du}{u} = \frac{\Phi(t)}{t}\Bigg|_{1/n}^{\delta} + \int_{1/n}^{\delta} \frac{\Phi(t)}{t^2}\, dt. \tag{50.7}$$

From (50.4), (50.6) and (50.7) it follows that

$$\int_0^{\delta} |\varphi(u)| \left|\frac{\sin nu}{u}\right| du \leqslant n\Phi\left(\frac{1}{n}\right) + \frac{\Phi(\delta)}{\delta} + n\Phi\left(\frac{1}{n}\right) + \int_{1/n}^{\delta} \frac{\Phi(t)}{t^2}\, dt$$

$$= O(1) + \int_{1/n}^{\delta} \frac{\Phi(t)}{t^2}\, dt. \tag{50.8}$$

If for a given $\varepsilon > 0$ we choose $\delta$ so that $\Phi(t) < \varepsilon t$ for $0 \leqslant t \leqslant \delta$, which is possible from (50.1), then

$$\int_{1/n}^{\delta} \frac{\Phi(t)}{t^2}\, dt < \varepsilon \int_{1/n}^{\delta} \frac{dt}{t} = \varepsilon \ln n\delta = o(\ln n), \tag{50.9}$$

because $\varepsilon$ is as small as desired. But $o(1)$ is also $o(\ln n)$, therefore from (50.3), (50.8) and (50.9) we find that

$$|S_n(x) - f(x)| = o(\ln n).$$

But since $x$ is fixed, then $f(x)$ is constant, i.e. $|f(x)| = o(\ln n)$ and finally

$$S_n(x) = o(\ln n),$$

which is what was required to be proved.

*Note.* In § 36 it was proved that for a bounded function, which also means a continuous function, we have for all $x$ and $n > 1$

$$|S_n(x)| \leqslant CM \ln n \quad (n = 2, 3, \ldots),$$

if $|f(x)| \leqslant M$ ($C$ is an absolute constant). If $f(x)$ is continuous, then condition (50.1) is fulfilled and even uniformly; therefore, for continuous functions the estimate made earlier is replaced by a stronger one: $O(\ln n)$ is replaced by $o(\ln n)$.

## § 51. Convergence factors

It is usually said that the numbers $\{\mu_n\}$ are *convergence factors* for some series

$$u_0(x) + u_1(x) + \cdots + u_n(x) + \cdots$$

in the interval $[a, b]$, if the series

$$\sum u_n(x)\,\mu_n$$

converges almost everywhere in $[a, b]$.

The results of §§ 49 and 50 allow us to prove that it is possible to choose as convergence factors for a Fourier series in $[-\pi, \pi]$ the numbers

$$\mu_n = \frac{1}{\ln n}, \qquad n = 2, 3, \ldots$$

($\mu_0$ and $\mu_1$ can be chosen as desired); i.e. we have

THEOREM. *If $a_k$ and $b_k$ are Fourier coefficients ($k = 1, 2, \ldots$) then the series*

$$\sum_{k=2}^{\infty} \frac{a_k \cos kx + b_k \sin kx}{\ln k}$$

*converges almost everywhere in* $[-\pi, \pi]$.

To prove this we note that in § 50 it was proved that $S_n(x) = o(\ln n)$ almost everywhere. Therefore because the sequence $\mu_n$ is convex (the definition and properties of convex sequences are given in § 3 of Introductory Material), then it remains to apply Theorem 6 (see Appendix, § 12), assuming that $u_n(x) = a_n \cos nx + b_n \sin nx$.

## § 52. Comparison of Dirichlet and Fejér kernels

We know (see §§ 45 and 46) that continuous functions exist in which the Fourier series diverges at some point. On the other hand, for any continuous function $f(x)$, the series $\sigma(f)$ is summable to $f(x)$ at any point (see § 47).

We want to explain why such a phenomenon occurs and for this purpose we will compare the Dirichlet and Fejér kernels. As is known

$$S_n(x) = \frac{1}{\pi} \int_{-\pi}^{\pi} f(t)\, D_n(t - x)\, dt \tag{52.1}$$

and

$$\sigma_n(x) = \frac{1}{\pi} \int_{-\pi}^{\pi} f(t)\, K_n(t - x)\, dt, \tag{52.2}$$

where $D_n(u)$ is a Dirichlet kernel and $K_n(u)$ is a Fejér kernel.

If at the point $x_0$, the series $\sigma(f)$ converges to $f(x)$, then this means that $S_n(x_0) \to f(x_0)$; if it is summable by Fejér's method to $f(x)$, then $\sigma_n(x_0) \to f(x_0)$.

It is natural, therefore, to pose the question thus: let $f(x)$ be continuous and

$$f_n(x) = \int_{-\pi}^{\pi} f(t)\,\Phi_n(t - x)\,dt, \tag{52.3}$$

where $\Phi_n(u)$ is some function which we will also refer to as a *kernel;* we ask ourselves—what properties of this kernel influence the equality

$$\lim_{n\to\infty} f_n(x) = f(x)$$

or the existence of points $x_0$ where $f_n(x_0)$ does not tend to $f(x_0)$ or in general does not tend to any limit?

Before answering this question we will show that the problem of convergence of a Fourier series with respect to an arbitrary orthogonal system leads to another question of the same type and we will therefore solve both problems together.

Let $\{\varphi_n(x)\}$ be some orthonomal system in $(a, b)$. In order to study the convergence of a Fourier series for some function $f(x)$ with respect to this system, we will consider the partial sum of this series, i.e.

$$S_n(x) = \sum_{k=0}^{n} a_k \varphi_k(x),$$

in other words,

$$S_n(x) = \sum_{k=0}^{n} \varphi_k(x) \int_a^b f(t)\varphi_k(t)\,dt = \int_a^b f(t) \left[\sum_{k=0}^{n} \varphi_k(t)\varphi_k(x)\right] dt.$$

Supposing

$$\Phi_n(t, x) = \sum_{k=0}^{n} \varphi_k(t)\varphi_k(x),$$

we name the function $\Phi_n(t, x)$ the kernel of the system $\{\varphi_n(x)\}$. We have

$$S_n(x) = \int_a^b f(t)\Phi_n(t, x)\,dt. \tag{52.4}$$

Lebesgue was the first to pay attention to the importance of investigating the behaviour of functions of the type

$$\varrho_n(x) = \int_a^b |\Phi_n(t, x)|\,dt. \tag{52.5}$$

which are now usually called "*Lebesgue functions*" for the given system. The role of these functions in the problem of the convergence of a Fourier series becomes extremely clear, when the theorem is proved (see Lebesgue[2]).

THEOREM. *If for some point $x_0$ the sequence $\varrho_n(x_0)$ $(n = 1, 2, \ldots)$ is unbounded, then there exists a continuous function $f(x)$ for which the Fourier series with respect to the system $\{\varphi_n(x)\}$ diverges without bound at the point $x_0$.*

This theorem can be proved immediately, if we first establish the validity of the following more general assertion:

LEMMA. *Let*

$$f_n(x, f) = \int_a^b f(t)\Phi_n(t, x)\,dt, \tag{52.6}$$

*where $\Phi_n(t, x)$ for every fixed $x$ is summable with respect to the variable $t$ and $f(t)$ is bounded. Then, if*

$$\overline{\lim_{n\to\infty}}\, \varrho_n(x_0) = +\infty, \tag{52.7}$$

*a continuous function $f(x)$ is found for which*

$$\overline{\lim_{n\to\infty}}\, |f_n(x_0, f)| = +\infty. \tag{52.8}$$

Indeed, first, supposing that for a given $n$

$$g(t) = \operatorname{sign}\Phi_n(t, x_0),$$

we have

$$f_n(x_0, g) = \int_a^b g(t)\Phi_n(t, x_0)\,dt = \int_a^b |\Phi_n(t, x_0)|\,dt = \varrho_n(x_0). \tag{52.9}$$

This means that for any $n$ there exists a function $g(t)$ such that $|g(t)| \leqslant 1$ and for it

$$f_n(x_0, g) = \varrho_n(x_0). \tag{52.10}$$

If this were the same function $g(t)$ for all $n$ and if it were continuous, the theorem would be proved, because from (52.7) we would have

$$\overline{\lim_{n\to\infty}}\, |f_n(x_0, g)| = +\infty.$$

Therefore, we will first replace $g(t)$ by a continuous function $g^*(t)$, for which $f_n(x_0, g^*)$ is "large" and then we will transfer various functions for various $n$ to a single function.

We will first choose for a given $n$ a continuous $g^*(t)$ such that for $f_n(x, g^*)$ we have

$$f_n(x_0, g^*) \geqslant \tfrac{1}{2}\varrho_n(x_0). \tag{52.11}$$

For this it is sufficient to take $\varepsilon$ such that

$$\int_E |\Phi_n(t, x_0)|\,dt \leqslant \frac{1}{4}\varrho_n(x_0), \tag{52.12}$$

if $mE < \varepsilon$, which is possible, since for fixed $n$ and $x_0$ the function under the integral sign is a summable function of $t$, and therefore its integral is as small as desired, if the set over which the integration occurs is of sufficiently small measure. Because of the $C$-property we can find a continuous function $g^*(t)$ coinciding with $g(t)$ in the perfect set $P$, $mP > (b - a) - \varepsilon$, such that $|g^*(t)| \leqslant 1$. Then for this function from (52.6)

$$f_n(x_0, g^*) = \int_a^b g^*(t)\Phi_n(t, x_0)\,dt.$$

From (52.12) it follows that

$$|f_n(x_0, g^*) - f_n(x_0, g)| = \Big|\int_{CP} [g^*(t) - g(t)]\Phi_n(t, x_0)\,dt\Big|$$

$$\leqslant 2\int_{CP} |\Phi_n(t, x_0)|\,dt \leqslant \frac{1}{2}\varrho_n(x_0) \tag{52.13}$$

which means that (52.11) follows from (52.9) and (52.13).

For all $n$ we will denote by $g_n(t)$ the function which possesses the properties:

(a) $g_n(t)$ is continuous
(b) $|g_n(t)| \leqslant 1$
(c) $f_n(x_0, g_n) > \frac{1}{2} \varrho_n(x_0)$.

We have already seen that it is possible to establish such a function for all $n$. Now let $\varepsilon_n$ be a sequence of numbers such that

$$\varepsilon_n > 0, \sum_{n=1}^{\infty} \varepsilon_n < +\infty, \sum_{k=n+1}^{\infty} \varepsilon_k \leqslant \frac{1}{6} \varepsilon_n \tag{52.14}$$

(for example, it is possible to take $\varepsilon_n = 1/7^n$), let $n_k$ be an increasing sequence of integers which we will select later. Then, supposing

$$f(x) = \sum_{k=1}^{\infty} \varepsilon_k g_{n_k}(x), \tag{52.15}$$

we see that $f(x)$ is continuous, since $g_n(x)$ are continuous and all $|g_n(x)| \leqslant 1$ and $\sum \varepsilon_k < +\infty$, which means that the series (52.15) converges uniformly. It is clear that

$$f_n(x_0, f) = \int_a^b \sum_{k=1}^{\infty} \varepsilon_k g_{n_k}(t) \Phi_n(t, x_0)\, dt = \sum_{k=1}^{\infty} \varepsilon_k \int_a^b g_{n_k}(t) \Phi_n(t, x_0)\, dt$$

$$= \sum_{k=1}^{\infty} \varepsilon_k f_n(x_0, g_{n_k}).$$

Here the term-by-term integration is valid because of the uniform convergence of the series (52.15).

We will now show that for a suitable choice of the numbers $n_k$ we will have

$$\overline{\lim_{n\to\infty}} |f_n(x_0, f)| = +\infty. \tag{52.8}$$

If for even one of the functions $g_m(x)$ we had

$$\overline{\lim_{n\to\infty}} |f_n(x_0, g_m)| = +\infty,$$

then the theorem would be proved. We will assume that this is not the case. Let us define

$$\overline{\lim_{n\to\infty}} |f_n(x_0, g_m)| = \gamma_m. \tag{52.16}$$

We will choose by induction the numbers $n_k$ such that

$$\varepsilon_k \varrho_{n_k}(x_0) \to \infty \tag{52.17}$$

and

$$\sum_{p=1}^{k-1} \varepsilon_p \gamma_{n_p} \leqslant \frac{1}{12} \varepsilon_k \varrho_{n_k}(x_0). \tag{52.18}$$

This is possible, since $\{\varrho_n(x_0)\}$ is unbounded due to (52.7), which means that the numbers $n_k$ can be chosen such that $\varrho_{n_k}(x_0) \to \infty$ sufficiently quickly for conditions (52.17) and (52.18) to be fulfilled. Since

$$\left| f_n\left(x_0, \sum_{p=1}^{k-1} \varepsilon_p g_{n_p}\right) \right| = \left| \sum_{p=1}^{k-1} \varepsilon_p f_n(x_0, g_{n_p}) \right| < 2 \sum_{p=1}^{k-1} \varepsilon_p \gamma_{n_p}$$

as $n \to \infty$ due to (52.16), it is possible to choose $n_k$ so large that

$$\left| f_{n_k}\left(x_0, \sum_{p=1}^{k-1} \varepsilon_p g_{n_p}\right) \right| < 2 \sum_{p=1}^{k-1} \varepsilon_p \gamma_{n_p} \leqslant \frac{1}{6} \varepsilon_k \varrho_{n_k}(x_0) \tag{52.19}$$

because of (52.18).

On the other hand

$$\left| f_{n_k}\left(x_0, \sum_{p=k+1}^{\infty} \varepsilon_p g_{n_p}\right) \right| < \sum_{p=k+1}^{\infty} \varepsilon_p \varrho_{n_k}(x_0) \leqslant \frac{1}{6} \varepsilon_k \varrho_{n_k}(x_0), \tag{52.20}$$

because $|g_{np}(x)| \leqslant 1$ which means that

$$\left| \int_a^b g_{n_p}(t) \Phi_{n_k}(t, x_0)\, dt \right| \leqslant \int_a^b |\Phi_{n_k}(t, x_0)|\, dt = \varrho_{n_k}(x_0)$$

and moreover, we have (52.14).

Hence because of property (c) of the function $g_n(x)$, (52.19) and (52.20)

$$|f_{n_k}(x_0, f)| \geqslant f_{n_k}(x_0, \varepsilon_k g_{n_k}) - \left| f_{n_k}\left(x_0, \sum_{p=1}^{k-1} \varepsilon_p g_{n_p}\right) \right| - \left| f_{n_k}\left(x_0, \sum_{k+1}^{\infty} \varepsilon_p g_{n_k}\right) \right|$$

$$\geqslant \frac{1}{2} \varepsilon_k \varrho_{n_k}(x_0) - \frac{1}{6} \varepsilon_k \varrho_{n_k}(x_0) - \frac{1}{6} \varepsilon_k \varrho_{n_k}(x_0) \geqslant \frac{1}{6} \varepsilon_k \varrho_{n_k}(x_0),$$

and this tends to $+\infty$ as $k \to \infty$ due to (52.17). This means that (52.8) is valid and the theorem is proved.†

The validity of Lebesgue's theorem formulated above follows quickly from this. Indeed, if in the proved lemma the role played by $\Phi_n(t, x)$ is the kernel of the given orthogonal system, then $f_n(t, f)$ is converted into the partial sum of the Fourier series of $f(x)$ with respect to this system (due to (52.4) and (52.3)) and therefore, if at some point (52.7) is fulfilled, then a continuous $f(x)$ is found with a Fourier series which diverges at this point. Thus, Lebesgue's theorem is proved.

Let us now consider specially the case of a trigonometric system. If it is normalized, i.e. if the following system is taken

$$\frac{1}{\sqrt{2\pi}}, \quad \frac{\cos x}{\sqrt{\pi}}, \quad \frac{\sin x}{\sqrt{\pi}}, \ldots, \frac{\cos nx}{\sqrt{\pi}}, \quad \frac{\sin nx}{\sqrt{\pi}}, \ldots,$$

---

† Since on multiplying $f(t)$ by some constant $f_n(x, f)$ is multiplied by the same constant by virtue of (52.6), it is always possible to find $f(x)$ to satisfy the conditions of the lemma and such that $|f(t)| \leqslant 1$. This note is not necessary for Lebesgue's theorem but will be useful later in Chapter IV.

then the role of its kernel is played by the function

$$\Phi_n(t, x) = \frac{1}{2\pi} + \sum_{k=1}^{n} \frac{\cos kx \cos kt + \sin kx \sin kt}{\pi}$$

$$= \frac{1}{2\pi} + \frac{1}{\pi}\sum_{k=1}^{n} \cos k(t - x) = \frac{1}{\pi} D_n(t - x),$$

and therefore the Lebesgue functions (see (52.5)) have the form

$$\varrho_n(x) = \frac{1}{\pi}\int_{-\pi}^{\pi} |D_n(t - x)|\, dt.$$

But because of the periodicity of $D_n(u)$ we have

$$\varrho_n(x) = \frac{1}{\pi}\int_{-\pi}^{\pi} |D_n(t)|\, dt,$$

i.e. the Lebesgue functions do not depend on $x$ and are converted into the Lebesgue constants $L_n$ considered earlier (see § 35). But we know that $\lim_{n\to\infty} L_n = +\infty$ (because $L_n \approx (4/\pi^2)\ln n$) and therefore we now see that the existence of continuous functions with Fourier series, divergent at some point, is explained by the fact that the Lebesgue constants increase without bound with increase in $n$. We also note that since

$$\varrho_n(x) = L_n$$

for any $x$, then it is possible for any point $x$ to find a continuous $f(x)$ with a Fourier series divergent at this point.

Now we will return to the question of the summability of a Fourier series by Fejér's method. Comparing formulae (52.5) and (52.2), we see that if for

$$\varrho_n(t) = \frac{1}{\pi}\int_{-\pi}^{\pi} |K_n(t - x)|\, dt$$

(52.7) were fulfilled for even one value of $x_0$, then it would be possible to find a continuous $f(x)$ for which $\sigma_n(x, f)$ would not tend to any finite limit as $n \to \infty$, i.e. $\sigma(f)$ would be unsummable by Fejér's method at this point. But due to $K_n(u)$ being periodic and positive, we have

$$\varrho_n(x) = \frac{1}{\pi}\int_{-\pi}^{\pi} K_n(t)\, dt,$$

and then due to property (3) of Fejér kernels (see § 47)

$$\varrho_n(x) \equiv 1$$

for all $n$ and $x$. Thus, for a Fejér kernel the fulfilment of (52.7) at no point whatever is impossible.

In § 2 of Chapter VII we will see why Fejér's method is applicable almost everywhere (Fejér–Lebesgue theorem, § 49) whilst everywhere divergent Fourier series exist (Chapter V, § 20) – this is also the result of the different behaviour of Fejér and Dirichlet kernels.

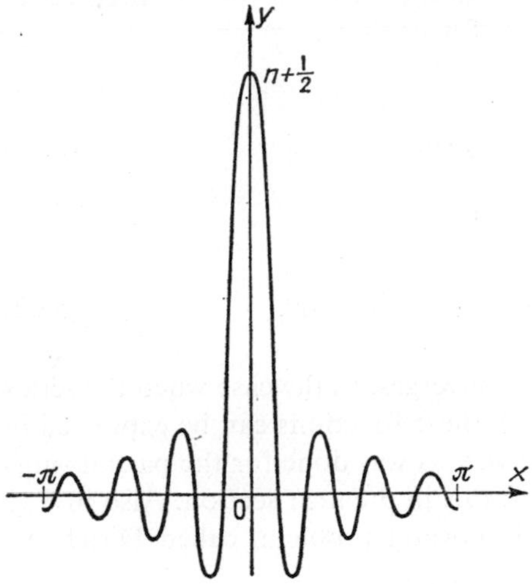


FIG. 9

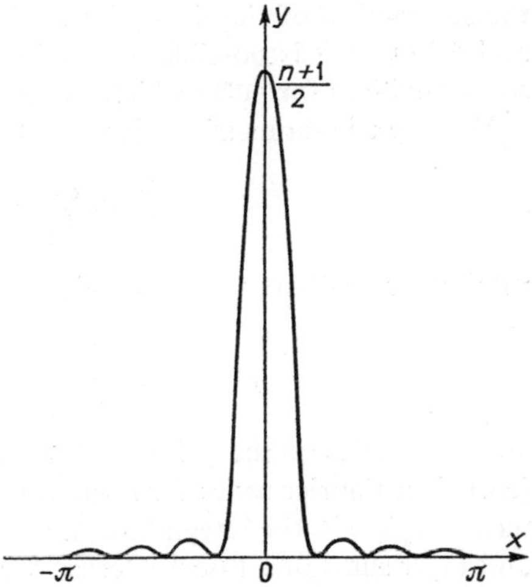


FIG. 10

To conclude this section, we think it appropriate to represent Dirichlet and Fejér kernels geometrically (see Figs. 9 and 10).

## § 53. Summation of Fourier series by the Abel–Poisson method

We will refer here to yet another classic and very important method of summation of Fourier series. For this we recall (see Introductory Material, § 7) that the series $\sum_{n=0}^{\infty} u_n(x)$ is said to be summable by Abel's method at a point $x_0$ to the value $S$, if for any $r$, $0 \leqslant r < 1$, the series $\sum_{n=0}^{\infty} u_n(x_0) r^n$ converges and supposing

$$S(x_0, r) = \sum_{n=0}^{\infty} u_n(x_0) r^n,$$

we have

$$\lim_{r \to 1} S(x_0, r) = S.$$

Poisson applied this method of summation to Fourier series, therefore the given method when it is applied to trigonometric series is usually referred to as *Poisson's method or the Abel–Poisson method.*

Since we know (see Introductory Material, § 7) that Abel's method is stronger than the method $(C, 1)$, then the following theorem immediately results from Fejér's theorem and the Fejér–Lebesgue theorem (see §§ 47 and 49):

THEOREM. *For any summable $f(x)$ the series $\sigma(f)$ is summable almost everywhere by the Abel–Poisson method to this function $f(x)$; it is summable to $\frac{1}{2}[f(x+0)+f(x-0)]$ at any point of discontinuity of the first kind and to $f(x)$ at any point of continuity.*

It can be seen that apart from these theorems little more need be said concerning the summation of Fourier series by Poisson's method; however, we will see in § 55 and § 56 that it is possible to obtain very much deeper results. We will first derive some auxiliary formulae which will be necessary for us there.

For any trigonometric series

$$\frac{a_0}{2}+\sum_{n=1}^{\infty}(a_n\cos nx+b_n\sin nx) \tag{53.1}$$

"Poisson sums" are the names given to the functions

$$f(r,x)=\frac{a_0}{2}+\sum_{n=1}^{\infty}(a_n\cos nx+b_n\sin nx)r^n, \tag{53.2}$$

when the series on the right-hand side of (53.2) converges. In the case when the series (53.1) is a Fourier series for some function $f(x)$, these functions can be expressed in terms of $f(x)$ in the integral form, in the same way as was done for the partial sums and Fejér sums of a Fourier series. We will find this in the next section. Also in § 57 we will use the results obtained to solve an important problem, called Dirichlet's problem.

## § 54. Poisson kernel and Poisson integral

We will first find a suitable expression for $f(r,x)$ if (53.1) is $\sigma(f)$. We have

$$a_n=\frac{1}{\pi}\int_{-\pi}^{\pi}f(t)\cos nt\,dt,\quad b_n=\frac{1}{\pi}\int_{-\pi}^{\pi}f(t)\sin nt\,dt,$$

and therefore

$$f(r,x)=\frac{1}{2\pi}\int_{-\pi}^{\pi}f(t)\,dt+\frac{1}{\pi}\sum_{n-1}^{\infty}r^n\int_{-\pi}^{\pi}f(t)\cos n(t-x)\,dt.$$

But since $0\leqslant r<1$, then the series $\sum_{n=1}^{\infty}r^n\cos n(t-x)$ for a given $r$ converges uniformly with respect to $t$ and therefore according to Lebesgue's theorem (Introductory Material, § 14) it is possible to integrate it term-by-term even after multiplying by $f(x)$; therefore

$$f(r,x)=\frac{1}{\pi}\int_{-\pi}^{\pi}f(t)\left[\frac{1}{2}+\sum_{n=1}^{\infty}r^n\cos n(t-x)\right]dt. \tag{54.1}$$

Let us now find a simpler expression for the series given in the square brackets in (54.1). Let

$$P(r,\alpha)=\frac{1}{2}+\sum_{n=1}^{\infty}r^n\cos n\alpha.$$

We consider the auxiliary series

$$\frac{1}{2} + \sum_{n=1}^{\infty} z^n$$

and suppose that $z = r(\cos\alpha + i\sin\alpha)$. If $|z| = r < 1$, then this series converges and

$$\frac{1}{2} + \sum_{n=1}^{\infty} z^n = \frac{1}{2} + \frac{z}{1-z} = \frac{1+z}{2(1-z)} = \frac{1 - r^2 + 2ir\sin\alpha}{2[1 - 2r\cos\alpha + r^2]}.$$

But, on the other hand

$$\frac{1}{2} + \sum_{n=1}^{\infty} z^n = \frac{1}{2}\sum_{n=1}^{\infty} r^n(\cos n\alpha + i\sin n\alpha).$$

Therefore, separating the real and purely imaginary parts, we find

$$\frac{1}{2} + \sum_{n=1}^{\infty} r^n \cos n\alpha = \frac{1-r^2}{2[1 - 2r\cos\alpha + r^2]}$$

and

$$\sum_{n=1}^{\infty} r^n \sin n\alpha = \frac{r\sin\alpha}{1 - 2r\cos\alpha + r^2}.$$

Thus we have established that

$$P(r, \alpha) = \frac{1-r^2}{2[1 - 2r\cos\alpha + r^2]}. \tag{54.2}$$

This expression is known as a *Poisson kernel* and the expression

$$Q(r, \alpha) = \frac{r\sin\alpha}{1 - 2r\cos\alpha + r^2} \tag{54.3}$$

as *the kernel conjugate to it.*

Later, the fact that the Poisson kernel at $0 \leqslant r < 1$ is a positive value (as is also the Fejér kernel) will be very important. In fact, since

$$1 - r^2 > 0 \quad \text{and} \quad 1 - 2r\cos\alpha + r^2 = (1-r)^2 + 4r\sin^2\frac{\alpha}{2} > 0,$$

then $P(r, \alpha) > 0$ at $0 \leqslant r < 1$.

Let us return to formula (54.1). We have

$$f(r, x) = \frac{1}{\pi}\int_{-\pi}^{\pi} f(t)\, P(r, t-x)\, dt = \frac{1}{2\pi}\int_{-\pi}^{\pi} f(t)\, \frac{1-r^2}{1 - 2r\cos(t-x) + r^2}\, dt. \tag{54.4}$$

The integral on the right-hand side of (54.4) is known as a *Poisson integral.*

It is very important to understand the meaning of a Poisson kernel geometrically (see Fig. 11). For this purpose we will take a plane circle with centre at the origin and unit radius; if a radius is drawn through the point $M$ with polar co-ordinates $(r, \omega)$ and the perpendicular is drawn to it, then denoting by $Q$ one of its points of intersection with the circumference, we find

$$\overline{MQ}^2 = 1 - r^2.$$

If $P$ is a point with polar co-ordinates $(1, t)$, then

$$\overline{MP}^2 = 1 - 2r\cos(\omega - t) + r^2,$$

and therefore

$$\frac{1 - r^2}{1 - 2r\cos(\omega - t) + r^2} = \left(\frac{\overline{MQ}}{\overline{MP}}\right)^2.$$

Thus, we again see that the Poisson kernel is a positive magnitude, and the Poisson integral can be written in the form

$$f(r, \omega) = \frac{1}{2\pi}\int_{-\pi}^{\pi} f(t)\left(\frac{\overline{MQ}}{\overline{MP}}\right)^2 dt.$$

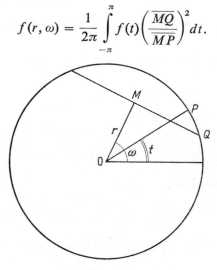

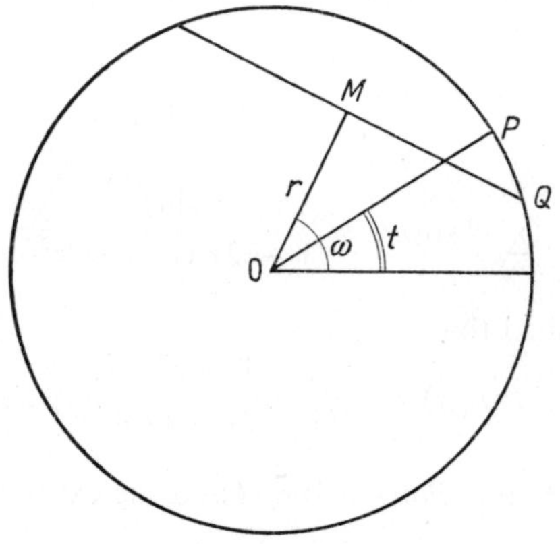


FIG. 11

Theorem § 53 could be expressed thus: if the point $M(r, \omega)$ tends to the point $P(1, \omega)$, i.e. to the point on the circumference lying on the same radius, then for almost all values of $\omega$ we have

$$f(r, \omega) \to f(\omega) \quad \text{as} \quad r \to 1$$

and this is true, in particular, for all those $\omega$ where $f(\omega)$ is continuous. But we want to prove that a considerably more general statement holds. We will now turn to this.

## § 55. Behaviour of the Poisson integral at points of continuity of a function

Let us prove the following theorem due to Fatou[1].

THEOREM. *If $f(\omega)$ is continuous at some point $P(1, \omega_0)$, then for the Poisson integral*

$$f(r, \omega) = \frac{1}{\pi}\int_{-\pi}^{\pi} f(t)\, P(r, \omega - t)\, dt \tag{55.1}$$

*we have*

$$f(r, \omega) \to f(\omega_0)$$

*no matter how $M(r, \omega)$ tends to $P(1, \omega_0)$, provided it remains inside the circle of unit radius.*

First we will note the following properties of a Poisson kernel:

(a) $P(r, t) \geqslant 0$ at any $t$ and $0 \leqslant r < 1$.

(b) We have

$$\frac{1}{\pi}\int_{-\pi}^{\pi} P(r, t)\, dt = 1.$$

Indeed from (54.4) supposing $f(t) \equiv 1$, we find that

$$1 = \frac{1}{\pi}\int_{-\pi}^{\pi} P(r, t-\omega)\, dt = \frac{1}{\pi}\int_{-\pi}^{\pi} P(r, t)\, dt. \tag{55.2}$$

(c) If $|t| \geqslant \delta$, then we have

$$m(r, \delta) = \max_{\delta \leqslant |t| \leqslant \pi} P(r, t) \to 0 \quad \text{as} \quad r \to 1. \tag{55.3}$$

Indeed

$$1 - 2r\cos t + r^2 \geqslant 1 - 2r\cos\delta + r^2 \quad \text{for} \quad \delta \leqslant |t| \leqslant \pi,$$

and therefore

$$0 \leqslant P(r, t) \leqslant \frac{1 - r^2}{2(1 - 2r\cos\delta + r^2)},$$

which also proves our statement.

From this and from (b) it immediately follows for any $\delta > 0$ that:

(d)

$$\lim_{r\to 1} \frac{2}{\pi}\int_{0}^{\delta} P(r, t)\, dt = 1. \tag{55.4}$$

Indeed, due to the evenness of $P(r, t)$ we have from (b)

$$1 = \frac{2}{\pi}\int_{0}^{\pi} P(r, t)\, dt = \frac{2}{\pi}\int_{0}^{\delta} P(r, t)\, dt + \frac{2}{\pi}\int_{\delta}^{\pi} P(r, t)\, dt,$$

and the latter integral does not exceed $(2/\pi)\, m(r, \delta)$.

Now in order to prove the theorem we note first that, multiplying (55.2) by $f(\omega_0)$, we have

$$f(\omega_0) = \frac{1}{\pi}\int_{-\pi}^{\pi} f(\omega_0)\, P(r, t-\omega)\, dt.$$

Subtracting this equation from (55.1) we find

$$f(r,\omega)-f(\omega_0)=\frac{1}{\pi}\int_{-\pi}^{\pi}[f(t)-f(\omega_0)]\,P(r,t-\omega)\,dt. \tag{55.5}$$

Let $\varepsilon > 0$ be given. We choose $\delta$ so that

$$|f(t)-f(\omega_0)|<\varepsilon \quad \text{for} \quad |t-\omega_0|<\delta, \tag{55.6}$$

and divide the integral (55.5) into three: for the range $\omega_0-\delta<t<\omega_0+\delta$ and for the ranges $(-\pi<t<\omega_0-\delta)$ and $(\omega_0+\delta<t<\pi)$. Due to the Poisson kernel being positive, and from (55.6) and (55.2) we have

$$\left|\frac{1}{\pi}\int_{\omega_0-\delta}^{\omega_0+\delta}[f(t)-f(\omega_0)]\,P(r,t-\omega)\,dt\right|<\frac{\varepsilon}{\pi}\int_{\omega_0-\delta}^{\omega_0+\delta}P(r,t-\omega)\,dt$$

$$<\frac{\varepsilon}{\pi}\int_{-\pi}^{\pi}P(r,t-\omega)\,dt=\varepsilon.$$

As regards the integrals in the remaining intervals, in them $|t-\omega|\geqslant\delta$ and therefore due to (55.3) it is possible to obtain

$$P(r,t-\omega)<\varepsilon,$$

provided $r$ is taken sufficiently close to 1. Then the modulus of each of these integrals does not exceed

$$\frac{\varepsilon}{\pi}\int_{-\pi}^{\pi}[|f(t)|+|f(\omega_0)|]\,dt,$$

i.e. it can be made as small as desired.

The theorem is proved.

## § 56. Behaviour of a Poisson integral in the general case

We proved in § 55 that if $f(\omega)$ is continuous at $\omega=\omega_0$, then the Poisson integral tends to $f(\omega_0)$ independently of the path by which $M(r,\omega)$ tends to the point $P(1,\omega_0)$ (provided it remains inside the circle of unit radius).

In the case when $f(\omega)$ is not continuous at $\omega=\omega_0$, matters become more complicated. However, here it is possible to obtain good results only if $M$ tends towards $P$ not by any path but by non-tangential paths to the circle. This means that we permit the point $M$ to move towards $P$ provided it remains the whole time within some angle $\varphi$ of magnitude $2\varphi<\pi$ with the bisector coinciding with $OP$ (see Fig. 12).

Before studying the behaviour of the Poisson integral in the general case, we will prove a theorem by Fatou, concerning the behaviour of the partial derivative of $f(r,\omega)$ with respect to $\omega$.

THEOREM 1. *If $f(\omega)$ possesses a finite derivative at the point $P(1, \omega_0)$, then*

$$\frac{\partial f(r, \omega)}{\partial \omega} \to f'(\omega_0),$$

*if the point $M(r, \omega) \to P(1, \omega_0)$ by any non-tangential path.*

In order to prove this, we will first prove a lemma.

LEMMA 1. *Let $f(u)$ have a bounded derivative $f'(\omega)$ in some interval $(\omega', \omega'')$ and let $f'(\omega)$ be continuous at some point $\omega_0$ of this interval. Then*

$$\frac{\partial f(r, \omega)}{\partial \omega} \to f'(\omega_0),$$

*where $M(r, \omega) \to P(1, \omega_0)$ along any path, provided it remains within a unit circle.*

We have from (55.1)

$$\frac{\partial f(r, \omega)}{\partial \omega} = \frac{1}{\pi} \int_{-\pi}^{\pi} f(t) \frac{\partial P(r, t-\omega)}{\partial \omega} dt. \tag{56.1}$$

Since

$$\frac{\partial P(r, u)}{\partial u} = \frac{-(1-r^2)\, 2r \sin u}{[1 - 2r \cos u + r^2]^2}, \tag{56.2}$$

then $\partial P(r, u)/\partial u$ is an odd function, negative or equal to zero in $[0, \pi]$, whilst for any $\delta > 0$ we have

$$\max_{\delta \leqslant |u| \leqslant \pi} \left| \frac{\partial P(r, u)}{\partial u} \right| \leqslant \frac{2(1-r^2)}{[1 - 2r\cos\delta + r^2]^2} \to 0 \quad \text{as} \quad r \to 1. \tag{56.3}$$

We choose $\delta$ so that $(\omega_0 - \delta, \omega_0 + \delta)$ lies within $(\omega', \omega'')$ and divide the integral (56.1) into two for the interval $(\omega_0 - \delta, \omega_0 + \delta)$ and for the remaining part of the

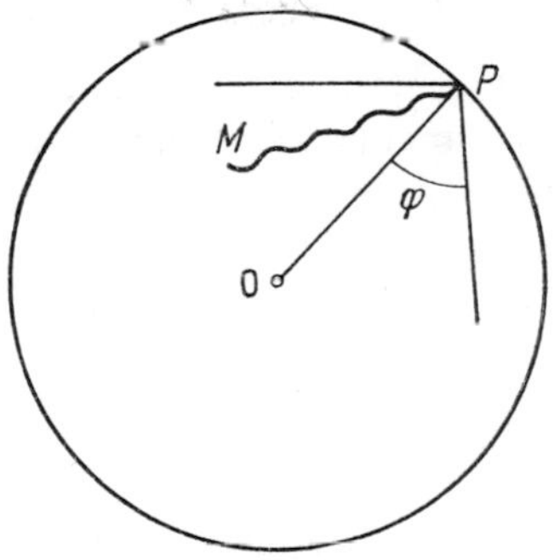


FIG. 12

circle. In the second integral for any $\varepsilon > 0$, provided $M$ becomes sufficiently close to $P$, the modulus of the factor $\partial P(r, t-\omega)/\partial \omega$ becomes less than $\varepsilon$ by virtue of (56.3), which means that the whole integral will not exceed $\varepsilon \int_{-\pi}^{\pi} |f(t)|\, dt$. As regards the first integral, integrating by parts, we have

$$\frac{1}{\pi}\int_{\omega_0-\delta}^{\omega_0+\delta} f(t)\frac{\partial P(r,t-\omega)}{\partial\omega}\,dt = -\frac{1}{\pi}\int_{\omega_0-\delta}^{\omega_0+\delta} f(t)\frac{\partial P(r,t-\omega)}{\partial t}\,dt$$

$$= -\frac{1}{\pi}[f(t)\,P(r,t-\omega)]\Big|_{\omega_0-\delta}^{\omega_0+\delta}$$

$$+\frac{1}{\pi}\int_{\omega_0-\delta}^{\omega_0+\delta} f'(t)\,P(r,t-\omega)\,dt.$$

Here the integrated term tends to zero when $M \to P$, because the Poisson kernel tends to 0, and $f(t)$ is bounded as far as the integral is concerned, so that it is possible to consider it to be the Poisson integral of the function equal to $f'(t)$ in $(\omega_0-\delta, \omega_0+\delta)$ and zero in the remaining part of the circle; this function, by hypothesis, is continuous at $\omega=\omega_0$, and therefore on the basis of the preceding results, this integral tends to $f'(\omega_0)$, no matter how $M$ tends to $P$.

Thus our assertion concerning $\partial f(r,\omega)/\partial\omega$ is true and Lemma 1 is proved.

We shall now prove Theorem 1. First, we refute the hypothesis that $f'(\omega)$ is continuous at $\omega_0$ and confine ourselves to the fact that it exists and is finite; then we will consider movement along non-tangential paths.

For simplicity of argument, we will suppose that $\omega_0 = 0$ and $f(0) = f'(0) = 0$ (this does not decrease the generality, as it is possible to consider instead of $f(\omega)$ the function $f_1(\omega) = f(\omega) - f(0) - \omega f'(0)$ and to study the behaviour of the Poisson integral for it).

Thus, we should prove that if $f(0) = f'(0) = 0$, then

$$\frac{\partial f(r,\omega)}{\partial\omega} \to 0, \tag{56.4}$$

if $M(r,\omega) \to P(1,0)$ by any tangential path.

First we note that because of our conditions we have $\lim_{t\to 0}(f(t)/t) = 0$, and therefore for any $\varepsilon > 0$ it is possible to find $\delta > 0$ such that

$$\left|\frac{f(t)}{t}\right| < \varepsilon \quad \text{at} \quad |t| \leqslant \delta. \tag{56.5}$$

For the remainder it is convenient to take $\delta < \pi/2$.

Let $\Psi(t) = 0$ in $(-\delta, \delta)$, $\Psi(t) = f(t)$ in $\delta \leqslant |t| \leqslant \pi$ and $\Psi(t+2\pi) = \Psi(t)$. It is clear then that denoting its Poisson integral by $\Psi(r,\omega)$, we have

$$\frac{\partial\Psi(r,\omega)}{\partial\omega} = \frac{1}{\pi}\int_{\delta\leqslant|t|\leqslant\pi} f(t)\frac{\partial P(r,t-\omega)}{\partial\omega}\,dt. \tag{56.6}$$

On the other hand, since $\Psi(t)$ satisfies the conditions of Lemma 1 in $(-\delta, \delta)$ and $\Psi'(0) = 0$, then $\partial\Psi(r,\omega)/\partial\omega \to 0$, when $M(r,\omega) \to P(1,0)$ along any path. Hence it follows that the integral on the right-hand side of (56.6) tends to zero, and therefore it follows from (56.1) that (56.4) will be true, if we prove that the integral

$$I = \frac{1}{\pi} \int_{-\delta}^{\delta} f(t) \frac{\partial P(r, t-\omega)}{\partial \omega} dt$$

can be made less than $C\varepsilon$ where $C$ is a constant. But by virtue of (56.5) we have

$$|I| < \frac{\varepsilon}{\pi} \int_{-\delta}^{\delta} \left| t \frac{\partial P(r, t-\omega)}{\partial \omega} \right| dt.$$

We now prove that the expression

$$Q = t \frac{\partial P(r, t-\omega)}{\partial \omega} \tag{56.7}$$

remains bounded in $-\delta \leqslant t \leqslant \delta$, when the point $M(r, \omega) \to P(1, 0)$ along any non-tangential path.

In order to prove this, we remark first that on the basis of (56.2)

$$|Q| = |t| \frac{|2r \sin(t-\omega)(1-r^2)|}{|e^{it} - re^{i\omega}|^2} \leqslant \frac{2|t|\,|\sin(t-\omega)|}{|e^{it} - re^{i\omega}|^2}.$$

Since

$$|e^{it} - re^{i\omega}| = |e^{i(t-\omega)} - r| \leqslant |\sin(t-\omega)|,$$

because the modulus of a complex quantity is not less than the modulus of its imaginary part, then

$$|Q| \leqslant \frac{2|t|}{|e^{it} - re^{i\omega}|}.$$

Moreover, we note that $\delta \leqslant \pi/2$ and therefore $|t| \leqslant (\pi/2)|\sin t|$, whence

$$|Q| \leqslant \pi \frac{|\sin t|}{|e^{it} - re^{i\omega}|}. \tag{56.8}$$

We can confine ourselves to considering the case $-\pi/2 \leqslant \omega \leqslant \pi/2$, because $M(r, \omega) \to P(1, 0)$. Figure 13 holds for $\omega > 0$ but the case $\omega < 0$ is treated in an exactly similar manner.

Since we are concerned with non-tangential paths, there exists an angle $KPK'$ with a vertex at $P$ and the bisector $OP$ such that the point $M$ as it approaches $P$ cannot go outside this angle. Letting $\alpha = KPy'$ where $Py'$ is a line, passing through $P$, parallel to the axis $Oy$, we see that the vector $PM$ forms with the positive direction of the abscissa axis an angle $\varphi$, where $\varphi \geqslant \pi/2 + \alpha$ (if $\omega < 0$, then we will have $\varphi \leqslant 3\pi/2 - \alpha$) whence it is clear that $re^{i\omega} = 1 + \varrho e^{i\varphi}$, where $\varrho$ is the length of the vector $MP$ and $\pi/2 + \alpha \leqslant \varphi \leqslant 3\pi/2 - \alpha$, i.e. $\alpha \leqslant \varphi - \pi/2 \leqslant \pi - \alpha$.

Thus

$$\varrho e^{i\varphi} = \varrho e^{i\frac{\pi}{2}} e^{i\left(\varphi - \frac{\pi}{2}\right)} = i\varrho e^{i\left(\varphi - \frac{\pi}{2}\right)} = i\varrho e^{i\Psi},$$

where $\alpha \leqslant \Psi \leqslant \pi - \alpha$. Therefore

$$\left| e^{it} - re^{i\omega} \right| = \left| e^{it} - 1 - i\varrho e^{i\Psi} \right| = \left| \frac{e^{it} - 1}{i} e^{-i\Psi} - \varrho \right|$$

$$= \left| \frac{e^{i\frac{t}{2}} - e^{-i\frac{t}{2}}}{2i} 2e^{i\left(\frac{t}{2} - \Psi\right)} - \varrho \right| = \left| 2 \sin\frac{t}{2} e^{i\left(\frac{t}{2} - \Psi\right)} - \varrho \right|$$

$$\geqslant 2 \left| \sin\frac{t}{2} \sin\left(\frac{t}{2} - \Psi\right) \right|. \tag{56.9}$$

(Here we again use the fact that the modulus of a complex quantity is not less than the modulus of its imaginary part.)

Now from (56.8) and (56.9) we conclude

$$|Q| \leqslant \pi \frac{|\sin t|}{2 \left|\sin\frac{t}{2}\right| \left|\sin\left(\frac{t}{2} - \Psi\right)\right|} \leqslant \frac{\pi}{\left|\sin\left(\frac{t}{2} - \Psi\right)\right|}.$$

If $|t| < \alpha$, then $|\sin(t/2 - \Psi)| \geqslant \sin(\alpha/2)$ and then

$$|Q| \leqslant \frac{\pi}{\sin\frac{\alpha}{2}},$$

i.e. $Q$ is bounded. If $\delta \geqslant |t| \geqslant \alpha$, then for $M(r, \omega) \to P(1, 0)$ the denominator in (56.8) is bounded below, which means that $|Q|$ is again bounded. This concludes the proof of Theorem 1.

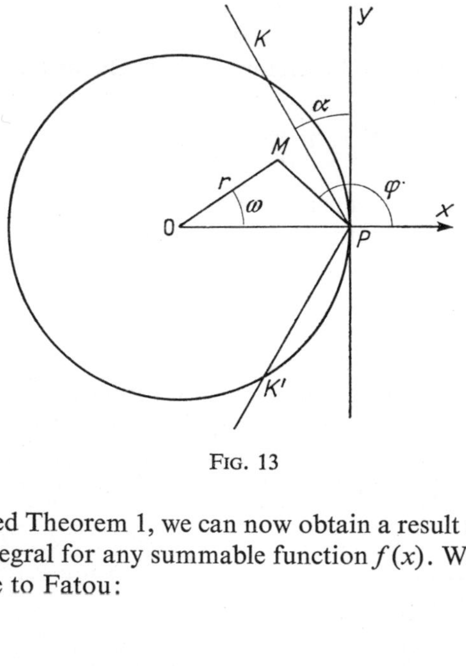


FIG. 13

Using the proved Theorem 1, we can now obtain a result referring to the behaviour of the Poisson integral for any summable function $f(x)$. We will prove the following theorem, also due to Fatou:

THEOREM 2. *At any point $\omega_0$, where $f(\omega)$ is the derivative of its indefinite integral, the Poisson integral $f(\omega, r) \to f(\omega_0)$, if the point $M(r, \omega)$ tends to the point $P(1, \omega_0)$ along any non-tangential path.*

In particular it follows that *the Fourier series of any summable function is summable by Poisson's method to this function almost everywhere.*†

In order to prove this we will suppose that

$$F(\omega) = \int_{-\pi}^{\omega} f(t)\, dt.$$

We have, integrating by parts,

$$f(r, \omega) = \frac{1}{\pi} [F(t)\, P(r, t-\omega)] \Big|_{-\pi}^{\pi} - \frac{1}{\pi} \int_{-\pi}^{\pi} F(t) \frac{\partial}{\partial t} [P(r, t-\omega)]\, dt.$$

The integrated term tends to zero when $M \to P(1, \omega_0)$ provided $\omega \neq -\pi$ and $\omega \neq \pi$. As regards the integral, it is possible to rewrite it in the form

$$\frac{\partial}{\partial \omega} \left\{ \frac{1}{\pi} \int_{-\pi}^{\pi} F(t)\, P(r, t-\omega)\, dt \right\} = \frac{\partial}{\partial \omega} F(r, \omega), \tag{56.10}$$

and therefore, only on the basis of the result just obtained, if $M(r, \omega) \to P(1, \omega_0)$ along a non-tangential path, the expression (56.10) tends to $F'(\omega_0)$ everywhere, where $F'(x)$ exists and is finite. Consequently, at any point where $f(\omega_0) = F'(\omega_0)$ we have $f(r, \omega) \to f(\omega_0)$ and this is what was required to be proved.

Since from the theory of the Lebesgue integral it is known that the equality $F'(\omega) = f(\omega)$ holds almost everywhere, then it follows in particular that for almost all values of $\omega$

$$f(r, \omega') \to f(\omega),$$

where $M(r, \omega') \to P(1, \omega)$ along any non-tangential path. This occurs even more so, when $M(r, \omega) \to P(1, \omega)$ as $r \to 1$, whence it is evident that the theorem of § 53 is a corollary of Fatou's theorem.

We will now look at the role played by the Poisson integral in solving the celebrated Dirichlet problem.

## § 57. The Dirichlet problem

This problem was set by Dirichlet in the following form: Given a closed contour and a function $f(x)$, continuous on it, it is required to find a harmonic†† function inside this contour tending to given values on the contour when the point tends by any method from inside to the periphery.

† Moreover, it is summable almost everywhere to $f(x)$ by method $A^*$ (see the definition of $A^*$ in § 7 of the Introductory Material).

†† That is, it satisfies Laplace's equation

$$\frac{\partial^2 F}{\partial x^2} + \frac{\partial^2 F}{\partial y^2} = 0.$$

We will discuss the particular case when the contour under consideration is a circle of unit radius with centre at the origin. If we denote by $x$ and $y$ the Cartesian co-ordinates of the point $M(r, \omega)$ then we have

$$F(x, y) = f(r, \omega) = \frac{a_0}{2} + \sum_{n=1}^{\infty} (a_n \cos n\omega + b_n \sin n\omega) r^n,$$

where $a_n$ and $b_n$ are the Fourier coefficients for $f(x)$ and therefore $F(x, y)$ is the real part of the analytic function inside the circle of unit radius, defined by the power series

$$\frac{a_0}{2} + \sum_{n=1}^{\infty} (a_n - ib_n) z^n, \quad z = re^{i\omega}.$$

But it is known that the real (and imaginary) part of any analytic function is a harmonic function, that is, it follows from the theorem of § 55 that the function $F(x, y)$ gives the solution of the Dirichlet problem for a circle.

If the Dirichlet problem is extended by not requiring the values of the function given on the boundary to define a continuous function, but permitting the point to tend from inside to the periphery only along non-tangential paths, then $F(x, y)$ tends to $f(\omega)$ almost everywhere and thus gives the solution of the generalized Dirichlet problem.

## § 58. Summation by Poisson's method of a differentiated Fourier series

Let

$$\sigma(F) = \frac{A_0}{2} + \sum (A_0 \cos nx + B_n \sin nx). \tag{58.1}$$

We know that the series

$$\sum n(B_n \cos nx - A_n \sin nx), \tag{58.2}$$

obtained by differentiating (58.1) should not be a Fourier series, since its coefficients

$$a_n = nB_n \quad \text{and} \quad b_n = -nA_n$$

should not even tend to zero. Therefore, the preceding theorems cannot be applied to series (58.2). But instead we have the following:

FATOU'S THEOREM. *If at some point $x$ the function $F(x)$ has a symmetrical derivative equal to the value $l$, then by differentiating the series $\sigma(F)$, we obtain a series which is summable at the point $x$ to the value $l$ by Poisson's method.*

Since $\lim\limits_{h\to 0} [F(x+h) - F(x-h)]/2h$, if this limit exists, is the symmetrical derivative, then by the condition of the theorem

$$\lim_{h\to 0} \frac{F(x+h) - F(x-h)}{2h} = l. \tag{58.3}$$

Supposing, as always

$$F(r, x) = \frac{A_0}{2} + \sum_{n=1}^{\infty} (A_n \cos nx + B_n \sin nx) r^n,$$

we can write

$$\frac{\partial F(r, x)}{\partial x} = \sum_{n=1}^{\infty} (B_n \cos nx - A_n \sin nx) r^n. \tag{58.4}$$

Here term-by-term differentiation is valid, since at $r < 1$ series (58.4) converges uniformly relative to $x$. It is necessary for us to prove that

$$\frac{\partial F(r, x)}{\partial x} \to l \quad \text{as} \quad r \to 1.$$

But

$$\frac{\partial F(r, x)}{\partial x} = \frac{1}{\pi} \int_{-\pi}^{\pi} F(t) \frac{\partial P(r, t - x)}{\partial x} dt = -\frac{1}{\pi} \int_{-\pi}^{\pi} F(t) \frac{\partial P(r, t - x)}{\partial t} dt, \tag{58.5}$$

and since $\partial P(r, u)/\partial u$ is an odd function (see (56.2)), then

$$\frac{\partial F(r, x)}{\partial x} = -\frac{1}{\pi} \int_{-\pi}^{\pi} F(x + u) \frac{\partial P(r, u)}{\partial u} du$$

$$= -\frac{1}{\pi} \int_{0}^{\pi} [F(x + u) - F(x - u)] \frac{\partial P(r, u)}{\partial u} du.$$

By virtue of (56.3) for any $\varepsilon > 0$ and $\delta > 0$ it is possible to choose $r_0 < 1$ such that $|\partial P(r, u)/\partial u| < \varepsilon$ for $\delta \leqslant u \leqslant \pi$ and $r_0 \leqslant r < 1$. Therefore

$$\frac{\partial F(r, x)}{\partial x} = -\frac{1}{\pi} \int_{0}^{\delta} [F(x + u) - F(x - u)] \frac{\partial P(r, u)}{\partial u} du + I_1, \tag{58.6}$$

where

$$|I_1| \leqslant \frac{2\varepsilon}{\pi} \int_{-\pi}^{\pi} |F(t)| \, dt < C\varepsilon, \tag{58.7}$$

where $C$ is a constant. From (58.3) it is possible to suppose that the number $\delta$ is so small that

$$\left| \frac{F(x + u) - F(x - u)}{2u} - l \right| < \varepsilon. \tag{58.8}$$

Then from (58.6), (58.7) and (58.8)

$$\frac{\partial F(r, x)}{\partial x} = -\frac{l}{\pi} \int_{0}^{\delta} \frac{F(x + u) - F(x - u)}{2u} 2u \frac{\partial P(r, u)}{\partial u} du + I_1$$

$$= I_1 - \frac{1}{\pi} \int_{0}^{\delta} \left[ \frac{F(x + u) - F(x - u)}{2u} - l \right] 2u \frac{\partial P(r, u)}{\partial u} du$$

$$- \frac{l}{\pi} \int_{0}^{\delta} 2u \frac{\partial P(r, u)}{\partial u} du = I_1 + I_2 + I_3. \tag{58.9}$$

Due to (58.8) we have

$$|I_2| < \frac{2\varepsilon}{\pi} \int_0^\delta \left| u \frac{\partial P(r, u)}{\partial u} \right| du < C_1 \varepsilon, \tag{58.10}$$

where $C_1$ is a constant. Indeed, from (56.2) we see that

$$\left| u \frac{\partial P(r, u)}{\partial u} \right| \leqslant \left| \frac{2u \sin u}{\sin^2 u} \right| \leqslant \pi, \quad \text{for} \quad 0 \leqslant u \leqslant \frac{\pi}{2}.$$

For $I_3$, integrating by parts, we find that

$$I_3 = -\frac{2l}{\pi} \int_0^\delta u \frac{\partial P(r, u)}{\partial u} du = -\frac{2l}{\pi} \delta P(r, \delta) + \frac{2l}{\pi} \int_0^\delta P(r, u)\, du \to l. \tag{58.11}$$

because $P(r, \delta) \to 0$ and from formula (55.4).

Now from (58.7), (58.10) and (58.11) we obtain

$$\frac{\partial F(r, x)}{\partial x} \to l \quad \text{as} \quad r \to 1,$$

and the theorem is proved.

*Note.* Since the presence of the normal derivative at some point guarantees the existence of a symmetrical derivative at that point and their equality, then from this it follows in particular that:

*If at some point $x$ the derivative $F'(x)$ exists and is finite, then $\partial F(r, x)/\partial x \to F'(x)$ as $r \to 1$, i.e. when $F(x)$ has a finite derivative, the differentiated Fourier series is summable to this derivative by Poisson's method.*

In § 56 we have essentially already obtained this result (only it is formulated in different terms). Now we will see that the requirement of the existence of $F'(x)$ can be replaced by the weaker requirement of the existence of a symmetrical derivative. But whereas in the theorem of this section $M(r, x_0) \to P(1, x_0)$ along the radial path, in § 56 it was proved that $M(r, x) \to P(1, x_0)$ along any non-tangential path.

## § 59†. Poisson–Stieltjes integral

*The Poisson–Stieltjes integral* is the name given to the expression

$$u(re^{i\omega}) = \frac{1}{\pi} \int_{-\pi}^{\pi} P(r, t - \omega)\, d\Psi(t),$$

where $\Psi(t)$ is some function of bounded variation in $[-\pi, \pi]$. Integrating by parts, we obtain

$$u(re^{i\omega}) = \frac{1}{\pi} P(r, t - \omega)\, \Psi(t) \Big|_{-\pi}^{\pi} - \frac{1}{\pi} \int_{-\pi}^{\pi} \Psi(t) \frac{\partial}{\partial t} P(r, t - \omega)\, dt.$$

† This section can be omitted at a first reading.

If $\omega \neq \pm\pi$, then the integrated term as $r \to 1$ tends to zero. As regards the integral, from Theorem 1, § 56 it should tend to $\Psi'(\omega_0)$ at any point $\omega_0$, where $\Psi'(\omega)$ exists and is finite, only if the point $M(re^{i\omega})$ tends to the point $P(e^{i\omega_0})$ along any non-tangential path.

In particular

$$u(re^{i\omega}) \to \Psi'(\omega) \quad \text{as} \quad r \to 1,$$

if $\Psi'(\omega)$ exists and is finite.

Hence as a corollary we obtain: *the Fourier–Stieltjes series is summable by the Abel–Poisson method almost everywhere.*

Later we will find it useful to prove that if $\omega \neq \pm\pi$ and $\Psi'(\omega) = +\infty$, then we have

$$u(re^{i\omega}) \to +\infty \quad \text{as} \quad r \to 1.$$

In order to prove this, from what has been said concerning the integrated term, it is sufficient to prove that

$$I = -\frac{1}{\pi}\int_{-\pi}^{\pi} \Psi(t)\frac{\partial}{\partial t}P(r, t-\omega)\,dt \to +\infty \quad \text{as} \quad r \to 1.$$

It is just the same kind of integral as (58.5), therefore we see immediately that for any $\varepsilon > 0$

$$I = -\frac{1}{\pi}\int_0^{\delta} [\Psi(\omega+u) - \Psi(\omega-u)]\frac{\partial P(r,u)}{\partial u}du + I_1 = I_1 + I_2,$$

where $|I_1| < \varepsilon$, if $\delta$ is fixed and $r$ is taken sufficiently close to 1. Now we represent $I_2$ in the form

$$I_2 = -\frac{1}{\pi}\int_0^{\delta} [\Psi(\omega+u) - \Psi(\omega)]\frac{\partial P(r,u)}{\partial u}du$$

$$-\frac{1}{\pi}\int_0^{\delta} [\Psi(\omega) - \Psi(\omega-u)]\frac{\partial P(r,u)}{\partial u}du = I_3 + I_4. \tag{59.1}$$

We will show that $I_3 \to +\infty$ and $I_4 \to +\infty$. The proof for both integrals is completely identical. We will carry it through for $I_3$.

Since $\Psi'(x) = +\infty$, we can, if $A$ is given, suppose that $\delta$ is so small that

$$\Psi(\omega+u) - \Psi(\omega) > Au \quad \text{for} \quad 0 \leqslant u \leqslant \delta.$$

We have

$$I_3 = -\frac{1}{\pi}\int_0^{\delta} \frac{\Psi(\omega+u) - \Psi(u)}{u}\left[u\frac{\partial P(r,u)}{\partial u}\right]du,$$

but $-u\,\partial P(r,u)/\partial u \geqslant 0$ (see (56.2)), therefore

$$I_3 > A\frac{1}{\pi}\int_0^{\delta}\left[-u\frac{\partial P(r,u)}{\partial u}\right]du$$

and we have seen (see (58.11)) that

$$\frac{2}{\pi}\int_0^\delta \left[-u\frac{\partial P(r,u)}{\partial u}\right] du \to 1 \quad \text{as} \quad r \to +1,$$

whence it follows that as $r \to 1$ it is possible to make $I_3 > A/2$ where $A$ is previously given and the proof is concluded.

*Note.* That the Fourier–Stieltjes series or the series obtained after differentiation of the Fourier series for a function of bounded variation (see § 23) cannot be a Fourier series is evident from this simple example: the series

$$\sum_{n=1}^{\infty} \frac{\sin nx}{n},$$

as we know (see § 41) is the Fourier series of a function monotonic in $[0, 2\pi]$; however after its differentiation we obtain the series

$$\sum_{n=1}^{\infty} \cos nx,$$

which is not a Fourier series because its coefficients do not tend to zero.

## § 60. Fejér and Poisson sums for different classes of functions

We will now prove a number of theorems which will show that it is possible to judge the properties of a function by studying the sequence of its Fejér or Poisson sums.

THEOREM 1. *In order for the trigonometric series to be a Fourier series for a continuous function, it is necessary and sufficient for the sequence of its Fejér sums $\{\sigma_n(x)\}$ to converge uniformly.*

The necessity of the condition is given simply by Fejér's theorem (see § 47). To prove its sufficiency, we note that if the given trigonometric series is

$$\frac{a_0}{2} + \sum_{n=1}^{\infty} (a_n \cos nx + b_n \sin nx),$$

then

$$\sigma_n(x) = \sum_{k=0}^{n} \left(1 - \frac{k}{n+1}\right)(a_k \cos kx + b_k \sin kx), \tag{60.1}$$

and therefore for $k \leqslant n$

$$\left.\begin{aligned} \left(1 - \frac{k}{n+1}\right) a_k &= \frac{1}{\pi}\int_{-\pi}^{\pi} \sigma_n(t) \cos kt\, dt, \\ \left(1 - \frac{k}{n+1}\right) b_k &= \frac{1}{\pi}\int_{-\pi}^{\pi} \sigma_n(t) \sin kt\, dt. \end{aligned}\right\} \tag{60.2}$$

If the sequence $\sigma_n(x)$ converges uniformly, then supposing $f(x) = \lim_{n\to\infty} \sigma_n(x)$, we see that $f(x)$ is continuous. As $n \to \infty$ from equations (60.2) by passing to the limit we obtain

$$a_k = \frac{1}{\pi}\int_{-\pi}^{\pi} f(t)\cos kt\,dt \quad (k = 0, 1, \ldots),$$

$$b_k = \frac{1}{\pi}\int_{-\pi}^{\pi} f(t)\sin kt\,dt \quad (k = 1, 2, \ldots),$$

and this is what was required to be proved.

THEOREM 2. *For the trigonometric series to be a Fourier series for a bounded function, it is necessary and sufficient for a constant K to be found for which*

$$|\sigma_n(x)| \leqslant K \quad (n = 1, 2, \ldots;\ 0 \leqslant x \leqslant 2\pi).$$

The necessity of this condition was proved in § 48. To prove its sufficiency we note that if it is satisfied, then

$$\frac{1}{\pi}\int_{-\pi}^{\pi} \sigma_n^2(x)\,dx \leqslant 2K^2.$$

But due to Parseval's equality we obtain from (60.1)

$$\frac{1}{\pi}\int_{-\pi}^{\pi} \sigma_n^2(x)\,dx = \frac{a_0^2}{2} + \sum_{k=1}^{n}\left(1 - \frac{k}{n+1}\right)^2 (a_k^2 + b_k^2).$$

From this it follows that if $m$ is any integer, $m \leqslant n$, then

$$\frac{a_0^2}{2} + \sum_{k=1}^{m}\left(1 - \frac{k}{n+1}\right)^2 (a_k^2 + b_k^2) \leqslant 2K^2.$$

Letting $n \to \infty$ and keeping $m$ constant, we conclude from this that

$$\frac{a_0^2}{2} + \sum_{k=1}^{m} (a_k^2 + b_k^2) \leqslant 2K^2$$

and since $m$ is any number, the series $\sum(a_k^2 + b_k^2) < +\infty$.

This means that the trigonometric series under consideration is a Fourier series of some function $f(x) \in L^2$. But since $\sigma_n(x) \to f(x)$ almost everywhere, then from $|\sigma_n(x)| \leqslant K$ it follows that $|f(x)| \leqslant K$ and the theorem is proved.

THEOREM 3. *For the trigonometric series to be a Fourier series for $f(x) \in L^p (p > 1)$, it is necessary and sufficient that*

$$\|\sigma_n(x)\|_{L^p} \leqslant K \quad (n = 1, 2, \ldots), \tag{60.3}$$

*where K is a constant.*

To prove the necessity we note that

$$\sigma_n(x) = \frac{1}{\pi}\int_{-\pi}^{\pi} f(t)K_n(t-x)\,dt.$$

Therefore, noting that $(1/\pi)\int_{-\pi}^{\pi} K_n(u)\,du = 1$ and that $K_n(u) \geqslant 0$ and applying the lemma proved in § 9 of the Introductory Material, we immediately find

$$\|\sigma_n(x)\|_{L^p} \leqslant \|f(x)\|_{L^p} \tag{60.4}$$

and since the right-hand side of (60.4) does not vary with $n$, the proof is concluded.

To prove the sufficiency we will consider the functions

$$F_n(x) = \int_0^x \sigma_n(t)\,dt \tag{60.5}$$

and prove that they are uniformly absolutely continuous, i.e. for any $\varepsilon$ there exists $\delta$ such that for any system of non-overlapping intervals $(a_i, b_i)$ with a sum $\sum(b_i - a_i) < \delta$ we have

$$\sum|F_n(b_i) - F_n(a_i)| < \varepsilon. \tag{60.6}$$

Indeed, denoting by $S$ this system of intervals, because of (60.3), we have

$$\sum|F_n(b_i) - F_n(a_i)| \leqslant \sum\int_{a_i}^{b_i} |\sigma_n(t)|\,dt$$

$$= \int_S |\sigma_n(t)|\,dt \leqslant \left(\int_S |\sigma_n(t)|^p dt\right)^{1/p}\left(\int_S 1^q\,dt\right)^{1/q} \leqslant \delta^{1/q}\|\sigma_n\|_{Lp} \leqslant \delta^{1/q}K < \varepsilon,$$

if $\delta$ is sufficiently small.

Arguing this, we see that the complete variations of these functions are all bounded. Therefore, from Helly's theorem (see Introductory Material, § 17) it is possible to extract from them the sub-sequence $F_{n_j}(x)$ which converges at every point to some function $F(x)$; according to Helly's theorem it should be of bounded variation, but from the uniform absolute continuity of the function $F_n(x)$ it immediately follows that it is absolutely continuous.

In fact, if in formula (60.6) instead of $n$ we write $n_j$ and pass to the limit as $j \to \infty$, then we obtain

$$\sum|F(b_i) - F(a_i)| < \varepsilon.$$

Let us prove now that the series under consideration is $\sigma(f)$ where $f(x) = F'(x)$. Indeed, we have

$$\int_0^{2\pi} \sigma_n(t)\cos kt\,dt = F_n(t)\cos kt\Big|_0^{2\pi} + k\int_0^{2\pi} F_n(t)\sin kt\,dt = F_n(2\pi) + k\int_0^{2\pi} F_n(t)\sin kt\,dt$$

and

$$\int_0^{2\pi} \sigma_n(t)\sin kt\,dt = -k\int_0^{2\pi} F_n(t)\cos kt\,dt.$$

Letting $n \to \infty$ for the sequence $n_j$, for which $F_{n_j}(x) \to F(x)$, we obtain from formula (60.2)

$$a_k = \frac{1}{\pi} F(2\pi) + \frac{k}{\pi} \int_0^{2\pi} F(t) \sin kt\, dt, \quad b_k = -\frac{k}{\pi} \int_0^{2\pi} F(t) \cos kt\, dt$$

(passage to the limit under the integral sign is valid here due to Lebesgue's theorem (see Introductory Material, § 14)).

After integration by parts of the last two integrals we conclude from this that

$$a_k = \frac{1}{\pi} \int_0^{2\pi} f(t) \cos kt\, dt, \quad b_k = \frac{1}{\pi} \int_0^{2\pi} f(t) \sin kt\, dt,$$

and this is what was required to be proved.

It remains to prove that $f(x) \in L^p$. But for this it is sufficient to note that $\sigma_n(x) \to f(x)$ almost everywhere, then, using the inequality (60.3) and Fatou's lemma (see Introductory Material, § 14), we immediately obtain $\|f(x)\|_{L^p} \leqslant K$.

COROLLARY. *If* $f(x) \in L^p$, $p > 1$, then

$$\int_0^{2\pi} |f(x) - \sigma_n(x)|^p dx \to 0 \quad \text{as} \quad n \to \infty. \tag{60.7}$$

We already know (see (60.4)) that if $f(x) \in L^p$, then

$$\|\sigma_n(x)\|_{L^p} \leqslant \|f(x)\|_{L^p}.$$

Let $\varepsilon > 0$ be given. It is possible to find (see § 28) a trigonometric polynomial $T(x)$ such that

$$\|f(x) - T(x)\|_{L^p} < \varepsilon. \tag{60.8}$$

Consequently, for any $n$

$$\|\sigma_n(x, f - T)\|_{L^p} < \varepsilon,$$

i.e.

$$\|\sigma_n(x, f) - \sigma_n(x, T)\|_{L^p} < \varepsilon. \tag{60.9}$$

But since $T(x)$ is a trigonometric polynomial, then the continuous function $\sigma_n(x, T)$ tends to $T(x)$ uniformly, and even more so

$$\|\sigma_n(x, T) - T(x)\|_{L^p} < \varepsilon \tag{60.10}$$

provided $n$ becomes sufficiently large. Therefore, from (60.8), (60.9) and (60.10) we have

$$\|f(x) - \sigma_n(x, f)\|_{L^p} \leqslant \|f(x) - T(x)\|_{L^p} + \|T(x) - \sigma_n(x, T)\|_{L^p}$$
$$+ \|\sigma_n(x, T) - \sigma_n(x, f)\|_{L^p} \leqslant 3\varepsilon,$$

if $n$ is sufficiently large and thus (60.7) is proved.

Below, in the proof of Theorem 4, we shall see that this assertion holds too for $p = 1$, i.e. if $f(x) \in L$, then

$$\int_0^{2\pi} |f(x) - \sigma_n(x)|\, dx \to 0 \quad \text{as} \quad n \to \infty.$$

However, Theorem 3 holds only for $p > 1$. In fact, if $p = 1$, i.e. if

$$\int_0^{2\pi} |\sigma_n(x)|\, dx \leqslant K,$$

then we cannot assert that the series under consideration is a Fourier series (see the note to Theorem 5 below). The case of a Fourier series is considered in the following theorem:

THEOREM 4. *In order for a trigonometric series to be a Fourier series, it is necessary and sufficient that*

$$\int_0^{2\pi} |\sigma_m(x) - \sigma_n(x)|\, dx \to 0 \quad \textit{as} \quad m \to \infty \quad \textit{and} \quad n \to \infty.$$

We know (see § 47) that

$$\sigma_n(x) - f(x) = \frac{1}{\pi} \int_{-\pi}^{\pi} [f(x+t) - f(x)] K_n(t)\, dt.$$

Therefore, supposing that

$$\Psi(t) = \int_{-\pi}^{\pi} |f(x+t) - f(x)|\, dx,$$

we have

$$\int_{-\pi}^{\pi} |\sigma_n(x) - f(x)|\, dx \leqslant \int_{-\pi}^{\pi} \left\{ \frac{1}{\pi} \int_{-\pi}^{\pi} |f(x+t) - f(x)|\, K_n(t)\, dt \right\} dx$$

$$= \frac{1}{\pi} \int_{-\pi}^{\pi} \Psi(t) K_n(t)\, dt. \tag{60.11}$$

If we denote by $\sigma_n^*(x)$ the Fejér sum for $\sigma(\Psi)$, then

$$\sigma_n^*(x) = \frac{1}{\pi} \int_{-\pi}^{\pi} \Psi(t+x) K_n(t)\, dt,$$

and therefore, from (60.11)

$$\int_{-\pi}^{\pi} |\sigma_n(x) - f(x)|\, dx \leqslant \sigma_n^*(0).$$

But since $\Psi(t)$ is continuous and $\Psi(0) = 0$, then $\sigma_n^*(0) \to 0$ as $n \to \infty$, which means that

$$\int_{-\pi}^{\pi} |\sigma_n(x) - f(x)|\, dx \to 0. \tag{60.12}$$

From this we obtain

$$\int_{-\pi}^{\pi} |\sigma_n(x) - \sigma_m(x)|\, dx \leqslant \int_{-\pi}^{\pi} |\sigma_n(x) - f(x)|\, dx + \int_{-\pi}^{\pi} |f(x) - \sigma_m(x)|\, dx \to 0$$

and the necessity of our condition is proved.

To prove its sufficiency we note that from

$$\int_0^{2\pi} |\sigma_n(x) - \sigma_m(x)|\, dx \to 0 \quad \text{as} \quad m \to \infty,\ n \to \infty$$

the existence of the constant $K$, for which

$$\int_0^{2\pi} |\sigma_n(x)|\, dx \leqslant K \quad (n = 1, 2, \ldots).$$

follows. Supposing, as in Theorem 3,

$$F_n(x) = \int_0^x \sigma_n(t)\, dt.$$

then we will prove in the same way that the sequence of functions $F_n(x)$ is uniformly absolutely continuous. Here, using the notation of Theorem 3, we have

$$\sum |F_n(b_i) - F_n(a_i)| \leqslant \int_S |\sigma_n(t)|\, dt. \tag{60.13}$$

But

$$\int_S |\sigma_n(t)|\, dt \leqslant \int_S |\sigma_n(t) - \sigma_k(t)|\, dt + \int_S |\sigma_k(t)|\, dt$$

$$\leqslant \int_0^{2\pi} |\sigma_n(t) - \sigma_k(t)|\, dt + \int_S |\sigma_k(t)|\, dt. \tag{60.14}$$

Let $\varepsilon > 0$ be given. Due to the condition of the theorem it is possible to take $k$ so large that

$$\int_0^{2\pi} |\sigma_n(t) - \sigma_k(t)|\, dt < \frac{\varepsilon}{2} \quad \text{for} \quad n \geqslant k. \tag{60.15}$$

We will now fix $k$; then, taking $\delta$ sufficiently small, it can be proved that $\int_S |\sigma_p(t)|\, dt < \varepsilon/2$ at $p \leqslant k$ provided $mS < \delta$. But if this is so, then from (60.14) and (60.15)

$$\int_S |\sigma_n(t)|\, dt < \varepsilon$$

and consequently from (60.13)

$$\sum |F_n(b_i) - F_n(a_i)| < \varepsilon \quad \text{at} \quad \sum (b_i - a_i) < \delta.$$

Now as in Theorem 3 we see that it is possible to remove from the sequence $\{F_n(x)\}$ a sub-sequence converging to some $F(x)$ which should be absolutely continuous and moreover, the series under consideration is a Fourier series of $F'(x)$.

The theorem is proved.

*Note.* In the process of this proof we have established that for any $f(x) \in L$ we have

$$\int_0^{2\pi} |f(x) - \sigma_n(x)|\, dx \to 0 \quad \text{as} \quad n \to \infty. \tag{60.16}$$

Finally, we shall prove yet another theorem.

THEOREM 5. *In order for the trigonometric series to be a Fourier–Stieltjes*† *series, it is necessary and sufficient that*

$$\int_{-\pi}^{\pi} |\sigma_n(x)|\, dx \leqslant K \quad (n = 1, 2, \ldots),$$

*where K is a constant.*

The necessity of the condition follows from the fact that for a Fourier–Stieltjes series we have

$$\sigma_n(x) = \frac{1}{\pi}\int_{-\pi}^{\pi} K_n(t-x)\, dF(t) \tag{60.17}$$

(this formula is derived in just the same way as (47.2)). Therefore

$$|\sigma_n(x)| \leqslant \frac{1}{\pi}\int_{-\pi}^{\pi} K_n(t-x)\, |dF|,$$

where $|dF|$ is no different from $dV(t)$, if $V(t)$ is taken to be the complete variation of $F(x)$ in $0 \leqslant x \leqslant t$. Hence, by changing the order of integration, we obtain

$$\int_0^{2\pi} |\sigma_n(x)|\, dx \leqslant \int_0^{2\pi} \left\{ \frac{1}{\pi}\int_0^{2\pi} K_n(t-x)\, |dF(t)| \right\} dx$$

$$= \int_0^{2\pi} |dF(t)| \frac{1}{\pi}\int_0^{2\pi} K_n(t-x)\, dx = \int_0^{2\pi} |dF| = V,$$

where $V$ is the complete variation of $F(x)$ in $[0, 2\pi]$.

Thus, the necessity is proved.

In order to prove the sufficiency, we will again turn to considering the function $F_n(x)$ already considered in Theorems 3 and 4. It is true that we have not been able to prove that they are uniformly absolutely continuous but nevertheless they are of uniformly bounded variation, because

$$\sum |F_n(x_{i+1}) - F_n(x_i)| \leqslant \sum \int_{x_i}^{x_{i+1}} |\sigma_n(t)|\, dt = \int_0^{2\pi} |\sigma_n(t)|\, dt \leqslant K$$

for any division of the interval $[0, 2\pi]$ by the points $x_i$. Therefore, from Helly's first theorem (see Introductory Material, § 17) a subsequence $n_j$ exists such that $F_{n_j}(x) \to F(x)$ for any $x$ of $[0, 2\pi]$, where $F(x)$ is of bounded variation. It remains to prove that the given series is the Fourier–Stieltjes series of $dF$.

---

† See § 23, point (9).

For this, as in the proof of Theorem 3, we have

$$\left(1 - \frac{k}{n+1}\right) a_k = \frac{1}{\pi} \int_0^{2\pi} \sigma_n(t) \cos kt \, dt = \frac{F_n(2\pi)}{\pi} + \frac{k}{\pi} \int_0^{2\pi} F_n(t) \sin kt \, dt$$

and then by integrating by parts we obtain

$$\left(1 - \frac{k}{n+1}\right) a_k = \frac{1}{\pi} \int_0^{2\pi} \cos kt \, dF_n(t).$$

Permitting $n$ to tend to infinity for the sub-sequence $n_j$, we find

$$a_k = \frac{1}{\pi} \int_0^{2\pi} \cos kt \, dF(t)$$

and similarly for $b_k$ (passage to the limit is valid from Helly's second theorem, Introductory Material, § 17).

The theorem is proved.

*Note.* We know (see § 59) that not every Fourier–Stieltjes series is a Fourier series. Thus, the condition

$$\int_{-\pi}^{\pi} |\sigma_n(x)| \, dx \leqslant K \quad (n = 1, 2, \ldots)$$

is not sufficient for the series to be a Fourier series and this shows that at $p = 1$ Theorem 3 no longer holds.

Taking into account that the Fourier–Stieltjes series is the result of differentiating the Fourier series for a function of bounded variation, we obtain as a corollary of Theorem 5 the following theorem:

THEOREM 6. *For the trigonometric series to be the Fourier series of a function of bounded variation, it is necessary and sufficient that*

$$\int_0^{2\pi} |\sigma_n'(x)| \, dx \leqslant K \quad (n = 1, 2, \ldots).$$

All the theorems that have been proved have referred to Fejér sums. If instead of them we consider Poisson sums, i.e.

$$f(r, x) = \frac{a_0}{2} + \sum_{n=1}^{\infty} (a_n \cos nx + b_n \sin nx) r^n$$

and note that

$$f(r, x) = \frac{1}{\pi} \int_{-\pi}^{\pi} f(t) P(r, t - x) \, dt,$$

where $P(r, u)$ is a Poisson kernel, then it is possible to prove completely analogous theorems; indeed, in this proof we used the whole time the expression $\sigma_n(x)$ in the form

$$\sigma_n(x) = \frac{1}{\pi}\int_{-\pi}^{\pi} f(t)K_n(t-x)\,dt$$

and we based the proof only on the facts that $K_n(u) \geqslant 0$ and

$$\frac{1}{\pi}\int_{-\pi}^{\pi} K_n(u)\,du = 1.$$

But we also have $P(r, u) \geqslant 0$ and

$$\frac{1}{\pi}\int_{-\pi}^{\pi} P(r, u)\,du = 1.$$

Therefore the whole argument can be carried out word for word (the fact that $r \to 1$ for all values of $r$, not just for a sequence, does not play a part, since it would be possible to consider the sequence $r_k \to 1$ as $k \to \infty$ and to use the kernels $P(r_k, u)$ in the discussion).

Thus the following theorems are obtained.

THEOREM 1′. *In order for a trigonometric series to be a Fourier series of a continuous function, it is necessary and sufficient for its Poisson sums $f(r, x)$ to tend uniformly to a limit as $r \to 1$.*

THEOREM 2′. *In order for a trigonometric series to be a Fourier series of a continuous function, it is necessary and sufficient that a constant $K$ exists, for which*

$$|f(r, x)| \leqslant K, \quad \begin{array}{l} 0 \leqslant r < 1, \\ 0 \leqslant x \leqslant 2\pi. \end{array}$$

THEOREM 3′. *In order for a trigonometric series to be a Fourier series for $f(x) \in L^p$ $(p > 1)$, it is necessary and sufficient for*

$$\| f(r, x)\|_{L^p} \leqslant K, \quad 0 \leqslant r < 1.$$

*Moreover, if $f(x) \in L^p$ $(p > 1)$, then*

$$\| f(r, x)\|_{L^p} \leqslant \| f(x)\|_{L^p}. \tag{60.18}$$

*We also have*

$$\int_0^{2\pi} | f(x) - f(r, x)|^p dx \to 0 \quad \text{as} \quad r \to 1, \tag{60.19}$$

*whilst this is true both for $p > 1$ and for $p = 1$.*

THEOREM 4′. *In order for the trigonometric series to be a Fourier series, it is necessary and sufficient that*

$$\int_0^{2\pi} | f(r, x) - f(\varrho, x)|\,dx \to 0 \quad \text{as} \quad r \to 1 \quad \text{and} \quad \varrho \to 1.$$

For the case of a Fourier–Stieltjes series the argument is somewhat more complicated. We will not go through it, but will confine ourselves to formulating the theorem analogous to Theorem 5, namely:

THEOREM 5′. *For the trigonometric series to be a Fourier–Stieltjes series, it is necessary and sufficient that*

$$\int_0^{2\pi} |f(r, x)|\, dx \leqslant K, \quad 0 \leqslant r < 1.$$

We note that in Chapter VIII (§ 14 and § 20) instead of Fejér or Poisson sums of a Fourier series we shall study its partial sums $S_n(x)$ and for them we shall consider the question of the behaviour of $\|S_n\|_{L^p}$ and $\|f - S_n\|_{L^p}$ at $p \geqslant 1$.

## § 61. General trigonometric series. The Lusin–Denjoy theorem

Up until now we have studied Fourier series. Now we will consider trigonometric series of the same general type and prove a number of very simple but important theorems concerning them. We will begin by considering the question of when the trigonometric series converges absolutely in a set of positive measure. Here we have a theorem proved simultaneously and independently by Lusin[3] and Denjoy[2].

THE LUSIN–DENJOY THEOREM. *If the trigonometric series*

$$\frac{a_0}{2} + \sum_{n=1}^{\infty} (a_n \cos nx + b_n \sin nx) \tag{61.1}$$

*converges absolutely in the set $E$, $mE > 0$, then*

$$\sum (|a_n| + |b_n|) < +\infty.$$

Let us define $\varrho_n = \sqrt{a_n^2 + b_n^2}$, $(n = 1, 2, \ldots)$ and let

$$a_0 = 0, \quad \frac{a_2}{2} = \varrho_0, \quad a_n = \varrho_n \cos\alpha_n, \quad b_n = \varrho_n \sin\alpha_n \quad (n = 1, 2, \ldots).$$

Then the series (61.1) takes the form

$$\sum_{n=0}^{\infty} \varrho_n \cos(nx - \alpha_n). \tag{61.2}$$

Absolute convergence of the series (61.2) in $E$ means that

$$\sum_{n=0}^{\infty} \varrho_n |\cos(nx - \alpha_n)| < +\infty \quad \text{for} \quad x \in E. \tag{61.3}$$

According to Yegorov's theorem, it is possible to find a perfect set $P \subset E$, $mP > 0$, in which the series (61.3) converges uniformly. Let $S(x)$ be its sum in $P$, then from the uniform convergence of (61.3)

$$\int_P S(x)\, dx = \sum_{n=0}^{\infty} \varrho_n \int_P |\cos(nx - \alpha_n)|\, dx.$$

But

$$\int_P |\cos(nx - \alpha_n)|\, dx \geqslant \int_P \cos^2(nx - \alpha_n)\, dx$$

$$= \frac{1}{2}\int_P [1 + \cos 2(nx - \alpha_n)]\, dx = \frac{1}{2} mP + \frac{1}{2}\int_P \cos 2(nx - \alpha_n) dx.$$

If $f(x)$ denotes a function equal to 1 in $P$ and zero outside it, then

$$\int_P \cos 2(nx - \alpha_n)\, dx = \int_{-\pi}^{\pi} f(x) \cos 2(nx - \alpha_n)\, dx$$

$$= \cos 2\alpha_n \int_{-\pi}^{\pi} f(x) \cos 2nx\, dx + \sin 2\alpha_n \int_{-\pi}^{\pi} f(x) \sin 2nx\, dx, \quad (61.4)$$

and therefore

$$\int_P \cos 2(nx - \alpha_n)\, dx \to 0 \quad \text{as} \quad n \to \infty,$$

since the integrals on the right-hand side of (61.4) differ only by a bounded multiplier from the Fourier coefficients of $f(x)$.

From this it follows that

$$\int_P |\cos(nx - \alpha_n)|\, dx > \frac{1}{4} mP$$

where $n$ is sufficiently large, which means that the convergence of series (61.3) implies the convergence of the series $\sum \varrho_n$, whence it follows that

$$\sum |a_n| < +\infty, \quad \sum |b_n| < +\infty.$$

The theorem is proved.

## § 62. The Cantor–Lebesgue theorem

We will now consider the coefficients of a trigonometric series, if it converges not absolutely but simply in a set of measure greater than zero.

Here we have

THE CANTOR–LEBESGUE THEOREM. *If a trigonometric series converges in a set $E$, $mE > 0$, then its coefficients tend to zero.*

In fact, if

$$\sum \varrho_n \cos(nx - \alpha_n) \quad (62.1)$$

converges in $E$, $mE > 0$, then we have

$$\lim_{n\to\infty} \varrho_n \cos(nx - \alpha_n) = 0 \quad \text{for} \quad x \in E.$$

If a sequence $n_1, n_2, \ldots, n_k, \ldots$ is found, such that

$$\varrho_{n_k} \geqslant \delta > 0, \quad (62.2)$$

then we evidently have

$$\lim_{k\to\infty} \cos(n_k x - \alpha_{n_k}) = 0, \quad x \in E.$$

We will prove that this is not possible. Indeed, then we would have

$$\lim_{k\to\infty} \cos^2(n_k x - \alpha_{n_k}) = 0, \quad x \in E.$$

According to Lebesgue's theorem on the validity of passage to the limit under the integral sign for all-bounded functions, we have, integrating for the set $E$

$$\lim_{k\to\infty} \int_E \cos^2(n_k x - \alpha_{n_k}) = 0.$$

But since by a similar argument to that in § 61, we have

$$\lim_{k\to\infty} \int_E \cos^2(n_k x - \alpha_{n_k})\,dx = \frac{1}{2} mE,$$

and $mE > 0$, then we arrive at a contradiction.

Consequently, it would be impossible to assume (62.2), therefore

$$\lim_{n\to 0} \varrho_n = 0, \tag{62.3}$$

and the theorem is proved.

*Note.* The name of this theorem is explained by the fact that Cantor proved it for the case when the series converges in some interval $[a, b]$ and Lebesgue generalized it for the case of any set of positive measure. We think it appropriate here to prove Cantor's theorem separately, as it does not require a knowledge of Lebesgue's integral.

Thus, let the series (62.1) converge in some interval $[a, b]$. For convenience we will rewrite it in the form

$$\sum \varrho_n \cos n(x - \alpha_n). \tag{62.4}$$

It is required to prove that $\varrho_n \to 0$. We will show that this is untrue; then $\delta > 0$ can be found such that

$$\varrho_n \geqslant \delta \tag{62.5}$$

for an infinite set of values of $n$.

We shall denote the length of the interval $[a, b]$ by $d$. When $x$ runs through $[a, b]$, then $x - \alpha_n$ runs through an interval of length $d$. Taking $n$, such that $n_1 d > 2\pi$, we see that $\cos n_1(x - \alpha_{n_1})$ can run through all its values, while $x$ runs through $[a, b]$, which means that it is possible to find an interval $[a_1, b_1]$ within $[a, b]$ such that this cosine $\geqslant \frac{1}{2}$. If $n$ is chosen so that (62.5) is satisfied, then

$$\varrho_{n_1} \cos n_1(x - \alpha_{n_1}) \geqslant \frac{\delta}{2}, \quad a_1 \leqslant x \leqslant b_1.$$

Let $d_1 = b_1 - a_1$. Arguing in the same way as before, we can choose $n_2$ so that (62.5) is satisfied for it and so that $n_2 d_1 > 2\pi$, then in the interval $[a_1, b_1]$ an interval $[a_2, b_2]$ is found for which $\cos n_2(x - \alpha_{n_2}) \geqslant \frac{1}{2}$ and therefore

$$\varrho n_2 \cos n_2(x - \alpha_{n_2}) \geqslant \frac{\delta}{2}, \quad a_2 \leqslant x \leqslant b_2.$$

This process can continue indefinitely, since the numbers $n$ satisfying the inequality (62.5) belong to an infinite set. We obtain a sequence of intervals $[a_k, b_k]$, enclosed within one another, whilst

$$\varrho_{n_k} \cos n_k(x - \alpha_{n_k}) \geqslant \frac{\delta}{2}. \tag{62.6}$$

There exists a point $\xi$, which belongs to all these intervals simultaneously. At this point $\xi$ the inequality (62.6) is fulfilled for all $k (k = 1, 2, \ldots)$ and therefore

$$\lim_{n\to\infty} \varrho_n \cos n(x - \alpha_n) \neq 0,$$

which means that the series $\sum \varrho_n \cos n(x - \alpha_n)$ should diverge at the point $\xi$. However, $\xi$ lies in the interval $[a, b]$ where the series converges and we arrive at a contradiction.

## § 63. An example of an everywhere divergent series with coefficients tending to zero

The question arises whether a trigonometric series with coefficients tending to zero converges in a set of positive measure. This problem was set by Fatou[1] and the first answer to it was given by Lusin[1], who gave the example of a trigonometric series with coefficients tending to zero and divergence almost everywhere (more detail will be given in §§ 1 and 2, Chapter VII). Then Steinhaus[1] gave the example of a trigonometric series with coefficients tending to zero and divergent at every point.

Here we will describe an example of Steinhaus given in a later report[5].

Consider the series

$$\sum_{k=3}^{\infty} \frac{\cos k(x - \ln \ln k)}{\ln k}. \tag{63.1}$$

Let $l_k = [\ln k]$, $v_k = \ln \ln k$ and

$$g_n(x) = \sum_{k=n+1}^{n+l_n} \frac{\cos k(x - v_k)}{\ln k}; \quad g_n = \sum_{k=n+1}^{n+l_n} \frac{1}{\ln k}.$$

First we note that

$$g_n - g_n(x) = \sum_{k=n+1}^{n+l_n} \frac{1}{\ln k} [1 - \cos k(x - v_k)] = 2 \sum_{k=n+1}^{n+l_n} \frac{\sin^2 k \left(\dfrac{x - v_k}{2}\right)}{\ln k},$$

whence

$$0 \leqslant g_n - g_n(x) \leqslant \frac{1}{2 \ln n} \sum_{k=n+1}^{n+l_n} k^2 (x - v_k)^2,$$

since $|\sin u| \leqslant |u|$. Let $v_n \leqslant x \leqslant v_{n+1}$ $(n \geqslant 3)$; then for $n + 1 \leqslant k \leqslant n + l_n$ we have, because of the monotonic increase in the numbers $v_k$:

$$v_n < v_k \leqslant v_{n+l_n},$$

and therefore

$$|x - v_k| \leqslant v_{n+l_n} - v_n.$$

Applying the mean value theorem to the difference $v_{n+l_n} - v_n = \ln\ln(n + l_n) - \ln\ln n$, we find that

$$|x - v_k| \leqslant \frac{l_n}{n \ln n} \leqslant \frac{1}{n},$$

and therefore for $v_n \leqslant x \leqslant v_{n+1}$

$$g_n - g_n(x) \leqslant \frac{1}{2\ln n}\frac{1}{n^2} l_n(n + l_n)^2 \leqslant \frac{1}{2}\left(1 + \frac{l_n}{n}\right)^2. \tag{63.2}$$

The right-hand side of the inequality (63.2) tends to $\frac{1}{2}$ as $n \to \infty$; therefore, for any $\varepsilon$ we can find $N$ such that

$$0 \leqslant g_n - g_n(x) \leqslant \frac{1}{2} + \varepsilon \quad \text{for} \quad n \geqslant N. \tag{63.3}$$

On the other hand

$$g_n \geqslant \frac{l_n}{\ln(n + l_n)} \to 1 \quad \text{as} \quad n \to \infty,$$

therefore

$$g_n \geqslant 1 - \varepsilon \quad \text{for} \quad n \geqslant N, \tag{63.4}$$

if $N$ is sufficiently great. If $\varepsilon < \frac{1}{8}$ is taken, then from (63.3) and (63.4)

$$g_n(x) > \frac{1}{2} - 2\varepsilon > \frac{1}{4} \quad \text{for} \quad v_n \leqslant x \leqslant v_{n+1} \quad \text{and} \quad n \geqslant N. \tag{63.5}$$

Now let $x$ be any point of the interval $[0, 2\pi]$. Let us prove that there exists an infinite set of those values of $n$ for which $g_n(x) > \frac{1}{4}$. In fact, if we mark off the points $v_3, v_4, \dots, v_n$, on the abscissa axis, then they tend monotonically to infinity, which means that the intervals $[v_n, v_{n+1}]$ $(n \geqslant 3)$ cover the whole of the abscissa axis.

Therefore, every point of the type $x + p \,.\, 2\pi$ certainly lies within some interval of the type $[v_n, v_{n+1}]$; but $g_n(x + p \,.\, 2\pi) = g_n(x)$ and therefore at the point $x$ the inequality (63.5) is satisfied, if $n \geqslant N$.

But for sufficiently large $p$ the inequality $x + p \,.\, 2\pi < v_{n+1}$ requires $n$ to be sufficiently large, therefore, for an infinite set of values of $n \geqslant N$ we will indeed have $g_n(x) > \frac{1}{4}$. This means that in the series (63.1) under consideration there is an infinite set of "segments" in which the sum of the terms has a value exceeding $\frac{1}{4}$ and therefore the series diverges. Since this has been proved for any $x$ in $[0, 2\pi]$, then the series diverges at every point.

## § 64. A study of the convergence of one class of trigonometric series

Fatou[1] proved a whole series of important theorems referring to series for which

$$a_n = o\left(\frac{1}{n}\right) \quad \text{and} \quad b_n = o\left(\frac{1}{n}\right). \tag{64.1}$$

But it appears that many of these theorems hold if a weaker requirement is satisfied, namely

$$\tau(n) = \sum_{k=1}^{n} k(|a_k| + |b_k|) = o(n). \tag{64.2}$$

It is clear that (64.2) follows from (64.1) but the converse, generally speaking, does not hold.

Trigonometric series, the coefficients of which satisfy condition (64.2), possess a whole series of interesting properties. They cannot be Fourier series (see Chapter VI, § 3), but this theorem holds:

THEOREM 1. *If the series*

$$\frac{a_0}{2} + \sum_{n=1}^{\infty} (a_n \cos nx + b_n \sin nx)$$

*with coefficients satisfying* (64.2) *is a Fourier series, then it converges almost everywhere; if it is* $\sigma(f)$, *where* $f(x)$ *is continuous, then this series converges uniformly.*

In fact, it is known that if for a trigonometric series $S_n(x)$ are the partial sums and $\sigma_n(x)$ are the Fejér sums, then

$$|S_n(x) - \sigma_n(x)| = \left| \frac{1}{n+1} \sum_{k=1}^{n} k(a_k \cos kx + b_k \sin kx) \right|$$

$$\leqslant \frac{1}{n+1} \sum_{k=1}^{n} k(|a_k| + |b_k|) = o(1) \tag{64.3}$$

because of (64.2). Therefore $S_n(x) - \sigma_n(x) \to 0$ uniformly by virtue of (64.3). But for any Fourier series $\sigma_n(x) \to f(x)$ almost everywhere, therefore $S_n(x) \to f(x)$ almost everywhere. If $f(x)$ is continuous, then $\sigma_n(x) \to f(x)$ uniformly and then $S_n(x) \to f(x)$ uniformly, and the theorem is proved.

As a corollary we deduce the theorem:

THEOREM 2. (Fatou). *If a trigonometric series has coefficients of the form*

$$a_n = o\left(\frac{1}{n}\right) \quad \text{and} \quad b_n = o\left(\frac{1}{n}\right),$$

*then it converges almost everywhere.*

*If moreover it is a Fourier series of a continuous function, then it converges uniformly.*

Indeed, it is clear above all that our series is a Fourier series, since $\sum(a_n^2 + b_n^2) < +\infty$. Moreover, as we have already said, (64.3) follows from (64.1), which means that we have conditions of applicability of the preceding theorem.

*Note.* The hypothesis relating to continuity is an additional requirement and does not follow from (64.1). It is possible to show that functions exist for which the Fourier coefficients satisfy condition (64.1) but, however, they are unbounded in any interval $\delta$, lying in $[-\pi, \pi]$ (see Chapter VIII, § 13).

## § 65. Lacunary sequences and lacunary series

Let us derive some corollaries from Theorem 1, § 64. For this we recall that in Introductory Material, § 4 we defined a sequence of natural numbers $\{n_k\}$ as satisfying condition $(L)$, if

$$\sum_{k=1}^{\infty} \frac{1}{n_k} < +\infty$$

and

$$\sum_{k=m}^{\infty} \frac{1}{n_k} = O\left(\frac{1}{n_m}\right) \quad (m = 1, 2, \ldots).$$

The sequence $\{n_k\}$ is named lacunary if there exists $\lambda > 1$ such that

$$\frac{n_{k+1}}{n_k} > \lambda > 1 \quad (k = 1, 2, \ldots). \tag{65.1}$$

Finally, it was proved that any lacunary sequence satisfies condition $(L)$.

Now we will define lacunary series.

DEFINITION. The series

$$\sum (a_k \cos n_k x + b_k \sin n_k x) \tag{65.2}$$

is named *lacunary* if the natural numbers $\{n_k\}$ form a lacunary sequence (i.e. satisfy the condition (65.1)).

If the sequence $\{n_k\}$ satisfies condition $(L)$ then we will say that series (65.2) is an $(L)$-series (thus, any lacunary series is an $(L)$-series, but the converse is generally not the case).

We will prove that if the coefficients of an $(L)$-series tend to zero, then it belongs to the class of series studied in § 64. Indeed, the function $\tau(n)$ defined in § 64 (see (64.2)) in the given case takes the form

$$\tau(n) = \sum_{k_n \leqslant n} n_k(|a_k| + |b_k|).$$

We will prove that $\tau(n) = o(n)$, then we will have the conditions of § 64. Since $a_k \to 0$ and $b_k \to 0$, then for any $\varepsilon > 0$, $p$ is found such that $|a_k| \leqslant \varepsilon$ and $|b_k| \leqslant \varepsilon$ at $k \geqslant p$. If $n_m$ is the greatest number of the sequence $\{n_k\}$ not exceeding $n$, then

$$\tau(n) = \sum_{k=1}^{m} n_k(|a_k| + |b_k|) \leqslant \sum_{k=1}^{p} n_k(|a_k| + |b_k|) + 2\varepsilon \sum_{k=p+1}^{m} n_k. \tag{65.3}$$

Since the first term on the right-hand side of (65.3) does not vary with $n$, then it is possible to make $n_0$ so large that this term will be less than $\varepsilon n$ for $n \geqslant n_0$. Then

$$\frac{\tau(n)}{n} \leqslant \varepsilon + \frac{2\varepsilon}{n_m} \sum_{k=p+1}^{m} n_k < c\varepsilon \quad (\text{for} \quad n \geqslant n_0),$$

where $c$ is a constant because for the sequences $\{n_k\}$ satisfying condition $(L)$ we have

$$\sum_{k=1}^{m} n_k = O(n_m)$$

(see Introductory Material, § 4).

Thus

$$\tau(n) \leqslant c\,\varepsilon_n,$$

and since $\varepsilon$ is as small as desired, then

$$\tau(n) = o(n)$$

and our statement is proved.

From the proved statement and Theorem 1, § 64, we immediately obtain:

COROLLARY 1. *If an (L)-series is a Fourier series, then it converges almost everywhere; if it is a Fourier series for a continuous function, it converges uniformly.*

From the note made above that any lacunary sequence satisfies condition (*L*) and from Corollary 1 we obtain Kolmogorov's theorem[6].

*If a lacunary series is a Fourier series, then it converges almost everywhere.*

Moreover, from Corollary 1 we also immediately obtain: *if a lacunary series is a Fourier series for a continuous function, then it converges uniformly.*

In Chapter XI, § 6 a stronger assertion will be proved, namely, that under the given conditions, the series should also converge absolutely.

We will now prove yet another theorem relating to sequences satisfying condition (*L*).

THEOREM. *Let $\{n_k\}$ be a sequence satisfying condition (L) and $f(x)$ be a function with an integrable square. Then*

$$S_{n_k}(x) \to f(x) \text{ almost everywhere as } k \to \infty.$$

*Proof.* Let

$$\frac{a_0}{2} + \sum (a_n \cos nx + b_n \sin nx)$$

be the Fourier series of $f(x)$, $S_n(x)$ and $\sigma_n(x)$ be its partial and Fejér sums. Since $\sigma_n(x) \to f(x)$ as $n \to \infty$ almost everywhere, then it is sufficient to prove that $S_{n_k}(x) - \sigma_{n_k}(x) \to 0$ almost everywhere.

We will prove that

$$\sum_{k=1}^{\infty} \int_{-\pi}^{\pi} [\sigma_{n_k}(x) - S_{n_k}(x)]^2 \, dx < +\infty, \tag{65.3'}$$

then according to Lebesgue's theorem (see Introductory Material, § 14) the series

$$\sum_{k=1}^{\infty} [\sigma_{n_k}(x) - S_{n_k}(x)]^2,$$

will converge almost everywhere and therefore its general term will tend to zero.

Thus, it remains to prove the convergence of series (65.3'). As is known,

$$S_n(x) - \sigma_n(x) = \frac{1}{n+1} \sum_{m=0}^{n} m(a_m \cos mx + b_m \sin mx).$$

Therefore due to Parseval's equality

$$\frac{1}{\pi} \int_{-\pi}^{\pi} [\sigma_{n_k}(x) - S_{n_k}(x)]^2 \, dx = \frac{1}{(n_k+1)^2} \sum_{m=0}^{n_k} m^2 (a_m^2 + b_m^2).$$

Let us estimate the sum of the first $p$ terms of series (65.3'); we have

$$\frac{1}{\pi} \sum_{k=1}^{p} \int_{-\pi}^{\pi} [S_{n_k}(x) - \sigma_{n_k}(x)]^2 \, dx = \sum_{k=1}^{p} \frac{1}{(n_k+1)^2} \sum_{m=0}^{n_k} m^2 (a_m^2 + b_m^2)$$

$$< \sum_{k=1}^{p} \frac{1}{n_k^2} \sum_{m=0}^{n_k} m^2 (a_m^2 + b_m^2). \tag{65.4}$$

To shorten the working-out, we introduce the notation

$$v_m = m^2(a_m^2 + b_m^2).$$

We have

$$\sum_{k=1}^{p} \frac{1}{n_k^2} \sum_{m=0}^{n_k} v_m = \sum_{k=1}^{n_1} v_k \sum_{m=1}^{p} \frac{1}{n_m^2} + \sum_{n_1+1}^{n_2} v_k \sum_{m=2}^{p} \frac{1}{n_m^2} + \cdots + \sum_{k=n_{p-1}+1}^{n_p} v_k \frac{1}{n_p^2}. \qquad (65.5)$$

But the sequence $\{n_k\}$ satisfies condition ($L$), and therefore $\{n_k^2\}$ does so, too (see Introductory Material, § 4) and therefore

$$\sum_{k=m}^{\infty} \frac{1}{n_k^2} < C \frac{1}{n_m^2}, \qquad (65.6)$$

where $C$ is a constant. But then, supposing $n_0 = 0$, we find from (65.5) and (65.6) that

$$\sum_{k=1}^{p} \frac{1}{n_k^2} \sum_{m=0}^{n_k} v_m < C \sum_{k=1}^{p} (v_{n_{k-1}+1} + \cdots + v_{n_k}) \frac{1}{n_k^2}.$$

Finally, it is clear from the definition of $v_m$ that

$$v_{n_{k-1}+1} + \cdots + v_{n_k} < n_k^2 \sum_{n_{k-1}+1}^{n_k} (a_m^2 + b_m^2) \qquad (65.7)$$

$$\sum_{k=1}^{p} \frac{1}{n_k^2} \sum_{m=0}^{n_k} v_m < c \sum_{k=1}^{p} \sum_{n_{k-1}+1}^{n_k} (a_m^2 + b_m^2) = c \sum_{m=1}^{n_p} (a_m^2 + b_m^2) \leqslant c \int_{-\pi}^{\pi} f^2(x)\,dx$$

for any $p$. Hence the convergence of the series on the right-hand side of (65.4) follows and this concludes the proof of the theorem.

COROLLARY 2. From the statement just, proved, Kolmogorov's[6] theorem follows. *If* $\{n_k\}$ *is a lacunary sequence and* $f(x) \in L^2$, *then*

$$S_{n_k}(x) \to f(x) \textit{ almost everywhere.}$$

## 66. Smooth functions

For the further investigation of the series which we considered in § 64 and also in many other problems, it will be useful to understand the concept of a smooth function.

DEFINITION. The function $F(x)$ is said to be *smooth at the point* $x$, if

$$\frac{F(x+h) + F(x-h) - 2F(x)}{h} \to 0 \quad \text{as} \quad h \to 0. \qquad (66.1)$$

Defining for brevity's sake

$$\Delta_h^2 F = F(x+h) + F(x-h) - 2F(x),$$

we can say that the smoothness of $F(x)$ is characterized by the equality

$$\Delta_h^2 F = o(h).$$

If equality (66.1) is fulfilled uniformly relative to $x$ for some interval $[a, b]$, then we say that $F(x)$ is *uniformly smooth* in this interval.

The word "smooth" is evidently introduced to represent the following idea: if $F(x)$ is smooth at some point, then this point cannot be angular. Indeed, if $\Delta_h^2 F = o(h)$ at the point $x$, then

$$\frac{F(x+h)+F(x-h)-2F(x)}{h} = \frac{F(x+h)-F(x)}{h} - \frac{F(x-h)-F(x)}{-h}$$
$$= o(1),$$

i.e. if a derivative exists on the right of the point $x$, then a derivative also exists on the left and they should be equal to one another. Moreover, if $F(x)$ is smooth at some point, then at the same point

$$D^+F = D^-F = \overline{D}F \quad \text{and} \quad D_+F = D_-F = \underline{D}F,$$

where $D^+F$ and $D^-F$ denote the upper right and upper left derivatives and $\overline{D}F$ the upper derivative (when they are equal); similar notation is used for the lower derivatives.

We note that if $f(x)$ is continuous at the point $x$ or only "symmetrically continuous," i.e.

$$f(x_0+h) - f(x_0-h) \to 0 \quad \text{as} \quad h \to 0,$$

then the primitive $F(x)$ of $f(x)$ satisfies the condition of smoothness at this point, since

$$F(x_0+h) + F(x_0-h) - 2F(x_0) = \int_0^h [f(x_0+t) - f(x_0-t)]\,dt = o(h)$$

as $h \to 0$.

However, smooth functions, in spite of their name, should not necessarily possess a derivative almost everywhere; moreover, they can be devoid of a derivative almost everywhere, as we will see later (see Chapter XI, § 4). However, the following theorem holds:

THEOREM 1. *If $F(x)$ is continuous and smooth in some interval $(a, b)$, then it possesses a derivative $F'(x)$ in a set $E$ of the power of the continuum in any interval $(\alpha, \beta)$ lying within $(a, b)$.*

To prove this we first note that if the function $F(x)$ possesses a maximum or minimum at some point $x_0$ within the interval $[a, b]$, then $F'(x_0)$ exists and equals zero. In fact, we have

$$\frac{F(x_0+h)+F(x_0-h)-2F(x_0)}{h} = \frac{F(x_0+h)-F(x_0)}{h} + \frac{F(x_0-h)-F(x_0)}{h}. \tag{66.2}$$

But at the maximum (or minimum) point neither terms on the right-hand side of (66.2) are positive for sufficiently small $h > 0$ (or correspondingly negative). Therefore since their sum tends to zero, it follows that each of them tends to zero, and then $F'(x_0)$ exists and equals zero.

Now let $[\alpha, \beta]$ be any interval within $(a, b)$ and $L(x) = mx + n$ be a linear function coinciding with $F(x)$ at $x = \alpha$ and $x = \beta$. The difference $g(x) = F(x) - L(x)$ is a smooth function returning to zero at the end points $\alpha$ and $\beta$. This means that $g(x)$

has an absolute maximum or minimum at some point $x_0$ inside $(\alpha, \beta)$. Therefore, $g'(x_0) = 0$, which means that $F'(x_0)$ exists and equals $m$. Hence, in particular, it follows that for continuous and smooth functions the first mean value theorem holds, i.e.

$$F(b) - F(a) = (b - a)F'(\xi), \quad a < \xi < b.$$

We have proved that in any $[\alpha, \beta]$ within $(a, b)$ there are points where $F'(x)$ exists. But it can be proved moreover that the set of these points is of the power of the continuum. Indeed, let $\gamma$ be given such that $\alpha < \gamma < \beta$. A point $x_0$ is found in $(\alpha, \gamma)$ where $F'(x)$ exists and equals the tangent of the angle of inclination of the chord connecting the points $(\alpha, F(\alpha))$ and $(\gamma, F(\gamma))$. If the inclinations corresponding to different $\gamma$ are different, then the corresponding points $x_0$ are also different. But if the curve $y = F(x)$ is not a rectilinear interval in $(\alpha, \beta)$ (if this were the case the theorem has already been proved), then the magnitudes of the tangents of these slopes form the interval, i.e. their set is of the power of the continuum and therefore the points of differentiability of $F(x)$ belong to a set with power of continuum in the whole interval. The theorem is proved.

We will now give a definition for later use.

DEFINITION. We say that *the function $f(x)$ possesses the property $D$ in some set $E$*, if for any two $\alpha \in E$ and $\beta \in E$ and for any number $C$, contained between $f(\alpha)$ and $f(\beta)$, a point $\gamma \in E$ is found lying between $\alpha$ and $\beta$ such that $f(\gamma) = C$.

The letter $D$ is derived from Darboux's name, since he noticed that this property was possessed not only by functions continuous in some interval but also by some discontinuous functions; in particular, if $f(x)$ is an exact derivative, i.e. if $F(x)$ exists such that $f(x) = F'(x)$ at every point of some interval, then it possesses property $D$ in that interval.

Let us prove a theorem.

THEOREM 2. *If $F(x)$ is continuous and smooth in some interval $(a, b)$, then its derivative $F'(x)$ possesses property $D$ in the set $E$ of all the points where it exists.*

This set $E$, as we can see from Theorem 1, is not only not empty but is of the power of the continuum in every interval $[\alpha, \beta]$ within $(a, b)$.

Let $\alpha \in E$, $\beta \in E$

$$A = F'(\alpha), \quad B = F'(\beta)$$

and let $C$ be contained between $A$ and $B$; for example, let us define $A < C < B$. We should prove the existence of $x_0$, $\alpha < x_0 < \beta$, $x_0 \in E$, such that $F'(x_0) = C$. If we subtract $Cx$ from $F(x)$ then it is possible to assume $C = 0$, and then $A < 0 < B$.

Let us suppose for a fixed $h$ that

$$g(x) = \frac{F(x + h) - F(x)}{h}.$$

We choose $h$ such that $0 < h < b - \beta$ and moreover we suppose its range to be so small that

$$g(\alpha) < 0, \quad g(\beta) > 0, \quad \frac{F(\beta) - F(\beta - h)}{h} > 0.$$

Since $g(x)$ is continuous in $[\alpha, \beta]$, then in this interval $[\alpha, \beta]$ there are points where it becomes zero. Let $\gamma$ be the furthest left of these points. From

$$g(\gamma) = \frac{F(\gamma + h) - F(\gamma)}{h} = 0$$

it follows that $F(\gamma + h) = F(\gamma)$. If $x_0$ is a point in $(\gamma, \gamma + h)$, where $F(x)$ reaches a maximum or minimum, then $F'(x_0) = 0 = C$. But since

$$g(\alpha) < 0 \quad \text{and} \quad g(\beta - h) = \frac{F(\beta) - F(\beta - h)}{h} > 0$$

because of the given choice of $h$, then

$$\alpha < \gamma < \beta - h$$

which means that $(\gamma, \gamma + h)$ lies inside $[\alpha, \beta]$, therefore $x_0$ is also inside $[\alpha, \beta]$. Moreover, since $F'(x_0)$ exists, then $x_0 \in E$. Thus we have found a point $x_0 \in E$, where $F'(x_0) = C$, and the proof is concluded.

We will apply the results obtained to the investigation of the behaviour of the sum of the trigonometric series considered in § 64. First we will prove this theorem:

THEOREM 3. *If the coefficients of the series*

$$\frac{a_0}{2} + \sum (a_n \cos nx + b_n \sin nx) \tag{66.3}$$

*satisfy the condition*

$$\tau(n) = \sum_{k=1}^{n} k(|a_k| + |b_k|) = o(n), \tag{66.4}$$

*then the sum of the integrated series*

$$F(x) = \frac{a_0}{2} x + C - \sum_{n=1}^{\infty} \frac{b_n \cos nx - a_n \sin nx}{n} \tag{66.5}$$

*is a function which is continuous and uniformly smooth in* $[0, 2\pi]$. *The series* (66.3) *converges at those points and only at those points where* $F'(x)$ *exists and besides, if* $N = [1/h]$ *then the equality*

$$\frac{F(x + h) - F(x - h)}{2h} - \left[\frac{a_0}{2} + \sum_{k=1}^{N} (a_k \cos kx + b_k \sin kx)\right] \to 0 \quad as \quad h \to 0 \tag{66.5}$$

*occurs uniformly relative to* $x$ *in* $[0, 2\pi]$.

In order to be able to speak correctly of the sum of an integrated series, it must be proved that it converges. But because

$$|a_k| + |b_k| = \frac{\tau(k) - \tau(k - 1)}{k} \quad (k = 1, 2, \ldots),$$

then the series (66.5) is majorized by the series

$$\sum_{k=1}^{\infty} \frac{|a_k| + |b_k|}{k} = \sum_{k=1}^{\infty} \frac{\tau(k) - \tau(k-1)}{k^2} \leqslant \sum_{k=1}^{\infty} \tau(k) \left(\frac{1}{k^2} - \frac{1}{(k+1)^2}\right)$$

$$= o\left(\sum_{k=1}^{\infty} \frac{1}{k^2}\right) < +\infty$$

(we applied Abel's transformation here). Hence it is clear that series (66.5) converges absolutely and uniformly. Let $F(x)$ be its sum, therefore, it is continuous in $[0, 2\pi]$.

Now in order to prove the theorem we suppose

$$A_k = a_k \cos kx + b_k \sin kx, \quad B_k = b_k \cos kx - a_k \sin kx.$$

Then

$$\frac{F(x+h) - F(x-h)}{2h} - S_N(x) = \sum_{k=1}^{N} A_k \left(\frac{\sin kh}{kh} - 1\right) + \sum_{k=N+1}^{\infty} A_k \frac{\sin kh}{kh}$$

$$= P + Q.$$

Since in the neighbourhood of the point $u = 0$, we have

$$\left|\frac{\sin u}{u} - 1\right| = O(u^2) < C|u|,$$

then

$$|P| < C|h| \sum_{k=1}^{N} (|a_k| + |b_k|)\, k \leqslant C \frac{1}{N} \tau(N) = o(1),$$

$$|Q| \leqslant \frac{1}{|h|} \sum_{k=N+1}^{\infty} \frac{|a_k| + |b_k|}{k} \leqslant \frac{1}{|h|} \sum_{k=N+1}^{\infty} \tau_k \left(\frac{1}{k^2} - \frac{1}{(k+1)^2}\right)$$

$$= \frac{1}{|h|} \sum_{k=N+1}^{\infty} o\left(\frac{1}{k^2}\right) = \frac{1}{|h|} o\left(\frac{1}{N}\right) = o(1)$$

and thus (66.2) is actually fulfilled, and moreover uniformly relative to $x$ in $[0, 2\pi]$.

Similarly we have

$$\frac{F(x+2h) + F(x-2h) - 2F(x)}{4h} = \sum_{k=1}^{\infty} B_k \frac{\sin^2 kh}{kh}$$

$$= \sum_{k=1}^{N} B_k \frac{\sin^2 kh}{kh} + \sum_{k=N+1}^{\infty} B_k \frac{\sin^2 kh}{kh}$$

$$= P_1 + Q_1.$$

Since $|\sin u| \leqslant |u|$, then

$$|P_1| \leqslant |h| \sum_{k=1}^{N} |B_k|\, k \leqslant |h| \sum_{k=1}^{N} (|a_k| + |b_k|)\, k = |h|\, \tau_N = o(1),$$

$$|Q_1| \leqslant \frac{1}{|h|} \sum_{k=N+1}^{\infty} \frac{|a_k| + |b_k|}{k} = o(1),$$

as we have already seen in estimating $Q$; therefore

$$F(x + 2h) + F(x - 2h) - 2F(x) = o(h),$$

i.e. $F(x)$ is uniformly smooth in $[0, 2\pi]$.

Finally, from (66.6) it is clear that series (66.3) converges at those points and only at those points where a symmetrical derivative of $F(x)$ exists, i.e.

$$\lim_{h \to 0} \frac{F(x + h) - F(x - h)}{2h}$$

and the sum $S(x)$ of this series equals its symmetrical derivative.

But since for smooth functions where a symmetrical derivative exists, the normal derivative also exists, then the latter part of the theorem is proved.

*Note.* The proved theorem is valid for lacunary series with coefficients tending to zero, since for them the conditions of Theorem 3 (see § 65) are fulfilled.

COROLLARY 1. *If for a trigonometric series the conditions of Theorem 3 are fulfilled, then the series converges in a set of the power of the continuum in any interval* $(a, b) \in [0, 2\pi]$ *and its sum* $S(x)$ *possesses property D in a set of those points where it exists.*

In particular, this property is possessed by any lacunary series, provided its coefficients tend to zero.

Indeed, by virtue of Theorem 3 $S(x)$ exists where and only where $F'(x)$ exists for a smooth function $F(x)$ defined by equality (66.5) and moreover $S(x) = F'(x)$; then, reference must be made to Theorem 2 and the proof is concluded.

COROLLARY 2. *If the coefficients of a trigonometric series satisfy the conditions of Theorem 3, then its sum cannot have points of discontinuity of the first kind.*

Indeed, in the neighbourhood of a point of discontinuity property $D$ would not be fulfilled.

For the case when the coefficients satisfy a stronger requirement

$$a_n = o\left(\frac{1}{n}\right), \quad b_n = o\left(\frac{1}{n}\right), \tag{66.7}$$

we have already obtained a similar result (see § 42).

*Note 1.* From Theorem 3 it is possible to obtain a new proof of Fatou's theorem (see § 64) that *a series with coefficients satisfying* (66.7) *converges almost everywhere.* Indeed, since from (66.7) it follows that $\sum (a_n^2 + b_n^2) < +\infty$, then the series $F(x)$ is a Fourier series. Therefore the sum $F(x)$ of an integrated series is an absolutely continuous function (see § 40) and therefore, $F'(x)$ exists almost everywhere. Then due to Theorem 3, the series (66.3) converges almost everywhere.

*Note 2.* If condition (66.4) only is fulfilled and not condition (66.7), then series (66.3) can even diverge almost everywhere. We meet examples of this kind in § 3 of Chapter XI.

## § 67. The Schwarz second derivative

The concept of a smooth function studied by us in § 66 will play a great part in later work; but before turning to its application, we must first introduce yet another new concept.

DEFINITION. Let the function $F(x)$ be defined in some neighbourhood of the point $x$; if the limit of the expression

$$\frac{F(x+h)+F(x-h)-2F(x)}{h^2} \tag{67.1}$$

exists as $h \to 0$, then it is said that $F(x)$ possesses at the point $x$ *a Schwarz second derivative* and we write

$$D^2 F(x) = \lim_{h\to 0} \frac{F(x+h)+F(x-h)-2F(x)}{h^2}. \tag{67.2}$$

If the relation (67.1) does not tend to a limit as $h \to 0$, then the values

$$\overline{D}^2 F(x) = \overline{\lim_{h\to 0}} \frac{F(x+h)+F(x-h)-2F(x)}{h^2}$$

and

$$\underline{D}^2 F(x) = \underline{\lim_{h\to 0}} \frac{F(x+h)+F(x-h)-2F(x)}{h^2}$$

are called respectively *the upper and lower Schwarz derivatives at the point x*.

We will show that if $F(x)$ possesses a normal second derivative $F''(x)$ at the point $x$, then $D^2 F(x)$ exists and

$$D^2 F(x) = F''(x). \tag{67.3}$$

Indeed, if $F''(x)$ exists at the point $x$, then $F'(x)$ is continuous at the point $x$ and therefore $F'(x)$ is bounded in the neighbourhood of the point $x$. It is clear that

$$\Delta_h^2 F = F(x+h)+F(x-h)-2F(x) = \int_0^h [F'(x+t)-F'(x-t)]dt. \tag{67.4}$$

Hence

$$\left|\frac{\Delta_h^2 F}{h^2} - F''(x)\right| = \left|\int_0^h \frac{2t}{h^2}\left[\frac{F'(x+t)-F'(x-t)}{2t} - F''(x)\right] dt\right|$$

$$\leqslant \max_{t\in(0,h)} \left|\frac{F'(x+t)-F'(x-t)}{2t} - F''(x)\right| \to 0 \quad \text{as} \quad h \to 0,$$

i.e. (67.3) is proved.

On the other hand it is clear that $D^2 F(x)$ can exist without $F''(x)$ existing; for example, if $F(x)$ is a continuous odd function, then at the point $x = 0$ we have

$$F(x+h)+F(x-h)-2F(x) = F(h)+F(-h) = 0$$

for all $h$, which means that $D^2 F = 0$ at $x = 0$, whilst $F''(0)$ cannot exist, if we only require that $F(x)$ be continuous and odd.

Thus, the Schwarz second derivative is a direct generalization of the normal second derivative.

We now note that, as in the case of the normal second derivative, we have: if $x$ is a maximum point and $D^2 F(x)$ exists at it, then $D^2 F(x) \leqslant 0$ and at a minimum

$D^2 F(x) \geqslant 0$. This follows from the fact that $\Delta_h{}^2 F(x) \leqslant 0$ for sufficiently small $h$ at the maximum point and $\Delta_h{}^2 F(x) \geqslant 0$ at the minimum point.

The analogy continues still further. Thus the following theorem holds.

THEOREM. *If $F(x)$ is continuous in $[a, b]$ and $D^2 F(x) \equiv 0$ in $a < x < b$, then $F(x)$ is linear in this interval.*

In order to prove this, take any $\varepsilon > 0$ and consider an auxiliary function

$$\varphi(x) = F(x) - F(a) - \frac{F(b) - F(a)}{b - a}(x - a) + \varepsilon(x - a)(x - b).$$

It is clear that $\varphi(a) = \varphi(b) = 0$. We will prove that it cannot assume positive values in $[a, b]$. Indeed, if this were the case, then because of the continuity of $\varphi(x)$ it would attain its maximum somewhere within $[a, b]$, i.e. a point $x_0$ would be found in this interval, where it would be known that $D^2\varphi(x_0) \leqslant 0$. But, on the other hand,

$$D^2\varphi(x_0) = D^2 F(x_0) + 2\varepsilon,$$

since the Schwarz second derivative of the sum equals the sum of the Schwarz second derivatives, and the term $\varepsilon(x - a)(x - b)$ has the normal second derivative equal to $2\varepsilon$, which means that the Schwarz second derivative has exactly the same magnitude.

But $D^2\varphi(x_0) \leqslant 0$, $D^2 F(x_0) = 0$, and we obtain $\varepsilon \leqslant 0$ which contradicts the choice of $\varepsilon$.

Thus $\varphi(x) \leqslant 0$ everywhere in $[a, b]$, i.e.

$$F(x) - F(a) - \frac{F(b) - F(a)}{b - a}(x - a) \leqslant \varepsilon(x - a)(b - x) \leqslant \varepsilon(b - a)^2.$$

If we were to put a minus sign in front of $\varepsilon$ in the expression for $\varphi(x)$, we would prove in exactly the same way that $\varphi(x) \geqslant 0$ everywhere, i.e.

$$F(x) - F(a) - \frac{F(b) - F(a)}{b - a}(x - a) \geqslant -\varepsilon(x - a)(b - x) \geqslant -\varepsilon(b - a)^2.$$

Therefore

$$\left| F(x) - F(a) - \frac{F(b) - F(a)}{b - a}(x - a) \right| \leqslant \varepsilon(b - a)^2. \tag{67.5}$$

But $\varepsilon$ is quite arbitrary, therefore the left-hand side of the inequality (67.5) should be equal to zero, whence

$$F(x) = F(a) + \frac{F(b) - F(a)}{b - a}(x - a),$$

which means that $F(x)$ is linear. The theorem has been proved.

We will now apply the concept of the Schwarz second derivative to a method of summation of trigonometric series.

## § 68. Riemann's method of summation

Let us consider the trigonometric series

$$\frac{a_0}{2} + \sum_{n=1}^{\infty} (a_n \cos nx + b_n \sin nx), \tag{68.1}$$

the coefficients of which tend to zero (or are only bounded). Then, integrating it twice term-by-term, we obtain

$$\frac{a_0}{4} x^2 + Cx + D - \sum_{n=1}^{\infty} \frac{a_n \cos nx + b_n \sin nx}{n^2}.$$

It is clear that this series converges absolutely and uniformly (because $a_n$ and $b_n$ are bounded); let us denote its sum by $F(x)$. It is a continuous function which we will name the *Riemann function* for the trigonometric series (68.1). Thus

$$F(x) = \frac{a_0}{4} x^2 + Cx + D - \sum_{n=1}^{\infty} \frac{a_n \cos nx + b_n \sin nx}{n^2}. \tag{68.2}$$

We assume that at some point $x_0$ the function $F(x)$ possesses a Schwarz derivative $D^2 F(x_0)$. Then we can say that *the series* (68.1) *is summable at the point* $x_0$ *by Riemann's method* and its Riemann sum equals $D^2 F(x_0)$.

In order to verify this statement, we will prove Riemann's theorem:

THEOREM 1. *If a trigonometric series with coefficients tending to zero converges at a point* $x_0$ *to a value* $S$*, then it is summable at this point by Riemann's method to the same value* $S$.

To prove this, we note first of all that it immediately follows from formula (68.2) after elementary trigonometric transformations that

$$\frac{F(x_0 + 2h) + F(x_0 - 2h) - 2F(x_0)}{4h^2}$$

$$= \frac{a_0}{2} + \sum_{n=1}^{\infty} (a_n \cos nx_0 + b_n \sin nx_0) \left(\frac{\sin nh}{nh}\right)^2. \tag{68.3}$$

For brevity's sake we assume

$$A_0 = \frac{a_0}{2}, \quad A_n = a_n \cos nx_0 + b_n \sin nx_0.$$

From formula (68.3) it is immediately evident that for the summability of series (68.1) by Riemann's method at the point $x_0$ to a value $S$ it is necessary and sufficient that

$$\lim_{h \to 0} \left[ A_0 + \sum_{n=1}^{\infty} A_n \left(\frac{\sin nh}{nh}\right)^2 \right] = S.$$

Thus, Theorem 1 will only be proved when we prove Theorem 2:

THEOREM 2. *Let the series* $A_0 + \sum_{n=1}^{\infty} A_n$ *converge and S be its sum; then*

$$\lim_{h\to 0}\left[A_0 + \sum_{n=1}^{\infty} A_n \left(\frac{\sin nh}{nh}\right)^2\right] = S. \tag{68.4}$$

We will now prove this latter assertion. Let us suppose

$$R_n = \sum_{k=n+1}^{\infty} A_k.$$

From the convergence of the series $\sum A_n$ it follows that for any $\varepsilon > 0$ it is possible to find $N$ such that

$$|R_n| < \varepsilon \quad \text{at} \quad n \geqslant N. \tag{68.5}$$

We now write

$$A_0 + \sum_{n=1}^{\infty} A_n \left(\frac{\sin nh}{nh}\right)^2 = A_0 + \sum_{n=1}^{N} A_n \left(\frac{\sin nh}{nh}\right)^2 + \sum_{N+1}^{\infty} A_n \left(\frac{\sin nh}{nh}\right)^2. \tag{68.6}$$

If $n$ is fixed and $h \to 0$, then $\dfrac{\sin nh}{nh} \to 1$, and therefore for sufficiently small $h$

$$\left| A_0 + \sum_{n=1}^{N} A_n \left(\frac{\sin nh}{nh}\right)^2 - (A_0 + A_1 + \cdots + A_N) \right| < \varepsilon. \tag{68.7}$$

Moreover,

$$\left| S - \sum_{k=0}^{N} A_k \right| = |R_N| < \varepsilon \tag{68.8}$$

due to (68.5), and therefore from (68.7) and (68.8)

$$\left| A_0 + \sum_{n=1}^{\infty} A_n \left(\frac{\sin nh}{nh}\right)^2 - S \right| < 2\varepsilon, \tag{68.9}$$

if only $h$ becomes sufficiently small.

Thus in order to prove (68.4) it is sufficient to prove that the last term on the right-hand side of formula (68.6) can be made as small as desired as $h \to 0$. But we have $A_n = R_{n-1} - R_n$, which means that

$$\sum_{N+1}^{\infty} A_n \left(\frac{\sin nh}{nh}\right)^2 = \sum_{N+1}^{\infty} (R_{n-1} - R_n) \left(\frac{\sin nh}{nh}\right)^2$$

$$= R_N \left(\frac{\sin(N+1)h}{(N+1)\,h}\right)^2 - \sum_{N+1}^{\infty} R_n \left[\left(\frac{\sin nh}{nh}\right)^2 - \left(\frac{\sin(n+1)h}{(n+1)h}\right)^2\right] \tag{68.10}$$

(Abel's transformation used here is valid, since as $n \to \infty$ and $h$ being any value

$R_n \left(\frac{\sin nh}{nh}\right)^2 \to 0$). But by virtue of (68.5) we obtain from (68.10)

$$\left|\sum_{N+1}^{\infty} A_n \left(\frac{\sin nh}{nh}\right)^2\right| \leqslant \varepsilon + \varepsilon \sum_{N+1}^{\infty} \left|\left(\frac{\sin nh}{nh}\right)^2 - \left(\frac{\sin (n+1)h}{(n+1)h}\right)^2\right|$$

$$= \varepsilon + \varepsilon \sum_{N+1}^{\infty} \left| \int_{nh}^{(n+1)h} \frac{d}{dt}\left(\frac{\sin t}{t}\right)^2 dt \right|$$

$$\leqslant \varepsilon + \varepsilon \int_{(N+1)h}^{\infty} \left|\frac{d}{dt}\left(\frac{\sin t}{t}\right)^2\right| dt < \varepsilon + \varepsilon \int_0^{\infty} \left|\frac{d}{dt}\left(\frac{\sin t}{t}\right)^2\right| dt \tag{68.11}$$

and it remains to prove that the last integral is finite, then the whole of the right-hand side of (68.11) is less than $C\varepsilon$, where $C$ is a constant, and since this is true for any $h$, then it is also true as $h \to 0$. Since

$$\frac{d}{dt}\left(\frac{\sin t}{t}\right)^2 = 2\,\frac{\sin t}{t}\,\frac{t\cos t - \sin t}{t^2},$$

then in the neighbourhood of $t = 0$ the function under the integral sign is bounded, moreover, as $t \to \infty$ we have

$$\left|\frac{d}{dt}\left(\frac{\sin t}{t}\right)^2\right| < 2\,\frac{t+1}{t^3} = O\left(\frac{1}{t^2}\right),$$

and therefore the integral in formula (68.11) does indeed have meaning and the proof is concluded.

*Note.* In the proof of Theorem 2, we considered the series $\sum_{n=0}^{\infty} A_n$ to be a numerical series, without being concerned with the fact that it was obtained from a given trigonometric series. It can be said in general that *the numerical series $\sum_{n=0}^{\infty} u_n$ is summable by Riemann's method to the value S, if*

$$\lim_{h\to 0}\left[u_0 + \sum_{n=1}^{\infty} u_n \left(\frac{\sin nh}{nh}\right)^2\right] = S.$$

In this case Theorem 2 is a statement that *Riemann's method is regular.*

Now it must be said that *the functional series $\sum u_n(x)$ is summable by Riemann's method uniformly to $S(x)$ in the set E, if*

$$\lim_{n\to\infty}\left[u_0(x) + \sum_{n=1}^{\infty} u_n(x)\left(\frac{\sin nh}{nh}\right)^2\right] = S(x)$$

*uniformly relative to x in E.*

From the proof of Theorem 2 it is immediately evident that the uniform convergence of $\sum u_n(x)$ in $E$ to $S(x)$ implies its uniform summability by Riemann's method to $S(x)$ in $E$.

This note will be used essentially in § 71.

We will now return to the study of the Riemann function $F(x)$ and will prove yet another theorem due to Riemann.

THEOREM 3. *If the coefficients of a trigonometric series tend to zero, then its Riemann function is uniformly smooth in* $[-\pi, \pi]$.

This theorem follows quite quickly from the results of § 66. Indeed, if we integrate the series

$$\frac{a_0}{2} + \sum (a_n \cos nx + b_n \sin nx), \tag{68.12}$$

where $a_n \to 0,\ b_n \to 0$, then we obtain a series with coefficients of order $o(1/n)$

$$\frac{a_0}{2} x + C - \sum \frac{b_n \cos nx - a_n \sin nx}{n}. \tag{68.13}$$

Integrating the series (68.13), we obtain according to the theorem of § 66 a series, the sum of which should be uniformly smooth. But this sum $F(x)$ is the sum of a series obtained by the double successive integration of (68.12), and therefore it is also the Riemann function for the series (68.12) and the theorem is proved.

We will use this theorem in § 70 but first we will consider the application of Riemann's method to Fourier series.

## § 69. Application of Riemann's method of summation to Fourier series

Riemann's method, as well as the methods of Fejér and Abel–Poisson, when applied to Fourier series, gives the following result:

THEOREM. *The Fourier series for any summable function $f(x)$ is summable by Riemann's method almost everywhere to this function.*

Indeed, let

$$f(x) \sim \frac{a_0}{2} + \sum_{n=1}^{\infty} (a_n \cos nx + b_n \sin nx). \tag{69.1}$$

We have $a_n \to 0$ and $b_n \to 0$, since these are Fourier coefficients. According to the theorem of § 40, the Fourier series can be integrated term by term; in other words, if

$$F(x) = \int_{-\pi}^{x} f(t)\, dt,$$

then

$$F(x) = C + \frac{a_0}{2} x - \sum_{n=1}^{\infty} \frac{b_n \cos nx - a_n \sin nx}{n}, \tag{69.2}$$

whilst because of the absolute continuity of $F(x)$ the series (69.2) converges everywhere to it and even uniformly in $[-\pi, \pi]$. Moreover, if $\Phi(x)$ is an indefinite integral of $F(x)$, then

$$\Phi(x) = \frac{a_0}{4} x^2 + Cx + D - \sum_{n=1}^{\infty} \frac{a_n \cos nx + b_n \sin nx}{n^2}$$

and therefore the Riemann function $\Phi(x)$ for the series (69.1) is the result of the double successive integration of $f(x)$. But since $F(x)$ is continuous, then $\Phi'(x) = F(x)$ at every point; moreover $F'(x) = f(x)$ almost everywhere; thus $\Phi''(x) = f(x)$ almost everywhere but since $D^2\Phi(x) = \Phi''(x)$ then, where $\Phi''(x)$ exists (§ 67), $D^2\Phi(x) = f(x)$ almost everywhere, and therefore the series (69.1) is summable almost everywhere to $f(x)$ by Riemann's method.

The theorem is proved.

We now begin to apply Riemann's method to general trigonometric series and especially to the very important question of the uniqueness of the expansion of a function into a trigonometric series.

## § 70. Cantor's theorem of uniqueness

Using Riemann's method of summation, we can answer the following important question; can two different trigonometric series exist which converge at every point to the same function $f(x)$? The answer to this question is in the negative. In order to prove this, we first prove the following important theorem:

CANTOR'S[1] THEOREM. *If the trigonometric series*

$$\frac{a_0}{2} + \sum (a_n \cos nx + b_n \sin nx) \tag{70.1}$$

*converges to zero at every point x of* $[0, 2\pi]$, *then all its coefficients equal zero.*

According to Cantor's Theorem, the coefficients of the series (70.1) tend to zero (this follows not from the Cantor–Lebesgue theorem, but from Cantor's own theorem — see § 62, note). If we construct the Riemann function $F(x)$ for series (70.1), it is continuous along the whole infinite straight line. According to the theorem in § 68, the series (70.1) should be summable to zero at every point, i.e.

$$D^2F(x) = 0 \quad -\pi \leqslant x \leqslant \pi.$$

Then according to the theorem of § 67 we have

$$F(x) = Ax + B. \tag{70.2}$$

But on the other hand since $F(x)$ is the Riemann function for the series (70.1), then

$$F(x) = \frac{a_0}{4}x^2 + Cx + D - \sum_{n=1}^{\infty} \frac{a_n \cos nx + b_n \sin nx}{n^2}. \tag{70.3}$$

From (70.2) and (70.3) we obtain

$$\frac{a_0}{4}x^2 + A_1 x + B_1 = \sum_{n=1}^{\infty} \frac{a_n \cos nx + b_n \sin nx}{n^2}, \tag{70.4}$$

where $A_1$ and $B_1$ are new constants. But the right-hand side of (70.4) has a period $2\pi$, which means that the same applies to the left-hand side and this is possible only for

$$a_0 = 0 \quad \text{and} \quad A_1 = 0. \tag{70.5}$$

We now have

$$B_1 = \sum_{n=1}^{\infty} \frac{a_n \cos nx + b_n \sin nx}{n^2}. \tag{70.6}$$

Series (70.6) converges uniformly; therefore (see § 12) its coefficients are the Fourier coefficients for its sum, but that is a constant number $B_1$ and therefore

$$\frac{a_n}{n^2} = \frac{b_n}{n^2} = 0 \quad (n = 1, 2, \ldots),$$

whence

$$a_n = b_n = 0 \quad (n = 1, 2, \ldots). \tag{70.7}$$

From (70.5) and (70.7) it follows that series (70.6) has all its coefficients equal to zero and thus Cantor's theorem is proved. He immediately generalized this theorem, by proving the following statement:

*If a trigonometric series converges to zero everywhere apart, perhaps, from a finite number of points, then all its coefficients equal zero.*

In fact, arguing in exactly the same way as in the proof of the preceding theorem, we see that the series under consideration has coefficients tending to zero and its Riemann function $F(x)$ should be linear in every interval where the series converges to zero, since then $D^2 F(x) \equiv 0$. But $F(x)$ should be smooth by virtue of Theorem 3 of § 68. Therefore it cannot possess angular points. Consequently it cannot consist of different rectilinear intervals and should be simply linear. But if this is so, then the proof is concluded as in the previous theorem, i.e. we prove that all the coefficients of the series equal zero.

*Note.* Cantor's theorem can be expressed in the following more general form: *if a trigonometric series with coefficients tending to zero is summable to zero by Riemann's method everywhere apart, perhaps, from a finite number of points, then all its coefficients equal zero.*

Indeed, in proving the theorem we only use the facts that the coefficients of the series tend to zero and $D^2 F(x) = 0$ everywhere apart, perhaps, from a finite number of points.

COROLLARY. *Let $f(x)$ be a function with period $2\pi$, which is finite at every point of* $[0, 2\pi]$. *Then, there do not exist two different trigonometric series, each of which converges to $f(x)$ everywhere in* $[0, 2\pi]$ *apart, perhaps, from a finite number of points.*

Indeed, we will suppose that two such trigonometric series do exist; then their difference would be the series

$$\frac{a_0}{2} + \sum_{n=1}^{\infty} (a_n \cos nx + b_n \sin nx), \tag{70.8}$$

in which not all the coefficients equal zero, but it converges to zero everywhere apart, perhaps, from a finite number of points. However, we have already seen that this is impossible.

Here, it is true, the requirement of convergence can be replaced by summability by the Riemann method (but in this case it is previously required that the coefficients tend to zero).

The theorem on the uniqueness of the expansion of a function into a trigonometric series permits considerable generalizations. We will devote Chapter XIV to this problem; here we will confine ourselves to formulating the most important results. For this purpose we introduce a definition.

DEFINITION. The set $E$, lying in $[-\pi, \pi]$, is known as *an M-set*, if there exists a trigonometric series

$$\frac{a_0}{2} + \sum_{n=1}^{\infty} (a_n \cos nx + b_n \sin nx),$$

in which not all the coefficients equal zero and which converges to zero everywhere in $[-\pi, \pi]$ outside the set $E$.

*If the set E is not an M-set, then we call it a U-set*†.

Using this definition, we can now formulate the two preceding theorems thus; *if E is an empty or finite set, then it is a U-set.*

Cantor himself proved that any reducible set (i.e. one for which the derived set is finite or denumerable) is again a $U$-set. Subsequently, Young[1] proved that any denumerable set is a $U$-set (see § 5, Chapter XIV).

On the other hand, it is easily proved that *any set* $E$, $mE > 0$, *is an M-set.* In fact let us take a perfect set $P \in E$, $mP > 0$, and suppose that $f(x) = 1$ in $P$ and $f(x) = 0$ outside $P$. From the principle of localization (see § 33) the series $\sigma(f)$ converges to zero in every interval adjoining $P$ and therefore everywhere outside $E$. Thus there exists a trigonometric series convergent to zero everywhere outside $P$ but with coefficients differing from zero (for example

$$a_0 = \frac{1}{\pi} \int_0^{2\pi} f(x)\, dx = \frac{1}{\pi} mP).$$

Consequently, $E$ is an $M$-set.

For a long time it was supposed that, on the contrary, any set of measure zero (not only finite and denumerable) should be a $U$-set. This hypothesis was refuted by Men'shov[11], who set up the first example of a perfect $M$-set of measure zero (see the proof in § 12, Chapter XIV).

## § 71. Riemann's principle of localization for general trigonometric series

The function $F(x)$ introduced by Riemann plays an important role not only in the question of the uniqueness of the expansion of a function into a trigonometric series but also in the examination of its convergence or divergence.

We recall that the following theorem was proved for Fourier series (see § 33): the convergence or divergence of a series $\sigma(f)$ at a point $x$ depends only on the behaviour of the function $f(x)$ in the neighbourhood of the point $x$.

We will now suppose that we are concerned with an arbitrary trigonometric series, not a Fourier series. It seems that it is then possible to judge its convergence by

† From the definition, it immediately follows that any part of a $U$-set is a $U$-set: on the other hand, a set containing an $M$-set is itself an $M$-set.

studying its Riemann function. Thus we have a theorem, analogous to the preceding theorem, which can be expressed in this form:

*For any trigonometric series with coefficients tending to zero, the convergence or divergence of the series at some point x depends only on the behaviour of the Riemann function $F(x)$ in the neighbourhood of the point $x$.*

This somewhat indistinct formulation will be stated more exactly later (see p. 200). Riemann proved this statement thus: he constructed a function $\lambda(x)$, equal to unity in $[\alpha, \beta]$, equal to zero outside $(a, b)$ and possessing continuous derivatives up to the fourth order inclusive in $[0, 2\pi]$. After this, he proved that the difference

$$\frac{a_0}{2} + \sum_{k=1}^{n} (a_k \cos kx + b_k \sin kx) - \frac{1}{\pi} \int_a^b F(t)\, \lambda(t) \frac{d^2}{dt^2} D_n(t - x)\, dt \qquad (71.1)$$

tends to zero uniformly in $[\alpha, \beta]$ and from this he drew the necessary conclusion.

At the present time the idea of introducing a function $\lambda(x)$ has been completely maintained but the proof of Riemann's theorem is usually carried out using the theory of the *formal multiplication of series*†; by the way, this theory also gives many other useful results which we will prove in Chapter XIV.

Thus, we begin with the concept of the formal product of two trigonometric series. For simplicity of exposition we will write the trigonometric series in its complex form

$$\sum_{n=-\infty}^{n=+\infty} c_n e^{inx} \qquad (c_{-n} = \bar{c}_n).$$

Let us consider two trigonometric series

$$\sum_{n=-\infty}^{n=+\infty} c_n e^{inx} \qquad (71.2)$$

and

$$\sum_{n=-\infty}^{n=+\infty} \gamma_n e^{inx}. \qquad (71.3)$$

Let us call their *formal product* the series

$$\sum_{n=-\infty}^{n=+\infty} K_n e^{inx}, \qquad (71.4)$$

where

$$K_n = \sum_{p=-\infty}^{p=+\infty} c_p \gamma_{n-p} \qquad (71.5)$$

on the supposition that all the series (71.5), defining $K_n$, converge ($n = 0, \pm 1, \pm 2, \ldots$).

In all that follows we will be concerned with the case when $\sum |\gamma_n| < +\infty$. Under these conditions series (71.3) converges absolutely and uniformly in $[-\pi, \pi]$ and is

† This theorem is due to Rajchman (see Rajchman[1] and also Zygmund[12]).

the Fourier series of some function $\lambda(x)$. As regards the series (71.2), it can be any series† providing that

$$c_n \to 0 \quad \text{as} \quad n \to \pm\infty.$$

Let us prove the following two lemmas due to Rajchman.

LEMMA 1. *If $c_n \to 0$ as $n \to \pm\infty$ and if the series $\sum |\gamma_n|$ converges, then all $K_n$ defined by formula* (71.5) *have meaning and $K_n \to 0$ as $n \to \pm\infty$.*

Indeed, if $M = \max |c_n|$, then as $n \to +\infty$

$$|K_n| \leqslant M \sum_{p=-\infty}^{\left[\frac{n}{2}\right]} |\gamma_{n-p}| + \max_{p<\left[\frac{n}{2}\right]} |c_p| \sum_{p=\left[\frac{n}{2}\right]+1}^{\infty} |\gamma_{n-p}|$$

$$\leqslant M \sum_{q=n-\left[\frac{n}{2}\right]}^{\infty} |\gamma_q| + \max_{p>\left[\frac{n}{2}\right]} |c_p| \sum_{q=-\infty}^{q=+\infty} |\gamma_q| \to 0 \quad \text{as} \quad n \to +\infty$$

and similarly we can carry out the proof for $n \to -\infty$. Lemma 1 is proved.

It is said that series (71.3) *converges rapidly* to $S$, if it converges to $S$ and if the series

$$\Gamma_0 + \Gamma_1 + \cdots + \Gamma_n + \cdots,$$

converges, where

$$\Gamma_n = \sum_{k=n}^{\infty} |\gamma_k|.$$

Thus, for example, if the coefficients of series (71.3) are of order $0(1/n^3)$, then $\Gamma_n = 0(1/n^2)$ and, therefore, series (71.3) converges rapidly. Subsequently we will frequently use the series $\sigma(\lambda)$ for the series (71.3), where $\lambda(x)$ is a function possessing three continuous derivatives. Then the coefficients of the series $\sigma(\lambda)$ will be of order $0(1/n^3)$ (see § 24) and $\sigma(\lambda)$ will converge rapidly to $\lambda(x)$.

We will now turn to proving the following lemma.

LEMMA 2. *If $c_n \to 0$ as $n \to \pm\infty$ and series* (71.3) *converges rapidly to zero in some set $E$, then the formal product* (71.4) *converges to zero uniformly in the set $E$.*

---

† It is appropriate to note here that if series (71.2) is the Fourier series of some function $f(x)$, then the formal product becomes the Fourier series of $f(x)\,\lambda(x)$. Indeed, if we denote by $K_n$ the Fourier coefficients of $f(x)\,\lambda(x)$, then

$$K_n = \frac{1}{2\pi}\int_{-\pi}^{\pi} f(t)\,e^{-int}\,\lambda(t)\,dt = \frac{1}{2\pi}\int_{-\pi}^{\pi} f(t)\,e^{-int} \sum_{q=-\infty}^{q=+\infty} \gamma_q\,e^{iqt}\,dt$$

$$= \sum_{q=-\infty}^{q=+\infty} \gamma_q \frac{1}{2\pi}\int_{-\pi}^{\pi} f(t)\,e^{-i(n-q)t}\,dt = \sum_{q=-\infty}^{q=+\infty} c_{n-q}\gamma_q = \sum_{p=-\infty}^{p=+\infty} c_p\gamma_{n-p}.$$

Here term-by-term integration was valid, since we had assumed that $\sum |\gamma_n| < +\infty$, and therefore series $\sigma(\lambda)$ converges uniformly.

Indeed, let $x_0 \in E$ and

$$R_k(x) = \sum_{n=k}^{\infty} \gamma_n e^{inx}.$$

We have for $k > 0$

$$|R_{-k}(x_0)| = \left|\sum_{-k}^{\infty} \gamma_n e^{inx_0}\right| = \left|\sum_{-(k+1)}^{-\infty} \gamma_n e^{inx_0}\right| = |R_{k+1}(x_0)| \leqslant \Gamma_{k+1} \tag{71.6}$$

which means that the series

$$\sum_{k=-\infty}^{k=+\infty} |R_k(x)|$$

converges uniformly for $x \in E$.

Then

$$Q_m(x_0) = \sum_{n=-m}^{n=+m} K_n e^{inx_0} = \sum_{n=-m}^{n=+m} e^{inx_0} \sum_{p=-\infty}^{p=+\infty} c_p \gamma_{n-p} = \sum_{p=-\infty}^{p=+\infty} c_p e^{ipx_0} \sum_{n=-m}^{n=+m} \gamma_{n-p} e^{i(n-p)x_0}$$

$$= \sum_{p=-\infty}^{p=+\infty} c_p e^{ipx_0} \sum_{q=-m-p}^{m-p} \gamma_q e^{iqx_0}$$

$$= \sum_{p=-\infty}^{p=+\infty} c_p e^{ipx_0} R_{-m-p}(x_0) - \sum_{p=-\infty}^{p=+\infty} c_p e^{ipx_0} R_{m-p+1}(x_0).$$

Therefore

$$|Q_m(x_0)| \leqslant \sum_{p=-\infty}^{p=+\infty} |c_p|\,|R_{-m-p}(x_0)| + \sum_{p=-\infty}^{p=+\infty} |c_p|\,|R_{m-p-1}(x_0)|,$$

and, taking into account the inequality (71.6), by the same arguments as in Lemma 1, we prove that $Q_m(x_0) \to 0$ as $m \to \infty$ and moreover uniformly for $x_0 \in E$, since the estimate of $R_k(x_0)$ in terms of $\Gamma_k$ or $\Gamma_{k+1}$ is valid for all $x \in E$.

From these two lemmas we can deduce a theorem:

THEOREM 1. *If the series* (71.3) *converges rapidly to some function* $\lambda(x)$ *and* $c_n \to 0$, *then the series*

$$\sum_{n=-\infty}^{n=+\infty} [K_n - \lambda(x)\, c_n]\, e^{inx} = \sum_{n=-\infty}^{n=+\infty} K_n e^{inx} - \lambda(x) \sum_{n=-\infty}^{n=+\infty} c_n e^{inx} \tag{71.7}$$

*converges uniformly to zero in* $[-\pi, \pi]$.

In order to prove this we suppose that

$$\gamma_0^* = \gamma_0 - \lambda(x),$$

$$\gamma_n^* = \gamma_n \qquad \text{for} \quad n \neq 0$$

and set up the formal product $\sum K_n^* e^{inx}$ of the series $\sum c_n e^{inx}$ and $\sum \gamma_n^* e^{inx}$. It is true that in the latter series $\gamma_0^*$ is not a constant value, but it is not difficult to show that the proof of Lemma 2 would not be changed, if we supposed $\gamma_0$ to be a bounded function of $x$, which occurs in our example. Therefore we can apply Lemma 2, since the series $\sum \gamma_n^* e^{inx}$ converges rapidly to zero in $[-\pi, \pi]$ and we find that $\sum K_n^* e^{inx}$ converges rapidly to zero uniformly in $[-\pi, \pi]$. But

$$K_n^* = \sum_{p=-\infty}^{p=+\infty} c_p \gamma_{n-p}^* = c_n[\gamma_0 - \lambda(x)] + \sum_{p\neq n}' c_p \gamma_{n-p} = K_n - \lambda(x)\, c_n,$$

and therefore

$$\sum K_n e^{inx} - \lambda(x) \sum c_n e^{inx}$$

converges to zero uniformly in $[-\pi, \pi]$ and Theorem 1 is proved.

Combining Lemma 2 and Theorem 1, we can express a proposition which we will use later.

COROLLARY 1. *Let $\lambda(x)$ be a function for which the Fourier series converges rapidly and $\sum c_n e^{inx}$ a series whose coefficients $c_n \to 0$ as $n \to \pm\infty$. Then the formal product of the series $\sum c_n e^{inx}$ and the Fourier series for $\lambda(x)$ converges to zero everywhere where $\lambda(x) = 0$ (even if the series $\sum c_n e^{inx}$ diverges). At those points where $\lambda(x) \neq 0$, it diverges if the series $\sum c_n e^{inx}$ diverges and it converges to $\lambda(x_0)\, S(x_0)$ if $\sum c_n e^{inx}$ converges to $S(x_0)$.*

*Note 1.* We will remark that this statement can be strengthened. Thus, if we suppose that $\lambda(x) \neq 0$ at some point then

$$\left.\begin{aligned} \overline{\lim}\, Q_n(x_0) &= \lambda(x_0)\, \overline{\lim}\, S_n(x_0), \\ \underline{\lim}\, Q_n(x_0) &= \lambda(x_0)\, \underline{\lim}\, S_n(x_0) \end{aligned}\right\} \quad \text{at} \quad \lambda(x_0) > 0$$

and

$$\left.\begin{aligned} \overline{\lim}\, Q_n(x_0) &= \lambda(x_0)\, \underline{\lim}\, S_n(x_0), \\ \underline{\lim}\, Q_n(x_0) &= \lambda(x_0)\, \overline{\lim}\, S_n(x_0) \end{aligned}\right\} \quad \text{at} \quad \lambda(x_0) < 0.$$

This follows immediately from an examination of the partial sums of the series

$$\sum K_n e^{inx} - \lambda(x) \sum c_n e^{inx},$$

which, as we have seen, converges to zero. Therefore, in particular, if $\overline{\lim}\, |S_n(x_0)| = +\infty$, then $\overline{\lim}\, |Q_n(x_0)| = +\infty$ also.

This result will be used specifically in Chapter XIV.

From Theorem 1 it also follows immediately that:

COROLLARY 2. *If the Fourier series for $\lambda(x)$ converges rapidly and $\sum c_n e^{inx}$ converges uniformly in $E$ to $S(x)$, then the formal product converges uniformly in $E$ to $\lambda(x)\, S(x)$. If in a set $F$ we have $|\lambda(x)| > a > 0$, then the uniform convergence of a formal product in $E$ implies the uniform convergence of $\sum c_n e^{inx}$ in it.*

*Note 2.* In Corollaries 1 and 2 the words "convergence" or "uniform convergence" can be replaced by "summability" or "uniform summability" by the Riemann method. In fact, according to Theorem 1,

$$\sum_{-\infty}^{+\infty} [K_n - \lambda(x)\, c_n]\, e^{inx}$$

converges to zero uniformly in $[-\pi, \pi]$. By virtue of the note to Theorem 2 of § 68 it follows that this series is uniformly summable to zero by the Riemann method in $[-\pi, \pi]$, and this means that the difference of the series

$$\sum K_n e^{inx} \quad \text{and} \quad \lambda(x) \sum c_n e^{inx}$$

is uniformly summable to zero by the Riemann method in $[-\pi, \pi]$, whence the required result immediately follows.

We can now prove the following important theorem:

THEOREM 2. *If a trigonometric series with coefficients tending to zero is summable by the Riemann method to zero at every point of some interval $(a, b)$, then it converges to zero at every point of $(a, b)$ and moreover uniformly in any interval lying entirely within $(a, b)$.*

Let $\lambda(x) = 1$ in $[\alpha, \beta]$, $\lambda(x) = 0$ outside $(a, b)$ and $\lambda(x)$ be interpolated between $[a, \alpha]$ and $[b, \beta]$ as desired, provided it possesses continuous derivatives up to the

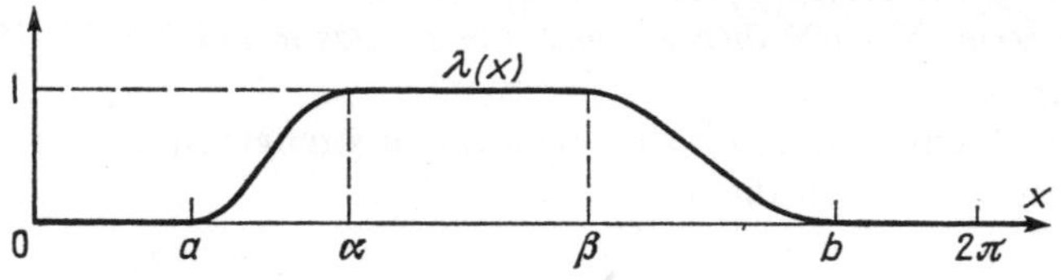


FIG. 14

hird order inclusive (see Fig. 14). We have already said that under these conditions he series $\sigma(\lambda)$ converges rapidly. Let

$$\sigma(\lambda) = \sum \gamma_n e^{inx}.$$

We will set up the formal product (71.4) of the given series and the series $\sigma(\lambda)$. Since $\lambda(x) = 0$ outside $(a, b)$, then by virtue of Corollary 1, the series (71.4) converges to zero outside $(a, b)$, which means that it is summable outside $(a, b)$ to zero by the Riemann method. Moreover, by virtue of Corollary 1 and Note 2 concerning summability, series (71.4) is summable to zero by the Riemann method at every point of $(a, b)$, because we have assumed that this holds for series (71.2) in $(a, b)$. Thus, series (71.4) is summable by the Riemann method to zero at every point in $[-\pi, \pi]$. If this is so, then according to the theorem of § 70 (see its note), it possesses all coefficients equal to zero. But according to Theorem 1 of this section the series

$$\sum K_n e^{inx} - \lambda(x) \sum c_n e^{inx}$$

converges to zero uniformly in $[-\pi, \pi]$. If all $k_n = 0$, then this means that

$$\lambda(x) \sum c_n e^{inx}$$

converges uniformly to zero in $[-\pi, \pi]$. But $\lambda(x) = 1$ in $[\alpha, \beta]$, therefore $\sum c_n e^{inx}$ converges uniformly to zero in $[\alpha, \beta]$, and the proof of Theorem 2 is concluded.

Now we will express in an exact form and prove a theorem which was formulated to some extent at the beginning of this section. So we have the following theorem which is known as Riemann's principle of localization.

RIEMANN'S PRINCIPLE OF LOCALIZATION. *Let $F_1(x)$ and $F_2(x)$ be Riemann functions for two trigonometric series with coefficients tending to zero; if these functions are equal in some interval $(a, b)$ or, perhaps, if their difference is a linear function in $(a, b)$, then the difference of the given trigonometric series is a series convergent to zero everywhere in $(a, b)$ and moreover, uniformly in any interval $[\alpha, \beta]$ lying entirely within $(a, b)$.*

To prove the theorem, let us consider two trigonometric series with coefficients tending to zero. Let (71.2) be the difference of these series, and $F_1(x)$ and $F_2(x)$ their Riemann functions. Then, according to the condition of the Riemann theorem, the sum $F(x)$ for series (71.2) is a linear function in $(a, b)$. If this is so,

$$D^2 F(x) = 0 \quad \text{in} \quad (a, b)$$

then, consequently, series (71. 2) is summable to zero by the Riemann method at every point of the interval $(a, b)$ and Theorem 2 can be applied.

From Riemann's principle of localization the truth of the statement made at the beginning of the section follows immediately, the convergence or divergence of a series with coefficients tending to zero depends only on the behaviour of the Riemann function.

Indeed, if for two series with coefficients tending to zero, we have $F_1(x) = F_2(x)$ in $(a, b)$, then the convergence or divergence of both series at any point $x \in (a, b)$ can only occur simultaneously (and also if they converge, they possess the same sum). It is in this sense that it should be understood that convergence or divergence depends only on the behaviour of the Riemann function.

It should be noted that the general Riemann principle of localization proved here includes, as a particular case, Riemann's principle of localization for Fourier series (see § 33). Indeed, if the two given series are Fourier series for $f_1(x)$ and $f_2(x)$, then the functions $F_1(x)$ and $F_2(x)$ are obtained as a result of the double successive integration of $f_1(x)$ and $f_2(x)$ (see § 70), and, therefore, if $f_1(x) = f_2(x)$ in $(a, b)$, then $F_1(x) - F_2(x)$ will be linear in this interval, and if the general principle of localization has already been proved, then it can be stated that $\sigma(f_1) - \sigma(f_2)$ converges to zero in $(a, b)$ everywhere and moreover uniformly in $[\alpha, \beta]$, lying within $(a, b)$.

In Chapter XIV we shall see the part played by Riemann's principle of localization which has been established here.

## § 72. du Bois-Reymond's theorem

Let $f(x)$ be a function which is finite at every point of $[-\pi, \pi]$. We have already seen (see § 70) that there cannot exist two different trigonometric series converging to it everywhere in $[-\pi, \pi]$. But if one such series exists, ought it to be its Fourier series?

This question, of course, only has meaning for summable $f(x)$, since otherwise it would be simply impossible to write down the Fourier series (we always mean Fourier–Lebesgue series).

Let us note that the convergence of a trigonometric series at every point does not in any way imply that it is a Fourier series. Indeed, for example, the series

$$\sum_{n=2}^{\infty} \frac{\sin nx}{\ln n}$$

converges everywhere, since this is a sine series with monotonically decreasing coefficients (see § 30); however, it is not a Fourier series (see § 40).

Therefore it is appropriate to pose the question thus: Let $f(x)$ be finite at every point and summable. Let there exist a trigonometric series converging to it everywhere in $[-\pi, \pi]$. Could this series be its Fourier series?

Here we can give a positive answer to this question in the case when $f(x)$ is a bounded function; it was in this form that the theorem was proved by Lebesgue who generalized the initial result obtained by du Bois-Reymond.† But before proving this theorem, we should demonstrate the validity of the following lemma:

LEMMA. *If $F(x)$ is continuous in $[a, b]$ and*

$$m \leqslant D^2 F(x) \leqslant M \quad \text{in} \quad (a, b),$$

*then for any $x_0$ and $h$ such that $a \leqslant x_0 - 2h < x_0 + 2h \leqslant b$, we have*

$$m \leqslant \frac{F(x_0 + 2h) + F(x_0 - 2h) - 2F(x_0)}{4h^2} \leqslant M.$$

To prove this, we consider the auxiliary function

$$\Psi(x) = F(x_0) + (x - x_0)\frac{F(x_0 + 2h) - F(x_0 - 2h)}{4h} + \frac{(x - x_0)^2}{2}\frac{F(x_0 + 2h) + F(x_0 - 2h) - 2F(x_0)}{4h^2}.$$

It is clear that $\Psi(x)$ is a polynomial of the second degree in $x$, whilst

$$\Psi(x_0 + 2h) = F(x_0 + 2h),\ \Psi(x_0) = F(x_0) \quad \text{and} \quad \Psi(x_0 - 2h) = F(x_0 - 2h),$$

i.e., the difference

$$r(x) = F(x) - \Psi(x)$$

becomes zero at $x = x_0 - 2h$, $x_0$ and $x_0 + 2h$. Moreover, $r(x)$ is continuous in $[a, b]$ and

$$D^2 r(x) = D^2 F(x) - \frac{F(x_0 + 2h) + F(x_0 - 2h) - 2F(x_0)}{4h^2}.$$

Since $r(x)$ possesses a minimum and maximum somewhere inside $(x_0 - 2h, x_0 + 2h)$, let them be the points $x_1$ and $x_2$, and at them it is known that $D^2 r(x_1) \geqslant 0$ and $D^2 r(x_2) \leqslant 0$, so it is immediately clear that

$$D^2 F(x_2) \leqslant \frac{F(x_0 + 2h) + F(x_0 - 2h) - 2F(x_0)}{4h^2} \leqslant D^2 F(x_1),$$

which proves the validity of the lemma.

We can now prove the theorem:

THE DU BOIS-REYMOND–LEBESGUE THEOREM: *If $f(x)$ is bounded in $[-\pi, \pi]$ and there exists a trigonometric series*

$$\frac{a_0}{2} + \sum_{n=1}^{\infty} (a_n \cos nx + b_n \sin nx), \tag{72.1}$$

*converging to it everywhere in this interval, then this series is its Fourier series.*

---

† du Bois-Reymond[2] considered only the case of bounded functions, integrable in the Riemann sense.

We will first note that from the convergence of series (72.1) it follows that $a_n \to 0$ and $b_n \to 0$ (see § 62). Therefore, it is possible to construct a Riemann function and to obtain, as in § 68

$$\frac{F(x_0 + 2h) + F(x_0 - 2h) - 2F(x_0)}{4h^2}$$

$$= \frac{a_0}{2} + \sum_{n=1}^{\infty} (a_n \cos nx_0 + b_n \sin nx_0) \left(\frac{\sin nh}{nh}\right)^2. \tag{72.2}$$

From Riemann's theorem (see § 68, Theorem 1) we have at every point

$$D^2 F(x) = f(x). \tag{72.3}$$

But $f(x)$ is given as bounded; which means that by the preceding lemma

$$\left|\frac{F(x + 2h) + F(x - 2h) - 2F(x)}{4h^2}\right| \leqslant M, \tag{72.4}$$

where $M$ is a constant (and this is for any $h$ and any $x$, $-\pi \leqslant x \leqslant \pi$). We also note that $f(x)$, as the sum of an everywhere convergent series of continuous functions, is measurable, which means that being measurable and bounded, it is summable.

From the uniform convergence of (72.2) it follows that it is the Fourier series of the function on the left-hand side of the equality, i.e.

$$a_n \left(\frac{\sin nh}{nh}\right)^2 = \frac{1}{\pi} \int_{-\pi}^{\pi} \frac{F(x + 2h) + F(x - 2h) - 2F(x)}{4h^2} \cos nx \, dx \tag{72.5}$$

and similarly

$$b_n \left(\frac{\sin nh}{nh}\right)^2 = \frac{1}{\pi} \int_{-\pi}^{\pi} \frac{F(x + 2h) + F(x - 2h) - 2F(x)}{4h^2} \sin nx \, dx. \tag{72.6}$$

But

$$D^2 F(x) = \lim_{h \to 0} \frac{F(x + 2h) + F(x - 2h) - 2F(x)}{4h^2}.$$

Therefore by virtue of (72.3)

$$\lim_{h \to 0} \frac{F(x + 2h) + F(x - 2h) - 2F(x)}{4h^2} = f(x).$$

If we now note that due to (72.4) the expressions under the integral sign in the integrals (72.5) and (72.6) are bounded at any $x$ and $h$ by the same value $M$ (this is true for any $n$), then it is possible to carry out the passage to the limit under the integral sign, and therefore

$$a_n = \lim_{h\to 0} a_n \left(\frac{\sin nh}{nh}\right)^2$$

$$= \lim_{h\to 0} \frac{1}{\pi} \int_{-\pi}^{\pi} \frac{F(x+2h)+F(x-2h)-2F(x)}{4h^2} \cos nx\, dx$$

$$= \frac{1}{\pi} \int_{-\pi}^{\pi} f(x) \cos nx\, dx$$

and similarly

$$b_n = \frac{1}{\pi} \int_{-\pi}^{\pi} f(x) \sin nx\, dx,$$

and this is what it was required to be proved.

*Note.* We assumed $f(x)$ to be bounded but the given theorem permits considerable generalization. It need not require convergence of the series at every point of $[0, 2\pi]$ (see Chapter XIV, § 4).

## § 73. Problems

1. The series

$$\sum_{n=1}^{\infty} \cos nx \quad \text{and} \quad \sum_{n=1}^{\infty} \cos 2^n x$$

do not possess points of convergence, if the series

$$\text{(a)} \quad \sum_{n=1}^{\infty} \sin nx$$

converges only at $x \equiv 0 \pmod{\pi}$, whilst the series

$$\text{(b)} \quad \sum_{n=1}^{\infty} \sin 2^n x$$

possesses an infinite (but denumerable) set of points of convergence in $(0, \pi)$.

The set of points of normal convergence of series (b) coincides with the set of points of its absolute convergence.

[In considering series (b), represent the points $x$ in the form $x = \pi y = \pi \sum_{n=1}^{\infty} \delta_k/2^k$ where $\delta_k = 0$ or 1. Consider the cases when $y$ is a binary rational number and when $y$ is not a binary rational number.]

2. The set $E \subset (-\infty, +\infty)$ of all the points of convergence of the series

$$\sum_{n=1}^{\infty} n \sin 2^{n!} x$$

has the power of the continuum in any interval $(a, b)$ where $a < b$ (although $mE = 0$).
This is also true for the series

$$\sum_{n=1}^{\infty} n \cos 2^{n!} x.$$

[Consider the set of points $E = \prod_{n=10}^{\infty} E_n$, where $E_n = \{-\infty < x < \infty : |\sin 2^{n!} x \leqq 1/n^3\}$.]

3. If the trigonometric series

$$\frac{a_0}{2} + \sum_{n=1}^{\infty} (a_n \cos nx + b_n \sin nx) \tag{73.1}$$

converges in measure in some set $E$ where $mE > 0$, then

$$\lim_{n\to\infty} \sqrt{a_n^2 + b_n^2} = 0.$$

[Refer to the proof of the Cantor–Lebesgue theorem in § 62.]

4. Consider a measurable function $\varphi(x)$ which is $2\pi$-periodic and not equal to a constant. Then for any $\alpha_n$ and $\lambda_n$ where $(\lambda_n) \to \infty$ as $n \to \infty$, the sequence of functions $\{\varphi(\lambda_n x - \alpha_n)\}$ diverges almost everywhere in $(-\infty, \infty)$.

5. If functions $g(x) \in C(0, 2\pi)$ and $f(x) \in C(0, 2\pi)$ exist such that $g(x) = f(x)$ for $x \in [1, 2]$, the Fourier series of $g(x)$ and $f(x)$ are however not uniformly equiconvergent in the interval $(1, 2)$.

6. The absolute convergence of trigonometric series is not a local property. There exists a $2\pi$-periodic absolutely-continuous function $f(x)$, the Fourier series of which is not absolutely convergent at any point $x \in [1, 2]$, although $f(x) = 0$ for $x \in [1, 2]$.

7. There exists a trigonometric series of the the form (73.1) which diverges everywhere in $(-\infty, \infty)$ and get this series is summable by the Abel–Poisson method for all $x \in (-\infty, \infty)$.

[Take the series $\sum_{n=1}^{\infty} n \sin nx$ and add to it a Fourier series (of a continuous function) which diverges only at the points $x \equiv O \pmod{\pi}$.]

8. Let $a_n \downarrow 0$ and

$$f(x) = \sum_{n=1}^{\infty} a_n \sin nx. \tag{73.2}$$

Then

(a) if $\lim_{x\to+0} f(x) = 0$, $a_n = o(1/n)$ and the series (73.2) converges uniformly in $[0, \pi]$;

(b) if $\overline{\lim_{x\to+0}} f(x) = A$, where $A$ is a finite number, $a_n = O(1/n)$ and

$$\Big|\sum_{n=1}^{k} a_n \sin nx\Big| \leqslant D \text{ for all } \begin{cases} k = 1, 2 \ldots \\ x \in [0, \pi] \end{cases}$$

where $D$ is a finite number.

9. Let

$$a_n \downarrow 0$$

and

$$f(x) = \sum_{n=1}^{\infty} a_n \cos nx. \tag{73.3}$$

Then

(a) if $\lim_{x\to+0} f(x) = A$, where $A$ is a finite number,

$$A = \frac{a_0}{2} + \sum_{n=1}^{\infty} a_n$$

and the series (73.3) converges absolutely in $(-\infty, \infty)$;

(b) if $\lim_{x\to+0} f(x) = +\infty$, $f(x) \in L(0, 2\pi)$ and the series (73.3) is a Fourier series;

(c) if the function $f(x)$ is non-integrable in $[0, \pi]$, then

$$-\infty = \varliminf_{x\to+0} f(x) < \varlimsup_{x\to+0} f(x) = +\infty.$$

10. (i) If a $2\pi$-periodic function $f(x) \in \mathrm{Lip}\,\alpha$, then

$$\|f(x) - \sigma_n(x,f)\|_c = \begin{cases} O(1/n^\alpha) & \text{for } 0 < \alpha < 1 \\ O((\log n)/n) & \text{for } \alpha = 1, \end{cases} \tag{73.4}$$

where $\sigma_n(x,f)$ are the arithmetic means of the partial sums of the Fourier series of the function $f$. The estimate (73.4) cannot be bettered.

S. N. BERNSTEIN

[The estimate (73.4) follows from the fact that (see § 47)

$$\|f - \sigma_n\|_c \leqslant \frac{1}{\pi} \left\| \int_0^{1/n} |f(x+t) + f(x-t) - 2f(x)|\, K_n(t)\, dt \right\|$$

$$+ \frac{8}{\pi(n+1)} \int_{1/n}^{\pi} \frac{\|f(x+t) + f(x-t) - 2f(x)\|}{t^2}\, dt.$$

If we take the function $f_0(x) \in \mathrm{Lip}\,\alpha$ such that $f_0(x) = |x|^\alpha$ where $|x| \leqslant 1$, then we prove that the estimate (73.4) cannot be bettered with respect to order.]

(ii) If $f(x) \in C(0, 2\pi)$, then

$$\|f(x) - \sigma_n(x,f)\|_c = O\left\{\frac{1}{n} \sum_{k=0}^{n} E_k(f)\right\}.$$

S. B. STECHKIN

11. Consider a $2\pi$-periodic function $f(x) = x \sin(\pi/x)$ where $0 < x < 1$ and $f(x) = 0$ for $1 \leqslant x \leqslant 2\pi$. Then

$$\|f(x) - \sigma_n(x,f)\|_c = O(1/\sqrt{n})$$

and this estimate cannot be bettered with respect to order.

[The modulus of continuity $\omega(\delta,f) = O(\delta^{1/2})$ and $\omega(\delta,f) \neq o(\delta^{1/2})$. The fact that the estimate cannot be bettered follows from Stechkin's result[5] (see also § 7 of the Appendix).]

12. For every $\alpha \in (0, 1)$ there exists a function $f \in \mathrm{Lip}\,\alpha$ such that

$$\varlimsup_{n\to\infty} n^\alpha |f(x) - \sigma_n(x,f)| > 0 \text{ for nearly all } x \in (-\infty, +\infty).$$

For $\alpha = 1$, a statement of this type is not valid.

A. I. RUBINSHTEIN

13. Consider a $2\pi$-periodic function

$$f(x) = \begin{cases} 1/q & \text{for} \quad x = 2\pi p/q \\ 0 & \text{for the remaining } x \text{ in } [0, 2\pi], \end{cases}$$

where $0 < p < q$ and $p/q$ is an irreducible fraction. Then there does not exist a trigonometric series which would converge everywhere to $f(x)$.

[Apply the du Bois-Reymond–Lebesgue Theorem of § 72.]

14. Construct some measurable set $E$ in $(0, 2\pi)$ such that for any interval $(a, b) \subset (0, 2\pi)$ the measures $m(a, b)\, E > 0$ and $m(a, b)\, CE > 0$ where $CE = [0, 2\pi] - E$.

15. Consider the $E$-set of problem 14. Then, if

$$f(x) = \begin{cases} 1 & \text{for} \quad x \in E \\ 0 & \text{for} \quad x \in CE \end{cases}$$

there does not exist a trigonometric series which would converge to $f(x)$ in some interval $(a, b)$.

[Assume the opposite and apply Baire's theorem concerning the limit of a sequence of continuous functions (see Lusin, A. 17, § 47).]

16. There does not exist a denumerable system of functions $f_n(x) \in C(0, 1)$ such that the set of all the functions

$$F(x) \equiv F(x; \{c_k\}, N) = \sum_{k=1}^{N} c_k f_k(x) \qquad (N = 1, 2, \ldots)$$

(where $c_k$ are arbitrary real numbers) coincides with the whole space $C(0, 1)$.

[Assume the opposite and consider the function

$$\varphi(x) = \sum_{n=1}^{\infty} \frac{\sqrt{\omega(x, f_n)}}{(A_n + 1)\, 2^n} \qquad (x \in [0, 1]),$$

where $A_n = \sup\limits_{x \in [0,1]} |f_n(x)|$ and $\omega(x, f)$ is the modulus of continuity of $f$.]

17. If

$$\sum_{k=1}^{\infty} |a_k \cos \sqrt{2}\pi k| < \infty,$$

then

$$\sum_{k=1}^{\infty} \frac{|a_k|}{k} < \infty.$$

A. A. Muromskii

18. (i) If there exists a set $E \subset [0, 1]$ with $mE = 1$ such that if

$$\sum_{k=1}^{\infty} |a_k \cos \pi k x_0| < \infty$$

at some point $x_0 \in E$, then

$$\sum_{k=2}^{\infty} \frac{|a_k|}{k (\ln k)^{1+\varepsilon}} < \infty$$

for any $\varepsilon > 0$.

(ii) Prove that the set $E$ (of part (i)) can be chosen such that it contains all the algebraic irrational points of the interval $(0, 1)$.

A. A. Muromskii

19. (i) If the series

$$\sum_{n=1}^{\infty} c_n(1 - \cos nx) \tag{73.5}$$

converges at every point of an interval $(a, b)$, then the series

$$\sum_{n=1}^{\infty} c_n \tag{73.6}$$

converges.

G. H. HARDY (A. 8)

(ii) If $c_n = \dfrac{(-1)^n}{\ln(n+1)}$, then the series (73.5) converges for all $x \in (0, \pi)$, although

$$\sum_{n=1}^{\infty} |c_n|^{\alpha} = \infty$$

for all real $\alpha > 0$.

20. If the series (73.5) converges absolutely at all the points of some set $E$ with $mE > 0$, then the series (73.6) converges absolutely.

[This statement is proved in the same way as the Lusin–Denjoy theorem of § 61.]

CHAPTER II

# FOURIER COEFFICIENTS

## § 1. Introduction

In this chapter we will set ourselves the following tasks:

A. Knowing the properties of the function, to estimate the rate at which its Fourier coefficients tend to zero (the fact that they should tend to zero was proved in Chapter I, § 19).

B. Given a sequence of numbers

$$a_0, a_1, a_2, \ldots, a_n, \ldots; \quad b_1, b_2, \ldots, b_n, \ldots,$$

to establish whether there exists a function possessing them as its Fourier coefficients, and if so what are its properties.

Unfortunately, these tasks are far short of being completely achieved. Therefore we have to partially solve them. Thus, for example, we study the rate of tending to zero of the Fourier coefficients for functions of bounded variation (see § 2), for functions of class Lip $\alpha$ (see § 3) and for functions of class $L^p (p > 1)$ (§§ 4 and 5). But at the same time we will prove that provided $f(x)$ is summable, then its coefficients can tend to zero as slowly as desired (§ 6). On the other hand, we will prove (see § 7) that if no account is taken of the signs of the values $a_n$ and $b_n$ and a limitation is imposed only on their absolute magnitudes, then it is impossible to solve problem B except for the case when $\sum(a_n^2 + b_n^2) < +\infty$ (this case has already been discussed in § 16 Chapter I).

Thus, the question of the behaviour of the Fourier coefficients for $f(x) \in L$ is a very delicate question. All the same in § 9 we give some necessity conditions for these coefficients and even in § 10 some necessary and sufficient conditions though these are rather obscure. The solution of task B or the so-called "trigonometric problem of moments" has been the subject of many reports but unfortunately here the formulation is such that for a precisely defined sequence of numbers it is neither possible to explain whether they are Fourier coefficients nor even to find the corresponding function. The majority of theorems are proved by referring the problem being cosidered to some other problem that is also extremely difficult. Therefore, we give the results obtained in § 11 without proof.

Section 12 is devoted to a problem of a somewhat different nature: can it be stated that a trigonometric series ought to be a Fourier series if all its partial sums are non-negative for any $x$? This problem, too, was not completely solved, but we thought it expedient to describe what is known in this connection. Finally in § 13 we consider the problem of the transformations of Fourier series.

## § 2. The order of Fourier coefficients for functions of bounded variation. Criterion for the continuity of functions of bounded variation

1. *The order of Fourier coefficients for functions of bounded variation.* We have seen (see Chapter I, § 22) that if $f(x)$ is a function of bounded variation, then

$$a_n = O\left(\frac{1}{n}\right) \quad \text{and} \quad b_n = O\left(\frac{1}{n}\right). \tag{2.1}$$

We know that if $f(x)$ is continuous, then it is impossible to improve on this estimate, since discontinuities in functions of bounded variation can only be of the first kind, and under these conditions improvement on estimate (1) is impossible (see Chapter I, § 42).

The question arises whether it is not possible to assert that

$$a_n = o\left(\frac{1}{n}\right) \quad \text{and} \quad b_n = o\left(\frac{1}{n}\right),$$

if $f(x)$, moreover, is still continuous. We will show that this too is not true.

For this purpose we set up in the interval $[0, 2\pi]$ a set, similar to the classical Cantor set, which is constructed in the interval $[0, 1]$, i.e. we first remove from the segment $[0, 2\pi]$ the interval $\delta_1^{(1)}$ with centre at the point $\pi$ and length $2\pi/3$, then from each of the two remaining segments we remove the intervals $\delta_1^{(2)}$ and $\delta_2^{(2)}$ of length $2\pi/3^2$ with centres in the middle of the intervals $[0, 2\pi/3]$ and $[4\pi/3, 2\pi]$, from which they are discarded, etc. If $\Phi(0) = 0$, $\Phi(2\pi) = 1$, $\Phi(x) = \frac{1}{2}$ in $\delta_1^{(1)}$, $\Phi(x) = \frac{1}{4}$ and $\frac{3}{4}$ respectively in $\delta_1^{(2)}$ and $\delta_2^{(2)}$, etc. and the function continues thus at the points of a Cantor set, then the classical Cantor stepped curve is obtained which increases from 0 to 1, whilst $\Phi'(x) = 0$ almost everywhere.

If we suppose that $f(x) = \Phi(x) - x/2\pi$, then $f(0) = f(2\pi) = 0$ and therefore $f(x)$ is continuous not only within the interval $[0, 2\pi]$, but along the whole infinite axis, if it is assumed that $f(x + 2\pi) = f(x)$. It is clear that it is of bounded variation, but, however, we now prove that its Fourier coefficients cannot be of order $o(1/n)$ but only $O(1/n)$. For this purpose we integrate by parts the integral on the right-hand side of equality

$$c_n = \frac{1}{2\pi}\int_0^{2\pi} f(x)\, e^{-inx}\, dx = \frac{1}{2\pi}\int_0^{2\pi}\left[\Phi(x) - \frac{x}{2\pi}\right] e^{-inx}\, dx,$$

which gives

$$c_n = \frac{1}{2\pi n i}\int_0^{2\pi} e^{-inx}\, d\Phi = \frac{P_n}{2\pi n i}$$

(here the integral is meant in the Stieltjes sense, see Introductory Material, § 16).

We will prove that for $n = 3^m$ $(m = 0, 1, \ldots)$ all the values $P_n$ are equal to one another and different from zero, whence it will follow that $c_n = O(1/n)$, but $c_n \neq o(1/n)$.

We have

$$P_n = \int_0^{2\pi} e^{-inx}\, d\Phi.$$

Therefore, since $\Phi(x)$ is constant in $\delta_1^{(1)}$ and in the segment $[4\pi/3, 2\pi]$ it varies just as in $[0, 2\pi/3]$, only increased by $\frac{1}{2}$, then

$$P_{3m} = \int_0^{2\pi} e^{-i\,3^m x}\, d\Phi = 2\int_0^{2\pi/3} e^{-i3^m x}\, d\Phi;$$

but by carrying out the substitution $3x = t$ here, we obtain

$$P_{3m} = 2\int_0^{2\pi} e^{-i3^{m-1}x}\, d\Phi\left(\frac{x}{3}\right) = \int_0^{2\pi} e^{-i3^{m-1}x}\, d\Phi = P_{3m-1},$$

since $\Phi(x/3) = \frac{1}{2}\,\Phi(x)$. Hence it is evident that

$$P_{3m} = P_{30} = P_1 = \int_0^{2\pi} e^{-ix}\, d\Phi.$$

It remains to prove that this magnitude $P_1 \neq 0$. For this we consider its real part, i.e.

$$\int_0^{2\pi} \cos x\, d\Phi = 2\int_0^{2\pi/3} \cos x\, d\Phi = 2\left(\int_0^{2\pi/9} \cos x\, d\Phi + \int_{4\pi/9}^{2\pi/3} \cos x\, d\Phi\right)$$

$$= 2\int_0^{2\pi/9}\left[\cos x + \cos\left(x + \frac{4\pi}{9}\right)\right] d\Phi = 4\int_0^{2\pi/9} \cos\left(x + \frac{2\pi}{9}\right)\cos\frac{2\pi}{9}\, x\, d\Phi$$

$$\geqslant 4\cos\frac{2\pi}{9}\cos\frac{4\pi}{9}\int_0^{2\pi/9} d\Phi = \frac{8\pi}{9}\cos\frac{2\pi}{9}\cos\frac{4\pi}{9} > 0,$$

and thus our statement is proved.

*Note* 1. The fact that the Fourier coefficients in the function that we have set up are not of order $o(1/n)$ can also be derived from general theorems concerning the problem of uniqueness of the expansion of a function into a trigonometric series (see Chapter XIV, § 7), but we preferred to use a direct method here, in order to avoid a restricted method in the case when very simple arguments can be used.

*Note* 2. The question arises whether, on the other hand, it is not possible to establish that the function is of bounded variation from the behaviour of the Fourier coefficients. We will prove here the Lorentz[1] sufficiency condition:

(1) if $1 \leqslant p \leqslant 2$ and

$$\left(\sum_{k=n}^{\infty} (|a_k|^p + |b_k|^p)\right)^{1/p} = O\left(\frac{1}{n}\right) \tag{2.2}$$

or

(2) if $2 \leqslant p \leqslant \infty$ and

$$\left(\sum_{k=n}^{\infty} (|a_k|^p + |b_k|^p)\right)^{1/p} = O\left(\frac{1}{n^{\frac{1}{2}+\frac{1}{p'}}}\right), \quad \text{where } \frac{1}{p} + \frac{1}{p'} = 1, \tag{2.3}$$

then $f(x)$ is of bounded variation. Lorentz proves by means of examples that the theorem holds if $1/n^\alpha$ is substituted for $1/n$ in formula (2.2) for $\alpha < 1$ or if $\frac{1}{2} + 1/p'$ in (2.3) is changed to any smaller number.

2. *Criterion for the continuity of a function of bounded variation.* We have proved that continuous functions of bounded variation exist in which the coefficients are of order $O(1/n)$ and not of $o(1/n)$. The question arises: is it not possible to draw conclusions on the continuity of a function of bounded variation from the character of the Fourier coefficients? The answer to this question can be given in several different forms. One of such forms is

WIENER'S[1] THEOREM. *In order for a function of bounded variation to be continuous, it is necessary and sufficient that*

$$\lim_{n\to\infty} \frac{\varrho_1 + 2\varrho_2 + \cdots + n\varrho_n}{n} = 0, \tag{2.4}$$

*where* $\varrho_n^2 = a_n^2 + b_n^2$;

We will first prove that the necessary and sufficient condition can be expressed in the form

$$\lim_{n\to\infty} n \sum_{k=1}^{\infty} \varrho_k^2 \sin^2 \frac{k\pi}{2n} = 0, \tag{2.5}$$

and we will then prove the equivalence of conditions (2.4) and (2.5).

If the Fourier series for $f(x)$ has the form

$$f(x) \sim \frac{a_0}{2} + \sum_{m=1}^{\infty} (a_m \cos mx + b_m \sin mx),$$

then

$$f(x+t) \sim \frac{1}{2} A_0(t) + \sum_{m=1}^{\infty} (A_m(t) \cos mx + B_m(t) \sin mx),$$

where

$$A_m(t) = a_m \cos mt + b_m \sin mt, \quad A_0(t) = \frac{a_0}{2},$$

$$B_m(t) = b_m \cos mt - a_m \sin mt,$$

consequently

$$f(x+t) - f(x) \sim \sum_{m=1}^{\infty} (\alpha_m(t) \cos mx + \beta_m(t) \sin mx),$$

where

$$\begin{aligned}
\alpha_m(t) &= A_m(t) - a_m = a_m(\cos mt - 1) + b_m \sin mt \\
&= 2 \sin m\frac{t}{2} \cos m\frac{t}{2} b_m - 2\sin^2 m\frac{t}{2} a_m \\
&= \left(b_m \cos m\frac{t}{2} - a_m \sin m\frac{t}{2}\right) 2 \sin m\frac{t}{2} = B_m\left(\frac{t}{2}\right) 2 \sin m\frac{t}{2};
\end{aligned}$$

$$\begin{aligned}
\beta_m(t) &= B_m(t) - b_m = b_m(\cos mt - 1) - a_m \sin mt \\
&= 2 \sin\frac{mt}{2}\left(- b_m \sin m\frac{t}{2} - a_m \cos m\frac{t}{2}\right) = -2 \sin\frac{mt}{2} A_m\left(\frac{t}{2}\right).
\end{aligned}$$

Therefore

$$f\left(x+\frac{\pi}{n}\right)-f(x)\sim 2\sum_{m=1}^{\infty}\left[B_m\left(\frac{\pi}{2n}\right)\cos mx - A_m\left(\frac{\pi}{2n}\right)\sin mx\right]\sin m\frac{\pi}{2n}$$

and consequently according to Parseval's equality

$$\frac{1}{\pi}\int_0^{2\pi}\left[f\left(x+\frac{\pi}{n}\right)-f(x)\right]^2 dx = 4\sum_{m=1}^{\infty}\left[A_m^2\left(\frac{\pi}{2n}\right)+B_m^2\left(\frac{\pi}{2n}\right)\right]\sin^2 m\frac{\pi}{2n}$$

$$= 4\sum_{m=1}^{\infty}\varrho_m^2\sin^2 m\frac{\pi}{2n}.$$

Because of the periodicity of the expression under the integral sign we have for any $k$

$$\frac{1}{\pi}\int_0^{2\pi}\left[f\left(x+k\frac{\pi}{n}\right)-f\left(x+(k-1)\frac{n}{\pi}\right)^2\right]dx = 4\sum_{m=1}^{\infty}\varrho_m^2\sin^2 m\frac{\pi}{2n}.$$

Letting $k$ pass through the values $1, 2, \ldots, 2n$ and combining all the equalities obtained, we find that

$$\int_0^{2\pi}\sum_{k=1}^{2n}\left[f\left(x+k\frac{\pi}{n}\right)-f\left(x+(k-1)\frac{\pi}{n}\right)\right]^2 dx = 8\pi n\sum_{m=1}^{\infty}\varrho_m^2\sin^2 m\frac{\pi}{2n}. \quad (2.6)$$

If it is noted that in the case of continuity of $f(x)$ we have

$$\left|f\left(x+k\frac{\pi}{n}\right)-f\left(x+(k-1)\frac{\pi}{n}\right)\right| \leqslant \omega\left(\frac{\pi}{n}\right),$$

where $\omega(\delta)$ is the modulus of continuity of $f(x)$ (see Introductory Material, § 25), then

$$\sum_{k=1}^{2n}\left[f\left(x+k\frac{\pi}{n}\right)-f\left(x+(k-1)\frac{\pi}{n}\right)\right]^2$$

$$\leqslant \omega\left(\frac{\pi}{n}\right)\sum_{k=1}^{2n}\left|f\left(x+k\frac{\pi}{n}\right)-f\left(x+(k-1)\frac{\pi}{n}\right)\right| \leqslant V\omega\left(\frac{\pi}{n}\right),$$

where $V$ is the complete variation of $f(x)$. Therefore by virtue of (2.6)

$$n\sum_{m=1}^{\infty}\varrho_m^2\sin^2 m\frac{\pi}{2n} \leqslant \frac{1}{4}V\omega\left(\frac{\pi}{n}\right)$$

which means that if $f(x)$ is continuous, then the condition (2.5) is indeed fulfilled.

We will now prove that $f(x)$ is discontinuous. This means that a point $\xi$ can be found such that $|f(\xi+0)-f(\xi-0)| = d \neq 0$.

We must first consider

$$f(\xi) = \frac{f(\xi+0)+f(\xi-0)}{2}.$$

Then for all sufficiently large $n$ any interval $[\alpha, \beta]$ of length $\pi/n$ containing the point $\xi$ is such that in it $|f(\beta) - f(\alpha)| > d/3$; consequently, for any $x$ the sum $\sum_{k=1}^{2n} [f(x + k\pi/n) - f(x + (k-1)\pi/n)]^2$ contains a term exceeding $d^2/9$, and therefore the integral of this sum is not less than $(2\pi/9)\, d^2$, i.e. it does not tend to zero as $n \to \infty$.

Thus, we have proved that the condition (2.5) is necessary and sufficient for the continuity of $f(x)$.

We will now prove that (2.5) is equivalent to the condition

$$\lim_{n\to\infty} \frac{1}{n} \sum_{k=1}^{n} k^2 \varrho_k^2 = 0. \tag{2.7}$$

Let us take any integer $r$, which we will define later, and denoting by $P_n$ the value on the left-hand side of formula (2.5) we divide $P_n$ into two terms

$$n \sum_{k=1}^{nr} \varrho_k^2 \sin^2 k \frac{\pi}{2n} \quad \text{and} \quad n \sum_{k=nr+1}^{\infty} \varrho_k^2 \sin^2 k \frac{\pi}{2n}.$$

We see that

$$P_n < n \sum_{k=1}^{nr} \varrho_k^2 \left(k \frac{\pi}{2n}\right)^2 + n \sum_{k=nr+1}^{\infty} \varrho_k^2.$$

Let us denote by $Q_n$ the sum on the left-hand side of (2.7). We know (see Chapter I, § 22) that

$$|a_k| \leqslant \frac{V}{k} \quad \text{and} \quad |b_k| \leqslant \frac{V}{k},$$

whence

$$\varrho_k^2 \leqslant 2 \frac{V^2}{k^2}$$

which means that

$$P_n < \frac{\pi^2}{4} r\, Q_{nr} + 2V_n^2 \sum_{nr+1}^{\infty} \frac{1}{k^2} < \frac{\pi^2}{4} r\, Q_{nr} + 2 \frac{V^2}{r}. \tag{2.8}$$

By making $r$ sufficiently large, we can make the second term on the right-hand side of (2.8) as small as desired. Then we fix $r$ and let $n$ tend to infinity, then as $Q_n \to 0$ we obtain $P_n \to 0$.

On the other hand, if $P_n \to 0$, then all the more

$$n \sum_{k=1}^{n} \varrho_n^2 \sin^2 \frac{k\pi}{2n} \to 0,$$

and since at $0 \leqslant u \leqslant \pi/2$ we have $\sin u \geqslant (2/\pi)\, u$ then

$$n \sum_{k=1}^{n} \varrho_k^2 \left(\frac{k}{n}\right)^2 \to 0,$$

which means that $Q_n \to 0$. Thus, the equivalence of (2.5) and (2.7) is established.

Supposing

$$T_n = \frac{1}{n} \sum_{k=1}^{n} k\, \varrho_k,$$

we have, from Bunyakovskii's inequality

$$T_n^2 = \frac{1}{n^2}\left(\sum_{k=1}^{n} k\,\varrho_k\right)^2 \leqslant \frac{1}{n^2}\,n\sum_{k=1}^{n}(k\,\varrho_k)^2 \leqslant Q_n$$

which means that it follows from $Q_n \to 0$ that $T_n \to 0$.

On the other hand, since

$$\varrho_k < \sqrt{2}\,\frac{V}{k},$$

then

$$Q_n = \frac{1}{n}\sum_{k=1}^{n}(k\,\varrho_k)^2 < \sqrt{2}\,V\frac{1}{n}\sum_{k=1}^{n}k\,\varrho_k = \sqrt{2}\,VT_n,$$

and therefore it follows from $T_n \to 0$ that $Q_n \to 0$.

Thus, (2.7) and (2.4) are equivalent and therefore (2.5) and (2.4) are equivalent. Consequently, the theorem is proved.

*Note 1.* From Wiener's theorem it follows that if $f(x)$ is of bounded variation and

$$a_n = o\left(\frac{1}{n}\right), \qquad b_n = o\left(\frac{1}{n}\right),$$

then $I(x)$ is continuous. This has already been proved in Chapter I, § 42.

*Note 2.* S.M. Lozinskii[2] gave another version of the condition, in which a function of bounded variation is shown to be continuous, namely: for this, it is necessary and sufficient that

$$\sum_{1}^{n}\varrho_k = o(\ln n),$$

where again $\varrho_k = \sqrt{a_k^2 + b_k^2}$.

## § 3. Concerning Fourier coefficients for functions of the class Lip α

Let

$$\sigma(f) = \frac{a_0}{2} + \sum_{n=1}^{\infty}(a_n \cos nx + b_n \sin nx).$$

Then (see Lorentz [1]) we have:

*If $f(x) \in \operatorname{Lip}\alpha$ and $\alpha > 1/p - \frac{1}{2}$ $(0 < p \leqslant 2)$, then*

$$\left(\sum_{k=n}^{\infty}(|a_k|^p + |b_k|^p)\right)^{1/p} \leqslant \frac{C}{n^{\alpha+\frac{1}{2}-\frac{1}{p}}}.$$

Indeed, since for $f(x+h) - f(x-h)$ the Fourier series has the form

$$2\sum_{n=1}^{\infty}(b_n \cos nx - a_n \sin nx)\sin nh, \tag{3.1}$$

then from Parseval's equality and $f \in \mathrm{Lip}\,\alpha$,

$$4\sum_{k=1}^{\infty}(a_k^2+b_k^2)\sin^2 kh = \frac{1}{\pi}\int_{-\pi}^{\pi}[f(t+h)-f(t-h)]^2\,dt \leqslant Ch^{2\alpha},$$

where $C$ is a constant. Therefore for any $n$

$$\sum_{k=n}^{2n-1}(a_k^2+b_k^2)\sin^2 kh \leqslant C\,|h|^{2\alpha}$$

and supposing $h=\pi/4n$ and noting that then $\sin^2 kh \geqslant \frac{1}{2}$ at $n \leqslant k \leqslant 2n-1$, we find that

$$\sum_{k=n}^{2n-1}(a_k^2+b_k^2) \leqslant C_1\frac{1}{n^{2\alpha}},$$

where $C_1$ is another constant.

Applying Hölder's inequality, we find that

$$\sum_{k=n}^{2n-1}(|a_k|^p+|b_k|^p) \leqslant \left\{\sum_{k=n}^{2n-1}(a_k^2+b_k^2)\right\}^{p/2}(2n)^{1-\frac{p}{2}},$$

whence

$$\sum_{k=n}^{2n-1}(|a_k|^p+|b_k|^p) \leqslant \frac{C_2}{n^{p\left(\alpha+\frac{1}{2}\right)-1}}.$$

But then from $\alpha > 1/p - \frac{1}{2}$ we conclude that

$$\left\{\sum_{k=n}^{\infty}(|a_k|^p+|b_k|^p)\right\}^{1/p} = \left\{\sum_{j=0}^{\infty}\sum_{k=2^j n}^{2^{j+1}n-1}(|a_k|^p+|b_k|^p)\right\}^{1/p}$$

$$\leqslant \frac{C_2}{n^{\alpha+\frac{1}{2}-\frac{1}{p}}}\left\{\sum_{j=0}^{\infty}\left(\frac{1}{2^{p\left(\alpha+\frac{1}{2}\right)-1}}\right)^j\right\}^{1/p} \leqslant \frac{C_3}{n^{\alpha+\frac{1}{2}-\frac{1}{p}}},$$

which is what was required to be proved.

COROLLARY 1. In particular, at $p=2$ we obtain for $f \in \mathrm{Lip}\,\alpha$

$$\left\{\sum_{k=n}^{\infty}(a_k^2+b_k^2)\right\}^{1/2} = O\left(\frac{1}{n^{\alpha}}\right).$$

COROLLARY 2. If $\alpha > \frac{1}{2}$, then the theorem can be applied at $p=1$, whence

$$\sum_{k=n}^{\infty}(|a_k|+|b_k|) = O\left(\frac{1}{n^{\alpha-\frac{1}{2}}}\right),$$

and since the right-hand side tends to zero as $n \to \infty$, then Bernstein's theorem follows: *if $f(x) \in \mathrm{Lip}\,\alpha$ at $\alpha > \frac{1}{2}$, then its Fourier series converges absolutely.*

(This theorem will also be proved in a different way in Chapter IX.)

Lorentz demonstrates by means of examples in what sense his theorem cannot be bettered. We will not dwell on this subject here but refer the reader to the author's work; however, here we will prove yet another theorem due to Lorentz, where, on the other hand, it can be concluded from the behaviour of the Fourier coefficients that $f(x)$ belongs to some Lipschitz class, namely:

*If*

$$\sum_{k=n}^{\infty}(|a_k| + |b_k|) = O\left(\frac{1}{n^{\alpha}}\right) \quad (0 \leqslant \alpha < 1).$$

*then* $f(x) \in \mathrm{Lip}\,\alpha$.

Indeed, from the condition of the theorem it follows that

$$\sum_{k=n}^{2n-1}(|a_k| + |b_k|) \leqslant \frac{C}{n^{\alpha}},$$

therefore

$$\sum_{k=n}^{2n-1} k(|a_k| + |b_k|) \leqslant 2\,Cn^{1-\alpha}.$$

Since the Fourier series for $f(x+h) - f(x-h)$ has the form (3.1), we have

$$|f(x+h) - f(x-h)| \leqslant 2\sum_{j=1}^{n}\sum_{k=2^{j-1}}^{2^j-1}(|a_k| + |b_k|)\,k\,|h| + 2\sum_{k=2^n}^{\infty}(|a_k| + |b_k|)$$

$$\leqslant C_1\,|h|\sum_{j=1}^{n} 2^{(1-\alpha)(j-1)} + 2\,\frac{C}{2^{\alpha n}} \leqslant C_2\left(|h|\,2^{(1-\alpha)n} + \frac{1}{2^{\alpha n}}\right).$$

If we choose $n$ such that

$$\frac{1}{2^n} < |h| \leqslant \frac{1}{2^{n-1}},$$

then it follows that

$$|f(x+h) - f(x-h)| \leqslant \frac{K}{2^{n\alpha}} \leqslant K\,|h|^{\alpha},$$

where $K$ is another constant and the theorem is proved.

COROLLARY. *If*

$$a_n = O\left(\frac{1}{n^{1+\alpha}}\right), \qquad b_n = O\left(\frac{1}{n^{1+\alpha}}\right),$$

*then*

$$f(x) \in \mathrm{Lip}\,\alpha \quad (0 < \alpha < 1).$$

Indeed, in this case $\sum_{k=n}^{\infty}(|a_k| + |b_k|) = O(1/n^{\alpha})$, and the conditions of the preceding theorem hold.

In Lorentz's work the reader can find a number of interesting theorems concerning functions belonging to the class Lip$\,\alpha$ and some of their generalizations.

## § 4. The relationship between the order of summability of a function and the Fourier coefficients

It is known (see Chapter I, §§ 13 and 16) that if $f(x) \in L^2$ and $\{c_n\}$ are its Fourier coefficients with respect to any normal orthogonal system $\{\varphi_n(x)\}$ then

$$\sum_{n=1}^{\infty}|c_n|^2 \leqslant \int_a^b |f(x)|^2\,dx,$$

and this inequality changes to an equality if the system is complete. On the other hand, if a sequence of numbers $\{c_n\}$ is given for which $\sum |c_n|^2 < +\infty$, then $f(x) \in L^2$ is found such that these numbers are Fourier coefficients and

$$\int_a^b |f(x)|^2\, dx = \sum_{n=1}^{\infty} |c_n|^2.$$

A question can now be asked: if $p$ is any number, provided that $p > 1$, and we know that $f(x) \in L^p$, then what can be said concerning its Fourier coefficients? On the other hand, if $\sum_{n=1}^{\infty} |c_n|^p < +\infty$, then does a function exist having these $c_n$ for its Fourier coefficients and what is its order of summability?

The answers to these questions for the case of a trigonometric system are given by a theorem due to Hausdorff[1] and W.H. Young[4], [5], and for the general orthogonal system by a theorem due to F. Riesz[2]. Before formulating them, we will introduce some notation. We will write

$$\|f\|_r = \left\{\int_a^b |f|^r\, dt\right\}^{1/r}$$

and

$$\|c\|_r = \left\{\sum_n |c_n|^r\right\}^{1/r},$$

where $r$ is any positive number. We will denote by $p$ a number satisfying the inequality

$$1 < p < 2$$

and by $q$ a number defined by the formula

$$\frac{1}{p} + \frac{1}{q} = 1.$$

Then $q > 2$. We have the following theorem:

Hausdorff–Young Theorem. (1) *Let*

$$f(t) \in L^p(0, 1)$$

*and let*

$$c_n = \int_0^1 f(t)\, e^{-2\pi i n t}\, dt \quad (n = 0, \pm 1, \pm 2, \ldots), \tag{4.1}$$

*i.e. $c_n$ are its Fourier coefficients with respect to the system $\{e^{2\pi i n t}\}$ normal and orthogonal in* $(0, 1)$. *Then*

$$\|c\|_q \leqslant \|f\|_p. \tag{4.2}$$

(2) *If $c_n$ $(n = 0, \pm 1, \pm 2, \ldots)$ are a sequence of numbers for which $\|c\|_p < +\infty$, then there exists $f(t) \in L^q(0, 1)$ such that the condition* (4.1) *is satisfied and*

$$\|f\|_q \leqslant \|c\|_p. \tag{4.3}$$

This theorem is a particular case of the more general theorem due to F. Riesz:

Riesz's Theorem. *Let $\{\varphi_n(t)\}$ be a normal orthogonal system consisting of functions which are all bounded*

$$|\varphi_n(t)| \leqslant M, \quad \begin{array}{l} a \leqslant t \leqslant b, \\ n = 1, 2, \ldots. \end{array} \tag{4.4}$$

(1) *If $f \in L^p(a, b)$, then the Fourier coefficients*

$$c_n = \int_b^a f \bar{\varphi}_n \, dt \tag{4.5}$$

*of $f(t)$ with respect to the system $\{\varphi_n(t)\}$ satisfy the condition*

$$\| c \|_q \leqslant M^{\frac{2}{p}-1} \, \|f\|_p. \tag{4.6}$$

(2) *If for a sequence of numbers $c_n$ we have $\| c \|_p < +\infty$, then there exists a function $f(t) \in L^p(a, b)$ satisfying* (4.5) *for all $n$ such that*

$$\|f\|_q \leqslant M^{\frac{2}{p}-1} \, \| c \|_p. \tag{4.7}$$

Several proofs of this theorem exist.† We give here the proof by Calderon and Zygmund[1], obtained by applying the Phragmen–Lindelöf principle (see Appendix, § 1).

PROOF OF THE RIESZ THEOREM. We start with the first part of the theorem and note that, without upsetting the generality of the theorem it is possible to make the following assumptions:

(a) the system $\{\varphi_n\}$ consists of a finite number of functions,
(b) the function $f$ is a step-function,
(c) $\|f\|_p = 1$.

Indeed, we can always select a step-function $f^*(t)$ such that $\|f - f^*\|_p < \varepsilon$; denoting its Fourier coefficients by $c_n^*$, we obtain from (4.5) using Hölder's inequality (see Introductory Material, § 9)

$$|c_n - c_n^*| \leqslant \|f - f^*\|_p \, \|\varphi_n\|_q \leqslant \varepsilon \left( \int_a^b |\varphi_n|^{q-2} \, |\varphi_n|^2 \, dx \right)^{\frac{1}{q}}$$

$$\leqslant \varepsilon \, M^{\frac{q-2}{q}} \left( \int_a^b |\varphi_n|^2 \, dx \right)^{\frac{1}{q}} \leqslant \varepsilon M^{1-\frac{2}{q}}. \tag{4.8}$$

Since we have assumed that the system $\{\varphi_n(x)\}$ consists of a finite number of functions, then the validity of the inequality (4.6) in the general case follows, provided it is proved for step-functions.

Also, if the inequality (4.5) is proved for any finite number of functions $\varphi_1, \varphi_2, \ldots, \varphi_N$, then, passing to the limit as $N \to \infty$, we see that it remains valid.

Finally, the validity of hypothesis (c) follows from the fact that, on multiplying $f$ by a constant, both sides of the inequality (4.5) are multiplied by the same constant.

Thus, not one of the assumptions made upsets the generality of the proved theorem.

We now note that it is always possible to choose numbers $d_n$ such that

$$\| c \|_q = \sum c_n d_n, \tag{4.9}$$

† The proof due to Riesz can be found in Kaczmarz and Steinhaus's book (ref. A 12).

where $\| d \|_p = 1$. Indeed, for this it is sufficient to take, for example,

$$d_n = |c_n|^{q-1} \frac{e^{-i \arg c_n}}{\| c \|_q^{q-1}}$$

(equality (4.9) is then obtained immediately and

$$\| d \|_p^p = \frac{\sum |c_n|^{p(q-1)}}{(\| c \|_q^{q-1})^p} = \frac{\sum |c_n|^q}{\sum |c_n|^q} = 1,$$

or $p(q-1) = q$).

Let us suppose

$$d_n = D_n^{1/p} \varepsilon_n, \quad \text{where} \quad |\varepsilon_n| = 1, \quad \text{and} \quad D_n \geqslant 0,$$

then

$$\sum D_n = 1. \tag{4.10}$$

Moreover, let us assume

$$f(t) = F^{1/p}(t)\, \eta(t), \quad \text{where} \quad F(t) \geqslant 0, \quad \text{and} \quad |\eta(t)| = 1,$$

then from $\| f \|_p = 1$ we have

$$\int_a^b F(t)\, dt = 1. \tag{4.11}$$

We can now express the coefficients $c_n$ thus:

$$c_n = \int_a^b F^{1/p}(t)\, \eta(t)\, \bar{\varphi}_n(t)\, dt$$

and taking into account (4.9)

$$\| c \|_q = \sum D_n^{1/p} \varepsilon_n \int_a^b F^{1/p}(t)\, \eta(t)\, \bar{\varphi}(t) dt.$$

If we now substitute $z$ for $1/p$, i.e. if we consider the function

$$\Phi(z) = \sum D_n^z \varepsilon_n \int_a^b F^z(t)\, \eta(t)\, \bar{\varphi}_n(t)\, dt, \tag{4.12}$$

then each of the integrals on the right-hand side of the equality (4.12) (because $f$ is a step-function) is a linear combination, with constant coefficients, of expressions of the type $\lambda^z$, where all the $\lambda$ are positive. But then $\Phi(z)$ is also a linear combination of this type and therefore it is bounded in any vertical zone in the $z$-plane.

Let us estimate the upper bound of $f(x)$ within the straight lines $x = \frac{1}{2}$, $x = 1$. For $x = 1$ from (4.10) and (4.11) we find that

$$|\Phi(z)| \leqslant \sum D_n |\varepsilon_n| \int_a^b F |\varphi_n|\, dt \leqslant M \sum D_n \int_a^b F\, dt = M.$$

For $z = \frac{1}{2} + iy$, applying Bunyakovskii's inequality to the right-hand side of (4.12) we find that

$$|\Phi| \leqslant (\sum D_n)^{1/2} \left( \sum \left| \int_a^b F^{\frac{1}{2} + iy}(t)\, \eta(t)\, \bar{\varphi}_n(t)\, dt \right|^2 \right)^{1/2}. \tag{4.13}$$

From Bessel's inequality, since the integrals on the right-hand side of the inequality (3.13) are the Fourier coefficients of $F^{1/2+iy}(t)\,\eta(t)$ we have

$$|\Phi| \leqslant (\sum D_n)^{1/2} \left(\int_a^b F\,dt\right)^{1/2} = 1.$$

Thus, $|\Phi(z)| \leqslant M$ on $x = 1$ and $|\Phi(z)| \leqslant 1$ on $x = \frac{1}{2}$. If we want to apply the second form of the Phragmen–Lindelöf principle (see Appendix, § 1) to the estimate of $\Phi(z)$ in the zone $\frac{1}{2} \leqslant x \leqslant 1$, then it is necessary to choose a linear function $L(t)$ such that it equals 0 at $t = 1$ and equals 1 at $t = \frac{1}{2}$. This function will be $L(t) = 2(1-t)$. Supposing $M_1 = 1$ and $M_2 = M$, we then find $|\Phi(x_0 + iy_0)| \leqslant 1^{2(1-x_0)} M^{1-2(1-x_0)}$ for $\frac{1}{2} \leqslant x_0 \leqslant 1$, $-\infty < y_0 < \infty$; whence, since

$$\|c\|_q = \Phi\left(\frac{1}{p}\right),$$

we find

$$\|c\|_q \leqslant 1^{2\left(1-\frac{1}{p}\right)} M^{\frac{2}{p}-1} = M^{\frac{2}{p}-1},$$

and this concludes the proof of the first half of the theorem.

In order to prove the second half we fix a number $N$ and suppose

$$f_N(t) = c_1\varphi_1(t) + c_2\varphi_2(t) + \cdots + c_N\varphi_N(t),$$

where $\{c_n\}$ is a given sequence of numbers.

Since $|\varphi_n| \leqslant M$, then $\varphi_n \in L^q$, which means that $f_N \in L^q$ also. We can always choose $g(t)$ such that $\|g\|_p = 1$ and

$$\|f_N\|_q = \int_a^b \bar{f}_N g\,dt. \tag{4.14}$$

Indeed, for this it is sufficient to suppose that

$$g(t) = |f_N(t)|^{q-1} \frac{e^{i \arg f_N(t)}}{\|f_N\|_q^{q-1}},$$

since (4.14) then follows from the fact that

$$\int_a^b \bar{f}_N g\,dt = \frac{\int_a^b \bar{f}_N |f_N|^{q-1} e^{i\arg f_N(t)} dt}{\left\{\int_a^b |f_N|^q\,dt\right\}^{\frac{q-1}{q}}} = \frac{\int_a^b |f_N|^q\,dt}{\left\{\int_a^b |f_N|^q\,dt\right\}^{\frac{q-1}{q}}} = \|f_N\|_q$$

and in this case

$$\|g\|_p^p = \int_a^b |g|^p\,dt = \frac{\int_a^b |\bar{f}_N|^{p(q-1)}\,dt}{\left(\int_a^b |f_N|^q\,dt\right)^{\frac{p(q-1)}{q}}} = \frac{\int_a^b |f_N|^q\,dt}{\int_a^b |f_N|^q\,dt} = 1.$$

Denoting by $d_n$ the Fourier coefficients of $g(t)$, we obtain

$$\|f_N\|_q = \int_a^b \bar{f}_N g\,dt = \sum \bar{c}_n d_n \leqslant \left(\sum_1^N |c_n|^p\right)^{1/p} \left(\sum_1^N |d_n|^q\right)^{1/q}.$$

But based on the first half of the theorem we obtain

$$(\sum |d_n|^q)^{1/q} \leqslant M^{\frac{2}{p}-1} \|g\|_p = M^{\frac{2}{p}-1},$$

and therefore

$$\|f_N\|_q \leqslant M^{\frac{2}{p}-1} \left(\sum_1^N |c_n|^p\right)^{1/p}. \tag{4.15}$$

Thus

$$\|f_{N+k} - f_N\|_q \leqslant M^{\frac{2}{p}-1} \left(\sum_{N+1}^{N+k} |c_n|^p\right)^{1/p}$$

for any $k$, whence it follows that $\{f_N\}$ converges in the norm of the space $L^q$. This means (see Introductory Material, § 21) that $f \in L^q$ is found such that $\|f - f_N\|_q \to 0$ as $N \to \infty$; then, permitting $N \to \infty$, we obtain from (4.15)

$$\|f\|_q \leqslant M^{\frac{2}{p}-1} \|c\|_p$$

and it only remains to prove that the numbers $c_n$ are the Fourier coefficients of $f$, for the theorem to be completely proved.

But since

$$\left|\int_a^b (f_N - f)\,\bar{\varphi}_n\,dt\right| \leqslant \|f_N - f\|_q \,\|\bar{\varphi}_n\|_k \leqslant M(b-a)^{1/p} \|f - f_N\|_q \to 0$$

as $N \to \infty$, then

$$c_n = \int_a^b f \bar{\varphi}_n\,dt,$$

and the proof is concluded.†

*Note 1.* We will not investigate here the problem concerning the transformation of the inequality in the Riesz theorem to an equality. We refer those who are interested to the work by Zygmund and Calderon.

*Note 2.* In the proof of the Riesz theorem the intrinsic assumption is made that $p > 1$. However, this same theorem due to Riesz and consequently the theorem due to Hausdorff and Young remain valid at $p = 1$ also. In this case $q = \infty$ and if it is defined (see Introductory Material, § 9) that

$$\|f\|_\infty = \sup |f|$$

and similarly it is assumed that

$$\|c\|_\infty = \frac{\max}{n} |c_n|,$$

then both assertions in Riesz's theorem are valid, as can be proved immediately.

---

† We will draw the attention of the reader to the work by Marcinkiewicz and Zygmund[4] where a certain generalization of this theorem is given.

*Note 3.* In the Riesz theorem just proved, it is assumed in both statement (1) and statement (2) that $p \leqslant 2$ whilst $q \geqslant 2$. Thus, from the summability of $|f|^p$ we drew conclusions concerning the convergence of $\sum |c_n|^q$ at $p \leqslant 2$, and also from the convergence of $\sum |c_n|^p$ we derived a result concerning the summability of $|f|^q$ at $p \leqslant 2$.

We want to prove that both statements cease to be correct if the numbers $p$ and $q$ are interchanged, in other words, if it is assumed that $p > 2$. This can be proved by examples. We will consider the case of a trigonometric system.

Indeed, if statement (1) were true for $p > 2$, then since a continuous function is summable to any degree $p$, it would be possible to state that for such a function the series

$$\sum (|a_n|^q + |b_n|^q),$$

converges on taking $q$ as near as desired to 1. However, in Chapter IV, § 14 we will prove that it is possible to construct a continuous function such that for any $\varepsilon > 0$

$$\sum (|a_n|^{2-\varepsilon} + |b_n|^{2-\varepsilon}) = +\infty.$$

In exactly the same way statement (2) ceases to be correct at $p > 2$. Indeed, if we consider the series

$$\sum_{n=1}^{\infty} \frac{\cos 2^n x}{\sqrt{n}},$$

then

$$\sum \left(\frac{1}{\sqrt{n}}\right)^p < +\infty$$

for any $p > 2$.

Consequently, if statement (2) were true at $p > 2$, then the series under consideration would be a Fourier series of $f(x) \in L^q$. However, in Chapter XI, § 3 we will prove that this series cannot be a Fourier series, as it will then be proved that a lacunary series is a Fourier series only when the series formed by the squares of its coefficients is convergent, and in our case this series is divergent.

We will demonstrate a simple fact, derived from the Hausdorff–Young theorem.

COROLLARY. *If $f(x) \in L^p$, $p > 1$, then both the series*

$$\sum \left|\frac{a_n}{n}\right| \quad \textit{and} \quad \sum \left|\frac{b_n}{n}\right|$$

*converge.*

Indeed, if $p \geqslant 2$, then $f \in L^p$ implies $f \in L^2$, and then it is sufficient to note that

$$\left|\frac{a_n}{n}\right| \leqslant \frac{1}{2} a_n^2 + \frac{1}{2} \frac{1}{n^2}$$

and similarly for $b_n$.

If $1 < p \leqslant 2$, then, according to the Hausdorff–Young theorem, the series $\sum (|a_n|^q + |b_n|^q)$ where $1/p + 1/q = 1$ should converge. But then for any $m$

$$\sum_{n=1}^{m} \left|\frac{a_n}{n}\right| \leqslant \left(\sum_{n=1}^{m} |a_n|^q\right)^{1/q} \left\{\sum_{n=1}^{m} \left(\frac{1}{n}\right)^p\right\}^{1/p} \leqslant C \left(\sum_{n=1}^{\infty} |a_n|^q\right)^{1/q},$$

where $C$ is a constant, since $\sum(1/n)^p < +\infty$ at $p > 1$. This means that $\sum |a_n/n| < +\infty$; the argument for $\sum b_n/n$ is exactly the same.

From the proved theorem, it follows in particular that the series

$$\sum \frac{a_n}{n} \quad \text{and} \quad \sum \frac{b_n}{n}$$

are convergent for $f(x) \in L^p$. With respect to the second of these series, it converges also for $f(x) \in L$ (see Chapter I, § 40), but this is not true for the first if $p = 1$. Indeed, in Chapter I, § 30 we proved that the series

$$\sum_{n=2}^{\infty} \frac{\cos nx}{\ln n}$$

is a Fourier series, although $\sum 1/(n \ln n) = +\infty$.

Hardy and Littlewood[5] found the necessary and sufficient conditions which had to be imposed on $f(x)$ for the series $\sum a_n/n$ to be convergent and also proved that if they are fulfilled then

$$\sum_{n=1}^{\infty} \frac{a_n}{n} = -\frac{1}{\pi} \int_0^{2\pi} f(x) \ln \left(2 \sin \frac{x}{2}\right) dx.$$

As regards the sum of the series $\sum b_n/n$, it is easy to prove the equality

$$\sum \frac{b_n}{n} = \frac{1}{2\pi} \int_0^{2\pi} (\pi - x) f(x)\, dx.$$

This formula is obtained by applying the Parseval equality to the function $f(x)$ and the function

$$\frac{\pi - x}{2} \sim \sum_{n=1}^{\infty} \frac{\sin nx}{n}$$

(see Chapter I, § 41) the use of the equality being valid, as will be proved in § 5, since this function is of bounded variation.

To conclude this section on the connection between the order of summability of a function and its Fourier coefficients, we will state without proof two theorems due to Paley[1].

Let us introduce the following notation: if $c_1, c_2, \ldots$ is any sequence of numbers (real or complex), then we will denote the numbers $|c_1|, |c_2|, \ldots, |c_n|, \ldots$ arranged in decreasing order by $\gamma_1, \gamma_2, \ldots, \gamma_n, \ldots$; if several of the numbers $|c_n|$ are equal, then in the sequence $\gamma_n$ there will be a corresponding number of repeated terms.

The following theorems hold:

PALEY'S THEOREMS. *Let* $\{\varphi_n(x)\}$ *be an orthogonal normal system in* $[a, b]$ *and* $|\bar{\varphi}_n(x)| \leqslant M$ $(n = 1, 2, \ldots)$, $a \leqslant x \leqslant b$.

(1) *If* $1 < p \leqslant 2$, $f(x) \in L^p$ *and* $c_1, c_2, \ldots, c_n, \ldots$ *be its Fourier coefficients with respect to the system* $\varphi_n(x)$, *then*

$$\left\{\sum_{n=1}^{\infty} |\gamma_n|^p n^{p-2}\right\}^{1/p} \leqslant A_p \left\{\int_a^b |f|^p dx\right\}^{1/p},$$

*where* $A_p$ *depends only on* $p$ *and* $M$.

(2) *If $q \geqslant 2$ and $c_1, c_2, \ldots, c_n, \ldots$ is a sequence of numbers for which*

$$\sum_{n=1}^{\infty} |\gamma_n|^q n^{q-2} < +\infty,$$

*then a function $f(x) \in L^q(a, b)$ exists, for which the numbers $c_n$ are Fourier coefficients with respect to the system $\{\varphi_n(x)\}$ and*

$$\left\{\int_a^b |f(x)|^q dx\right\}^{1/q} \leqslant B_p \left\{\sum_{n=1}^{\infty} |\gamma_n|^q n^{q-2}\right\}^{1/q},$$

*where $B_q$ depends only on $q$ and $M$.*

Proofs of these theorems can be found in Zygmund's book[A35] (see § 9.4) as well as in the present author's work.

Littlewood[5] too has investigated a problem with similar conclusions.

Finally, the theorems due to Hardy and Littlewood should be mentioned which refer to the connection between the order of summability of a function and its Fourier coefficients (see Zygmund[A35] § 9.5). Some particular cases of their results are reported in Chapter X, § 3.

## § 5. The generalization of Parseval's equality for the product of two functions

We have seen in Chapter I, § 18, that if $f(x) \in L^2$ and $\varphi(x) \in L^2$, whilst $a_n$ and $b_n$ are Fourier coefficients for $f(x)$ and $\alpha_n$ and $\beta_n$ for $\varphi(x)$, then we have Parseval's equality

$$\frac{1}{\pi}\int_{-\pi}^{\pi} f(x)\,\varphi(x)\,dx = \frac{a_0\alpha_0}{2} + \sum_{n=1}^{\infty}(a_n\alpha_n + b_n\beta_n). \tag{5.1}$$

Let us prove that the formula holds if $f \in L^p$, $\varphi \in L^q$ and $1/p + 1/q = 1$ $(p > 1)$. We already know (see Introductory Material, § 9) that in this case the product $f(x)\,\varphi(x)$ is summable.

Let us denote the partial sum of the Fourier series for $f(x)$ by $S_n(x)$. We then have

$$\frac{1}{\pi}\int_{-\pi}^{\pi} S_n(x)\,\varphi(x)\,dx = \frac{1}{\pi}\int_{-\pi}^{\pi}\left\{\frac{a_0}{2} + \sum_{k=1}^{n}\left(a_k \cos kx + b_k \sin kx\right)\right\}\varphi(x)\,dx$$

$$= \frac{a_0\alpha_0}{2} + \sum_{k=1}^{n}(a_k\alpha_k + b_k\beta_k).$$

Therefore it is sufficient to prove that

$$\frac{1}{\pi}\int_{-\pi}^{\pi} f(x)\,\varphi(x)\,dx = \lim_{n\to\infty}\frac{1}{\pi}\int_{-\pi}^{\pi} S_n(x)\,\varphi(x)\,dx$$

or that

$$\lim_{n\to\infty} \int_{-\pi}^{\pi} \varphi(x)\,[f(x) - S_n(x)]\,dx = 0.$$

But in Chapter VIII, § 20 it will be proved that at $p > 1$

$$\int_{-\pi}^{\pi} |f(x) - S_n(x)|^p\,dx \to 0 \quad \text{as} \quad n \to \infty,$$

if $f(x) \in L^p$. If this is so, then from Hölder's inequality

$$\int_{-\pi}^{\pi} |f(x) - S_n(x)|\,|\varphi(x)|\,dx \leqslant \| f(x) - S_n(x) \|_p \, \| \varphi(x) \|_q \to 0,$$

because $\varphi(x) \in L^q$.

Using this equality, we can obtain the following criterion for a certain series to be a Fourier series of $f(x) \in L^p$.

THEOREM. *For the series*

$$\frac{a_0}{2} + \sum_{n=1}^{\infty} (a_n \cos nx + b_n \sin nx) \tag{5.2}$$

*to be a Fourier series of the function $f(x) \in L^p$ $(p > 1)$, it is necessary and sufficient that, for every function $\varphi(x) \in L^q$ with coefficients $\alpha_n$, $\beta_n$, the series*

$$\frac{a_0 \alpha_0}{2} + \sum_{n=1}^{\infty} (a_n \alpha_n + b_n \beta_n) \tag{5.3}$$

*is convergent.*

*The necessity condition.* This has only just been proved. We even showed that the sum of this series is

$$\frac{1}{\pi} \int_{-\pi}^{\pi} f(x)\,\varphi(x)\,dx.$$

*The sufficiency condition.* Let us consider a function $\varphi(x) \in L^q$ with a series

$$\sigma(\varphi) = \frac{\alpha_0}{2} + \sum (\alpha_n \cos nx + \beta_n \sin nx). \tag{5.4}$$

We will denote by $\sigma_n(x)$ and $\tau_n$, respectively, the $(C, 1)$ means for the series (5.2) and (5.3). It is clear that

$$\tau_n = \frac{1}{\pi} \int_{-\pi}^{\pi} \varphi(t)\,\sigma_n(t)\,dt.$$

But $\tau_n = \tau_n(\varphi)$ is a linear functional in $L^q$, because $\sigma_n(t)$, as a trigonometric polynomial, belongs to $L^p$ for any $p$; the norm of this functional is $(1/\pi)\| \sigma_n \|_p$ (see Introductory Material, § 20).

Since the series (5.3) converges, which means that it is all the more $(C, 1)$ summable, then the values $\tau_n(\varphi)$ are bounded for every $\varphi \in L_q$, i.e.

$$\left| \frac{1}{\pi} \int_{-\pi}^{\pi} \varphi(t)\, \sigma_n(t)\, dt \right| \leqslant M(\varphi) < +\infty,$$

where $M$ is a constant dependent on $\varphi$ (but not on $n$).

Consequently, $\overline{\lim_{n\to\infty}}\ \tau_n(\varphi) < +\infty$. Therefore on the basis of the Banach–Steinhaus theorem (see Appendix, § 4) the norms of the functionals $\tau_n(\varphi)$ are bounded, i.e.

$$\|\sigma_n\|_p \leqslant K \quad (n = 1, 2, \ldots).$$

Hence, from Theorem 3 of § 60, Chapter I, it follows that series (5.2) is a Fourier series of some $f \in L^p$ and the proof is completed.

Let us return to Parseval's equality and prove the theorem:

*Parseval's equality holds, if $f(x)$ is of bounded variation, and $\varphi(x) \in L$.*

Indeed, in this case $f(x)$ too is bounded, and the functions $S_n(x)$ are all bounded, and therefore the product $\varphi(x)\,[f(x) - S_n(x)]$ is majorized by a summable function. On the other hand, $S_n(x) \to f(x)$ almost everywhere. On the basis of Lebesgue's theorem concerning passage to the limit under the integral sign we then have

$$\lim_{n\to\infty} \int_{-\pi}^{\pi} \varphi(x)\,[f(x) - S_n(x)]\, dx = 0,$$

and the proof is concluded as in the preceding case.

This argument does not apply, if $f(x)$ is only bounded and not of bounded variation. However, in this case, i.e. for $\varphi(x) \in L$ and bounded $f(x)$, Parseval's equality is valid, provided we consider the $(C, 1)$ summability of the series on the right-hand side instead of its convergence.

Indeed, let $\sigma_n(x)$ be the Fejér sums of the Fourier series of $f(x)$. Then $\sigma_n(x) \to f(x)$ almost everywhere and $|\sigma_n(x) - f(x)| \leqslant M$ and therefore

$$\lim_{n\to\infty} \int_{-\pi}^{\pi} \varphi(x)\,[f(x) - \sigma_n(x)]\, dx = 0.$$

But

$$\frac{1}{\pi}\int_{-\pi}^{\pi} \varphi(x)\,\sigma_n(x)\,dx = \frac{1}{\pi}\int_{-\pi}^{\pi} \varphi(x) \left\{ \frac{a_0}{2} + \sum_{k=1}^{n} \left(1 - \frac{k}{n+1}\right) \left(a_k \cos kx + b_k \sin kx\right) \right\} dx$$

$$= \frac{a_0 \alpha_0}{2} + \sum_{k=1}^{n} \left(1 - \frac{k}{n+1}\right) [a_k \alpha_k + b_k \beta_k]$$

and the right-hand side of this equality is none other than the $n$th Cesàro sum for the series (5.3). Therefore the statement is proved.

Returning to the case when $f(x)$ is of bounded variation, let us introduce a theorem which is used frequently.

*Any Fourier series after being multiplied by any function of bounded variation can be integrated term by term over any interval, i.e. if $\varphi(x)$ is of bounded variation and*

$$f(x) \sim \frac{a_0}{2} + \sum (a_n \cos nx + b_n \sin nx),$$

*then*

$$\int_a^b f(x)\,\varphi(x)\,dx = \frac{a_0}{2}\int_a^b \varphi(x)\,dx + \sum_{n=1}^{\infty}\left(a_n \int_a^b \varphi(x)\cos nx\,dx + b_n \int_a^b \varphi(x)\sin nx\,dx\right). \tag{5.5}$$

First of all, we note that it is sufficient to prove formula (5.5) for the case $[a, b] \equiv [0, 2\pi]$. In fact, if $0 < a < b < 2\pi$, it is sufficient to consider $\varphi(x) = 0$ outside $(a, b)$ and then integration can be carried out over the interval $[0, 2\pi]$; if the length of this interval $[a, b]$ exceeds $2\pi$, then it can be divided into a finite number of intervals, in each of which it is proved that the formula holds.

Thus, it is sufficient to prove that

$$\int_0^{2\pi} f(x)\,\varphi(x)\,dx = \frac{a_0}{2}\int_0^{2\pi} \varphi(x)\,dx + \sum a_n \int_0^{2\pi} \varphi(x)\cos nx\,dx + \sum b_n \int_0^{2\pi} \varphi(x)\sin nx\,dx. \tag{5.6}$$

After multiplying both sides of (5.6) by $1/\pi$, we see that this formula is transformed into Parseval's equality

$$\frac{1}{\pi}\int_0^{2\pi} f(x)\,\varphi(x)\,dx = \frac{a_0}{2}\alpha_0 + \sum (a_n\alpha_n + b_n\beta_n),$$

the validity of which has already been proved† for $f(x) \in L$ and $\varphi(x)$ of bounded variation.

## § 6. The rate at which the Fourier coefficients of summable functions tend to zero

Let us ask the following question: can a function $\lambda(n) \uparrow \infty$ be found such that for any summable function we have

$$a_n = o\left(\frac{1}{\lambda(n)}\right), \quad b_n = o\left(\frac{1}{\lambda(n)}\right)? \tag{6.1}$$

† It is possible to impose other limitations on $f(x)$ instead of "bounded variation". Thus, for example, Parseval's equality holds if $\varphi(x) \in L$, $f(x)$ is bounded, and moreover

$$\int_0^h [f(x+u) - f(x-u)]\,du = o\left(\frac{h}{\ln \frac{1}{h}}\right)$$

uniformly with respect to $x$ (see Izumi and Sâto[11]).

It seems that a negative answer must be given to this question; indeed, it is possible for any $\lambda(n) \uparrow \infty$ to find a continuous $f(x)$ for which the Fourier coefficients do not satisfy the relationship (6.1). In fact, we will choose the numbers $n_k$ such that

$$\sum_{k=1}^{\infty} \frac{1}{\lambda(n_k)} < +\infty$$

and suppose that $a_{n_k} = 1/\lambda(n_k)$, $b_{n_k} = 1/\lambda(n_k)$; $a_n = b_n = 0$, if $n \neq n_k$ $(k = 1, 2, \ldots)$. Then the series

$$\sum (a_n \cos nx + b_n \sin nx) = \sum \frac{1}{\lambda(n_k)} [\cos n_k x + \sin n_k x]$$

is a Fourier series of a continuous function, because it converges absolutely and uniformly, but at the same time the relationship (6.1) cannot hold, since

$$a_{n_k} \lambda(n_k) = 1 \quad \text{and} \quad b_{n_k} \lambda(n_k) = 1 \quad (k = 1, 2, \ldots).$$

Thus, even for continuous functions it is impossible to assert that the Fourier coefficients are obliged to tend to zero at some definite "rate".

However, if $f(x) \in L^p$ $(p > 1)$, then we have seen (§ 5) that at $p \leqslant 2$ we have $\sum (|a_n|^q + |b_n|^q) < +\infty$, and at $p > 2$ in any case $\sum (|a_n|^2 + |b_n|^2) < +\infty$, i.e. all such $a_n$ and $b_n$ cannot be "too great" for large values of $n$.

In other words, it is a matter of $f(x) \in L$, namely:

Provided $f(x)$ is summable, then its Fourier coefficients can tend to zero as slowly as desired. To express this more exactly:

*If $\varepsilon_n \downarrow 0$ as slowly as desired, then it is possible to find a Fourier series of the form*

$$\sum a_n \cos nx,$$

*such that $a_n \geqslant \varepsilon_n$ $(n = 1, 2, \ldots)$.*

This will be proved in Chapter X, § 2.

Banach[1] also observed that it is possible to find a sequence of positive $\lambda_n$ tending to $+\infty$ and a summable $f(x)$ for which

$$\sum_{n=1}^{\infty} (|a_n|^{\lambda_n} + |b_n|^{\lambda_n}) = +\infty.$$

Can all this indicate some *necessary* conditions for the Fourier coefficients of a summable function?

Here we will only recall that the series $\sum b_n/n$ should converge (see Chapter I, § 40) but this is not the case for $\sum a_n/n$ (see § 4); thus the coefficients $a_n$ and $b_n$ do not possess the same properties. In Chapter VIII we will see that the series conjugate to a Fourier series should not itself be a Fourier series. We will return to the question of necessary conditions in § 9 of this chapter. Now we will discuss the question of *sufficient* conditions. Unfortunately, what can be said consists almost entirely of negative facts in this connection.

It is known that the condition $\sum_{n=1}^{\infty} (a_n^2 + b_n^2) < +\infty$ is sufficient. But Orlicz[1] observed that it is possible to find a sequence of positive numbers $\gamma_n$, $\gamma_n \to 2$ as $n \to \infty$, such that the series

$$\sum (|a_n|^{\gamma_n} + |b_n|^{\gamma_n}) < +\infty,$$

however, $\sum (a_n \cos nx + b_n \sin nx)$ is not a Fourier series.

We will also note that any condition of the kind

$$a_n = O\left(\frac{1}{\lambda(n)}\right), \quad b_n = O\left(\frac{1}{\lambda(n)}\right),$$

where $\lambda(n) \uparrow \infty$ cannot be sufficient for the series $\sum (a_n \cos nx + b_n \sin nx)$ to be a Fourier series. We will prove this in § 8.

We recall too that in § 4 of this chapter it was remarked that: any condition of the kind

$$\sum (|a_n|^q + |b_n|^q) < +\infty,$$

where $q > 2$ is not sufficient for the series $\sum (a_n \cos nx + b_n \sin nx)$ to be a Fourier series.

Let us pay some attention to the following fact: if in a Fourier series some coefficients are changed to zero, then it may cease to be a Fourier series. Indeed, let $a_n = 1/\sqrt{\ln n}$, then the series $\sum a_n \cos nx$ is a Fourier series (see Chapter I, § 30). Now we make all the $a_n$ zero for $n \neq 2^k$ $(k = 1, 2, \ldots)$. We obtain the series $\sum a_{2^k} \cos 2^k x$ which is a lacur ary series; if it were a Fourier series, then (see Chapter XI, § 3) we should have had $\sum (a_{2^k})^2 < +\infty$, but however

$$\sum (a_{2^k})^2 \geqslant \sum \frac{1}{k \ln 2} = +\infty.$$

This proves our statement.

In § 8 we will indicate greater difficulties experienced in solving the problem of sufficiency conditions for Fourier coefficients; in order to do this, however, we must first refer to some auxiliary theorems.

## § 7. Auxiliary theorems concerning the Rademacher system

The definition of Rademacher functions was given in § 9 Chapter I. Now we will prove a few theorems concerning these functions and then apply them to the study of trigonometric series.

THEOREM 1†. *If* $\sum c_n^2 < +\infty$, *then the series*

$$\sum c_n \varphi_n(t), \tag{7.1}$$

*where* $\varphi_n(t)$ *is the n-th Rademacher function, is convergent almost everywhere.*

In fact, it follows from $\sum c_n^2 < +\infty$ that the series (7.1) is a Fourier series for some $(f x) \in L^2$, for which

$$\int_0^1 [f(x) - S_n(x)]^2 \, dx \to 0 \quad \text{as} \quad n \to \infty.$$

† See Rademacher[1], also Paley and Zygmund[1], and Kolmogorov[4].

We derive from this with the help of Bunyakovskii's inequality

$$\int_0^1 |f(x) - S_n(x)|\, dx \to 0.$$

Let $(a, b)$ be any interval in $[0, 1]$; then

$$\left| \int_a^b S_n(x)\, dx - \int_a^b f(x)\, dx \right| \leqslant \int_a^b \left| S_n(x) - f(x) \right| dx \leqslant \int_0^1 \left| S_n(x) - f(x) \right| dx \to 0,$$

i.e.

$$\int_a^b S_n(x)\, dx \to \int_a^b f(x)\, dx \quad \text{as} \quad n \to \infty. \tag{7.2}$$

Now let us denote the indefinite integral of $f(t)$ by $F(t)$, then $F'(t) = f(t)$ everywhere apart from some set $E$, $mE = 0$. Let $\mathscr{E}$ be obtained from $E$ by the addition of all the points $t$ of the type $t = p/2^k$, where $p$ and $k$ are any integers; again $m\mathscr{E} = 0$. We will prove that the series (7.1) converges everywhere outside $\mathscr{E}$. Indeed let $t \bar{\in} \mathscr{E}$. Then $t \in (p/2^k, (p+1)/2^k)$ where $k$ is any integer and $p$ takes one of the values $0, 1, 2, \ldots, 2^k - 1$.

For any $j \geqslant k$ in the interval $I = (p/2^k, (p+1)/2^k)$ we have

$$\int_I \varphi_j(x)\, dx = 0,$$

therefore

$$\int_I S_n(x)\, dx = \int_I S_{k-1}(x)\, dx \quad (n > k)$$

and from (7.2) it follows that $\int_I f(x)\, dx = \int_I S_{k-1}(x)\, dx$. But $S_{k-1}(x)$ is constant in $I$ and therefore

$$S_{k-1}(t) = \frac{1}{I} \int_I S_{k-1}(x)\, dx = \frac{1}{I} \int_I f(x)\, dx. \tag{7.3}$$

If $k \to \infty$, then the length of the interval $I$ tends to zero and because $t \bar{\in} E$, then the right-hand side of (7.3) tends to $f(t)$, which means that

$$\lim_{k \to \infty} S_{k-1}(t) = f(t),$$

and this concludes the proof of the theorem.

THEOREM 2 (Zygmund[7]). *If the series*

$$\sum_{n=1}^{\infty} c_n \varphi_n(t), \tag{7.4}$$

*where $\varphi_n(t)$ are Rademacher functions is summable by method $(C, 1)$ in the set $E$, $mE > 0$, then $\sum c_n^2 < +\infty$.*

*Proof.* For the $n$th Cesàro sum we have the series

$$\sigma_n(t) = \sum_{k=1}^{n} \left(1 - \frac{k}{n}\right) c_k \varphi_k(t) \tag{7.5}$$

and it is conditional that $\sigma_n(t)$ converges in $E$, $mE > 0$. This means that an $\mathscr{E}$ can be found, $m\mathscr{E} > 0$, where $\sigma_n(t)$ converges uniformly to $\sigma(t)$ and $\sigma(t)$ is continuous. Therefore for sufficiently large $N$ we have at $n > N$, for example,

$$|\sigma_n(t)| < |\sigma(t)| + 1, \quad t \in \mathscr{E},$$

i.e. an $M$ can be found such that

$$|\sigma_n(t)| < M \quad \text{for} \quad n > N \quad \text{and} \quad t \in \mathscr{E},$$

and, consequently, an $M$ can be found such that

$$|\sigma_n(t)| < M_1 \quad \text{for} \quad t \in \mathscr{E} \quad \text{and} \quad n = 1, 2, \dots. \tag{7.6}$$

Hence

$$\int_{\mathscr{E}} \sigma_n^2(t)\, dt < M_1^2 m\mathscr{E} \quad (n = 1, 2, \dots). \tag{7.7}$$

This means that

$$M_1^2 m\mathscr{E} \geqslant \sum_{k=1}^{n} \left(1 - \frac{k}{n}\right)^2 c_k^2 \int_{\mathscr{E}} \varphi_k^2(t)\, dt + \sum_{\substack{k=1 \\ k \neq j}}^{n} \sum_{j=1}^{n} \left(1 - \frac{k}{n}\right)\left(1 - \frac{j}{n}\right) c_k c_j \int_{\mathscr{E}} \varphi_k \varphi_j\, dt. \tag{7.8}$$

From the definition of Rademacher functions it is easily deduced that the system $\{\varphi_k(x)\varphi_j(x)\}$ where $k \neq j$ is also orthogonal. The numbers

$$b_{kj} = \int_{\mathscr{E}} \varphi_k(t)\, \varphi_j(t)\, dt$$

are the Fourier coefficients with respect to this system for the function $f(x)$, characteristic for the set $\mathscr{E}$ (i.e. $f(x) = 1$ in $\mathscr{E}$ and $f(x) = 0$ in $C\mathscr{E}$). This means that $\sum\sum b_{kj}^2 < +\infty$. In considering the summability of the series (7.5) by the $(C, 1)$ method and also the convergence of the series $\sum c_n^2$, a finite number of the first terms plays no part; therefore, without disturbing the generality, it is possible to consider that for some $N_1$ we have $c_n = 0$ for $n \leqslant N_1$.

This number $N_1$ can be made so large that

$$\sum_{k=N_1+1}^{\infty} \sum_{\substack{j=N_1+1 \\ (k \neq j)}}^{\infty} b_{kj}^2 < \left(\frac{m\mathscr{E}}{2}\right)^2. \tag{7.9}$$

On disregarding terms in the sum $\sigma_n(t)$ (i.e. by supposing that $c_1 = c_2 = \cdots = c_{N_1} = 0$) the constant $M_1$ in formula (7.6) should perhaps be changed into some $M_2$.

Applying Bunyakovskii's inequality to the latter sum in equality (7.8) and taking into account (7.9), we obtain

$$\left| \sum_{\substack{k=1 \\ (k \neq j)}}^{n} \sum_{k=1}^{n} \left(1 - \frac{k}{n}\right)\left(1 - \frac{j}{n}\right) c_k c_j \int_{\mathscr{E}} \varphi_k \varphi_j\, dt \right|$$

$$\leqslant \sqrt{\sum_{k=1}^{n} \left(1 - \frac{k}{n}\right)^2 c_k^2 \sum_{j=1}^{n} \left(1 - \frac{j}{n}\right)^2 c_j^2 \left(\frac{m\mathscr{E}}{2}\right)^2} = \frac{m\mathscr{E}}{2} \sum_{k=1}^{n} \left(1 - \frac{k}{n}\right)^2 c_k^2,$$

therefore, noting that $\varphi_n^2(t) = 1$ almost everywhere for any $n$, we find from (7.8)

$$M_2^2 m\mathscr{E} \geqslant \sum_{k=1}^{n} \left(1 - \frac{k}{n}\right)^2 c_k^2 m\mathscr{E} - \sum_{k=1}^{n} \left(1 - \frac{k}{n}\right)^2 c_k^2 \frac{m\mathscr{E}}{2} = \frac{m\mathscr{E}}{2} \sum_{k=1}^{n} \left(1 - \frac{k}{n}\right)^2 c_k^2 .$$

This means that

$$\sum_{k=1}^{n} \left(1 - \frac{k}{n}\right)^2 c_k^2 \leqslant 2M_2^2$$

for any $n$. Let $N_2$ be arbitrary.

If $N_3 > N_2$, then

$$\sum_{k=1}^{N_2} \left(1 - \frac{k}{N_3}\right)^2 c_k^2 \leqslant \sum_{k=1}^{N_3} \left(1 - \frac{k}{N_3}\right)^2 c_k^2 \leqslant 2M_2^2 .$$

But $N_3$ can be taken as large as desired; whence it follows that

$$\sum_{k=1}^{N_2} c_k^2 \leqslant 2M_2^2 ,$$

and since $N_2$ is any number, then $\sum_{k=1}^{\infty} c_k^2 < +\infty$.

Theorem 2 is proved.

*Note 1.* Theorem 2 can be somewhat strengthened, namely, if it is expressed in this form:

*If for the series $\sum c_n \varphi_n(t)$ the Cesàro sums satisfy the condition*

$$|\sigma_n(t)| \leqslant M \quad (n = 1, 2, \ldots) \tag{7.10}$$

*in some $\mathscr{E}$, $m\mathscr{E} > 0$, then $\sum c_n^2 < +\infty$.*

Indeed, during the proof of Theorem 2 we first detected the existence of a set of positive measure where condition (7.10) is completely fulfilled and we use only this fact.

*Note 2.* In order to simplify the proof we carried out the argument with method $(C, 1)$. In actual fact, a very much more general theorem holds.

THEOREM. *If the series $\sum c_n \varphi_n(t)$ is summable by any method $T$ or even $T^*$ in a set of measure greater than zero, then $\sum c_n^2 < +\infty$.*†

For the case of convergence this theorem was proved by Kolmogorov and Khintchin[1].

## § 8. Absence of criteria applicable to the moduli of coefficients

We want to show that if we disregard the signs of the numbers $a_n$ and $b_n$ and consider only their moduli, then no condition, apart from $\sum (a_n^2 + b_n^2) < +\infty$, is sufficient for the series

$$\sum (a_n \cos nx + b_n \sin nx)$$

† See Introductory Material, § 5 for methods $T$ and $T^*$.

to be a Fourier series. This fact was first detected by Littlewood[1] who proved that if the series $\sum \varrho_n^2$ diverges ($\varrho_n^2 = a_n^2 + b_n^2$), then it is possible to find numbers $\alpha_n$ such that the series

$$\sum \varrho_n \cos(nx - \alpha_n)$$

is not a Fourier series. Then Szidon[5] gave the following strengthening to Littlewood's theorem:

*If all the series*

$$\pm \frac{a_0}{2} + \sum_{n=1}^{\infty} \pm (a_n \cos nx + b_n \sin nx), \tag{8.1}$$

*where the plus and minus signs can be chosen as desired, are Fourier series, then* $\sum (a_n^2 + b_n^2) < +\infty$.

In other words, if $\sum (a_n^2 + b_n^2) = +\infty$, then it is always possible to choose the plus or minus signs so that among the series (8.1) a series can be obtained which is not a Fourier series.

This result in its turn is contained in a much stronger result obtained by Zygmund. In order to formulate it, we will consider the Rademacher functions. Let us suppose that

$$A_0(x) = \frac{a_0}{2}, \; A_n(x) = a_n \cos nx + b_n \sin nx$$

and we will consider series of the type

$$\sum_{n=0}^{\infty} \pm A_n(x). \tag{8.2}$$

If we include in the examination all the cases when $+1$ or $-1$ is encountered as the multiplier for $A_n(x)$ only a finite number of times, then we will obtain only a denumerable set of series of the type (8.2). All the remaining series can be written in the form

$$\sum_{n=1}^{\infty} A_n(x)\, \varphi_n(t), \tag{8.3}$$

where $\varphi_n(t)$ is the $n$th Rademacher function, and $t$ is some value in the interval (0, 1) whilst $t \neq p/2^q$ where $p$ and $q$ are integers. In fact for any $t \neq p/2^q$ we have $\varphi_n(t) = +1$ or $\varphi_n(t) = -1$ for any $n$, which means that series (8.3) takes the form (8.2); conversely, if series (8.2) is given and in it the plus and minus signs are encountered an infinite number of times, then it is easily seen that a completely definite $t_0 \neq p/2^q$ can be found for which $\varphi_n(t_0) = +1$ or $\varphi_n(t_0) = -1$ that is, it takes the same sign as occurs in $A_n(x)$.

We can say that *almost all series of the type* (8.2) *possess a certain property* if this property is also possessed by series (8.3) for almost all values of $t$ in the interval (0, 1).

Accepting this definition, we can formulate Zygmund's theorem thus:

THEOREM 1†. *If* $\sum_{n=1}^{\infty} (a_n^2 + b_n^2) = \infty$, *then almost all the series*

$$\pm \frac{a_0}{2} + \sum \pm(a_n \cos nx + b_n \sin nx)$$

† Zygmund proved a more general theorem, i.e. concerning the non-summability of these series by any $T^*$ method. However, because we base the proof on Theorem 2, § 7, which was proved only for the method $(C, 1)$, we obtain a weaker result here.

*are not summable* $(C, 1)$ *almost everywhere in* $[0, 2\pi]$ *and, consequently, are not Fourier series.*

This theorem does indeed cover Szidon's theorem formulated above.

In its turn, it can be obtained from Theorem 2 § 7. In fact, let us suppose that $\sum (a_n^2 + b_n^2) = +\infty$. We will first prove that

$$\sum_{n=1}^{\infty} A_n^2(x) = +\infty$$

for nearly all values of $x$.

Indeed let us assume that this is not so. Then an $E$ can be found, $mE > 0$, such that $\sum_{n=1}^{\infty} A_n^2(x)$ converges in $E$. Then an $\mathscr{E}$ can be chosen inside $E$, $m\mathscr{E} > 0$, in which the sum $\sum A_n^2(x)$ is bounded. Let

$$\sum_{n=1}^{\infty} A_n^2(x) < M \quad \text{in} \quad \mathscr{E}.$$

Supposing that $A_n(x) = \varrho_n \cos(nx + \alpha_n)$, we can integrate the series $\sum A_n^2(x)$ term by term in the set $\mathscr{E}$; then we obtain

$$\sum_{n=1}^{\infty} \varrho_n^2 \int_{\mathscr{E}} \cos^2(nx + \alpha_n)\, dx < Mm\mathscr{E}. \tag{8.4}$$

But

$$\int_{\mathscr{E}} \cos^2(nx + \alpha_n)\, dx = \frac{1}{2} \int_{\mathscr{E}} [1 + \cos 2(nx + \alpha_n)]\, dx \to \frac{1}{2} m\mathscr{E}$$

as $n \to \infty$; which means that for a sufficiently large $N$ every term of the series on the left-hand side of (8.4) at $n \geqslant N$ exceeds $\varrho_n^2 a$, where $a > 0$, therefore

$$\sum \varrho_n^2 < +\infty,$$

and this contradicts the hypothesis that $\sum (a_n^2 + b_n^2) = +\infty$.

Thus, we have proved that if $\sum (a_n^2 + b_n^2) = +\infty$, then $\sum A_n^2(x) = +\infty$ for almost all values of $x$.

Now let us denote by $E$ a plane set of points $(x, t)$ possessing this property: if $(x_0, t_0) \in E$, then the series

$$\sum A_n(x_0)\, \varphi_n(t_0)$$

is summable by the method $(C, 1)$, i.e. the corresponding series

$$\sum \pm A_n(x_0)$$

is summable by the Fejér method. Let us prove that $mE = 0$.

Indeed, $\sum A_n^2(x_0) = +\infty$ for nearly all $x$. Let $\mathscr{E}$ be a set of $x$ for which this is so, then $m\mathscr{E} = 2\pi$. If $x_0 \in \mathscr{E}$, then according to the preceding theorem due to Zygmund the set of all $t$ for which $\sum A_n(x_0)\varphi_n(t)$ is summable by the $(C, 1)$ method is of measure zero. This means that the set of points $(x_0, t) \in E$ is of measure zero and this is true for all $x_0 \in \mathscr{E}$. Consequently, for nearly all $x_0$ in $[0, 2\pi]$ the vertical straight line $x = x_0$ intersects $E$ in a set of measure zero. But then from Fubini's theorem (see Introductory Material, § 18) it follows that $mE = 0$. If this is so, then, again due to

Fubini's theorem, nearly any horizontal straight line intersects $E$ in a set of measure zero, i.e. for nearly all $t_0$ the series $\sum_{n=1}^{\infty} A_n(x)\varphi_n(t_0)$ can be summable by the $(C, 1)$ method only for a set of points of measure zero. But this means that "nearly all the series" $\sum \pm A_n(x)$ are summable by the Fejér method only in a set of measure zero, but since a Fourier series should be summable by the Fejér method almost everywhere, then nearly all the series $\sum \pm A_n(x)$ are not Fourier series, which concludes the proof.

*Note 1.* It is useful to note that if $\sum (a_n^2 + b_n^2) = +\infty$, then for nearly all the series $\sum \pm(a_n \cos nx + b_n \sin nx)$ the partial sums of a series are almost everywhere unbounded. Indeed, if the series $\sum (a_n \cos nx + b_n \sin nx)\varphi_n(t)$ possesses bounded partial sums in the plane set $E$, $mE > 0$, then on the basis of the note to Theorem 2, § 7, in a set of positive measure, $\sum (a_n \cos nx + b_n \sin nx)^2 < +\infty$, but this contradicts the hypothesis $\sum (a_n^2 + b_n^2) = +\infty$.

This note will be used in Chapter V, § 23.

*Note 2.* We have proved that if $\sum (a_n^2 + b_n^2) = +\infty$, then nearly all the series

$$\sum \pm(a_n \cos nx + b_n \sin nx)$$

are not Fourier series. It is interesting to note that *when* $\sum (a_n^2 + b_n^2) < +\infty$, *then nearly all these series converge.* This result follows quite quickly from Theorem 1, § 7.

## § 9. Some necessity conditions for Fourier coefficients

In § 6 we have already spoken of the difficulties encountered in finding the necessity conditions for the Fourier coefficients of summable functions.

Here, following Salem[1], we will demonstrate some necessity conditions, which are well-known and of considerable interest.

Let

$$\frac{a_0}{2} + \sum_{n=1}^{\infty} (a_n \cos nx + b_n \sin nx) \tag{9.1}$$

be the Fourier series of some summable function $f(x)$. Let $\varphi(x)$ be a function of bounded variation and $\alpha_n$ and $\beta_n$ be its Fourier coefficients; we will assume that $\alpha_0 = 0$. Then Parseval's equality (§ 5) is valid

$$\int_{-\pi}^{\pi} f(x)\,\varphi(x)\,dx = \pi \sum_{n=1}^{\infty} (a_n\alpha_n + b_n\beta_n).$$

Let $\mu$ be a variable parameter; let us consider a function equal to $\varphi(\mu x)$ in $(-\pi, \pi)$ with period $2\pi$. If $\alpha_n(\mu)$ and $\beta_n(\mu)$ are its Fourier coefficients, then we will have

$$\int_{-\pi}^{\pi} f(x)\,\varphi(\mu x)\,dx = \pi \left[\frac{a_0\alpha_0(\mu)}{2} + \sum_{n=1}^{\infty} (a_n\alpha_n(\mu) + b_n\beta_n(\mu))\right]. \tag{9.2}$$

Using Fejér's lemma (see Chapter I, § 20) and the fact that $\alpha_0 = \frac{1}{\pi}\int_0^{2\pi} \varphi(x)\,dx = 0$, we see that the integral on the left-hand side of (9.2) tends to zero as $\mu \to \infty$. Moreover

$$\alpha_0(\mu) = \frac{1}{\pi}\int_0^{2\pi} \varphi(\mu x)\,dx = \frac{1}{\mu\pi}\int_0^{\mu\cdot 2\pi} \varphi(y)\,dy \to 0 \quad \text{as} \quad \mu \to \infty,$$

again due to $\alpha_0 = 0$. Therefore, from (9.2) we obtain the following:

$$\lim_{\mu\to\infty} \sum_{n=1}^{\infty} [a_n\alpha_n(\mu) + b_n\beta_n(\mu)] = 0$$

which is a necessary condition for $a_n$ and $b_n$ to be Fourier coefficients.

In particular, if we suppose that $\varphi(x) = \cos x$ or $\varphi(x) = \sin x$ and consider $\mu$ to be non-integral, then we find that

$$\int_{-\pi}^{\pi} f(x)\cos\mu x\,dx = 2\mu\sin\mu\pi \sum_{n=1}^{\infty} \frac{(-1)^n a_n}{\mu^2 - n^2} + \frac{a_0\sin\mu\pi}{\mu},$$

$$\int_{-\pi}^{\pi} f(x)\sin\mu x\,dx = 2\sin\mu\pi \sum_{n=1}^{\infty} \frac{(-1)^n n b_n}{\mu^2 - n^2}.$$

If instead of $f(x)$ we consider $f(x + \pi)$, then we get rid of the multiplier $(-1)^n$. Let us now permit $\mu \to \infty$, assuming values which do not approximate to any integer values; for example, let us suppose that

$$\mu = p + \frac{1}{2},$$

where $p$ runs through all the integer values.

Hence we have these *necessary conditions for the numbers $a_n$ and $b_n$ to be Fourier coefficients:*

$$\lim_{p\to\infty} p \sum_{n=1}^{\infty} \frac{a_n}{\left(p + \frac{1}{2}\right)^2 - n^2} = 0; \quad \lim_{p\to\infty} \sum_{n=1}^{\infty} \frac{n b_n}{\left(p + \frac{1}{2}\right)^2 - n^2} = 0. \tag{9.3}$$

From the first of these conditions, it is possible to deduce this corollary as a particular case:

*If $a_n \downarrow 0$, then for the series*

$$\sum a_n \cos nx$$

*to be a Fourier series, it is necessary that*

$$\lim_{n\to\infty} (a_n - a_{n+1}) \ln n = 0. \tag{9.4}$$

To prove this statement we will first prove that if $a_n \downarrow 0$, then

$$\lim_{p\to\infty} p \sum_{2p+1}^{\infty} \frac{a_n}{\left(p + \frac{1}{2}\right)^2 - n^2} = 0. \tag{9.5}$$

Indeed, all the terms of the series in the formula (9.5) are negative, therefore the series

$$\sum_{2p+1}^{\infty} \frac{a_n}{n^2 - \left(p + \frac{1}{2}\right)^2}$$

has positive signs and since $a_n \downarrow 0$ its sum does not exceed

$$a_{2p+1} \sum_{n=2p+1}^{\infty} \frac{1}{n^2 - \left(p + \frac{1}{2}\right)^2};$$

but at $n \geqslant 2p + 1$ we have $n^2 - (p + \frac{1}{2})^2 \geqslant \frac{3}{4} n^2$ and therefore

$$\sum_{2p+1}^{\infty} \frac{1}{n^2 - \left(p + \frac{1}{2}\right)^2} \leqslant \frac{4}{3} \sum_{2p+1}^{\infty} \frac{1}{n^2} = O\left(\frac{1}{p}\right)$$

Consequently,

$$p \sum_{n=2p+1}^{\infty} \frac{a_n}{n^2 - \left(p + \frac{1}{2}\right)^2} \leqslant p a_{2p+1} O\left(\frac{1}{p}\right) = o(1),$$

and this proves (9.5).

Hence it follows that for $a_n \downarrow 0$ the necessity condition (9.3) can be rewritten in the form

$$\lim_{p\to\infty} p \sum_{n=1}^{2p} \frac{a_n}{\left(p + \frac{1}{2}\right)^2 - n^2} = 0. \tag{9.6}$$

But since

$$\frac{1}{\left(p + \frac{1}{2}\right)^2 - n^2} = \frac{2}{2p+1} \left[\frac{1}{2p + 1 + 2n} + \frac{1}{2p + 1 - 2n}\right],$$

then the condition (9.6) is just as strong as the condition

$$\lim_{p\to\infty} \sum_{n=1}^{2p} a_n \left[\frac{1}{2p + 1 + 2n} + \frac{1}{2p + 1 - 2n}\right] = 0. \tag{9.7}$$

Since

$$\sum_{n=1}^{2p} a_n \frac{1}{2p + 1 + 2n} < \frac{1}{2p} \sum_{n=1}^{2p} a_n \to 0$$

as $p \to \infty$, because $a_n \to 0$, then condition (9.7) takes the form

$$\lim_{p\to\infty} \sum_{n=1}^{2p} \frac{a_n}{2p + 1 - 2n} = 0$$

or

$$\frac{a_1}{2p-1} + \frac{a_2}{2p-3} + \cdots + \frac{a_p}{1} - \left[\frac{a_{p+1}}{1} + \frac{a_{p+2}}{3} + \cdots + \frac{a_{2p}}{2p-1}\right] \to 0,$$

or

$$\frac{a_p - a_{p+1}}{1} + \frac{a_{p-1} - a_{p+2}}{3} + \cdots + \frac{a_1 - a_{2p}}{2p - 1} \to 0. \tag{9.8}$$

But, supposing $\Delta n = a_n - a_{n+1}$, we see immediately that each of the numerical fractions in (9.8) is not less than $\Delta a_p$ (because it is conditional that all $\Delta a_n \geqslant 0$) and therefore (9.8) implies that

$$\Delta a_p \left(1 + \frac{1}{3} + \cdots + \frac{1}{2p - 1}\right) \to 0.$$

But then

$$\Delta a_p \ln p \to 0,$$

and our statement is proved.

This necessity condition permits us to set up an example of a cosine series:

$$\sum a_n \cos nx,$$

in which $a_n \downarrow 0$, but it is not a Fourier series†, however. For this it is sufficient to suppose, for example, that

$$a_n = \frac{1}{m} \quad \text{for } 2^{(m-1)^2} \leqslant n < 2^{m^2}, m = 1, 2, \ldots$$

Then monotonicity is present, but

$$(a_{2^{m^2}-1} - a_{2^{m^2}}) \ln 2^{m^2} = \left(\frac{1}{m} - \frac{1}{m+1}\right) m^2 \ln 2 \to \ln 2$$

as $m \to \infty$ and the necessity condition is not fulfilled.

## § 10. Salem's necessary and sufficient conditions

We wish to demonstrate now some conditions which arouse interest as being necessary and sufficient, although they are not clear. They were introduced by Salem[1].

Let us denote by $\{M\}$ a class of functions

$$\omega(x) = \sum_{n=1}^{\infty} (\alpha_n \cos nx + \beta_n \sin nx)$$

which are continuous and differentiable, $|\omega(x)| \leqslant 1$ and such that the Fourier series of $\omega'(x)$ converges absolutely.

THEOREM. *For the series*

$$\sum (a_n \cos nx + b_n \sin nx) \tag{10.1}$$

*to be a Fourier series it is necessary and sufficient for* (1) *the formally integrated series*

$$\sum \left(-\frac{b_n}{n} \cos nx + \frac{a_n}{n} \sin nx\right)$$

*to converge to a continuous function* $F(x)$;

† The first example of this type of series was set up by Szidon[1].

(2) *the expression*

$$\sum (a_n \alpha_n + b_n \beta_n)$$

*to tend to zero, when* $\omega$, *belonging to* $\{M\}$, *changes so that* $\sum_{n=1}^{\infty} (\alpha_n^2 + \beta_n^2)$ *tends to zero.*

*Necessity conditions.* Let us assume that (10.1) is the Fourier series of a summable function $f(x)$. The necessity of condition (1) is a classical result. Now let $\omega(x)$ belong to $\{M\}$ and let

$$\frac{1}{\pi} \int_{-\pi}^{\pi} \omega^2(x)\, dx = \sum_{n=1}^{\infty} (\alpha_n^2 + \beta_n^2) = \varepsilon. \tag{10.2}$$

We have

$$\frac{1}{\pi} \int_{-\pi}^{\pi} f(x)\, \omega(x)\, dx = \sum_{n=1}^{\infty} (a_n \alpha_n + b_n \beta_n). \tag{10.3}$$

The application of Parseval's equality is valid (see § 5), since $\omega'(x)$ possesses an absolutely convergent Fourier series, and therefore $\omega(x)$ is not only of bounded variation but is also absolutely continuous (moreover, the series on the right-hand side of (10.3) even converges absolutely).

Let $E$ be a set of points, where $|\omega(x)| \geqslant \varepsilon^{1/3}$; then from

$$\frac{1}{\pi} \int_{E} \omega^2(x)\, dx \geqslant \varepsilon^{2/3} \frac{1}{\pi}\, mE$$

and from the equation (10.2) it follows that $mE < \pi\varepsilon^{1/3}$. Denoting by $CE$ the complement to $E$ and taking into account that $|\omega(x)| \leqslant 1$, we have

$$\left| \int_{-\pi}^{\pi} f(x)\, \omega(x)\, dx \right| \leqslant \left| \int_{E} f(x)\, \omega(x)\, dx \right| + \left| \int_{CE} f(x)\, \omega(x)\, dx \right|$$

$$\leqslant \int_{E} |f(x)|\, dx + \varepsilon^{1/3} \int_{-\pi}^{\pi} |f(x)|\, dx,$$

and since $\varepsilon \to 0$, then the necessity of (2) is proved.

*Sufficiency conditions.* It will be sufficient to prove that $F(x)$ is absolutely continuous; indeed, $F(x)$ is then an indefinite integral of some summable $f(x)$, and since $-b_n/n$ and $a_n/n$ are Fourier coefficients of $F(x)$, then, integrating by parts, we will prove that $a_n$ and $b_n$ are Fourier coefficients of $f(x)$.

Let $(c_1, d_1), (c_2, d_2), \ldots, (c_\nu, d_\nu)$ be some system of non-overlapping intervals lying in $[-\pi, \pi]$. Let us choose a function $\omega'(x) = d\omega/dx$ in the following way; let $p$ be a positive integer which is as large as desired. Let us suppose for $i = 1, 2, \ldots, \nu$, that

$$\omega'(x) = \frac{1}{2} \frac{p\pi}{c_i} \sin\left(\frac{2p\pi}{c_i} x\right) \quad \text{for} \quad c_i < x < c_i\left(1 + \frac{1}{2p}\right),$$

$$\omega'(x) = \frac{1}{2} \frac{p\pi}{d_i} \sin\left(\frac{2p\pi}{d_i} x\right) \quad \text{for} \quad d_i\left(1 - \frac{1}{2p}\right) < x < d_i$$

and $\omega'(x) = 0$ for all the remaining points of $[-\pi, \pi]$.

It is clear that the free term of the Fourier series for $\omega'(x)$ equals 0, that its Fourier series converges absolutely and that

$$|\omega(x)| = \left|\int_0^x \omega'(x)\,dx\right| < 1,$$

i.e., $\omega(x)$ belongs to class $\{M\}$. Let

$$\omega(x) = \sum_{n=1}^{\infty} (\alpha_n \cos nx + \beta_n \sin nx).$$

Then the coefficients of the Fourier series for $\omega'(x)$ have the form $n\beta_n$ and $-n\alpha_n$, therefore

$$\frac{1}{\pi}\int_{-\pi}^{\pi} F(x)\omega'(x)\,dx = \sum_{n=1}^{\infty}\left(-\frac{b_n}{n}\right)n\beta_n - \left(\frac{a_n}{n}\right)n\alpha_n = -\sum_{n=1}^{\infty}(a_n\alpha_n + b_n\beta_n). \quad (10.3')$$

On the other hand

$$\sum_{n=1}^{\infty}(\alpha_n^2 + \beta_n^2) = \frac{1}{\pi}\int_{-\pi}^{\pi}\omega^2(x)\,dx < \frac{1}{\pi}\sum_{i=1}^{\nu}(d_i - c_i),$$

since $\omega(x) = 0$ outside all $(c_i, d_i)$ and $|\omega(x)| < 1$ everywhere.

Therefore, if $\sum_{i=1}^{\nu}(d_i - c_i)$ tends to zero, then $\sum_{n=1}^{\infty}(\alpha_n^2 + \beta_n^2) \to 0$ and then, from the condition of the theorem, $\sum_{n=1}^{\infty}(a_n\alpha_n + b_n\beta_n) \to 0$ also and therefore from (10.3′)

$$\int_{-\pi}^{\pi} F(x)\omega'(x)\,dx \to 0. \quad (10.4)$$

We will prove that it follows from this that $\sum_{i=1}^{\nu}|F(d_i) - F(c_i)| \to 0$ and then the absolute continuity of $F(x)$ will be established. We have

$$\int_{-\pi}^{\pi} F(x)\omega'(x)\,dx = \sum_{i=1}^{\nu}\int_{c_i}^{c_i\left(1+\frac{1}{2p}\right)} F(x)\omega'(x)\,dx + \int_{d_i\left(1-\frac{1}{2p}\right)}^{d_i} F(x)\omega'(x)\,dx.$$

Applying the first mean value theorem and denoting by $\gamma_i$ some point such that $c_i < \gamma_i < c_i(1 + 1/2p)$ and by $\delta_i$ some point such that $d_i(1 - 1/2p) < \delta_i < d_i$, we have

$$\int_{c_i}^{c_i\left(1+\frac{1}{2p}\right)} F(x)\omega'(x)\,dx = F(\gamma_i)\int_{c_i}^{c_i\left(1+\frac{1}{2p}\right)} \frac{1}{2}\frac{p\pi}{c_i}\sin\left(\frac{2p\pi}{c_i}x\right)dx = \frac{1}{2}F(\gamma_i),$$

$$\int_{d_i\left(1-\frac{1}{2p}\right)}^{d_i} F(x)\omega'(x)\,dx = F(\delta_i)\int_{d_i\left(1-\frac{1}{2p}\right)}^{d_i} \frac{1}{2}\frac{p\pi}{d_i}\sin\left(\frac{2p\pi}{d_i}x\right)dx = -\frac{1}{2}F(\delta_i).$$

This means that

$$\int_{-\pi}^{\pi} F(x)\omega'(x)\,dx = \frac{1}{2}\sum_{i=1}^{\gamma}[F(\gamma_i) - F(\delta_i)]. \tag{10.5}$$

But the expression on the right-hand side of (10.5) can be as close as desired to $\frac{1}{2}\sum_{i=1}^{\nu}[F(d_i) - F(c_i)]$, if $p$ is sufficiently large, i.e. it follows from the fact that the integral on the left-hand side of (10.5) tends to zero (see (10.4)) that $\sum_{i=1}^{\nu}[F(d_i) - F(c_i)] \to 0$, and this concludes the proof.

## § 11. The trigonometric problem of moments

The problem as to when the given numbers $\{a_n\}$ and $\{b_n\}$ can be Fourier coefficients, or the more specific problem as to when they are Fourier coefficients of a function satisfying an additional requirement (for example, bounded or non-negative, or monotonic) can be expressed in terms of the so-called "trigonometric problem of moments".

It is convenient to refer to the values

$$\mu_n = \int_a^b f(x)x^n\,dx \quad (n = 0, 1, 2, \ldots) \tag{11.1}$$

as the "moments" of the function $f(x)$ and the values

$$c_n = \int_0^{2\pi} f(t)e^{int}\,dt \quad (n = 0, \pm 1, \pm 2, \ldots). \tag{11.2}$$

as "trigonometric moments".

The problem of moments is the name given to the following problem; given a sequence of numbers $\mu_n$, does an $f(x)$ exist such that the relation (11.1) holds for it? The trigonometric problem of moments is expressed in a similar way. Since the system $\{e^{int}\}$ is complete in $[0, 2\pi]$, then it is only possible for all the moments of a function to equal zero if the function equals zero almost everywhere, and therefore the function is expressed uniquely by its trigonometric moments. But, it is true that any sequence of numbers is far from being a sequence of moments of a particular function. The problem of moments occupied a whole succession of authors, starting with P.L.Chebyshev. The reader can find fundamental data on the power problem of moments in I.P.Natanson's book[A, 22], Part II, Chapter VII. A detailed account of results, referring to both the power and the trigonometric problem of moments, can be found in the book by N.I.Achieser and M.G.Krein[A, 1]. Here it is impossible for us to describe these results, since it would require too much space. We will confine ourselves to describing the formulation of one of them, as an example. For this we must start with a definition.

Let $c_0$ be real, $c_0 \neq 0$, $c_1, c_2, \ldots, c_n, \ldots$ be complex numbers. Let us consider the the trigonometric polynomials

$$T_n(z) = \sum_{k=-n}^{n} A_k e^{ikt} \quad (z = e^{it})$$

with complex coefficients, generally speaking; let

$$\sigma(T_n) = \sum_{k=-n}^{n} A_k c_k,$$

where

$$c_{-k} = \bar{c}_k \quad (k = 1, 2, \ldots, n).$$

It is evident that if $T_n(e^{it})$ is a trigonometric polynomial with real coefficients ($A_{-k} = \bar{A}_k$, $k = 1, 2, \ldots, n$), then $\sigma(T_n)$ is also a real number.

We will define a *finite* sequence

$$c_0, c_1, c_2, \ldots, c_n$$

*as non-negative on the circle* $0 \leqslant t \leqslant 2\pi$, if it always follows from the relationships

$$T_n(e^{it}) \not\equiv 0, \quad T_n(e^{it}) \geqslant 0, \quad 0 \leqslant t \leqslant 2\pi$$

that

$$\sigma(T_n) \geqslant 0.$$

We refer to an *infinite* sequence

$$c_0, c_1, \ldots, c_n, \ldots$$

as being *non-negative on the circle*, if for any $n$ the sequence

$$c_0, c_1, \ldots, c_n$$

possesses this property.

A number of criteria exist for the sequence $c$ to be non-negative on the circle as, for example, the Toeplitz criterion; for this it is necessary and sufficient for the quadratic form

$$\sum_{0}^{m} c_{i+k} x_i x_k, \quad \text{where} \quad m = \left[\frac{n}{2}\right],$$

to be non-negative.

Using this definition, we formulate the following theorem due to Achieser and Krein[A, 1].

*In order for a function $f(x)$ satisfying the relationships*

$$-L \leqslant f(t) \leqslant L,$$

$$c_k = \int_0^{2\pi} f(t) e^{ikt} dt \quad (k = 0, 1, \ldots),$$

*to exist, it is necessary and sufficient for the inequality*

$$-2\pi L < c_0 < 2\pi L$$

*to be fulfilled and for the following sequence to be non-negative on the circle:*

$$\gamma_0, \gamma_1, \ldots, \gamma_n, \ldots,$$

*where*

$$\gamma_0 = 2 \cos \frac{c_0}{4L},$$

*and the sequence* $\gamma_1, \gamma_2, \ldots$ *is defined by the expansion*

$$e^{\frac{i}{2L}\left(\frac{c_0}{2}+c_1 z+\cdots+c_{n-1}z^{n-1}+\cdots\right)} = \gamma + \gamma_1 z + \cdots + \gamma_{n-1} z^{n-1} + \cdots.$$

Thus, on the one hand, it seems that the problem for the case of the bounded function has been completely solved, but, on the other hand, it is extremely difficult in practice to verify whether for a given sequence of numbers a bounded function exists which possesses them as its Fourier coefficients and even more difficult to find this function.

There exist other criteria which are just as definite and final from the purely theoretical point of view but are at the same time extremely difficult to apply to concrete cases. Such an example is given by Carathéodory's[1],[2] theorem:

*For the numbers* $1, a_1, a_2, \ldots, a_n, \ldots; b_1, b_2, \ldots, b_n, \ldots$ *to be the Fourier coefficients of a positive function, it is necessary and sufficient for the point* $(a_1, a_2, \ldots, a_n, b_1, b_2, \ldots, b_n)$ *in a* $2n$*-dimensional space to belong to the body* $K_n$ *which is the smallest convex body containing the curve*

$$x_1 = 2\cos\varphi, \quad x_2 = 2\cos 2\varphi, \quad \ldots, \quad x_n = 2\cos n\varphi,$$
$$y_1 = -2\sin\varphi, \quad y_2 = -2\sin 2\varphi, \quad \ldots, \quad y_n = -2\sin n\varphi$$
$$(n = 1, 2, \ldots).$$

In this connection reference should be made to the work by Baiada[1], Ghizzetti[1],[2],[3] and Pagni[1].

## § 12. Coefficients of trigonometric series with non-negative partial sums

In Helson's[1] work it is shown that the following problem was set by Steinhaus: In the trigonometric series

$$\sum_{-\infty}^{+\infty} c_n e^{inx} \tag{12.1}$$

let all the partial sums $\sum_{n=-N}^{N} c_n e^{inx}$ be non-negative for any $x$. Does it follow from this that it is a Fourier series?

This problem arose in connection with the fact that Steinhaus[4] proved this theorem: if a trigonometric series converges everywhere and its sum is positive, then this series is a Fourier series†.

The problem in this form has not yet been solved. We want to describe here two results which are closely connected with the solution of the problem set. First we note that if Steinhaus's problem is solved in the positive sense, then in any case from

$$\sum_{n=-N}^{N} c_n e^{inx} \geqslant 0 \quad \text{for all} \quad N \text{ and } x \tag{12.2}$$

it should follow that $c_n \to 0$ as $|n| \to \infty$.

† The proof of this theorem by Steinhaus (and even of the more general result) will be given in Chapter XIV, § 4.

Here it will be proved that this really does occur. This result will follow from Helson's theorem in which an even stronger statement is proved (see Helson's theorem below).

On the other hand, an example will be given due to Turán[1] which shows that for non-negative partial sums of the series (12.1) the case $\sum c_n^2 = +\infty$ is possible all the same. Consequently, when (12.2) is fulfilled, the series is not necessarily the Fourier series of $f \in L^2$. Whether it should be a Fourier series nevertheless remains still unexplained†.

We will now formulate Helson's theorem:

HELSON'S THEOREM. *If*

$$\int_0^{2\pi} \left| \sum_{n=-N}^{N} c_n e^{inx} \right| dx < A \tag{12.3}$$

*as* $N \to \infty$, *then* $c_n \to 0$ *as* $|n| \to \infty$.

Before proving this theorem we note that in the case when (12.2) is fulfilled then condition (12.3) is also fulfilled, since then

$$\int_0^{2\pi} \left| \sum_{n=-N}^{N} c_n e^{inx} \right| dx = \int_0^{2\pi} \sum_{n=-N}^{N} c_n e^{inx} dx = c_0 \cdot 2\pi.$$

Therefore, from Helson's theorem it quickly follows that if all the partial sums of the trigonometric series are non-negative for any $x$, then its coefficients tend to zero.

PROOF OF HELSON'S THEOREM. If the Fejér sums of the series (12.1) are denoted by $\sigma_n(x)$, then from equation (12.3) it immediately follows that

$$\int_0^{2\pi} |\sigma_N(x)|\, dx < A, \tag{12.4}$$

and therefore (see Chapter I, § 60) the series (12.1) under consideration is a Fourier–Stieltjes series of some function $\mu(x)$, i.e.

$$c_n = \frac{1}{2\pi} \int_0^{2\pi} e^{-inx} d\mu \quad (n = 0, \pm 1, \ldots). \tag{12.5}$$

Let us assume the opposite to what we wish to prove, i.e. $c_n \not\to 0$. This means that an $\varepsilon > 0$ and a sequence of integers $n_j$ can be found such that

$$|c_{n_j}| \geqslant \varepsilon, \quad j = 1, 2, \ldots. \tag{12.6}$$

---

† For the case when the series converges everywhere, apart from one point, to the non-negative function $f(x)$, it can only be asserted that $f(x) \in L$ but it is not possible to assert that $f(x) \in L^p$ for $p > 1$. Indeed, we know (see Chapter I, § 30) that the series $\sum_{n=2}^{\infty} (\cos nx)/\ln n$ converges everywhere apart from $x \equiv 0 \pmod{2\pi}$, and its sum $f(x)$ is non-negative. However $f(x) \bar{\in} L^p$, whatever $p > 1$, since, if $f(x) \in L^p (p > 1)$ were the case, then (see § 4) we would have

$$\sum_{n=1}^{\infty} \frac{|a_n|}{n} < +\infty,$$

which does not occur at $a_n = 1/\ln n$.

If we define the functions $g_n(x)$ by the condition

$$g_n(x) = \int_0^x e^{-int}\,d\mu,$$

then $\{g_{n_j}(x)\}$ are all bounded and possess the same complete variation; therefore according to Helly's first theorem (see Introductory Material, § 17) it is possible to separate from the sequence $\{g_{n_j}(x)\}$ a sub-sequence converging at every point to some $\gamma(x)$ of bounded variation. In order not to change the notation, we will assume that the whole sequence $\{n_j\}$ possesses this property. Then by virtue of Stieltjes' theorem concerning the passage to the limit under the integral sign (see Introductory Material, § 17) we have for any continuous $\varphi(x)$

$$\int_0^{2\pi} \varphi(x)\,d\gamma = \lim_{j\to\infty} \int_0^{2\pi} \varphi(x) e^{-in_j x}\,d\mu. \tag{12.7}$$

If we resolve $\mu(x)$ into the sum of two functions, one of which is singular (see Appendix, § 17) and the other is absolutely continuous, then the equality (12.7) holds for the singular part, whilst for the absolutely continuous part the corresponding integral should tend to zero.

In formula (12.7) we will consider as $\varphi(x)$ the continuous functions with modulus not exceeding unity, which become zero outside some interval $(a, b)$. We have

$$\sup_{\varphi} \int_0^{2\pi} \varphi(x)\,d\gamma = \sup_{|\varphi|\leqslant 1} \int_a^b \varphi(x)\,d\gamma = \operatorname*{Var}_{(a,b)} \gamma$$

due to the properties of the norms of linear functionals (see § 19 Introductory Material). But from (12.7) we see that for such $\varphi$

$$\left|\int_a^b \varphi(x)\,d\gamma\right| = \left|\int_0^{2\pi} \varphi(x)\,d\gamma\right| \leqslant \int_a^b |d\mu| = \operatorname*{Var}_{(a,b)} \mu, \tag{12.8}$$

i.e.

$$\operatorname*{Var}_{(a,b)} \gamma \leqslant \operatorname*{Var}_{(a,b)} \mu. \tag{12.9}$$

Since $\mu(x)$ is singular, then $\operatorname*{Var}_{(0,x)} \mu$ is also a singular function of $x$ (see Appendix, § 17) and therefore, because (12.9) holds for any $a$ and $b$, we have

$$\left|\frac{\gamma(x+h)-\gamma(x)}{h}\right| \leqslant \frac{\operatorname*{Var}_{[x,x+h]} \gamma(x)}{h} \leqslant \frac{\operatorname*{Var}_{[x,x+h]} \mu(x)}{h} \to 0 \quad \text{as} \quad h \to 0$$

for nearly all $x$. Therefore $\gamma'(x) = 0$ almost everywhere. We will prove that $\gamma(x)$ is singular. For this it is only necessary to prove that $\gamma(x) \neq \text{const}$. But, supposing in (12.7) that $\varphi(x) = 1$, we see that due to (12.5) and (12.6)

$$\int_0^{2\pi} d\gamma = \lim_{j\to\infty} \int_0^{2\pi} e^{-in_j x}\,d\mu = \lim_{j\to\infty} 2\pi c_{n_j} \neq 0,$$

and then it is clear that $\gamma(x) \neq \text{const}$. Thus $\gamma(x)$ is singular.

We will now consider for all such $n_j$ the functions $h_n(x)$ defined thus:

$$h_n(x) = \int_0^x e^{-int} \sum_{k=-n}^{n} c_k e^{ikt} dt.$$

Due to condition (12.3) their complete variations are all bounded and so are they themselves; therefore it is possible by the same argument as before to state that a $\gamma^*(x)$ exists for which for any continuous $\varphi(x)$

$$\int_0^{2\pi} \varphi(x) d\gamma^* = \lim_{j\to\infty} \int_0^{2\pi} (e^{-im_jx} \sum_{n=-m_j}^{m_j} c_n e^{inx})\varphi(x) dx.$$

Here the sequence $\{m_j\}$ is contained in $\{n_j\}$.

We will prove that for any $k > 0$ we have

$$a_k^* = \frac{1}{2\pi} \int_0^{2\pi} e^{-ikx} d\gamma^* = 0,$$

i.e. the Fourier–Stieltjes coefficients $a_k^*$ of $\gamma^*(x)$ become zero for all $k > 0$.

Indeed, we have

$$2\pi a_k^* = \int_0^{2\pi} e^{-ikx} d\gamma^* = \lim_{j\to\infty} \int_0^{2\pi} \sum_{n=-m_j}^{m_j} c_n e^{i(n-m_j-k)x} dx = 0, \tag{12.8'}$$

since $n - m_j \leqslant 0$ and consequently $n - m_j - k < 0$ at $k > 0$, and therefore every integral on the right-hand side of (12.8′) equals zero.

We will now prove that if $a_k$ are Fourier–Stieltjes coefficients for $\gamma(x)$, then

$$a_k^* = a_k \quad \text{at} \quad k \leqslant 0.$$

Indeed, on the one hand

$$2\pi a_k^* = \lim_{j\to\infty} \int_0^{2\pi} \sum_{n=-m_j}^{m_j} c_n e^{i(n-m_j-k)x} dx = 2\pi \lim_{j\to\infty} c_{m_j+k}, \tag{12.9'}$$

since the integral on the right-hand side of (12.9′) differs from zero only when $n = m_j + k$. On the other hand, by virtue of (12.7), substituting $\varphi(x) = e^{-ikx}$, we find that

$$2\pi a_k = \int_0^{2\pi} e^{-ikx} d\gamma = \lim_{j\to\infty} \int_0^{2\pi} e^{-i(n_j+k)x} d\mu = 2\pi \lim_{j\to\infty} c_{n_j+k}.$$

Since $\lim_{j\to\infty} c_{n_j+k}$ exists and the sequence $\{m_j\}$ is contained in $\{n_j\}$, then $\lim_{j\to\infty} c_{m_j+k} = \lim_{j\to\infty} c_{n_j+k}$, and therefore

$$a_k = a_k^*, \quad k \leqslant 0.$$

Consequently, for the function $\gamma(x) - \gamma^*(x)$ all the Fourier–Stieltjes coefficients with non-positive indices equal zero, and therefore $\gamma(x) - \gamma^*(x)$ is absolutely continuous according to F. and M. Riesz's theorem (see Chapter VIII, § 12). But according to the same theorem it follows from $a_k^* = 0$ at $k > 0$ that $\gamma^*(x)$ is absolutely continuous. This means that $\gamma(x)$ is also absolutely continuous and we have proved earlier that it is singular.

It follows from the contradiction obtained that (12.3) and (12.6) are incompatible and therefore

$$\lim |c_n| = 0 \quad \text{as} \quad |n| \to +\infty,$$

and the theorem is proved.

The question remains open: should not the function $\mu(x)$ be absolutely continuous when condition (12.3) holds? If this were true, then the validity of Steinhaus's hypothesis would be proved, because the series $\sum_{n=-\infty}^{n=+\infty} c_n e^{inx}$ would be simply a Fourier series.

*Note.* Not only for trigonometric series satisfying only the condition $c_n \to 0$ as $|n| \to \infty$, but even for Fourier series, Helson's condition

$$\int_0^{2\pi} |S_n(x)| \, dx < C$$

(where $S_n(x)$ is the sum of the first $n$ terms of the series) does not hold, generally speaking. This will be proved in Chapter VIII, § 22. Thus, Helson's theorem is known to be irreversible.

We will now return to Turán's example, referred to at the beginning of this section and prove that the non-negativeness of the partial sums of the trigonometric series does not in any case imply that it is a Fourier series of $f(x) \in L^2$.

TURÁN'S THEOREM. *There exists a trigonometric series*

$$\sum_{n=0}^{\infty} a_n \cos nx, \tag{12.10}$$

*in which the partial sums are* $S_n(x) \geqslant 0 \quad (-\pi \leqslant x \leqslant \pi), \quad n = 1, 2, \ldots,$ *and yet* $\sum a_n^2 = +\infty$.

For the coefficients $a_n$, Turán used the coefficients obtained by the expansion into a Taylor series of $(1 - z)^{-1/2}$, which are

$$\frac{1}{\sqrt{1 - z}} = 1 + \sum_{n=1}^{\infty} \frac{(2n - 1)!!}{(2n)!!} z^n, \tag{12.11}$$

where the series converges for $|z| < 1$. Supposing that

$$a_0 = 1, \quad a_n = \frac{(2n - 1)!!}{(2n)!!}, \tag{12.12}$$

we will prove that the series (12.10) satisfies the conditions of Turán's theorem.

For this we will note first of all that

$$\frac{\pi}{2} = \left[\frac{(2n)!!}{(2n - 1)!!}\right]^2 \frac{1}{2n + \theta_n}, \quad \text{where} \quad 0 < \theta_n < 1$$

(as proved when deriving Wallis's formula, see, for example, Fikhtengol'ts,[A.7] Vol. II, p. 169) whence it immediately follows that for $n = 1, 2, \ldots$

$$a_n^2 = \frac{2}{\pi} \frac{1}{2n + \theta_n}, \tag{12.13}$$

and therefore

$$\sum a_n^2 = +\infty .$$

Now it must be proved that the partial sums of series (12.10) are all non-negative. For this purpose we note first that from (12.13) it follows that

$$a_n < \frac{1}{\sqrt{\pi n}} \quad (n = 1, 2, \ldots). \tag{12.14}$$

Now we will prove the lemma:

LEMMA. *If*

$$g(x) = d_0 + d_1 \cos x + \cdots + d_n \cos nx$$

*is a trigonometric polynomial in which the coefficients are positive and decrease (or increase) monotonically, then* $g(x)$ *does not become zero in the interval*

$$0 < x < \frac{\pi}{n}. \tag{12.15}$$

For the proof we will rewrite $g(x)$ in the form

$$g(x) = \sum_{\nu=0}^{[n/2]} d_\nu \cos\nu x + \sum_{\nu=[n/2]+1}^{n} d_\nu \cos\nu x .$$

In the first sum the number of terms is not less than in the second, and due to (12.15) all these terms are non-negative. Consequently, if each term $d_\nu \cos\nu x$ of the second sum is combined with the term $d_{n-\nu} \cos(n-\nu)x$ of the first sum, then

$$g(x) \geqslant \sum_{\nu=[n/2]+1}^{n} [d_\nu \cos\nu x + d_{n-\nu} \cos(n-\nu)x]. \tag{12.16}$$

But for the values of $\nu$ under consideration it is evident from (12.15) that

$$0 \leqslant (n-\nu)x \leqslant \frac{\pi}{2}.$$

Moreover

$$(n-\nu)x < \nu x < \pi - (n-\nu)x.$$

Consequently,

$$|\cos\nu x| < |\cos(n-\nu)x| = \cos(n-\nu)x. \tag{12.17}$$

Since we supposed the coefficients of the polynomial $g(x)$ to be monotonically decreasing, then

$$d_\nu \leqslant d_{n-\nu},$$

whence it follows from (12.17) that all the terms of the sum standing in square brackets in (12.16) are positive and therefore the lemma is proved.

Now we will return to proving the theorem. If we take the partial sum $S_n(x)$ of series (12.10), then since the numbers $a_n$ are positive and monotonically decreasing (see (12.12)), we have the conditions of the lemma, i.e. we have

$$S_n(x) \geqslant 0 \quad \text{at} \quad 0 \leqslant x \leqslant \frac{\pi}{n}.$$

Since the polynomial $S_n(x)$ is even, it is now sufficient to prove that it is non-negative for $\pi/n < x \leqslant \pi$.

Moreover, for $n \leqslant 2$ the statement is evident, since

$$a_0 = 1, \quad a_1 = \frac{1}{2}, \quad a_2 = \frac{3}{8},$$

and the polynomials

$$S_0 = 1, \quad S_1(x) = 1 + \frac{1}{2}\cos x, \quad S_2(x) = 1 + \frac{1}{2}\cos x + \frac{3}{8}\cos 2x$$

are non-negative simply because $1 - [\frac{1}{2} + \frac{3}{8}] > 0$.

Thus it is sufficient to consider $S_n(x)$ for

$$n \geqslant 3 \quad \text{and} \quad \frac{\pi}{n} < x \leqslant \pi. \tag{12.18}$$

Since the coefficients in the expansion of $1/\sqrt{1-z}$ decrease monotonically, then according to Abel's theorem the series (12.11) converges not only for $|z| < 1$, but also for $z = e^{it}$, provided $t \not\equiv 0 \pmod{2\pi}$.

Consequently, under these conditions

$$\sum_{\nu=0}^{\infty} a_\nu e^{it\nu} = \frac{1}{\sqrt{1-e^{it}}}, \quad 0 < t < 2\pi.$$

Separating out the real part, we have

$$\operatorname{Re}\sum_{\nu=0}^{\infty} a_\nu e^{it\nu} = \sum_{\nu=0}^{\infty} a_\nu \cos\nu t = \operatorname{Re}\,[(1-e^{it})^{-1/2}] = \operatorname{Re}\left[e^{-i\frac{t}{4}}\left(e^{-i\frac{t}{2}} - e^{i\frac{t}{2}}\right)^{-1/2}\right]$$

$$= \operatorname{Re}\left[e^{-i\frac{t}{4}}\left(-2i\sin\frac{t}{2}\right)^{-1/2}\right] = \operatorname{Re}\frac{e^{i\frac{\pi-t}{4}}}{\sqrt{2\sin\frac{t}{2}}} = \frac{\cos\frac{\pi-t}{4}}{\sqrt{2\sin\frac{t}{2}}}.$$

Hence it follows that for $0 < x < 2\pi$

$$S_n(x) = \frac{\cos\frac{\pi-x}{4}}{\sqrt{2\sin\frac{x}{2}}} - \sum_{\nu=n+1}^{\infty} a_\nu \cos\nu x.$$

But from (12.18) in any case $\cos(\pi-x)/4 > 1/\sqrt{2}$, whence

$$S_n(x) > \frac{1}{2\sqrt{\sin\frac{x}{2}}} - \sum_{\nu=n+1}^{\infty} a_\nu \cos\nu x. \tag{12.19}$$

We will now estimate the series on the right-hand side of (12.19) from above.

Applying Abel's lemma (see Introductory Material, § 1) and taking into account that

$$|D_\nu(x)| \leqslant \frac{1}{2\sin\frac{x}{2}}, \quad \nu = 1, 2, \ldots; \quad 0 < x \leqslant \pi,$$

we have

$$\left|\sum_{\nu=n+1}^{\infty} a_\nu \cos\nu x\right| \leqslant \frac{a_{n+1}}{\sin\frac{x}{2}}. \tag{12.20}$$

But since due to (12.14) we have

$$a_{n+1} < \frac{1}{\sqrt{\pi(n+1)}}, \tag{12.21}$$

then from (12.19), (12.20) and (12.21) it follows that

$$S_n(x) > \frac{1}{2\sqrt{\sin\frac{x}{2}}} - \frac{1}{\sqrt{\pi(n+1)}\sin\frac{x}{2}} > \frac{1}{\sqrt{\sin\frac{x}{2}}}\left(\frac{1}{2} - \frac{1}{\sqrt{\pi n \sin\frac{x}{2}}}\right). \tag{12.22}$$

From this we should now conclude that $S_n(x) \geqslant 0$. First let

$$\frac{4}{n} < x \leqslant \pi.$$

Then

$$\sin\frac{x}{2} \geqslant \frac{x}{\pi} > \frac{4}{n\pi},$$

and therefore

$$\sqrt{\pi n \sin\frac{x}{2}} > 2,$$

and this implies that $S_n(x) > 0$ by virtue of (12.22).

We will now consider the case

$$\frac{\pi}{n} < x \leqslant \frac{4}{n}. \tag{12.23}$$

In this case since at $x > 0$

$$\sin x > x - \frac{x^3}{6},$$

we have from (12.23)

$$\sin\frac{x}{2} \geqslant \frac{x}{2} - \frac{x^3}{48} \geqslant \frac{x}{2}\left(1 - \frac{1}{24}\cdot\frac{16}{n^2}\right) \geqslant \frac{\pi}{2n}\left(1 - \frac{2}{3n^2}\right). \tag{12.24}$$

But we have already noted that it is sufficient to consider the case $n \geqslant 3$, and moreover for $n \geqslant 2$ we have from (12.24)

$$\frac{1}{\sqrt{\pi n \sin\frac{x}{2}}} \leqslant \sqrt{\frac{2}{\pi^2\left(1 - \frac{2}{3n^2}\right)}} \leqslant \sqrt{\frac{2}{\pi^2\left(1 - \frac{1}{6}\right)}} = \frac{1}{\pi}\sqrt{\frac{12}{5}} < \frac{1}{2},$$

and therefore from (12.22) we again conclude that $S_n(x) > 0$, and the theorem is completely proved.

*Note 1.* The author notes that at the last stage of the proof the use of inequality

$$a_n \leqslant \frac{1}{\sqrt{\pi n}},$$

was essential, since if it were assumed, for example, that $a_n \leqslant 1/\sqrt{2n}$, then the argument could not follow along the lines given.

*Note 2.* If, instead of the interval $0 < x < \pi/n$, the smaller interval $0 < x < \pi/2n$ were considered in the lemma, then the fact that $g(x)$ does not become zero would be trivial; hence this fact would be insufficient for proving the theorem.

On the other hand, although this is not necessary for the proof, it may be noted that it is not possible to extend the interval $(0, \pi/n)$. Indeed, if for $n \geqslant 1$ we consider the polynomial

$$g_0(x) = 1 + \cos x + \cdots + \cos nx,$$

then since

$$g_0(x) = \frac{1}{2} + D_n(x),$$

where $D_n(x)$ is the Dirichlet kernel, we see that

$$g_0(x) = \frac{1}{2} + \frac{\sin\left(n + \frac{1}{2}\right)x}{2\sin\frac{x}{2}} = \frac{\sin\frac{n+1}{2}x\cos\frac{n}{2}x}{\sin\frac{x}{2}}.$$

But it is clear from this that $g_0(x)$ becomes zero at $x = \pi/n$ and it also satisfies the conditions of the lemma.

A number of interesting points in addition to the given problem are contained in the cited work by Turán[1].

## § 13. Transformation of Fourier series

Several authors have studied the following problem: let us assume that

$$f(x) \sim \frac{a_0}{2} + \sum_{n=1}^{\infty} (a_n \cos nx + b_n \sin nx). \tag{13.1}$$

Under what conditions imposed on the numbers $\lambda_n$ does the series

$$\frac{a_0}{2}\lambda_0 + \sum_{n=1}^{\infty} (a_n \cos nx + b_n \sin nx)\lambda_n \tag{13.2}$$

become again a Fourier series, and if it is $\sigma(F)$, then what can be said about this function $F(x)$ knowing the properties of $f(x)$? We will not consider here the cases which have already been discussed in Zygmund's book[A. 35], § 4.60, but we will describe some later work in this connection.

Thus, for example, Salem[1] shows that it is always possible to choose $\lambda_n$ such that $\lambda_n \uparrow \infty$, that the sequence $\{\lambda_n\}$ is concave, whilst the series of a continuous $f(x)$ transforms into a series of continuous $F$ and similarly for the case $f \in L$ and $F \in L$.

A. F. Timan[3] gives the effective necessary condition for $\{\lambda_n\}$, for the Fourier series of any bounded or continuous or integrable function to be transformed into a Fourier series of a function of the same class (and also a Fourier–Stieltjes series into a Fourier–Stieltjes series). This condition is as follows:

$$\sum_{k=1}^{\infty} \frac{\lambda_{|k-n|} - \lambda_{k+n}}{k},$$

converges uniformly with respect to $n$. In particular, if $\{\lambda_n\}$ is monotonic, then it follows that $\lambda_n - \lambda_{n+1} = O(1/\ln n)$.

A. A. Konyushkov[1] showed that if $0 < \alpha < 1$, $1 \leqslant p \leqslant \infty$ and $f(x) \in \mathrm{Lip}(\alpha, p)$, i.e.

$$\| f(x+h) - f(x) \|_p = O(h^\alpha),$$

then for any convex sequence $\{\lambda_n\}$ where $\lambda_n \to 0$ the series (13.2) will be the Fourier series of $F \in \mathrm{Lip}(\alpha, p)$, i.e.

$$\| F(x+h) - F(x) \|_p = o(h^\alpha).$$

The problem of the transformation of a Fourier series can be generalized, namely: given a matrix $\| a_{kj} \|$, we will carry out the transformation defined by this matrix on the coefficients $a_n$ and $b_n$, i.e. we will take

$$A_k = \sum_{j=0}^{\infty} a_{kj} a_j; \quad B_k = \sum_{j=0}^{\infty} a_{kj} b_j. \tag{13.3}$$

Supposing that these series converge, i.e. $A_k$ and $B_k$ are defined for any $k$, the question is: under what conditions, imposed on the matrix, does the series

$$\frac{A_0}{2} + \sum_{k=1}^{\infty} (A_k \cos kx + B_k \sin kx) \tag{13.4}$$

again become a Fourier series and what is the function defined by it?

In particular, Hardy[2] first considered considered this question for the case where

$$f(x) \sim \sum_{k=1}^{\infty} a_k \cos kx,$$

$$A_k = \frac{a_1 + a_2 + \cdots + a_k}{k}$$

(i.e. the matrix is the type used in method $(C, 1)$). Hardy showed that this matrix transformed a Fourier series into a Fourier series, and if $f(x) \in L^p$ $(1 < p < \infty)$, then $F(x) \in L^p$ too. Also Bellman[2] considered the case when

$$A_k = \sum_{n=k}^{\infty} \frac{a_n}{n}.$$

In this case for an arbitrary Fourier series the numbers $A_k$ can have no meaning, but if $f \in L^p$ at $p > 1$, then he showed that the newly obtained series will be the Fourier series of $F \in L^p$. Bellman's matrix is transposed in relation to Hardy's matrix.

Other authors also examined Hardy's matrix, but for a sine series, and Bellman's matrix also for this case, imposing various conditions on $f(x)$.

As it is impossible to dwell on all the individual results, we will note one fairly general result due to F.Young[1]. He studied arbitrary matrices $\| a_{kj} \|$ and found the conditions under which they transformed the series of $f \in L^p$ into a series of $F \in L^p$. In particular, it follows from his results that if the matrix possesses this property, then it is also transposed, and therefore Bellman's theorem could have been derived from Hardy's theorem.

We also note that there is a theorem similar to Bellman's theorem in the cited report by Konyushkov, namely:

If $g(x) \sim \sum b_n \sin nx$ and $g(x) \in \text{Lip}\,\alpha$, $0 < \alpha < 1$, then for $G(x) \sim \sum B_n \sin nx$, where $B_n = \sum_{k=n}^{\infty} b_k/k$ we also have $G(x) \in \text{Lip}\,\alpha$.

This work also includes theorems concerning the transformations of Fourier series for functions of the $\text{Lip}(\alpha, p)$ classes.

Finally, speaking of the transformation of Fourier series, we note the work by Rudin[1] where the problem is set: for what conditions imposed on the function $\varphi(z)$, starting from $\sum c_n e^{inx}$ being a Fourier series, does it follow that $\sum \varphi(c_n) e^{inx}$ is also a Fourier series? It is shown that it is necessary that $\varphi(z)$ satisfies the Lipschitz condition in the neighbourhood of zero. This condition is insufficient, since $\varphi(z) = |z|$ satisfies the condition Lip 1, and moreover $\sum |c_n|\, e^{inx}$ cannot also be a Fourier series; this follows from Kahane's[1] results.

## § 14. Problems

1. It is known (see § 3) that if $f \in \text{Lip}\,\alpha (0 < \alpha \leqslant 1)$, then

$$|a_n(f)| = O(1/n^\alpha) \quad \text{and} \quad |b_n(f)| = O(1/n^\alpha),$$

where $a_n(f)$ and $b_n(f)$ are the Fourier coefficients of the function $f$.

Prove that there exists an absolutely continuous function $\varphi(x)$, the Fourier series of which converges absolutely for every $x$, and yet $\varphi(x) \,\bar{\in}\, \text{Lip}\,\varepsilon$ for any $\varepsilon > 0$, although

$$a_n(\varphi) = O(1/n) \quad \text{and} \quad b_n(\varphi) = O(1/n).$$

[It is sufficient to take $\varphi(x) = \sum_{n=2}^{\infty} \frac{\sin nx}{n \log^2 n}$ and to note that $\sum_{n=2}^{\infty} \frac{\cos nx}{\log^2 n}$ is a Fourier series (see § 30 of Chapter I)].

2. Constructan example of a Fourier series for the continuous function

$$\frac{a_0}{2} + \sum_{n=1}^{\infty} (a_n \cos nx + b_n \sin nx)$$

such that the series

$$\frac{|a_0|}{2} + \sum_{n=1}^{\infty}(|a_n| \cos nx + |b_n| \sin nx)$$

is not a Fourier series of a continuous function.

[Consider the Fourier series of the continuous function $f(x)$ in the Lebesgue example (see Chapter I, § 46)].

3. If the function $f \in C(0, 2\pi)$, then $|a_n(f)| \leqslant 2E_{n-1}(f)$ and $|b_n(f)| \leqslant 2E_{n-1}(f)$.

[The statement follows from the fact that

$$a_n(f) = \frac{1}{\pi}\int_0^{2\pi} f(x) \cos nx\, dx = \frac{1}{\pi}\int_0^{2\pi} [f(x) - T_{n-1}(x)] \cos nx\, dx,$$

where $T_{n-1}(x)$ is the trigonometric polynomial of order $(n - 1)$ of best approximation for the function $f$.]

4. Consider $\varepsilon_n \geqslant 0$ where $\varepsilon_n \to 0$. Then there exists a Fourier series

$$\sum_{n=1}^{\infty} a_n \cos nx, \tag{14.1}$$

for which $a_n \geqslant \varepsilon_n$ for every $n = 1, 2, \ldots$.

[Use Theorem 4 of § 30, Chapter I.]

5. Values of $\varepsilon_n \geqslant 0$ where $\varepsilon_n \to 0$ exist such that any series of the form (14.1) with $|a_n| \geqslant \varepsilon_n$ for $n = 1, 2, \ldots$ is not the Fourier series of any function $f \in L^{1+\delta}(0, 2\pi)$ for any $\delta > 0$.

[It is sufficient to take $\varepsilon_n = 1/(\ln \ln n)$ for $n \geqslant n_0$ and apply the corollary of the Hausdorff–Young Theorem (see § 4)].

6. For any sequence $\varepsilon_n \downarrow 0$ there exists a function $f(x) \in C(0, 2\pi)$, which possesses a finite derivative everywhere in $[0, 2\pi]$ although

$$b_n(f) \neq O(\varepsilon_n) \quad \text{as} \quad n \to \infty.$$

[Assume

$$f(x) = \begin{cases} (\sin^3 n_{k+1} x)/n_k^3 & \text{for } x \in (\pi/n_k, 2\pi/n_k) \quad (k = 1, 2, \ldots) \\ 0 & \text{for the remaining } x \in [0, 2\pi] \\ f(x + 2\pi) & \text{for all } x \in (-\infty, \infty), \end{cases}$$

where the increasing sequence of integers $n_k$ is chosen so that

$$n_1 = 2; \quad n_{k+1} \text{ is a multiple of } n_k; \quad n_{k+1} > (2n_k)^5;$$

$$\int_{\pi/n_k}^{2\pi/n_k} \sin^4 n_{k+1} x\, dx > 1/5\, n_k \quad \text{and} \quad \sqrt{\varepsilon_{n_{k+1}}} + \left| \int_{\pi/n_{k-1}}^{\pi} f(x) \sin n_{k+1} x\, dx \right| \leqslant 1/n_k^5.$$

Then consider

$$\pi b_{n_{k+1}}(f) = \int_0^{2\pi/n_{k+1}} f(x) \sin n_{k+1} x\, dx + \int_{\pi/n_k}^{2\pi/n_k} f(x) \sin n_{k+1} x\, dx + \int_{\pi/n_{k-1}}^{\pi} f(x) \sin n_{k+1} x\, dx,$$

where the middle integral is the largest.]

7. If the function $f(x) \in V(0, 2\pi)$ (i.e. it is of bounded variation in $[0, 2\pi]$ and has a finite derivative at every point $x \in [0, 2\pi]$, then

$$a_n(f) = o(1/n) \quad \text{and} \quad b_n(f) = o(1/n).$$

[This statement follows from the fact that under the given conditions the function $f(x)$ is absolutely continuous in $[0, 2\pi]$ (see A. 30).]

8. There exists a function $f(x) \in C(0, 2\pi)$ which possesses a finite derivative at every point $x \in [0, 2\pi]$ and

$$\sum_{n=1}^{\infty} (|a_n(f)| + |b_n(f)|) = \infty.$$

9. Let

$$\text{(a) } \alpha_k \downarrow 0 \quad \text{and} \quad \sum_{k=1}^{\infty} \frac{\alpha_k}{k} = \infty,$$

or

$$\text{(b) } \alpha_k > 0 \text{ and } \alpha_k \uparrow \text{ but } \alpha_k \leqslant k^p \ (k = 1, 2, \ldots) \text{ for some } p > 0.$$

Then for the function $f(x) \in V(0, 2\pi)$ to be equivalent to a continuous function, it is necessary and sufficient for the relationship

$$\sum_{k=1}^{n} \alpha_k \varrho_k = 0 \left\{ \sum_{k=1}^{n} \frac{\alpha_k}{k} \right\} \quad (\text{as } n \to \infty)$$

to be fulfilled, where $\varrho_k = \sqrt{a_k^2(f) + b_k^2(f)}$.

In particular, a necessary and sufficient condition is the fulfilment of the relationship

$$\sum_{k=2}^{n} \frac{\varrho_k}{\ln k} = o(\ln \ln n).$$

V. A. Matveyev

[This can be proved by combining the arguments of Wiener[1] and Losinskii[2] (see also § 2).]

10. A Fourier series

$$\sum_{n=1}^{\infty} (a_n \cos nx + b_n \sin nx) \tag{14.2}$$

exists such that for all $\alpha > 0$

$$\sum_{n=1}^{\infty} \frac{(|a_n|^\alpha + |b_n|^\alpha)}{n} = \infty$$

[Consider the series $\sum_{n=10}^{n} \frac{\cos nx}{\ln \ln n}$ (see Chapter I, § 30).]

11. Construct a Fourier series of the form (14.2) such that

$$\sum_{n=1}^{\infty} \frac{|b_n|}{n} = \infty$$

(compare with the result of § 40, Chapter I).

[Consider the Fourier series of the function $f(x) = [\varphi(x - \pi/3) - \varphi(x + \pi/3)]/2$, where $\varphi(x) = \sum_{n=2}^{\infty} \frac{\cos nx}{\ln n}$.]

12. There exists a Fourier series of the form (14.2) such that the series

$$\sum_{n=1}^{\infty} (a_{2^n} \cos 2^n x + b_{2^n} \sin 2^n x)$$

is not a Fourier series, i.e. a function $F(x) \in L(0, 2\pi)$ does not exist for which

$$a_{2^n}(F) = a_{2^n}, \quad b_{2^n}(F) = b_{2^n} \quad \text{and} \quad a_k(F) = b_k(F) = 0 \quad \text{for} \quad k \neq 2^n.$$

[It is sufficient to consider the series $\sum_{n=10}^{\infty} \frac{\cos nx}{\ln \ln n}$.]

13. Prove that if

$$\text{(a)} \sum_{n=1}^{\infty} a_n \cos nx \quad \text{and} \quad \text{(b)} \sum_{n=1}^{\infty} b_n \sin nx$$

are Fourier series, then the series

$$\sum_{n=1}^{\infty} a_n^{\alpha} \cos nx, \quad \sum_{n=1}^{\infty} b_n^{2\alpha-1} \sin nx \quad \text{and} \quad \sum_{n=1}^{\infty} b_n^{2\alpha} \cos nx$$

are also Fourier series for any given integer $\alpha = 1, 2, \dots$

14. Construct an example of a Fourier series of the form in problem 13(b) such that the series

$$\sum_{n=1}^{\infty} b_n^{2\alpha} \sin nx$$

are not Fourier series for any given $\alpha = 1, 2, \dots$

[According to Banach's theorem[1], there exists an odd function $f \in L(0, 2\pi)$ for which $a_{2^n}(f) = 1/\log(n+1)$ $(n = 1, 2, \dots)$. The Fourier series of the function $f$ is also required.]

15. Let $b_n \downarrow 0$ and the series (b) of problem 13 becomes a Fourier series. Then the series

$$\sum_{n=1}^{\infty} b_n^{\alpha} \sin nx$$

is a Fourier series for every real $\alpha > 1$.

16. Prove that if a Fourier series of the form (14.2) is given, then the series

$$\sum_{n=1}^{\infty} (a_{pn} \cos nx + b_{pn} \sin nx)$$

is a Fourier series for any given $p = 1, 2, \dots$.

In particular, for any Fourier series (14.2), the series

$$\sum_{n=1}^{\infty} \frac{b_{pn}}{n} \quad (p = 1, 2, \dots)$$

converges.

[Let the series (14.2) be the Fourier series of the function $f(x) \in L(0, 2\pi)$. Consider the Fourier series of the function $F(x) = \frac{1}{p}\sum_{k=0}^{p-1} f\left(\frac{x + 2\pi k}{p}\right)$.]

17. Derive an example of a Fourier series of the form (14.2) such that the series

$$\sum_{n=1}^{\infty} (a_{1+4n} \cos(1 + 4n) x + b_{1+4n} \sin(1 + 4n) x)$$

is not a Fourier series.

[Consider the Fourier series of the function $f(x) = \varphi(x - \pi/2) - \varphi(x + \pi/2)$ where $\varphi(x) = \sum_{n=1}^{\infty} \frac{\cos nx}{\ln(n + 1)}$.]

18. Let $f_k(x)$ and $F(x)$ be monotonely increasing bounded functions in $[0, 2\pi]$. If

$$|f_k(x)| \leqslant D \quad \text{for all} \quad \begin{cases} k = 1, 2, \dots \\ x \in [0, 2\pi] \end{cases}$$

where $D$ is a constant and

$$\lim_{k\to\infty} a_n(f_k) = a_n(F), \quad \lim_{k\to\infty} b_n(f_k) = b_n(F),$$

then at all points of continuity of the function $F(x)$

$$\lim_{k\to\infty} f_k(x) = F(x).$$

N. DUNFORD, J. SCHWARZ

[First of all, establish that for all functions $\Phi(x) \in L[0, 2\pi]$

$$\lim_{k\to\infty} \int_0^{2\pi} f_k \Phi \, dx = \int_0^{2\pi} F\Phi \, dx. \tag{*}$$

Then consider the point $x_0 \in (0, 2\pi)$ which is a point of continuity of the function $F(x)$. Next take sufficiently small numbers $h > 0$ and consider the functions

$$\Phi_1(x) = \begin{cases} 1 & \text{for} \quad x \in [x_0, x_0 + h] \equiv I_h \\ 0 & \text{for} \quad x \in [0, 2\pi] - I_h, \end{cases}$$

$$\Phi_2(x) = \begin{cases} 1 & \text{for} \quad x \in [x_0 - h, x_0] \equiv J_h \\ 0 & \text{for} \quad x \in [0, 2\pi] - J_h \end{cases}$$

which are then substituted in the equality (*).]

19. Consider a $2\pi$-periodic function $\varphi(x) \in L^2(0, 2\pi)$ such that $\varphi(x)$ is not equal to a constant. Let the sub-sequence of natural numbers $n_k \uparrow \infty$ be such that $\overline{\lim_{k\to\infty}} (n_{k+1} - n_k) < \infty$. If in the series

$$\sum_{n=1}^{\infty} a_n \varphi(nx - \alpha_n) \quad (\alpha_n \text{ are any given real numbers})$$

the partial sums $S_n(x)$ converge in measure in some set $E$ with $mE > 0$, then $\lim_{n\to\infty} a_n = 0$.

S. B. STECHKIN, P. L. UL'YANOV

20. Let $F(t)$ be an analytic function in [0, 1]. If a series with respect to the Rademacher system (see § 7)

$$\sum_{n=1}^{\infty} a_n \varphi_n(t)$$

converges to $F(x)$ at every point of some set $E \subset [0, 1]$ with $mE > 1/2$, then $F(t) = C(1 - 2t)$ and

$$a_n = C/2^n \quad (n = 1, 2, \ldots)$$

where $C$ is some constant.

S. B. STECHKIN, P. L. UL'YANOV

CHAPTER III

# THE CONVERGENCE OF A FOURIER SERIES AT A POINT

## § 1. Introduction

In Chapter I we have already considered some tests for the convergence of a Fourier series at a given point. Here we mean to examine some more tests and also to compare the various tests with one another. It is said that some sufficient test $A$ is *stronger* than test $B$, if

(1) every time the convergence of a series can be deduced by test $B$, the same result can also be obtained using test $A$, but

(2) cases occurs when the convergence can be proved by test $A$, whilst it is not possible to apply test $B$.

If condition (1) is fulfilled and nothing is known concerning condition (2), then we say that test $A$ is *not weaker* than test $B$.

Two tests $A$ and $B$ are said to be *non-comparable*, when cases can be demonstrated where $A$ is applicable but $B$ not, or vice versa.

We conclude this chapter with some remarks concerning uniform convergence, which will be examined in more detail in Chapter IV.

## § 2. Comparison of the Dini and Jordan tests

In Chapter I, § 38 it was established that if $x$ is a point of regularity for $f(x)$ and if

$$\int_0^\delta \frac{|f(x+t)+f(x-t)-2f(x)|}{t}\,dt$$

has meaning, then the series $\sigma(f)$ converges to $f(x)$ at this point (Dini's test).

On the other hand, it follows from Jordan's theorem (Chapter I, § 39) that if $f(x)$ is of bounded variation in the neighbourhood of the point $x$ and $x$ is a point of regularity, then $\sigma(f)$ converges to $f(x)$ at this point.

We will prove that *the Dini and Jordan tests are non-comparable.* Indeed, let us suppose that

$$f(x) = \frac{1}{\left|\ln \dfrac{x}{2\pi}\right|} \quad \text{in} \quad 0 < x \leqslant \pi,$$

$$f(0) = 0,$$

$$f(-x) = f(x).$$

It is then clear that $f(x)$ is monotonic in $(0, \pi)$ and in $(-\pi, 0)$, and therefore it is of bounded variation in $[-\pi, \pi]$. Moreover, it is everywhere continuous, especially at $x = 0$. Therefore, applying Jordan's test, we see that its Fourier series converges to it everywhere and, in particular, at $x = 0$.

However, we cannot apply Dini's test at $x = 0$, since the integral

$$\int_0^\delta \left| \frac{f(x+t)+f(x-t)-2f(x)}{t} \right| dt = 2\int_0^\delta \frac{f(t)}{t}\, dt = 2\int_0^\delta \frac{dt}{t\left|\ln \frac{t}{2\pi}\right|} = +\infty.$$

On the contrary, if we consider the function

$$\psi(x) = \sqrt{x}\sin\frac{1}{x} \quad \text{for} \quad 0 < x \leqslant \pi,$$
$$\psi(0) = 0,$$
$$\psi(-x) = \psi(x),$$

then Dini's test shows that its Fourier series converges at the point 0, since the integral

$$2\int_0^\delta \frac{|\psi(t)|}{t}\, dt \leqslant 2\int_0^\delta \frac{\sqrt{t}}{t}\, dt = 2\int_0^\delta \frac{dt}{\sqrt{t}}$$

has meaning. However, the function $\psi(x)$ is of bounded variation in any neighbourhood of the point 0 and therefore Jordan's test is not applicable.

We will describe in the following paragraphs a number of tests for convergence at a point. Let us recall (see Chapter I, § 37) that for the convergence of $\sigma(f)$ to $f(x)$ it is necessary and sufficient that

$$\lim_{n\to\infty} \int_0^\delta \varphi_x(u)\frac{\sin nu}{u}\, du,$$

where

$$\varphi_x(u) = f(x+u) + f(x-u) - 2f(x).$$

We will use this criterion.

## § 3. The de la Vallée-Poussin[1] test and its comparison with the Dini and Jordan tests

Let

$$\chi(t) = \frac{1}{t}\int_0^t \varphi_x(u)\,du, \quad \chi(0) = 0$$

and

$$\chi(t) \to 0 \quad \text{as} \quad t \to 0.$$

*If $\chi(t)$ is a function of bounded variation in some interval $0 \leqslant t \leqslant \delta$, then $\sigma(f)$ converges to $f(x)$ at the point $x$.*

We have by definition

$$t\chi(t) = \int_0^t \varphi_x(u)\,du,$$

and therefore

$$\varphi_x(t) = [t\chi(t)]'$$

almost everywhere.

Consequently,

$$\int_0^\delta \varphi_x(u)\frac{\sin nu}{u}\,du = \int_0^\delta [u\chi(u)]'\frac{\sin nu}{u}\,du$$

$$= \int_0^\delta u\chi'(u)\frac{\sin nu}{u}\,du + \int_0^\delta \chi(u)\frac{\sin nu}{u}\,du$$

$$= \int_0^\delta \chi'(u)\sin nu\,du + \int_0^\delta \chi(u)\frac{\sin nu}{u}\,du. \tag{3.1}$$

The first integral on the right-hand side of (3.1) tends to zero as $n \to \infty$, because $\chi(u)$ is of bounded variation, which means that $\chi'(u)$ is summable in $(0, \delta)$. We will prove that the second integral also tends to zero. For this, we note that $\chi(u)$ is continuous at the point 0 and is of bounded variation in its neighbourhood. Therefore $\sigma(\chi)$ converges to 0 at $u = 0$. But then

$$\lim_{n\to\infty}\int_0^\delta [\chi(0+u)+\chi(0-u)-2\chi(0)]\frac{\sin nu}{u}\,du = 0$$

or

$$\lim_{n\to\infty}\int_0^\delta [\chi(u)+\chi(-u)]\frac{\sin nu}{u}\,du = 0,$$

and since $\varphi_x(u)$ is even, then $\chi(u)$ is also even, which means that it follows that

$$\lim_{n\to\infty}\int_0^\delta \chi(u)\frac{\sin nu}{u}\,du = 0.$$

We see that

$$\lim_{n\to\infty}\int_0^\delta \varphi_x(u)\frac{\sin nu}{u}\,du = 0,$$

and therefore $\sigma(f)$ converges to $f(x)$, and the theorem is proved.

We will now prove that

*The de la Vallée-Poussin test is stronger than the Dini or the Jordan test.*

Indeed, if $f(x)$ is of bounded variation, then $\varphi_x(u)$ is also. It follows that $\varphi_x(u)$ is the difference of two monotonic functions, but then it seems that $\chi(t)$ is also the difference of two monotonic functions, and consequently will be of bounded variation. Moreover, $\chi(t) \to 0$ as $t \to 0$. Indeed, if $f(x) = [f(x+0) + f(x-0)]/2$, then $\varphi_x(u) \to 0$ as $u \to 0$, consequently $\chi(t) \to 0$ too.

Thus, if the Jordan test is fulfilled, then the de la Vallée-Poussin test is also fulfilled.

Now we will assume that the Dini test is fulfilled. Since

$$\chi'(t) = \frac{1}{t}\varphi_x(t) - \frac{1}{t^2}\int_0^t \varphi_x(u)du$$

almost everywhere, then

$$|\chi'(t)| \leqslant \left|\frac{\varphi_x(t)}{t}\right| + \frac{1}{t^2}\int_0^t |\varphi_x(u)|\, du. \tag{3.2}$$

The first term on the right-hand side of (4.2) is summable from Dini's condition. Then, integrating by parts

$$\int_\varepsilon^\delta \left\{\frac{1}{t^2}\int_0^t |\varphi_x(u)|\, du\right\} dt = \frac{1}{\varepsilon}\int_0^\varepsilon |\varphi_x(u)|\, du - \frac{1}{\delta}\int_0^\delta |\varphi_x(u)|\, du + \int_\varepsilon^\delta \frac{|\varphi_x(u)|}{u} du, \tag{3.3}$$

we see that as $\varepsilon \to 0$ the right-hand side of (3.3) tends to a limit, therefore the second term on the right-hand side of (3.2) is summable in $(0, \delta)$, which means that $\chi'(t)$ is summable in $(0, \delta)$. Hence it follows that $\chi(t)$ is of bounded variation in $(0, \delta)$.

Moreover, $\chi(t) \to 0$ as $t \to 0$, since

$$\left|\frac{1}{t}\int_0^t \varphi_x(u)\, du\right| \leqslant \int_0^t \frac{|\varphi_x(u)|}{u} du \to 0 \quad \text{as} \quad t \to 0.$$

Thus if the Dini test is fulfilled, then the de la Vallée-Poussin test is also fulfilled.

We have proved that the de la Vallée-Poussin test is not weaker than the Jordan test and not weaker than the Dini test. But since the last two tests are non-comparable (see § 2), then the de la Vallée-Poussin test is stronger than either of them.

## § 4. The Young† test

The following conditions are given:

(a) $\varphi_x(t) \to 0$ as $t \to 0$,

(b) the function

$$\theta(t) = t\varphi_x(t)$$

is of bounded variation in some interval $(0, \delta)$,

† W.H. Young[7].

(c) denoting the complete variation of $\theta(t)$ in the interval $(0, h)$ by $V(h)$, we have

$$V(h) = O(h).$$

Then $\sigma(f)$ converges to $f(x)$ at the point $x$.

To prove this we will again use the criterion of convergence

$$\lim_{n\to\infty} \int_0^\delta \varphi_x(t) \frac{\sin nt}{t} dt = 0,$$

where $\delta$ is some value such that $\theta(t)$ is of bounded variation in $(0, \delta)$.

We have

$$\int_0^\delta \varphi_x(t) \frac{\sin nt}{t} dt = \int_0^{k\frac{\pi}{n}} \varphi_x(t) \frac{\sin nt}{t} dt + \int_{k\frac{\pi}{n}}^\delta \varphi_x(t) \frac{\sin nt}{t} dt. \tag{4.1}$$

Here $k$ is some fixed value which we will define later. From condition (a) we know that

$$\sup_{0\leqslant t\leqslant k\frac{\pi}{n}} |\varphi_x(t)| \to 0 \quad \text{as} \quad n \to \infty,$$

and therefore

$$\left| \int_0^{k\frac{\pi}{n}} \varphi_x(t) \frac{\sin nt}{t} dt \right| \leqslant n \sup_{0\leqslant t\leqslant k\frac{\pi}{n}} |\varphi_x(t)|\, k\frac{\pi}{n} = o(1), \tag{4.2}$$

so there remains the estimate of the second integral in (4.1).

Let us suppose that

$$\xi_n(t) = \begin{cases} \dfrac{\varphi_x(t)}{t} = \dfrac{\theta(t)}{t^2} \quad \text{in} \quad \left(k\dfrac{\pi}{n}, \delta\right), \\ 0 \quad \text{outside this interval.} \end{cases}$$

Then the function $\xi_n(t)$ is of bounded variation due to condition (b). If we denote by $W_n$ its complete variation in $[-\pi, \pi]$, then since

$$\int_{k\frac{\pi}{n}}^\delta \varphi_x(t) \frac{\sin nt}{t} dt = \int_{-\pi}^\pi \xi_n(t) \sin nt\, dt,$$

we see (Chapter I, § 22) that

$$\left| \frac{1}{\pi} \int_{k\frac{\pi}{n}}^\delta \varphi_x(t) \frac{\sin nt}{t} dt \right| \leqslant \frac{W_n}{n}.$$

We note that $W_n$ depends on how we choose $k$. We will prove that for any $\varepsilon > 0$ it is possible to choose $k$ so that

$$W_n < \varepsilon n.$$

If this is proved, then we will have

$$\left| \int_{k\frac{\pi}{n}}^{\delta} \varphi_x(t) \frac{\sin nt}{t} dt \right| \leqslant \pi\varepsilon,$$

and by virtue of (4.1) and (4.2) the theorem will be proved.

Thus, it remains to estimate the complete variation $W_n$ of the function $\xi_n$. We have

$$\xi_n\left(\frac{k\pi}{n}\right) = \frac{\theta\left(\frac{k\pi}{n}\right)}{\left(\frac{k\pi}{n}\right)^2} = \frac{\frac{k\pi}{n}\varphi_x\left(\frac{k\pi}{n}\right)}{\left(\frac{k\pi}{n}\right)^2} = \frac{n}{k\pi}\varphi_x\left(\frac{k\pi}{n}\right) = o(n)$$

and $\xi_n(\delta) = \theta(\delta)/\delta^2 = o(1)$; therefore, if we prove that the complete variation of $\xi_n(t)$ in $(k\pi/n, \delta)$ is $o(n)$ for the given choice of $k$, then this will be true too for $(-\pi, \pi)$, because the jumps of the function at the points $k\pi/n$ and $\delta$ equal $o(n)$ and $O(1)$.

In this estimate we note that due to condition (c) we have the inequality $V(t) < At$, where $A$ is a constant, for the complete variation $V(t)$ of the function $\theta(t)$. Therefore $\theta(t)$ can be represented in the form $\theta(t) = \theta_1(t) - \theta_2(t)$, where $\theta_1$ and $\theta_2$ are monotonic and

$$|\theta_1(t)| < At, \quad |\theta_2(t)| < At.$$

For any division of the interval $(k\pi/n, \delta)$ by the points of separation

$$t_0 = \frac{k\pi}{n}, \; t_1, \; t_2, \; \dots, \; t_m = \delta$$

we have

$$\sum_{i=0}^{m-1}\left|\frac{\theta_1(t_{i+1})}{t_{i+1}^2} - \frac{\theta_1(t_i)}{t_i^2}\right| \leqslant \sum_{i=0}^{m-1}\frac{1}{t_{i+1}^2}\left|\theta_1(t_{i+1}) - \theta_1(t_i)\right| + \sum_{i=0}^{m-1}\left|\theta_1(t_i)\right|\left|\frac{1}{t_{i+1}^2} - \frac{1}{t_i^2}\right|$$

$$\leqslant \sum_{i=0}^{m-1}\frac{1}{t_{i+1}^2}\left|V(t_{i+1}) - V(t_i)\right| + 2\int_{k\pi/n}^{\delta}\frac{|\theta_1(t)|}{t^3}dt$$

$$\leqslant \int_{k\pi/n}^{\delta}\frac{dV(t)}{t^2} + 2A\int_{k\pi/n}^{\delta}\frac{dt}{t^2}.$$

A similar estimate holds for $\theta_2(t)$. Therefore

$$\sum_{i=0}^{m-1}\left|\frac{\theta(t_{i+1})}{t_{i+1}^2} - \frac{\theta(t_i)}{t_i^2}\right| \leqslant 2\int_{k\pi/n}^{\delta}\frac{dV(t)}{t^2} + 4A\int_{k\pi/n}^{\delta}\frac{dt}{t^2}$$

$$= 2\frac{V(t)}{t^2}\Big|_{k\pi/n}^{\delta} + 4\int_{k\pi/n}^{\delta}\frac{V(t)}{t^3}dt + 4A\int_{k\pi/n}^{\delta}\frac{dt}{t^2}$$

$$\leqslant 2\frac{V(\delta)}{\delta^2} + 8A\int_{k\pi/n}^{\delta}\frac{dt}{t^2} \leqslant \frac{2V(\delta)}{\delta^2} + 8A\frac{n}{k\pi}.$$

Finally

$$\sum_{i=0}^{m-1}\left|\frac{\theta(t_{i+1})}{t_{i+1}^2}-\frac{\theta(t_i)}{t_i^2}\right|<\frac{2V(\delta)}{\delta^2}+\varepsilon n=o(n)$$

for sufficiently large $n$ and therefore

$$W(n)=o(n),$$

which was what was required to be proved.

## § 5. The relationship between the Young test and the Dini, Jordan and de la Vallée-Poussin tests†

We will prove that *the Young test is stronger than the Jordan test.*

Indeed, if $f(x)$ is of bounded variation, then $\varphi_x(t)$ is also. If the value of the function at the point $x$ being considered is $f(x)$, then $\varphi_x(t) \to 0$ as $t \to 0$. The function $\theta(t) = t\,\varphi_x(t)$ is a function of bounded variation, being the product of two functions of bounded variation.

Finally, in order to evaluate the complete variation $V(h)$ of the function $\theta(t)$ in $(0, h)$, we note that for any two functions $\psi(t)$ and $g(t)$ of bounded variation and any interval $(a, b)$

$$\operatorname*{Var}_{(a,b)}\psi(t)g(t) \leqslant \max_{a\leqslant t\leqslant b}|g(t)|\operatorname*{Var}_{(a,b)}\psi+\max_{a\leqslant t\leqslant b}|\psi(t)|\operatorname*{Var}_{(a,b)}g$$

(where $\operatorname*{Var}_{(a,b)} F$ denotes the complete variation of $F$ in $(a, b)$) and therefore, if $|\varphi_x(t)| \leqslant M$ for $0 \leqslant t \leqslant h$, then

$$V(h)=hM+h\operatorname*{Var}_{0\leqslant t\leqslant h}\varphi_x(t)=O(h),$$

i.e. the Young test is fulfilled and, consequently, it is proved that the Young test is not weaker than the Jordan test.

Below we will show that cases exist where the Young test can be applied but the de la Vallée-Poussin test cannot be applied; therefore, it is even more true that we cannot apply the Jordan test, and therefore we see that

*The Young test is not only not weaker but is stronger than the Jordan test.*

Our statement has been proved.

We will now prove that

*The Young test is not stronger than the Dini test.*

Indeed, let us consider an example which has already figured in the comparison of the Dini and Jordan tests (see § 2):

$$\psi(x)=\sqrt{x}\sin\frac{1}{x}\quad\text{in}\quad 0<x\leqslant\pi,$$

$$\psi(0)=0,$$

$$\psi(-x)=\psi(x).$$

† A comparison of the different convergence tests was made by Hardy[4].

It is clear that, supposing $x = 0$, we have $\varphi_0(t) = 2\sqrt{t}\sin(1/t)$. Therefore

$$\theta(t) = 2t^{3/2}\sin\frac{1}{t}.$$

This means that

$$d\theta(t) = \left(3t^{1/2}\sin\frac{1}{t} - \frac{2}{\sqrt{t}}\cos\frac{1}{t}\right)dt.$$

If the Young test were satisfied, then we should have

$$\int_0^h |d\theta(t)| = O(h),$$

and moreover

$$\int_0^h \frac{\left|\cos\frac{1}{t}\right|}{\sqrt{t}}\,dt \geqslant C\sqrt{h},$$

where $C$ is a positive constant i.e. the Young test is not fulfilled although the Dini test can be applied.

On the other hand, the Dini test is not stronger than the Young test. Indeed, we have given an example, where the Dini test is not applicable but the Jordan test is applicable. But in this case the Young test is also applicable.

From the last two statements there follows a

COROLLARY. *The Young and Dini tests are non-comparable.*

We will proceed with a comparison of the Young test with the de la Vallée-Poussin test. We will prove first that

*The Young test is not stronger than the de la Vallée-Poussin test.*

Indeed, if the Young test were stronger than the de la Vallée-Poussin test, then by virtue of the results in § 3 it would be far stronger than the Dini test, but we have only just proved this is not true.

We will now prove that conversely:

*The de la Vallée-Poussin test is not stronger than the Young test.*

Indeed, let us take any number $a$, $0 < a < 1$ and suppose that

$$f(x) = \frac{\sin|\ln x|}{|\ln x|} \quad \text{for} \quad 0 < x \leqslant a,$$

$$f(x) = 0 \quad \text{for} \quad a < x \leqslant \pi,$$

$$f(0) = 0,$$

$$f(-x) = f(x).$$

From this definition

$$\varphi_0(t) = 2f(t) = 2\frac{\sin|\ln t|}{|\ln t|} \quad \text{for} \quad 0 < t \leqslant a$$

and

$$\theta(t) = 2t\frac{\sin|\ln t|}{|\ln t|} = 2t\frac{\sin \ln t}{\ln t}.$$

Since

$$\theta'(t) = 2\frac{\sin \ln t}{\ln t} + 2\frac{\cos \ln t}{\ln t} - 2\frac{\sin \ln t}{\ln^2 t}$$

remains bounded as $t \to 0$, then $\theta(t)$ is of bounded variation and

$$V(h) \leqslant \int_0^h |\theta'(t)|\, dt = O(h),$$

i.e. the Young test is fulfilled.

If we assume that

$$\chi(t) = \frac{1}{t}\int_0^t \varphi_0(u)\,du = \frac{2}{t}\int_0^t \frac{\sin \ln u}{\ln u}\,du,$$

then to fulfil the de la Vallée-Poussin test, it would be necessary for $\chi(t)$ to be of bounded variation in some $(0, \delta)$ and then $\chi'(t)$ should be summable in $(0, \delta)$. We will show that $\chi'(t)$ is not summable near the point $t = 0$.

To prove this, we note that

$$\chi'(t) = -\frac{2}{t^2}\int_0^t \frac{\sin \ln u}{\ln u}\,du + \frac{2}{t}\,\frac{\sin \ln t}{\ln t}. \tag{5.1}$$

But

$$\int_0^t \frac{\sin \ln u}{\ln u}\,du = \int_0^t \frac{u}{\ln u}\sin \ln u\, d(\ln u) = -\frac{t}{\ln t}\cos \ln t + \int_0^t \cos \ln u \frac{\ln u - 1}{\ln^2 u}\,du$$

$$= -\frac{t}{\ln t}\cos \ln t + \int_0^t \cos \ln u \frac{du}{\ln u} - \int_0^t \frac{\cos \ln u}{\ln^2 u}\,du. \tag{5.2}$$

Also we find that

$$\int_0^t \frac{\cos \ln u}{\ln u}\,du = \frac{t}{\ln t}\sin \ln t - \int_0^t \frac{\sin \ln u}{\ln u}\,du + \int_0^t \frac{\sin \ln u}{\ln^2 u}\,du,$$

whence, substituting in (5.2), we obtain

$$2\int_0^t \frac{\sin \ln u}{\ln u}\,du = \frac{t}{\ln t}[\sin \ln t - \cos \ln t] + \int_0^t \frac{\sin \ln u - \cos \ln u}{\ln^2 u}\,du. \tag{5.3}$$

Since for small and positive values of $u$ the function $\ln^2 u$ decreases with increasing $u$, then

$$\left|\int_0^t \frac{\sin \ln u - \cos \ln u}{\ln^2 u}\,du\right| \leqslant \frac{2t}{\ln^2 t},$$

and therefore, from (5.3)

$$\frac{2}{t}\int_0^t \frac{\sin \ln u}{\ln u}\,du = \frac{\sin \ln t - \cos \ln t}{\ln t} + O\left(\frac{1}{\ln^2 t}\right)$$

and, substituting in (5.1), we find that

$$\chi'(t) = \frac{\sin \ln t + \cos \ln t}{t \ln t} + O\left(\frac{1}{t \ln^2 t}\right).$$

But since $1/(t \ln^2 t)$ is summable near $t = 0$, then it remains to prove that

$$\frac{\sin \ln t + \cos \ln t}{t \ln t}$$

is not summable near $t = 0$. This means that

$$\int_0^\delta \left|\frac{\sin \ln t + \cos \ln t}{t \ln t}\right| dt = +\infty.$$

Assuming $\ln t = -u$, we obtain

$$\int_0^\delta \left|\frac{\sin \ln t + \cos \ln t}{t \ln t}\right| dt = \int_{\ln \frac{1}{\delta}}^\infty \frac{|\cos u - \sin u|}{u}\,du = \sqrt{2}\int_{\ln \frac{1}{\delta}}^\infty \frac{\left|\sin\left(\frac{\pi}{4} - u\right)\right|}{u}\,du = +\infty$$

(see Chapter I, § 41).

Consequently, we have proved the non-summability of $\chi'(t)$, and the theorem is proved.

From the last two theorems it follows that *the Young and de la Vallée-Poussin tests are non-comparable.*

## § 6. The Lebesgue test

Lebesgue derived a convergence test which is stronger than all the preceding ones. This test was expressed by Lebesgue himself in several different forms. We will prove it first in the following form:

THE LEBESGUE THEOREM. *If*

$$\int_h^\delta \left|\frac{\varphi_x(u+h)}{u+h} - \frac{\varphi_x(u)}{u}\right| du \to 0 \tag{6.1}$$

*as* $h \to +0$, *then the series* $\sigma(f)$ *converges to* $f(x)$ *at the point* $x$.

We will use the following lemma:

LEMMA 1. *If condition* (6.1) *is fulfilled, then supposing that*

$$\Phi_x(t) = \int_0^t |\varphi_x(u)|\, du, \tag{6.2}$$

*we have*

$$\Phi_x(t) = o(t). \tag{6.3}$$

For the proof we note that it follows from (6.1) that it is all the more true that

$$\int_h^\delta \frac{|\varphi_x(u+h)|}{u+h}\, du - \int_h^\delta \frac{|\varphi_x(u)|}{u}\, du \to 0. \tag{6.4}$$

Carrying out a change of variable $u = v - h$ in the first integral of (6.4), we find after elementary calculation that

$$\int_h^{2h} \frac{|\varphi_x(u)|}{u}\, du \to 0. \tag{6.5}$$

Let $\varepsilon > 0$ be given. We will choose $h_0$ so that

$$\int_h^{2h} \frac{|\varphi_x(u)|}{u}\, du < \varepsilon \quad \text{at} \quad h \leqslant h_0.$$

Then it is all the more true that

$$\frac{1}{2h} \int_h^{2h} |\varphi_x(u)|\, du < \varepsilon$$

or

$$\int_h^{2h} |\varphi_x(u)|\, du \leqslant 2\varepsilon h \quad \text{at} \quad h \leqslant h_0.$$

It is convenient to rewrite this in the form

$$\int_{h_1/2}^{h_1} |\varphi_x(u)|\, du \leqslant \varepsilon h_1 \quad \text{at} \quad h_1 < 2h_0. \tag{6.6}$$

Now let $t \leqslant 2h_0$. Then by virtue of (6.6) we have for any $n = 0, 1, 2, \ldots$

$$\int_{t/2^{n+1}}^{t/2^n} |\varphi_x(u)|\, du < \varepsilon \frac{t}{2^n}.$$

But from this

$$\Phi_x(t) = \int_0^t |\varphi_x(u)|\, du = \sum_{n=0}^{\infty} \int_{t/2^{n+1}}^{t/2^n} |\varphi_x(u)|\, du < \varepsilon t \sum_{n=0}^{\infty} \frac{1}{2^n} = 2\varepsilon t,$$

i.e.

$$\Phi_x(t) \leqslant 2\varepsilon t,$$

but this means that

$$\Phi_x(t) = o(t),$$

i.e. (6.3) is proved.

We will now proceed with the proof of the Lebesgue theorem. To prove the validity of this theorem, it is sufficient to prove that for some $\delta > 0$ we have

$$\lim_{n\to\infty} \int_0^{\delta} \frac{\varphi_x(u)}{u} \sin nu \, du = 0. \tag{6.7}$$

For this purpose we suppose that

$$I = \int_{\pi/n}^{\delta} \frac{\varphi_x(u)}{u} \sin nu \, du. \tag{6.8}$$

We will first show that

$$I = \int_{2\frac{\pi}{n}}^{\delta+\frac{\pi}{n}} \frac{\varphi_x(u)}{u} \sin nu \, du + o(1). \tag{6.9}$$

Indeed, due to Lemma 1, we have

$$\left| \int_{\pi/n}^{2\frac{\pi}{n}} \frac{\varphi_x(u)}{u} \sin nu \, du \right| \leqslant n \int_{\pi/n}^{2\frac{\pi}{n}} |\varphi_x(u)| \, du$$

$$= n \left[ \Phi\left(2\frac{\pi}{n}\right) - \Phi\left(\frac{\pi}{n}\right) \right] \leqslant n\Phi\left(2\frac{\pi}{n}\right) = o(1). \tag{6.10}$$

Moreover,

$$\int_{\delta}^{\delta+\frac{\pi}{n}} \frac{\varphi_x(u)}{u} \sin nu \, du = o(1) \quad \text{as} \quad n \to \infty, \tag{6.11}$$

because $\varphi_x(u)/u$ is summable in $(\delta, \pi)$.

From (6.10) and (6.11), the validity of (6.9) follows.

Now, substituting the variable $u + \pi/n$ for $u$, we find that

$$I = - \int_{\pi/n}^{\delta} \frac{\varphi_x\left(u + \frac{\pi}{n}\right)}{u + \frac{\pi}{n}} \sin nu \, du + o(1). \tag{6.12}$$

Combining (6.8) and (6.12), we obtain

$$I = \frac{1}{2}\int_{\pi/n}^{\delta}\left[\frac{\varphi_x(u)}{u} - \frac{\varphi_x\left(u+\frac{\pi}{n}\right)}{u+\frac{\pi}{n}}\right]\sin nu\,du + o(1).$$

But then

$$|I| \leqslant \frac{1}{2}\int_{\pi/n}^{\delta}\left|\frac{\varphi_x(u)}{u} - \frac{\varphi_x\left(u+\frac{\pi}{n}\right)}{u+\frac{\pi}{n}}\right| du + o(1) = o(1), \tag{6.13}$$

which follows from (6.1) where $h = \pi/n$.

Moreover, we have

$$\left|\int_0^{\pi/n}\frac{\varphi_x(u)}{u}\sin nu\,du\right| \leqslant n\int_0^{\pi/n}|\varphi_x(u)|\,du = o(1), \tag{6.14}$$

because due to Lemma 1, (6.3) follows from (6.1). But

$$\int_0^{\delta}\frac{\varphi_x(u)}{u}\sin nu\,du = I + \int_0^{\pi/n}\frac{\varphi_x(u)}{u}\sin nu\,du,$$

and therefore (6.7) follows from (6.13) and (6.14) and the theorem is proved.

We want to prove that Lebesgue's convergence test, expressed by condition (6.1), can be described in a somewhat different form, more suitable for application to concrete cases.† Let us prove this lemma:

LEMMA 2. *The condition*

$$\int_h^{\delta}\left|\frac{\varphi_x(u+h)}{u+h} - \frac{\varphi_x(u)}{u}\right| du = o(1) \quad as \quad h \to 0 \tag{6.1}$$

*is equivalent to the combination of the two conditions*

$$\Phi_x(t) = \int_0^t |\varphi_x(u)|\,du = o(t), \tag{6.3}$$

$$\int_h^{\delta}\left|\frac{\varphi_x(u+h) - \varphi_x(u)}{u}\right| du = o(1) \quad as \quad h \to 0. \tag{6.15}$$

In other words, we can express the following statement which can also be called Lebesgue's test of convergence.

† As regards the form given, it is suitable for the comparison of this test with others (see § 7).

*If at some point x the conditions* (6.3) *and* (6.15) *are fulfilled, then* $\sigma(f)$ *converges to* $f(x)$ *at this point.*

In order to prove Lemma 2, we note first of all that if (6.1) is fulfilled, then (6.3) is also fulfilled, which was stated in Lemma 1. Also, we have

$$\frac{\varphi_x(u+h)}{u+h} - \frac{\varphi_x(u)}{u} = \frac{\varphi_x(u+h) - \varphi_x(u)}{u} - h\,\frac{\varphi_x(u+h)}{(u+h)u}. \tag{6.16}$$

Let us prove that it follows from (6.3) that

$$h\int_h^\delta \frac{|\varphi_x(u+h)|}{u(u+h)}\,du = o(1). \tag{6.17}$$

Let $\varepsilon > 0$ be given. Let us choose $\eta > 0$ so small that $\Phi_x(t) < \varepsilon t$ at $t \leqslant 2\eta$ (which is possible due to (6.3)). Since

$$h\int_\eta^\delta \frac{|\varphi_x(u+h)|}{(u+h)u}\,du \leqslant \frac{h}{\eta^2}\int_\eta^\delta |\varphi_x(u+h)|\,du < \varepsilon, \tag{6.18}$$

if $h$ is sufficiently small, then it remains to estimate

$$h\int_h^\eta \frac{|\varphi_x(u+h)|}{u(u+h)}\,du.$$

But

$$\int_0^t |\varphi_x(u+h)|\,du = \Phi_x(t+h) - \Phi_x(h).$$

and therefore

$$\int_h^\eta \frac{|\varphi_x(u+h)|}{u(u+h)}\,du \leqslant \int_h^\eta \frac{|\varphi_x(u+h)|}{u^2}\,du = \frac{\Phi_x(u+h)}{u^2}\Bigg|_h^\eta + 2\int_h^\eta \frac{\Phi_x(u+h) - \Phi_x(h)}{u^3}\,du. \tag{6.19}$$

From the choice of the number $\eta$ we have for $h \leqslant u \leqslant \eta$

$$\Phi_x(u+h) - \Phi_x(h) \leqslant \Phi_x(u+h) < \varepsilon(u+h) < 2\varepsilon u,$$

therefore

$$2\int_h^\eta \frac{\Phi_x(u+h) - \Phi_x(h)}{u^3}\,du < 4\varepsilon\int_h^\eta \frac{du}{u^2} < \frac{4\varepsilon}{h}. \tag{6.20}$$

Moreover, the integrated term is

$$\frac{\Phi_x(\eta+h)}{\eta^2} - \frac{\Phi_x(2h)}{h^2} \leqslant \frac{\Phi_x(2\eta)}{\eta^2} + \frac{\Phi_x(2h)}{h^2} < \frac{2\varepsilon}{\eta} + \frac{2\varepsilon}{h}. \tag{6.21}$$

From (6.19), (6.20) and (6.21) it follows that

$$h\int_h^\eta \frac{|\varphi_x(u+h)|}{u(u+h)}\,du < 6\varepsilon + 2\varepsilon\,\frac{h}{\eta} \leqslant 8\varepsilon$$

since $h \leqslant \eta$, and taking into account (6.18), we see that the integral (6.17) can be made less than $9\varepsilon$, and since $\varepsilon$ is arbitrarily small, then (6.17) is proved.

Thus, we have proved that (6.17) follows from (6.3). But since from (6.16) we have

$$\left|\frac{\varphi_x(u+h)-\varphi_x(u)}{u}\right| \leqslant \left|\frac{\Phi_x(u+h)}{u+h}-\frac{\varphi_x(u)}{u}\right| + \left|h\frac{\varphi_x(u+h)}{u(u+h)}\right|,$$

then integrating with respect to $u$ from $h$ to $\delta$, we see that (6.3) and (6.13) follow from (6.1) and (6.17). In conclusion: (6.1) implies (6.3) and (6.15).

On the other hand, if (6.3) and (6.15) are fulfilled, then since (6.3) implies (6.17) and from (6.16) we have

$$\left|\frac{\varphi_x(u+h)}{u+h}-\frac{\varphi_x(u)}{u}\right| \leqslant \left|\frac{\varphi_x(u+h)-\varphi_x(u)}{u}\right| + \left|h\frac{\varphi_x(u+h)}{(u+h)u}\right|,$$

we also prove completely that (6.1) holds.

Thus, (6.1) implies (6.3) and (6.15), and they in their turn imply (6.1); so Lemma 2 is proved.

## § 7. A comparison of the Lebesgue test with all the preceding tests

Now we want to prove that *the Lebesgue test is stronger than the Jordan, Dini, de la Vallée-Poussin and Young tests.*

For this, following Hardy[4], we prove first that the Lebesgue test is not weaker than the de la Vallée-Poussin and Young tests.

*The Lebesgue test is not weaker than the de la Vallée-Poussin test.*

To prove this proposition we show that if

$$\chi(t) = \frac{1}{t}\int_0^t \varphi_x(u)\,du \tag{7.1}$$

is a function of bounded variation in some $(0, \delta)$ and $\chi(t) \to 0$ as $t \to 0$, then

$$\int_h^\delta \left|\frac{\varphi_x(u+h)}{u+h}-\frac{\varphi_x(u)}{u}\right| du = o(1) \quad \text{as} \quad h \to 0. \tag{7.2}$$

For this purpose we note that almost everywhere

$$\varphi_x(t) = [t\chi(t)]' = \chi(t) + t\chi'(t). \tag{7.3}$$

and therefore (7.2) will be valid if

$$\int_h^\delta \left|\frac{\chi(u+h)}{u+h}-\frac{\chi(u)}{u}\right| du = o(1) \tag{7.4}$$

and

$$\int_h^\delta |\chi'(u+h)-\chi'(u)|\,du = o(1). \tag{7.5}$$

It is not necessary to prove (7.5) since if $\chi(t)$ is of bounded variation in $(0, \delta)$, then $\chi'(t)$ is summable in $(0, \delta)$ and then (see Introductory Material, § 25) even

$$\int_0^\delta |\chi'(u+h) - \chi'(u)|\, du = o(1).$$

Thus, everything reduces to proving (7.4).

But since it is conditional that $\chi(t) \to 0$ as $t \to 0$, then it is even more true that

$$\int_0^t |\chi(u)|\, du = o(t),$$

and therefore it will follow† from Lemma 2 (§ 6) that (7.4) is valid, if we prove that

$$\int_h^\delta \left| \frac{\chi(t+h) - \chi(t)}{t} \right| dt = o(1). \tag{7.6}$$

We now note that it is immediately evident from (7.1) that in any interval, not containing the point $t = 0$, the function $\chi(t)$ is absolutely continuous. Therefore if $t > 0$, then

$$|\chi(t+h) - \chi(t)| \leqslant \int_t^{t+h} |\chi'(u)|\, du,$$

and therefore for any $\eta > h$

$$\int_h^\eta \frac{|\chi(t+h) - \chi(t)|}{t}\, dt \leqslant \int_h^\eta \left\{ \int_t^{t+h} |\chi'(u)|\, du \right\} \frac{dt}{t}$$

$$= \left[ \ln t \int_t^{t+h} |\chi'(u)|\, du \right]_h^\eta - \int_h^\eta \ln t [\,|\chi'(t+h)| - |\chi'(t)|\,]\, dt$$

$$= \ln \eta \int_\eta^{\eta+h} |\chi'(u)|\, du - \ln h \int_h^{2h} |\chi'(u)|\, du - \int_{2h}^{\eta+h} \ln(t-h) |\chi'(t)|\, dt$$

$$+ \int_h^\eta \ln t\, |\chi'(t)|\, dt$$

$$= \int_h^{2h} \ln\left(\frac{t}{h}\right) |\chi'(t)|\, dt + \int_{2h}^\eta \ln \frac{t}{t-h} |\chi'(t)|\, dt + \int_\eta^{\eta+h} \ln \frac{\eta}{t-h} |\chi'(t)|\, dt.$$

In each of these three integrals the logarithmic factor is bounded, and therefore the sum of all these integrals does not exceed some constant multiplied by

$$\int_h^{\eta+h} |\chi'(u)|\, du$$

---

† In the proof of Lemma 2 the properties of $\varphi_x(u)$ are nowhere applied; therefore the lemma holds for any summable function, and in particular for $\chi(t)$.

and, consequently, can be made as small as desired, if $\eta$ is taken to be sufficiently small. If $\eta$ is fixed, then

$$\int_{\eta}^{\delta} \left| \frac{\chi(t+h) - \chi(t)}{t} \right| dt = o(1) \quad \text{as} \quad h \to 0,$$

which means that (7.6) is valid and the proof is concluded.

We will now prove the following theorem (see Hardy[4]):

*The Lebesgue test is not weaker than the Young test.*

Let the conditions of Young's theorem be fulfilled, i.e.

(a) $\varphi_x(t) \to 0$ as $t \to 0$

(b) the function $\theta(t) = t\,\varphi_x(t)$ be of bounded variation in $(0, 2\delta)$,

(c) the complete variation $V(h)$ of the function $\theta(t)$ in the interval $(0, h)$ satisfy the condition

$$V(h) = O(h).$$

Due to (a) we have

$$\Phi_x(t) = \int_0^t |\varphi_x(u)|\, du = o(t),$$

and therefore it is sufficient to prove that

$$\int_h^{\delta} \left| \frac{\varphi_x(u+h) - \varphi_x(u)}{u} \right| du = o(1) \quad \text{as} \quad h \to 0,$$

in order to prove that the conditions are fulfilled leading to the Lebesgue test, and then the theorem will be proved.

Due to (b) we can represent $\theta(t)$ in the form

$$\theta(t) = g_1(t) - g_2(t),$$

where $g_1(t)$ and $g_2(t)$ are monotonically non-decreasing, $g_1(0) = g_2(0) = 0$ and

$$g_1(t) + g_2(t) = V(t),$$

and, consequently, due to (c)

$$\frac{g_1(t)}{t} = O(1) \quad \text{and} \quad \frac{g_2(t)}{t} = O(1). \tag{7.7}$$

Let $m$ be an integer for which $mh < \delta$; we will define it later. We have

$$\int_h^{\delta} \left| \frac{\varphi_x(t+h) - \varphi_x(t)}{t} \right| dt = \int_h^{mh} \left| \frac{\varphi_x(t+h) - \varphi_x(t)}{t} \right| dt + \int_{mh}^{\delta} \left| \frac{\varphi_x(t+h) - \varphi_x(t)}{t} \right| dt$$

$$= I_1 + I_2. \tag{7.8}$$

If we suppose that

$$\mu = \sup_{[h,(m+1)h]} |\varphi_x(t)|,$$

then

$$I_1 = \int_h^{mh} \frac{|\varphi_x(t+h)|}{t}\, dt + \int_h^{mh} \frac{|\varphi_x(t)|}{t}\, dt \leqslant 2\mu \ln m. \tag{7.9}$$

But if $m$ is fixed and $h \to 0$, then from $\varphi_x(t) \to 0$ it follows that $\mu \to 0$ and therefore

$$I_1 = o(1). \tag{7.10}$$

Now since $\varphi_x(t) = \theta(t)/t$ we have

$$I_2 = \int_{mh}^{\delta} \left| \frac{\theta(t+h)}{t+h} - \frac{\theta(t)}{t} \right| \frac{dt}{t}$$

$$\leqslant \int_{mh}^{\delta} \left| \frac{g_1(t+h)}{t+h} - \frac{g_1(t)}{t} \right| \frac{dt}{t} + \int_{mh}^{\delta} \left| \frac{g_2(t+h)}{t+h} - \frac{g_2(t)}{t} \right| \frac{dt}{t}. \tag{7.11}$$

It is clear that both integrals are estimated in the same way, therefore it is sufficient to estimate the first; we have

$$\int_{mh}^{\delta} \left| \frac{g_1(t+h)}{t+h} - \frac{g_1(t)}{t} \right| \frac{dt}{t}$$

$$\leqslant \int_{mh}^{\delta} \left| \frac{g_1(t+h) - g_1(t)}{(t+h)t} \right| dt + \int_{mh}^{\delta} |g_1(t)| \left( \frac{1}{t} - \frac{1}{t+h} \right) \frac{dt}{t} = I_3 + I_4. \tag{7.12}$$

If

$$k = \sup_{0 \leqslant t \leqslant \delta} \left| \frac{g_1(t)}{t} \right|$$

(and this magnitude is finite due to (7.7)), then

$$I_4 < k \ln \frac{t}{t+h} \Bigg|_{mh}^{\delta} = k \ln \frac{\delta(m+1)h}{(\delta+h)mh} < k \ln \frac{m+1}{m}. \tag{7.13}$$

This magnitude can be made as small as desired, if $m$ is chosen to be sufficiently large, but we will make the choice of $m$ later.

We will now estimate $I_3$. Due to $g_1(t)$ being monotonic it can be written thus

$$I_3 = \int_{mh}^{\delta} \frac{g_1(t+h) - g_1(t)}{(t+h)t}\, dt.$$

Therefore

$$
\begin{aligned}
I_3 &= \int_{mh}^{\delta} \frac{g_1(t+h)}{(t+h)t}\,dt - \int_{mh}^{\delta} \frac{g_1(t)}{t(t+h)}\,dt \\
&= \int_{(m+1)h}^{\delta+h} \frac{g_1(u)}{u(u-h)}\,du - \int_{mh}^{\delta} \frac{g_1(u)}{u(u+h)}\,du \\
&= \int_{(m+1)h}^{\delta+h} \frac{g_1(u)}{u(u+h)}\,du + 2h \int_{(m+1)h}^{\delta+h} \frac{g_1(u)}{u(u^2-h^2)}\,du - \int_{mh}^{\delta} \frac{g_1(u)}{u(u+h)}\,du \\
&= \int_{\delta}^{\delta+h} \frac{g_1(u)}{u(u+h)}\,du - \int_{mh}^{(m+1)h} \frac{g_1(u)}{u(u+h)}\,du + 2h \int_{(m+1)h}^{\delta+h} \frac{g_1(u)}{u(u^2-h^2)}\,du. \qquad (7.14)
\end{aligned}
$$

Since in all these integrals $|g_1(u)/u| \leqslant k$, then

$$
\left| \int_{\delta}^{\delta+h} \frac{g_1(u)}{u(u+h)}\,du \right| \leqslant k \ln(u+h) \Big|_{\delta}^{\delta+h} \leqslant k \ln \frac{\delta+2h}{\delta+h} \qquad (7.15)
$$

can be made as small as desired if $h$ is sufficiently small; also

$$
\left| \int_{mh}^{(m+1)h} \frac{g_1(u)}{u(u+h)}\,du \right| \leqslant k \ln(u+h) \Big|_{mh}^{(m+1)h} = k \ln \frac{m+2}{m+1} \qquad (7.16)
$$

and finally

$$
\begin{aligned}
\left| 2h \int_{(m+1)h}^{\delta+h} \frac{g_1(u)}{u(u^2-h^2)}\,du \right| &\leqslant 2kh \int_{(m+1)h}^{\delta+h} \frac{du}{u^2-h^2} = k \ln \frac{u-h}{u+h} \Big|_{(m+1)h}^{\delta+h} \\
&= k \ln \frac{\delta(m+2)h}{(\delta+2h)mh} \leqslant k \ln \frac{m+2}{m}. \qquad (7.17)
\end{aligned}
$$

If we first choose $m$ so that

$$
k \ln \frac{m+2}{m} < \eta, \qquad (7.18)
$$

where $\eta > 0$ is given, after this we choose $h$ so that

$$
k \ln \frac{\delta+2h}{\delta+h} < \eta \quad \text{as} \quad mh < \delta, \qquad (7.19)
$$

and finally we require that

$$
2\mu \ln m < \eta \qquad (7.20)
$$

(which is possible since $\mu \to 0$ if $mh \to 0$), then due to (7.13) and (7.18) we will have

$$|I_4| < \eta$$

and due to (7.14)–(7.19)

$$|I_3| < 3\eta,$$

which concludes the proof of the theorem.

We have proved that the Lebesgue test is not weaker than the de la Vallée-Poussin test and is not weaker than the Young test. We will now prove that:

*The Lebesgue test is stronger than the Jordan, Dini, de la Vallée-Poussin and Young tests.*

In order to prove this, it is sufficient to make a simple note: we know that the de la Vallée-Poussin and Young tests are non-comparable. This means that it is possible to find a case where the de la Vallée-Poussin test can be applied, but the Young test cannot. However, the Lebesgue test is not weaker than the de la Vallée-Poussin test, which means that it can also be applied in the case under consideration. Thus, the Lebesgue test is stronger than the Young test. We can also conclude that it is stronger than the de la Vallée-Poussin test. But the latter is stronger than the Dini and Jordan tests. This means that the Lebesgue test is stronger than the last two tests and the proof of our statement is concluded.

Unfortunately, as was noted by Lebesgue himself, the practical application of this test was rather difficult, therefore it is frequently necessary to try out weaker tests which are at the same time more convenient to verify. Lebesgue made the following useful remark: if we can divide the function $f(x)$ into the sum of two functions, to each of which we can apply some test, then the series $\sigma(f)$ converges as the sum of two convergent series. As regards his own test, it is automatically fulfilled for the sum if it is fulfilled for each of the terms of the sum.

## § 8. The Lebesgue–Gergen test

The following theorem† can be proved, in which a somewhat less restrictive condition than for the Lebesgue test is required:

THEOREM. *If*

$$\int_0^t \varphi_x(u)\,du = o(t)$$

*and*

$$\int_h^\delta \left|\frac{\varphi_x(u+h)-\varphi_x(u)}{u}\right| du = o(1) \quad \text{as} \quad h \to 0,$$

*then the series $\sigma(f)$ converges to $f(x)$ at the point $x$.*

Consequently, here, whilst maintaining the second condition of the Lebesgue theo-

† Some authors refer to this theorem as the Lebesgue–Gergen theorem, although Gergen[1] examined a somewhat different condition.

rem, we replace $|\varphi_x(u)|$ by $\varphi_x(u)$ in the first condition. In order to prove the theorem, we will prove as always that at some $\delta$ we have

$$\int_0^\delta \frac{\varphi_x(u)}{u} \sin nu\, du = o(1) \quad \text{as} \quad n \to \infty. \tag{8.1}$$

Again, having assumed that

$$I = \int_{\pi/n}^{\delta} \frac{\varphi_x(u)}{u} \sin nu\, du, \tag{8.2}$$

we will show that

$$I = \int_{2\frac{\pi}{n}}^{\delta+\frac{\pi}{n}} \frac{\varphi_x(u)}{u} \sin nu\, du + o(1). \tag{8.3}$$

Indeed, since $\varphi_x(u)/u$ is summable in $(\delta, \pi)$, then the added integral

$$\int_{\delta}^{\delta+\frac{\pi}{n}} \frac{\varphi_x(u)}{u} \sin nu\, du = o(1).$$

As regards the integral

$$\int_{\pi/n}^{2\frac{\pi}{n}} \frac{\varphi_x(u)}{u} \sin nu\, du, \tag{8.4}$$

we will argue thus: supposing

$$\Phi_x^*(t) = \int_0^t \varphi_x(u)\, du,$$

we have $\Phi_x^*(t) = o(t)$. Also

$$\int_{\pi/n}^{2\frac{\pi}{n}} \varphi_x(u) \frac{\sin nu}{u}\, du = \Phi_x^*(u) \frac{\sin nu}{u} \Bigg|_{\pi/n}^{2\frac{\pi}{n}} - \int_{\pi/n}^{2\frac{\pi}{n}} \Phi_x^*(u) \frac{d}{du}\left(\frac{\sin nu}{u}\right) du. \tag{8.5}$$

The integrated term equals zero. Under the integral sign $\Phi_x^*(u) = o(u)$ and

$$\frac{d}{du}\left(\frac{\sin nu}{u}\right) = \frac{nu \cos nu - \sin nu}{u^2} = O\left(\frac{n}{u}\right).$$

Therefore, noting that the length of the interval of integration is $\pi/n$, we see that the integral in (8.5) is $o(1)$.

Thus (8.3) is established. Again from (8.2) and (8.3) we find (as in the proof of the Lebesgue theorem) that

$$I = \frac{1}{2}\int_{\pi/n}^{\delta}\left[\frac{\varphi_x(u)}{u} - \frac{\varphi_x\left(u+\frac{\pi}{n}\right)}{u+\frac{\pi}{n}}\right]\sin nu\,du + o(1). \tag{8.6}$$

This can be written differently in the form

$$I = \frac{1}{2}\int_{\pi/n}^{\delta}\left[\frac{\varphi_x(u) - \varphi_x\left(u+\frac{\pi}{n}\right)}{u+\frac{\pi}{n}}\right]\sin nu\,du$$

$$+\frac{1}{2}\int_{\pi/n}^{\delta}\varphi_x(u)\left[\frac{1}{u} - \frac{1}{u+\frac{\pi}{n}}\right]\sin nu\,du + o(1). \tag{8.7}$$

From the second condition of our theorem we have that

$$\left|\int_{\pi/n}^{\delta}\frac{\left[\varphi_x(u) - \varphi_x\left(u+\frac{\pi}{n}\right)\right]}{u+\frac{\pi}{n}}\sin nu\,du\right| \leqslant \int_{\pi/n}^{\delta}\left|\frac{\varphi_x(u) - \varphi_x\left(u+\frac{\pi}{n}\right)}{u}\right|du = o(1)$$

as $n \to \infty$, and therefore from (8.7)

$$I = \frac{\pi}{2n}\int_{\pi/n}^{\delta}\varphi_x(u)\frac{\sin nu}{u\left(u+\frac{\pi}{n}\right)}du + o(1). \tag{8.8}$$

We will prove that

$$\frac{\pi}{2n}\int_{\pi/n}^{2\frac{\pi}{n}}\varphi_x(u)\frac{\sin nu}{u\left(u+\frac{\pi}{n}\right)}du = o(1). \tag{8.9}$$

Indeed, here the proof is the same as in the evaluation of the integral (8.4), only

$$\frac{d}{du}\frac{\sin nu}{u\left(u+\frac{\pi}{n}\right)} = O\left(\frac{n}{u^2}\right),$$

and therefore

$$\int_{\pi/n}^{2\frac{\pi}{n}} \varphi_x(u) \frac{\sin nu}{u\left(u+\dfrac{\pi}{n}\right)} du = -\int_{\pi/n}^{2\frac{\pi}{n}} \Phi_x^*(u) \frac{d}{du}\left(\frac{\sin nu}{u\left(u+\dfrac{\pi}{n}\right)}\right) du$$

$$= \int_{\pi/n}^{2\frac{\pi}{n}} o(u) O\left(\frac{n}{u^2}\right) du = o(n) \int_{\pi/n}^{2\frac{\pi}{n}} \frac{du}{u} = o(n) \ln 2 = o(n).$$

Consequently (8.9) is proved. Moreover, it is evident that

$$\int_{\delta}^{\delta+\frac{\pi}{n}} \varphi_x(u) \frac{\sin nu}{u\left(u+\dfrac{\pi}{n}\right)} du = o(1) \tag{8.10}$$

even without multiplying by $\pi/2n$; therefore from (8.9) and (8.10) it follows that it is possible to rewrite (8.8) thus:

$$I = o(1) + \frac{\pi}{2n} \int_{2\frac{\pi}{n}}^{\delta+\frac{\pi}{n}} \varphi_x(u) \frac{\sin nu}{u\left(u+\dfrac{\pi}{n}\right)} du$$

$$= o(1) - \frac{\pi}{2n} \int_{\pi/n}^{\delta} \varphi_x\left(u+\frac{\pi}{n}\right) \frac{\sin nu}{\left(u+\dfrac{\pi}{n}\right)\left(u+\dfrac{2\pi}{n}\right)} du. \tag{8.11}$$

Combining the two different expressions for $I$, namely (8.8) and (8.11), we obtain

$$I = o(1) + \frac{\pi}{4n} \int_{\pi/n}^{\delta} \left[\frac{\varphi_x(u)}{u\left(u+\dfrac{\pi}{n}\right)} - \frac{\varphi_x\left(u+\dfrac{\pi}{n}\right)}{\left(u+\dfrac{\pi}{n}\right)\left(u+2\dfrac{\pi}{n}\right)}\right] \sin nu \, du.$$

Here we will again separate out the portion that can be estimated according to the second condition of the theorem, and therefore we can write

$$I = o(1) + \frac{\pi}{4n}\int_{\pi/n}^{\delta}\left[\frac{\varphi_x(u) - \varphi_x\left(u+\frac{\pi}{n}\right)}{\left(u+\frac{\pi}{n}\right)\left(u+\frac{2\pi}{n}\right)}\right]\sin nu\,du$$

$$+ \frac{\pi}{4n}\int_{\pi/n}^{\delta}\varphi_x(u)\left[\frac{1}{u\left(u+\frac{\pi}{n}\right)} - \frac{1}{\left(u+\frac{\pi}{n}\right)\left(u+\frac{2\pi}{n}\right)}\right]\sin nu\,du.$$

The modulus of the first integral is less than

$$\frac{\pi}{4n}\int_{\pi/n}^{\delta}\left|\frac{\varphi_x(u) - \varphi_x\left(u+\frac{\pi}{n}\right)}{u^2}\right|du \leqslant \int_{\pi/n}^{\delta}\left|\frac{\varphi_x(u) - \varphi_x\left(u+\frac{\pi}{n}\right)}{u}\right|du = o(1),$$

and therefore

$$I = o(1) + \frac{\pi^2}{2n^2}\int_{\pi/n}^{\delta}\varphi_x(u)\frac{\sin nu}{u\left(u+\frac{\pi}{n}\right)\left(u+2\frac{\pi}{n}\right)}\,du. \tag{8.12}$$

We will again integrate by parts; taking into account that $\Phi_x^*(u) = o(u)$ and

$$\frac{d}{du}\left(\frac{\sin nu}{u\left(u+\frac{\pi}{n}\right)\left(u+2\frac{\pi}{n}\right)}\right) = O\left(\frac{n}{u^3}\right),$$

we find that

$$\int_{\pi/n}^{\delta}\varphi_x(u)\frac{\sin nu}{u\left(u+\frac{\pi}{n}\right)\left(u+2\frac{\pi}{n}\right)}\,du = \Phi_x^*(u)\frac{\sin nu}{u\left(u+\frac{\pi}{n}\right)\left(u+2\frac{\pi}{n}\right)}\Bigg|_{\pi/n}^{\delta}$$

$$- \int_{\pi/n}^{\delta}\Phi_x^*(u)\frac{d}{du}\left[\frac{\sin nu}{u\left(u+\frac{\pi}{n}\right)\left(u+2\frac{\pi}{n}\right)}\right]du$$

$$= O(1) + \int_{\pi/n}^{\delta}o(u)O\left(\frac{n}{u^3}\right)du = o(n^2).$$

Substituting this in (8.12) we find that

$$I = o(1).$$

But the integral on the left-hand side of (8.1) differs from $I$ by the magnitude $o(1)$, since

$$\int_0^{\pi/n} \frac{\varphi_x(u)}{u} \sin nu\, du = \Phi_x^*(u) \frac{\sin nu}{u}\Bigg|_0^{\pi/n} - \int_0^{\pi/n} \Phi_x^*(u) d\left(\frac{\sin nu}{u}\right)$$

$$= \int_0^{\pi/n} o(u) O\left(\frac{n}{u}\right) du = o(1)$$

(here the argument is the same as in the estimation of the integral of (8.4)). This concludes the proof.

*Note.* The test that we have just proved is somewhat stronger than the Lebesgue test; however, this strengthening is not significant. It is important to note that the condition

$$\Phi_x(t) = \int_0^t |\varphi_x(u)|\, du = o(t)$$

is fulfilled almost everywhere for any summable function $f(x)$ (see Introductory Material, § 15), therefore although at an individual point this condition has not got to be fulfilled, a set of such points where it is not fulfilled is only of measure zero. Thus, subsequently, when we will study the convergence of Fourier series in sets and not at individual points, the superiority of the Lebesgue–Gergen test over the Lebesgue test cannot be perceived.

However, at the present moment, we are concerned with convergence at an individual point.†

We will describe yet another convergence test due to Izumi[1], namely: if $f(x)$ is an even periodic function and

$$\int_0^t |f(x)|\, dx = o(t) \quad \text{as} \quad t \to 0 \tag{8.13}$$

and if the condition

$$\int_0^{\pi/n} \psi(n, t) dt = o\left(\frac{1}{n}\right), \tag{8.14}$$

is fulfilled where

$$\psi(n, t) = \sum_{k=1}^{\frac{n-1}{2}} \int_{t+\frac{2k\pi}{n}}^{t+\frac{(2k+1)\pi}{n}} \frac{f(x) - f\left(x - \frac{\pi}{n}\right)}{x} dx,$$

then the Fourier series of $f(x)$ converges at the point $x = 0$.

† For the result of a comparison of different convergence tests at a point, see also the work by Morse and Transue[1].

This condition is a generalization of the Lebesgue criterion, since if (8.13) is fulfilled and

$$\lim_{\delta\to 0}\int_{\delta}^{\pi}\left|f(t+\delta)-f(t)\right|\frac{dt}{t}=0,$$

then (8.14) also holds.

The author also asserts that if for even $f(x)$, (8.13) is fulfilled, then for the convergence of the Fourier series of $f(x)$ at the point $x = 0$ it is necessary and sufficient that

$$\lim_{n\to\infty}\int_0^{\pi/n}\psi(n, t)\cos nt\, dt = 0.$$

## § 9. Concerning the necessity conditions for convergence at a point

The question arises: to what extent are the sufficiency conditions of convergence obtained necessary? We will now prove that not only the condition

$$\Phi_x(t)=\int_0^t|\varphi_x(u)|\,du=o(t),$$

but even the less restrictive

$$\Phi_x^*(t)=\int_0^t\varphi_x(u)\,du=o(t)$$

is not necessary for the convergence of a Fourier series at the point $x$.

To be exact, the following theorem holds (see Izumi, Matsuyama, Tsuchikura[1]).

THEOREM. *For any function $\varepsilon(t)$, provided that $\varepsilon(t)\geqslant 0$ and $\varepsilon(t)\to 0$ as $t\to 0$, there exists a summable $f(x)$ such that the series $\sigma(f)$ converges at a point $x$ and at the same time*

$$\left|\int_0^t\varphi_x(u)\,du\right|\geqslant\varepsilon(t) \tag{9.1}$$

*for an infinite set of values $t$.*

*Proof.* We will assume that $x = 0, f(0) = 0$ and take $f(x)$ as even, then

$$\varphi_x(t)=\varphi_0(t)=2f(t).$$

Let us consider a sequence of positive numbers $t_n$, $t_n\downarrow 0$ and two sequences of positive numbers $\{u_n\}$ and $\{v_n\}$ such that

$$\sum_{n=1}^{\infty}\varepsilon(t_n)<+\infty, \tag{9.2}$$

$$\frac{v_n}{u_n}\to 0\quad\text{as}\quad n\to\infty \tag{9.3}$$

and the intervals

$$(t_n-u_n,\quad t_n+u_n)\quad(n=1,2,\ldots) \tag{9.4}$$

do not overlap and lie in $(0,\pi]$.

Let us consider the sets

$$\Delta_n = (t_n - u_n, t_n - v_n) + (t_n + v_n, t_n + u_n) \quad (n = 1, 2, \ldots).$$

We define the even function $f(t)$ thus

$$f(t) = \frac{c_n t}{t_n - t} \quad \text{for} \quad t \in \Delta_n \quad (n = 1, 2, \ldots) \tag{9.5}$$

and $f(t) = 0$ at the remaining points of $(0, \pi)$, where $\{c_n\}$ is a sequence of positive numbers which we will define later.

We have

$$\int_0^\pi |f(t)|\, dt = \sum_{n=1}^\infty c_n \int_{\Delta_n} \left| \frac{t}{t_n - t} \right| dt = \sum_{n=1}^\infty \left[ c_n \int_{t_n - u_n}^{t_n - v_n} \frac{t}{t_n - t}\, dt + c_n \int_{t_n + v_n}^{t_n + u_n} \frac{t}{t - t_n}\, dt \right]$$

$$= \sum_{n=1}^\infty c_n \left[ -(u_n - v_n) - t_n \ln |t_n - t| \Big|_{t_n - u_n}^{t_n - v_n} \right.$$

$$\left. + (u_n - v_n) + t_n \ln |t - t_n| \Big|_{t_n + v_n}^{t_n + u_n} \right] = 2 \sum_{n=1}^\infty c_n t_n \ln \frac{u_n}{v_n}.$$

Consequently, if

$$\sum_{n=1}^\infty c_n t_n \ln \frac{u_n}{v_n} < +\infty, \tag{9.6}$$

then the function $f(x)$ is summable.

Also

$$\int_0^\pi f(t) \frac{\sin mt}{t}\, dt = \sum_{n=1}^\infty c_n \int_{\Delta_n} \frac{\sin mt}{t_n - t}\, dt$$

$$= \sum_{n=1}^\infty c_n \int_{\Delta_n} \frac{\sin mt_n \cos m(t - t_n) + \cos mt_n \sin m(t - t_n)}{t_n - t}\, dt$$

$$= \sum_{n=1}^\infty c_n \cos mt_n \int_{\Delta_n} \frac{\sin m(t - t_n)}{t_n - t}\, dt = -2 \sum_{n=1}^\infty c_n \cos mt_n \int_{v_n}^{u_n} \frac{\sin mt}{t}\, dt, \tag{9.7}$$

because the two intervals containing $\Delta_n$ are positioned symmetrically relative to $t_n$, and we take into account the even nature of the cosine and the odd nature of the sine.

Let us assume that

$$\sum_{n=1}^\infty c_n < +\infty \tag{9.8}$$

and prove that then the right-hand side of (9.7) tends to zero as $n \to \infty$.

Indeed, since

$$\left| \int_{\alpha}^{\beta} \frac{\sin mt}{t} \, dt \right| \leqslant \pi$$

for any $\alpha$ and $\beta$ in $(0, \infty)$ (see Chapter I, § 41) and moreover

$$\lim_{m\to\infty} \int_{\alpha}^{\beta} \frac{\sin mt}{t} \, dt = 0, \tag{9.9}$$

if $\alpha$ and $\beta$ are positive, then it is possible for any $\varepsilon > 0$ to find $N$ such that

$$\sum_{N+1}^{\infty} c_n < \varepsilon,$$

and then

$$\left| \sum_{N+1}^{\infty} c_n \cos mt_n \int_{u_n}^{v_n} \frac{\sin mt}{t} \, dt \right| < \varepsilon\pi;$$

moreover, when $N$ is fixed

$$\sum_{n=1}^{N} c_n \cos mt_n \int_{u_n}^{v_n} \frac{\sin mt}{t} \, dt = o(1),$$

since every term is $o(1)$ due to (9.9).

On the other hand we have

$$\int_{\Delta_n} f(t) \, dt = c_n \int_{t_n-u_n}^{t_n-v_n} \frac{t}{t_n - t} \, dt + c_n \int_{t_n+v_n}^{t_n+u_n} \frac{t}{t_n - t} \, dt$$

$$= - c_n(u_n - v_n) - c_n t_n \ln |t_n - t| \Big|_{t_n-u_n}^{t_n-v_n}$$

$$- c_n(u_n - v_n) - c_n t_n \ln |t_n - t| \Big|_{t_n+v_n}^{t_n+u_n} = 2c_n(v_n - u_n) \tag{9.10}$$

and

$$\left| \int_{t_n-u_n}^{t_n} f(t) \, dt \right| = c_n \int_{t_n-u_n}^{t_n-v_n} \frac{t}{t_n - t} \, dt = c_n \left\{ t_n \ln \frac{u_n}{v_n} - (u_n - v_n) \right\}$$

$$\geqslant c_n t_n \left( \ln \frac{u_n}{v_n} - \frac{u_n}{t_n} \right) \geqslant c_n t_n \left( \ln \frac{u_n}{v_n} - 1 \right) \geqslant \frac{1}{2} c_n t_n \ln \frac{u_n}{v_n}. \tag{9.11}$$

We will assume that the condition

$$\sum_{i=n+1}^{\infty} c_i(u_i - v_i) < \frac{1}{8} c_n t_n \ln \frac{u_n}{v_n}, \tag{9.12}$$

is fulfilled and also that

$$\frac{1}{4} c_n t_n \ln \frac{u_n}{v_n} \geqslant \varepsilon(t_n). \tag{9.13}$$

Then from (9.11), (9.13), (9.12) and (9.10) we obtain

$$\left| \int_0^{t_n} f(u)\, du \right| = \left| \sum_{i=n+1}^{\infty} \int_{\Delta_i} f(t)\, dt + \int_{t_n-u_n}^{t_n} f(t)\, dt \right|$$

$$\geqslant \frac{1}{2} c_n t_n \ln \frac{u_n}{v_n} - 2 \sum_{n+1}^{\infty} c_i(u_i - v_i) \geqslant \frac{1}{4} c_n t_n \ln \frac{u_n}{v_n} \geqslant \varepsilon(t_n).$$

We now proceed thus: supposing that $t_n$ are chosen as desired, provided that

$$\sum_{n=1}^{\infty} \varepsilon(t_n) < +\infty,$$

we require that

$$\frac{1}{4} c_n t_n \ln \frac{u_n}{v_n} = \varepsilon(t_n), \tag{9.14}$$

then (9.13) is known to be satisfied. The relationship (9.14) gives greater scope in the choice of $c_n$, $u_n$ and $v_n$. We will choose $c_n$ so small that

$$\sum_{i=n+1}^{\infty} c_i < \frac{1}{2} \varepsilon(t_n).$$

Then (9.12), which by virtue of (9.14) takes the form

$$\sum_{i=n+1}^{\infty} c_i(u_i - v_i) < \frac{1}{2} \varepsilon(t_n),$$

will be true, provided that $u_i \leqslant 1$ and moreover (9.8) will be valid. Finally we note that by decreasing $c_n$ we will only permit $u_n/v_n$ to increase, which means that it is always possible to satisfy (9.3) and by choosing $u_n$ intelligently (it is sufficient that $u_n + v_{n+1} < t_n - t_{n+1}$) we will prove that (9.4) also holds. Thus all the conditions are fulfilled and the theorem is proved.

*Note.* We have proved that the convergence of the series $\sigma(f)$ to $f(x)$ at some point $x$ is not implied by the fulfilment alone of the condition

$$\int_0^t \varphi_x(u)\, du = o(t). \tag{9.15}$$

However, it can be remarked that if certain limitations are imposed on the coefficients of the series or on the rapidity of its convergence, then condition (9.15) appears to be necessary.

Thus, for example, Hardy and Littlewood[9] proved that if

$$a_n = O\left(\frac{1}{n^\delta}\right) \quad \text{and} \quad b_n = O\left(\frac{1}{n^\delta}\right), \quad \delta > 0$$

and moreover

$$|S_n(x) - f(x)| = O\left(\frac{1}{\ln n}\right),$$

then condition (9.15) is fulfilled.

P. L. Ul'yanov[10], imposing no limitations on the coefficients of the series but some on the rapidity of its convergence, also derived the necessity of (9.15); to be exact, he proved that from

$$|S_n(x) - f(x)| = O\left(\frac{1}{\ln^{1+\varepsilon} n}\right), \quad \varepsilon > 0,$$

it follows that

$$\int_0^t \varphi_x(u)\,du = O\left(\frac{t}{\ln^\varepsilon \frac{1}{t}}\right).$$

## § 10. Sufficiency convergence tests at a point with additional restrictions on the coefficients of the series

In the convergence tests discussed in §§ 2–8 we have imposed restrictions only on the function $f(x)$, whilst studying the convergence of the series $\sigma(f)$. If additional assumptions are made concerning the rate at which the coefficients of the series tend to zero, then it is possible to obtain a number of new tests. We will recall that it has already been proved in Chapter I, § 64 that for the convergence of the series

$$\frac{a_0}{2} + \sum_{n=1}^{\infty} (a_n \cos nx + b_n \sin nx) \tag{10.1}$$

under the condition

$$\sum_{k=1}^{n} k(|a_k| + |b_k|) = o(n)$$

it is necessary and sufficient that the derivative $F'(x)$ exists of the function $F(x)$ obtained as a result of integrating the series (10.1).

Other conditions of this kind can also be demonstrated. For example, Hardy and Littlewood[4] proved that if

$$a_n = O\left(\frac{1}{n}\right) \quad \text{and} \quad b_n = O\left(\frac{1}{n}\right),$$

then the necessary and sufficient condition of convergence of the series to $f(x)$ at the point $x$ is the condition

$$\lim_{h \to 0} \frac{1}{2h} \int_{x-h}^{x+h} f(t)\,dt = f(x).$$

Here we give the proof of another theorem, also due to Hardy and Littlewood[9], giving a sufficiency test of convergence based both on the behaviour of the function at the point under consideration and on the rate at which the coefficients of the series tend to zero.

*The Hardy and Littlewood test. If*

$$a_n = O\left(\frac{1}{n^\delta}\right), \quad b_n = O\left(\frac{1}{n^\delta}\right), \quad \delta > 0, \tag{10.2}$$

*and if*

$$f(x+h) - f(x) = o\left(\frac{1}{\ln\dfrac{1}{|h|}}\right), \tag{10.3}$$

*then $\sigma(f)$ converges to $f(x)$ at the point $x$.*

As usual, we will prove that for some $a$

$$\lim_{n\to\infty} \int_0^a \varphi_x(t) \frac{\sin nt}{t} dt = 0. \tag{10.4}$$

By virtue of condition (10.3) we have

$$\varphi_x(t) \to 0 \quad \text{as} \quad t \to 0,$$

and, therefore, all the more so

$$\int_0^t |\varphi_x(u)|\, du = o(t)$$

which means that

$$\left| \int_0^{1/n} \varphi_x(t) \frac{\sin nt}{t} dt \right| < n \int_0^{1/n} |\varphi_x(u)| du = o(1). \tag{10.5}$$

Also it follows from (10.3) that

$$|\varphi_x(t)| \ln \frac{1}{t} \to 0 \quad \text{as} \quad t \to 0.$$

Let us assume that $r = \delta/2$ where $\delta$ is the quantity in (10.2). It can always be considered that $\delta < 1$, since if the coefficients of the series satisfy condition (10.2) at $\delta \geqslant 1$, this is even more true at $\delta < 1$. Therefore $r < 1$. We have

$$\left| \int_{1/n}^{1/n^r} \varphi_x(t) \frac{\sin nt}{t} dt \right| \leqslant \int_{1/n}^{1/n^r} |\varphi_x(t)| \ln \frac{1}{t} \frac{dt}{t \ln \dfrac{1}{t}} = o(1) \int_{1/n}^{1/n^r} \frac{dt}{t \ln \dfrac{1}{t}} = o(1) \ln \frac{1}{r} = o(1). \tag{10.6}$$

Finally, it remains to estimate the integral in the interval $(1/n^r, a)$. If we prove that

$$\int_{1/n^r}^{a} \varphi_x(t) \frac{\sin nt}{t} dt = o(1), \tag{10.7}$$

then combining (10.5), (10.6) and (10.7), we see that (10.4) is proved. Thus, it remains to prove (10.7).

From the definition of $\varphi_x(t)$ it is clear that its Fourier coefficients are of the same order as those for $f(x)$; moreover, it is even.

Thus

$$\sigma[\varphi_x(t)] = \frac{\alpha_0}{2} + \sum_{k=1}^{\infty} \alpha_k \cos kt.$$

But any Fourier series after being multiplied by a function of bounded variation can be integrated term by term (see Chapter II, § 5), therefore

$$\int_{1/n^r}^{a} \varphi_x(t)\frac{\sin nt}{t}\,dt = \frac{\alpha_0}{2}\int_{1/n^r}^{a}\frac{\sin nt}{t}\,dt + \sum_{k=1}^{\infty}\alpha_k \int_{1/n^r}^{a}\frac{\cos kt \sin nt}{t}\,dt$$

$$= \frac{\alpha_0}{2}\int_{1/n}^{a}\frac{\sin nt}{t}\,dt + \frac{1}{2}\alpha_n\int_{1/n^r}^{a}\frac{\sin 2nt}{t}\,dt$$

$$+ \frac{1}{2}\sum_{\substack{k=1\\k\neq n}}^{\infty}{}' \alpha_k \int_{1/n^r}^{a}\frac{\sin(n+k)t + \sin(n-k)t}{t}\,dt. \tag{10.8}$$

But for any $m \neq 0$, applying the second mean value theorem, we have

$$\int_{1/n^r}^{a}\frac{\sin mt}{t}\,dt = \frac{1}{|m|}O(n^r),$$

and therefore from (10.2) and (10.8) we conclude that

$$\int_{1/n^r}^{a}\varphi_x(t)\frac{\sin nt}{t}\,dt = O(n^{r-1}) + O\left(\frac{1}{n^\delta}\right)n^{r-1} + O\left(\sum_{k\neq n}{}'\frac{1}{k^\delta}n^r\frac{k}{|k-n|}\right)$$

$$= o(1) + O\left(\sum_{k\neq 1}{}'\frac{1}{k^\delta|k-n|}\right)n^{\delta/2},$$

since $r = \delta/2$.

But

$$\sum_{k\neq 1}{}'\frac{1}{k^\delta|k-n|} = \sum_{k=1}^{[n/2]}\frac{1}{k^\delta(n-k)} + \sum_{[n/2]+1}^{2n}{}'\frac{1}{k^\delta|k-n|} + \sum_{2n+1}^{\infty}\frac{1}{k^\delta(k-n)}$$

$$= S_1 + S_2 + S_3,$$

$$S_1 < \frac{2}{n}\sum_{k=1}^{[n/2]}\frac{1}{k^\delta} = \frac{2}{n}O(n^{-\delta+1}) = O(n^{-\delta}),$$

$$S_2 \leqslant \left(\frac{2}{n}\right)^\delta \sum_{1}^{2n}{}'\frac{1}{|k-n|} < 2\left(\frac{2}{n}\right)^\delta\sum_{1}^{n}\frac{1}{k} = O\left(\frac{\ln n}{n^\delta}\right),$$

$$S_3 \leqslant 2\sum_{2n+1}^{\infty}\frac{1}{k^{\delta+1}} = O(n^{-\delta})$$

and since $r - \delta = -\delta/2$, then finally

$$\int_{1/n^r}^{a} \varphi_x(t) \frac{\sin nt}{t} dt = o(1) + n^r O(n^{-\delta} \ln n) = o(1),$$

which concludes the proof of the theorem.

*Note.* It is important to notice that if we were to suppose that only the second condition of the Hardy and Littlewood theorem, i.e.

$$f(x+h) - f(x) = o\left[\left(\ln \frac{1}{|h|}\right)^{-1}\right],$$

were fulfilled, then the series $\sigma(f)$ would not have to converge at the point $x$ under consideration. We will prove this in Chapter IV, § 4.

## § 11. A note concerning the uniform convergence of a Fourier series in some interval

Even in 1905, Fatou[1] noted that any condition of convergence at a point can be transformed into a condition for uniform convergence in some interval, provided the required condition is fulfilled uniformly in this interval or in a somewhat larger interval containing it. We will explain exactly what this means.

It is known (see Chapter I, § 37) that for bounded functions

$$S_n(x) - f(x) = \frac{1}{\pi} \int_0^{\delta} \varphi_x(t) \frac{\sin nt}{t} dt + o(1),$$

where $o(1)$ is understood to be a quantity which tends uniformly to zero in $0 \leqslant x \leqslant 2\pi$. Thus, for the uniform convergence of $\sigma(f)$ in some $[a, b]$ it is necessary and sufficient that for some $\delta > 0$ the equality

$$\lim_{n \to \infty} \int_0^{\delta} \varphi_x(t) \frac{\sin nt}{t} dt = 0 \tag{11.1}$$

holds uniformly for $a \leqslant x \leqslant b$.

All the convergence tests at a point are proved according to the following principle: if some condition $A$ is fulfilled at a given point $x$, then (11.1) holds for this $x$ and therefore the series converges. Fatou conceived the idea that usually when the condition $A$ is fulfilled uniformly in $(a, b)$, then (11.1) also holds uniformly in $(a, b)$. Here however, one important circumstance must not be overlooked.

In order for the series to converge uniformly in $(a, b)$, it is necessary for $f(x)$ to be continuous in $(a, b)$ including its end points: if there are discontinuities at its end points, then it can be expected that uniform convergence occurs only in the interval $[a', b']$ lying entirely inside $(a, b)$. Therefore all the tests of uniform convergence are formulated in a corresponding manner. We will not repeat everything anew and will confine ourselves to a single example.

In examining the proof of the validity of the Lebesgue test, it is possible to obtain the theorem:

*If $f(x)$ is continuous in $(a, b)$, including its end points, and if*

$$\int_h^\delta \left| \frac{\varphi_x(u+h)}{u+h} - \frac{\varphi_x(u)}{u} \right| du \to 0 \quad as \quad h \to 0$$

*uniformly in $(a, b)$, then $\sigma(f)$ converges to $f(x)$ uniformly in $(a, b)$.*

We now note that the reverse transformation from an interval to a point is not permissible, i.e. if some condition which the function satisfies uniformly in the interval implies uniform convergence of a series within this interval, then it does not follow that its fulfilment at a point implies convergence at that point.

For example, in Chapter IV, § 4, it will be proved that if

$$f(x+h) - f(x) = o\left(\frac{1}{\ln \frac{1}{|h|}}\right) \tag{11.2}$$

in some $[a, b]$, then $\sigma(f)$ converges uniformly in any $[a', b']$ lying entirely within $(a, b)$. However, at the end of the preceding section we have already proved that the fulfilment of condition (11.2) at a point does not guarantee the convergence of a series at that point.

Finally, we note that a number of conditions for the uniform convergence of a Fourier series in the interval $[a, b]$ can be obtained from the conditions of uniform convergence in $[0, 2\pi]$ with the help of the principle of localization, which is obviously used in each individual case. This problem will be examined in Chapter IV, § 9. In the same chapter the conditions for uniform convergence over the whole interval $[0, 2\pi]$ will be investigated.

## § 12. Problems

1. Functions $f(x) \in C(0, 2\pi)$ and $g(x) \in C[0, 2\pi)$ exist such that $f(x) = g(x)$ for $x \in [1, 2]$ and yet the Fourier series of $f$ and $g$ are not equi-convergent at the points $x = 1$ and $x = 2$.

2. An odd function $f(x) \in C(0, 2\pi)$ exists such that its Fourier series converges absolutely for all $x \in (-\infty, \infty)$ but the Fourier series of the function

$$F(x) = \begin{cases} f(x) & \text{for} \quad 0 \leqslant x \leqslant \pi \\ 0 & \text{for} \quad -\pi \leqslant x \leqslant 0 \end{cases}$$

diverges at the point $x = 0$.

$\left[\text{Assume that } f(x) = \sum_{n=1}^{\infty} \frac{1}{n^n} \sin n^{n^n} x.\right]$

3. In the Dini test (see Chapter I, § 38 and Chapter III, § 2) the assumption is essential that the function

$$\frac{\varphi_{x_0}(t)}{t} = \frac{f(x_0 + t) + f(x_0 - t) - 2f(x_0)}{t}$$

is absolutely integrable.

Construct the function $f(x) \in C(0, 2\pi)$, the Fourier series of which diverges at some point $x_0$ and yet has finite limit

$$\lim_{\varepsilon \to +0} \int_{\varepsilon}^{\pi} \frac{\varphi_{x_0}(t)}{t}\, dt.$$

[The Lebesgue construction (see Chapter I, § 46) can be used as the starting point of the construction.]

4. Prove that, whatever the function $\omega(t)$ positive in $(0, \pi)$ and monotonely tending to zero as $t \to +0$, a continuous function $f(x)$ can be found such that at some point $x_0$ a finite limit

$$\lim_{\varepsilon \to +0} \int_{0}^{\pi} \frac{f(x_0 + t) + f(x_0 - t) - 2f(x_0)}{\omega(t)}\, dt$$

exists and the Fourier series of $f(x)$ diverges at the point $x_0$.

A. I. SHMUKLER

5. Prove that if the second condition in the Lebesgue–Gergen test (see § 8) is discarded, the test is no longer valid.

6. Whatever positive sequence $\varepsilon_n$ with $\lim\limits_{n\to\infty} \varepsilon_n = 0$ is taken, there exists a function $f(x) \in C(0, 2\pi)$, the Fourier series of which converges uniformly in $[0, 2\pi]$ and moreover

$$\overline{\lim_{n\to\infty}} \frac{|S_n(x,f) - f(x)|}{\varepsilon_n} = \infty$$

for all $x \in [0, 2\pi]$.

A. I. SHMUKLER

7. Whatever $a_n \downarrow 0$ with $\sum\limits_{n=1}^{\infty} a_n = \infty$ are given, it is possible to find $b_n (n = 1, 2, \ldots)$ such that

(a) $|b_n| \leqslant a_n \quad (n = 1, 2, \ldots)$.

(b) the series $\sum\limits_{n=1}^{\infty} b_n$ converges

and yet the point $x = 0$ is the limiting point of the set $E$ where $E$ is the set of all the points of the simultaneous divergence of the series

$$\sum_{n=1}^{\infty} b_n \cos nx, \quad \sum_{n=1}^{\infty} b_n \sin nx. \tag{12.1}$$

[Consider the points $x_k = \pi/2^{k+1}$ $(k = 1, 2, \ldots)$. Since $\sum\limits_{n=1}^{\infty} \varepsilon_n^{(k)} a_2 k_n \cos 2^k n x_k = \infty$ and $\sum\limits_{n=1}^{\infty} \eta_n^{(k)} a_{2^k n} \sin 2^k n x_k = \infty$ for $\varepsilon_n^{(k)} = \operatorname{sign} \cos 2^k n x_k$ and $\eta_n^{(k)} = \operatorname{sign} \sin 2^k n x_k$, then it is possible to construct non-intersecting polynomials

$$T_i^{(k)}(x) = \sum_{n=p_i^{(k)}}^{q_i^{(k)}} \varepsilon_n^{(k)} a_{2^k n} \cos 2^k nx, \quad U_i^{(k)}(x) = \sum_{n=\bar{p}_i^{(k)}}^{\bar{q}_i^{(k)}} \eta_n^{(k)} a_{2^k n} \sin 2^k nx$$

with

$$p_i^{(k)} < q_i^{(k)} < \bar{p}_i^{(k)} < \bar{q}_i^{(k)} < p_{i+1}^{(k)} < \dots$$

such that

$$|T_i^{(k)}(x_k)| > 2^i \quad \text{and} \quad |U_i^{(k)}(x_k)| > 2^i \quad \left(\begin{matrix} k = 1, 2, \dots \\ i = 1, 2, \dots \end{matrix}\right).$$

The sum of the polynomials $T_{i_\alpha}^{(k)}(x)$ and the polynomials $\overline{U}_{i_\alpha}^{(k)}(x)$ gives the first series of (12.1), which for every given $k$ ($k = 1, 2, \dots$) should contain an infinite number of polynomials such as $T_i^{(k)}(x)$ and $\overline{U}_i^{(k)}(x)$.]

CHAPTER IV

# FOURIER SERIES OF CONTINUOUS FUNCTIONS

## § 1. Introduction

We already know (see Chapter I, §§ 44, 45) that the Fourier series of a continuous function not only need not converge uniformly but it can even diverge. We begin this chapter with an investigation of the conditions under which the series does converge uniformly. These conditions can be divided into the following four types:

(1) The conditions imposed on the coefficients of a trigonometric series, from which its uniform convergence follows. Not counting those strong limitations under which absolute (which also means uniform) convergence of a series occurs, it is possible to quote the following condition as an example: if $b_n \downarrow 0$ and $nb_n \to 0$, then $\sum b_n \sin nx$ converges uniformly (see Chapter I, § 30).

(2) The conditions imposed on the function under which its series is uniformly convergent, for example, the Jordan test (see Chapter I, § 39), its generalization (see § 5 of the present chapter), the Dini–Lipschitz test and its generalization (we will study them in § 4 and § 8).

(3) Combined conditions, namely those where it is already known that $f(x)$ is continuous and moreover its coefficients satisfy a certain condition (for example, the theorems due to Paley, Szász and others – see § 2), the Satô test (§ 10).

(4) The conditions arising from a comparison of the given function with others possessing uniformly convergent Fourier series (see, for example, § 11).

The comparison of functions with other functions is useful in the study of the problem when a given series converges uniformly in some interval of length less than $2\pi$ (see § 9).

In § 13 and § 15 the question is studied of how the Fourier series of a continuous function is obtained either by the rearrangement of the signs of the terms of the series or by the choice of the arguments $\alpha_n$ in the series $\sum_{n=1}^{\infty} \varrho_n \cos(nx - \alpha_n)$ for fixed $\varrho_n$.

Section 16 is devoted to the question of what can be said generally concerning the Fourier coefficients of a continuous function.

We also ask: what operations can be carried out on continuous functions to obtain uniformly convergent Fourier series? Section 12 is devoted to this problem.

We then continue with the study of those singularities which can occur in the Fourier series of continuous functions. We will show (see § 18) that they can converge non-uniformly not only near one point as was the case in Chapter I, § 44 but also in any interval $\Delta$ lying in $[0, 2\pi]$. Also the divergence of a series of a continuous function can occur both in any denumerable set (§ 21) and in a set of the power of the continuum

(§ 20 and § 22). This phenomenon can occur, for example, for $f^2(x)$, although $\sigma(f)$ converges uniformly (§ 23).

Finally, in §§ 24 and 25 the problem is considered of dividing the Fourier series of a continuous function into two, each of which already possesses certain "good" properties.

## § 2. Sufficiency conditions for uniform convergence, expressed in terms of Fourier coefficients

We will not describe here the strong limiting conditions under which

$$\sum (|a_n| + |b_n|) < +\infty,$$

holds, since this leads to the absolute convergence of the trigonometric series; the study of absolute convergence will be described in Chapter IX. Conditions exist which are very much less limiting, for example: if $b_n \downarrow 0$ and $nb_n \to 0$, then the series

$$\sum_{n=1}^{\infty} b_n \sin nx$$

converges uniformly. This has already been proved (see Chapter I, § 30).

Now we want to describe some conditions to be imposed on the coefficients of the series, which guarantee its uniform convergence, if we already know that it is the Fourier series of a continuous function.

We will refer first to a simple theorem which has already been proved in Chapter I, § 64.

THEOREM. *If $f(x)$ is continuous and the condition*

$$\sum_{k=1}^{n} k(|a_k| + |b_k|) = o(n), \tag{2.1}$$

*is fulfilled for its Fourier coefficients, then its Fourier series converges uniformly.*†

Hence, in particular, it follows that if $f(x)$ is continuous and its Fourier series is lacunary, then it converges uniformly. It is true that it will be proved in Chapter XI that a lacunary Fourier series of a continuous $f(x)$ converges absolutely, but this is a restricted result due to Szidon with a complicated proof, whilst here the theorem is obtained very easily.

We note that in the proved theorem the requirement of continuity was essential, since even those series where instead of condition (4.1) the coefficients satisfy the stronger requirement

$$a_n = o\left(\frac{1}{n}\right), \quad b_n = o\left(\frac{1}{n}\right),$$

† In Chapter II, § 2 we have seen that if a function of bounded variation is continuous, then condition (2.1) is fulfilled for it, and therefore, using only the formulated theorem, it is possible to obtain new proof of the fact that the Fourier series for a continuous function of bounded variation converges uniformly.

can be the Fourier series of functions which are not bounded in any interval (see Chapter VIII, § 13) and consequently they cannot converge uniformly.

We will now prove the following theorem due to Paley[2]:

PALEY'S THEOREM. If $f(x)$ is continuous and its Fourier coefficients are non-negative, then its Fourier series converges uniformly.

To prove this theorem it is expedient to consider separately the cases of even and odd functions. We will prove two auxiliary theorems:

THEOREM 1. *If $f(x)$ is even and bounded, whilst*

$$f(x) \sim \frac{a_0}{2} + \sum_{n=1}^{\infty} a_n \cos nx,$$

*where $a_n \geqslant 0$ $(n = 0, 1, 2, \ldots)$ then $\sum_{n=1}^{\infty} a_n < +\infty$ which means that the series $\sigma(f)$ converges uniformly.*

We have for the Fejér sum of order $2n$ at the point $x = 0$

$$\sigma_{2n}(0) = \frac{1}{2n+1} \sum_{k=0}^{2n} S_k(0) \geqslant \frac{1}{2n+1} \sum_{k=n}^{2n} S_k(0) \geqslant \frac{n+1}{2n+1} S_n(0) \geqslant \frac{1}{2} S_n(0),$$

and since $\sigma_n(x)$ for a bounded function are bounded, then $S_n(0) \leqslant M$ $(n = 1, 2, \ldots)$, where $M$ is a constant, i.e.

$$\frac{a_0}{2} + \sum_{k=1}^{n} a_k < M \quad \text{and} \quad \sum_{k=1}^{\infty} a_k < +\infty.$$

Incidentally it would be sufficient to assume the boundedness of $f(x)$ merely near the point $x = 0$.

THEOREM 2. *If $f(x)$ is odd and bounded, whilst*

$$f(x) \sim \sum_{n=1}^{\infty} b_n \sin nx,$$

*where $b_n \geqslant 0$ $(n = 1, 2, \ldots)$ then the partial sums of the Fourier series for $f(x)$ are all bounded. If $f(x)$, moreover, is continuous, then its Fourier series converges uniformly.*

Let $|f(x)| \leqslant M$, then $|\sigma_n(x)| \leqslant M$ also, but

$$\sigma_n(x) = \sum_{k=1}^{n} \left(1 - \frac{k}{n+1}\right) b_k \sin kx.$$

Supposing $n = 2m$ and $x = \pi/(4m)$, we obtain for $1 \leqslant k \leqslant 2$ the inequality

$$\sin k \frac{\pi}{4m} \geqslant \frac{2}{\pi} k \frac{\pi}{4m} = \frac{k}{2m}$$

which means that from

$$0 \leqslant \sum_{k=1}^{2m} \left(1 - \frac{k}{2m+1}\right) b_k \sin k \frac{\pi}{4m} \leqslant M$$

it follows that

$$0 \leqslant \sum_{k=1}^{2m} \left(1 - \frac{k}{2m+1}\right) k b_k \leqslant 2mM. \tag{2.2}$$

But for $1 \leqslant k \leqslant m$ all the quantities in brackets in formula (2.2) are not less than $\frac{1}{2}$ and therefore

$$0 \leqslant \frac{1}{2} \sum_{k=1}^{m} k b_k \leqslant 2mM$$

which means that it is all the more true that

$$\left| \sum_{k=1}^{m} k b_k \sin kx \right| \leqslant 4mM.$$

But since

$$|\sigma_m(x)| \leqslant \left| \sum_{k=1}^{m} \left(1 - \frac{k}{m+1}\right) b_k \sin kx \right| \leqslant M,$$

it follows that

$$\left| \sum_{k=1}^{m} b_k \sin kx \right| \leqslant 5M.$$

Thus, the uniform boundedness of the partial sums for bounded $f(x)$ is proved.

Now let $f(x)$ be continuous, then $\sigma_n(x) \to f(x)$ uniformly. Consequently if $\varepsilon$ is given, then it is possible to find $n$ such that

$$|f(x) - \sigma_n(x)| < \varepsilon, \quad 0 \leqslant x \leqslant 2\pi.$$

Since all $b_k \geqslant 0$ and the coefficients in the expansion of $\sigma_n(x)$ have the form

$$(1 - k/(n+1))b_k$$

(for $m = 1, 2, \ldots, n$), then the function $g(x) = f(x) - \sigma_n(x)$ possesses non-negative Fourier coefficients. Moreover, $|g(x)| < \varepsilon$. Therefore, according to what has just been proved for the partial sums $S_m(g, x)$ of its Fourier series, we should have

$$|S_m(g, x)| < 5\varepsilon \quad \text{for any } m \text{ and } x.$$

On the other hand, if $p \geqslant n$, then

$$S_p(\sigma_n, x) = \sigma_n(x),$$

and therefore for any $p$ and $q$, if $q > p \geqslant n$, we have $S_q(\sigma_n, x) = S_p(\sigma_n, x)$ and then

$$\begin{aligned} S_q(f, x) - S_p(f, x) &= S_q(\sigma_n, x) - S_q(\sigma_n, x) + S_q(g, x) - S_p(g, x) \\ &= S_q(g, x) - S_p(g, x) \end{aligned}$$

which means that

$$|S_q(f, x) - S_p(f, x)| \leqslant |S_q(g, x)| + |S_p(g, x)| \leqslant 10\varepsilon.$$

Consequently, the Fourier series of $f(x)$ converges uniformly.

*Note.* It is clear that in the case of odd $f(x)$ the requirement of continuity was necessary, since, for example, the series

$$\sum_{n=1}^{\infty} \frac{\sin nx}{n}$$

with positive coefficients converges non-uniformly (see Chapter I, § 41).

Now, to prove Paley's theorem, it remains to note that if $f(x)$ is continuous, then both the functions

$$\varphi(x) = \frac{f(x) + f(-x)}{2} \quad \text{and} \quad \psi(x) = \frac{f(x) - f(-x)}{2}$$

will be continuous. One of them has a Fourier series $a_0/2 + \sum a_n \cos nx$ and the other $\sum b_n \sin nx$. By virtue of Theorems 1 and 2 just proved, since all $a_n$ and $b_n$ are non-negative, the Fourier series of $\varphi(x)$ and $\psi(x)$ converge uniformly, which means that this is true also for the series $\sigma(f)$, since $f(x) = \varphi(x) + \psi(x)$.

Paley's theorem was generalized by Szász[2] who proved that.

*If $f(x)$ is continuous and*

$$na_n \geqslant -K,$$

$$nb_n \geqslant -K,$$

*where $K > 0$, then the series $\sigma(f)$ converges uniformly.*†

## § 3. Sufficiency conditions for uniform convergence in terms of the best approximations

Let $f(x)$ be a continuous function and $E_n(f)$ be its best approximation by trigonometric polynomials of order not higher than $n$.

First of all we will establish the validity of the following inequality due to Lebesgue[A.14]:

*If $R_n(x,f) = f(x) - S_n(x,f)$, then*

$$|R_n(x,f)| < CE_n(f) \ln n, \tag{3.1}$$

*where $C$ is an absolute constant.*

In fact, let $T_n(x)$ be the trigonometric polynomial of order $n$, which gives the best approximation for $f(x)$; then

$$|f(x) - T_n(x)| \leqslant E_n. \tag{3.2}$$

Let us consider the partial sum of index $n$ for the Fourier series of $f(x) - T_n(x)$; we have

$$S_n(x, f - T_n) = S_n(x,f) - S_n(x, T_n) = S_n(x,f) - T_n(x), \tag{3.3}$$

since the $n$th partial sum of the Fourier series for a polynomial of order $n$ coincides with this polynomial.

But according to Lebesgue's theorem (see Chapter I, § 36) we have by virtue of (3.2)

$$|S_n(x, f - T_n)| \leqslant C_1 E_n \ln n, \tag{3.4}$$

where $C_1$ is an absolute constant, and then due to (3.2), (3.3) and (3.4)

$$|R_n(x,f)| = |S_n(x,f) - f(x)| \leqslant |S_n(x,f) - T_n(x)| + |T_n(x) - f(x)|$$
$$\leqslant E_n(f)(1 + C_1 \ln n) < CE_n(f) \ln n,$$

and this is what was required to be proved.

† See also Szász[3] and the literature referred to there.

As a corollary to Lebesgue's inequality we obtain the theorem:
THEOREM. *If*

$$\lim_{n\to\infty} E_n(f)\ln n = 0, \tag{3.5}$$

*then the Fourier series of $f(x)$ converges uniformly.*

Indeed, from (3.5) and (3.1) it immediately follows that $R_n(x,f)\to 0$ uniformly.

*Note.* If we consider the best approximation of $f(x)$ in some interval $[a, b]\subset[-\pi, \pi]$, then it is also possible to obtain a certain estimate $R_n(x,f)$ which is somewhat more complicated but all the same is useful. Namely, supposing that $f_1(x)=f(x)$ for $a\leqslant x\leqslant b$ and choosing it anyhow in $(0, a)$ and $(b, 2\pi)$, provided that it is continuous in $[0, 2\pi]$ and $f_1(0)=f_1(2\pi)$, we have

$$|R_n(x,f)|\leqslant AE_n(f_1)\ln n+o(1) \tag{3.6}$$

uniformly in any $[a', b']\subset(a, b)$; here $A$ is an absolute constant.

It follows from this that for $x\in[a', b']$

$$|R_n(x,f)|=|S_n(x,f)-f(x)|\leqslant|S_n(x,f)-S_n(x,f_1)|+|S_n(x,f_1)-f_1(x)|,$$

and since $S_n(x,f)-S_n(x,f_1)=o(1)$ uniformly in $(a', b')$ and formula (3.1) applies to the second term, then (3.6) follows from this.

Therefore, if it is possible to choose $f_1(x)$ so that $E_n(f_1)\ln n\to 0$, then $R_n(x,f)\to 0$ uniformly in $[a', b']$, i.e. the series $\sigma(f)$ converges uniformly in $[a', b']\subset(a, b)$.

## § 4. The Dini–Lipschitz test

As a corollary of the theorem in § 3 we can immediately obtain
*The Dini–Lipschitz test. If*

$$f(x+h)-f(x)=o\left(\frac{1}{\ln\frac{1}{|h|}}\right) \tag{4.1}$$

*uniformly for $0\leqslant x\leqslant 2\pi$, then $\sigma(f)$ converges uniformly in this interval.*

*If condition* (4.1) *is fulfilled uniformly in some $[a, b]\subset[-\pi, \pi]$, then $\sigma(f)$ converges uniformly in any $[a', b']$, $a<a'<b'<b$.*

Indeed, from the fact that condition (4.1) is fulfilled uniformly for $0\leqslant x\leqslant 2\pi$ it immediately follows that for the modulus of continuity $\omega(\delta,f)$ of the function $f(x)$ under consideration we have

$$\lim_{\delta\to 0}\omega(\delta,f)\ln\frac{1}{\delta}=0. \tag{4.2}$$

But on the basis of Jackson's theorem (see Appendix, § 7)

$$E_n\leqslant C\omega\left(\frac{1}{n}\right),$$

and since from (4.2) it follows that

$$\lim_{n\to\infty}\omega\left(\frac{1}{n}\right)\ln n=0,$$

then

$$\lim_{n\to\infty} E_n \ln n = 0$$

and then the conditions of the theorem in § 3 hold, which means that $\sigma(f)$ converges uniformly.

If condition (4.1) is fulfilled uniformly in $[a, b]$, then

$$\lim_{\delta\to\infty} \omega(\delta, f, a, b) \ln \frac{1}{\delta} = 0,$$

whence

$$\lim_{n\to\infty} \omega\left(\frac{1}{n}, f, a, b\right) \ln n = 0.$$

Therefore if $f_1(x)$ is taken as continuous over the whole interval $[0, 2\pi]$ and coincident with $f(x)$ in $(a, b)$, then by Jackson's theorem

$$E_n(f_1) \ln n \leqslant C\omega\left(\frac{1}{n}, f_1\right) \ln n \leqslant C\omega\left(\frac{1}{n}, f, a, b\right) \ln n.$$

and then we have the conditions of the note to the theorem in § 3 and consequently $\sigma(f)$ converges uniformly in any $[a', b']$, $a < a' < b' < b$.

*Note.* The Dini–Lipschitz test can also be proved without the theory of approximation of a function (for example, by using the Lebesgue test (Chapter III, § 6)). But we considered it expedient to demonstrate how easily it can be proved using the results of this theory. Note that below (in § 5 and in § 8) theorems will be given, from which the Dini–Lipschitz test follows as a corollary.

Now we want to stress that the Dini–Lipschitz test should be fulfilled *uniformly* over the whole interval $[0, 2\pi]$ or over some interval $[a, b]$ in order to be able to draw conclusions concerning the convergence of the series. On the other hand, if condition (4.1) is fulfilled only at some point $x$, then it does not follow from this that $\sigma(f)$ converges at this point.

In order to confirm this, we will prove this theorem.

THEOREM. *Let $\mu(t)$ be positive and continuous in $[0, \pi]$, $\mu(0) = 0$, $\mu(t)/t$ increase as $t \to 0$ and $\mu(t)/t$ be not summable near $t = 0$. Then there exists a continuous $f(t)$ for which*

$$|f(t) - f(0)| \leqslant \mu(t),$$

*but whose Fourier series diverges at $t = 0$.*

If this theorem is proved, then supposing, for example, that

$$\mu(t) = \frac{1}{\ln \frac{2\pi}{|t|} \ln \ln \frac{2\pi}{|t|}},$$

we see that $\mu(t)$ satisfies the conditions of the theorem and moreover

$$\mu(h) = o\left(\frac{1}{\ln \frac{1}{|h|}}\right)$$

and therefore the validity of the statement made concerning the Dini–Lipschitz condition will be true.

To prove this theorem, two lemmas are necessary.

LEMMA 1. *If $\mu(t)$ is positive and continuous in $(0,\pi)$, $\mu(t)/t$ increases as $t \to 0$ and is not summable near $t = 0$, then*

$$\overline{\lim_{n\to\infty}} \int_0^\pi \left| \frac{\mu(t)\sin nt}{t} \right| dt = +\infty.$$

The proof is based on the same principle as that on which the proof depends that the Lebesgue constants increase without bound with increase of $n$ (Fig. 15).

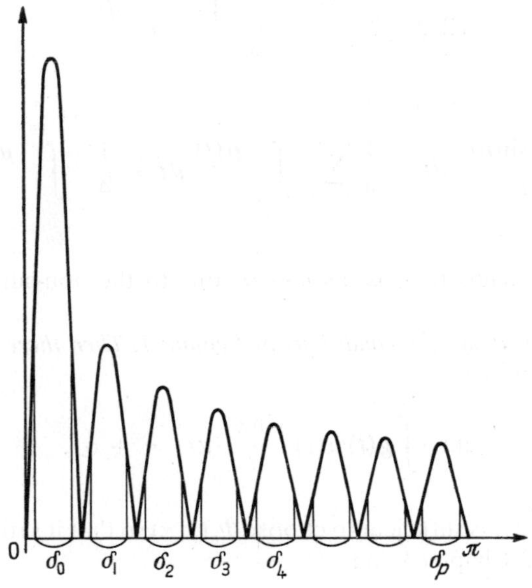


FIG. 15

Let us consider the intervals $\delta_p$ $(p = 0, 1, \ldots, n-1)$, lying in $(0,\pi)$ where $|\sin nt| \geqslant \frac{1}{2}$. This will be for

$$p\pi + \frac{\pi}{6} \leqslant nt \leqslant \frac{5}{6}\pi + p\pi,$$

i.e.

$$\delta_p = \left( \pi \frac{\frac{1}{6} + p}{n}, \pi \frac{\frac{5}{6} + p}{n} \right) \quad (p = 0, 1, \ldots, n-1).$$

We have for these intervals

$$\int_{\delta_p} \left| \frac{\mu(t)\sin nt}{t} \right| dt \geqslant \frac{1}{2} \int_{\delta_p} \frac{\mu(t)}{t} dt.$$

If we denote by $\sigma_p$ the segment lying between $\delta_{p-1}$ and $\delta_p$, i.e.

$$\sigma_p = \left[\pi\frac{\frac{5}{6}+(p-1)}{n},\ \pi\frac{\frac{1}{6}+p}{n}\right],$$

then

$$\int_{\delta_p}\frac{\mu(t)}{t}\,dt \geqslant \int_{\sigma_{p+1}}\frac{\mu(t)}{t}\,dt,$$

since the length $\sigma_{p+1}$ is less than the length $\delta_p$ and, moreover, $\mu(t)/t$ decreases with increase in $t$. Hence

$$\frac{1}{2}\int_{\delta_p}\frac{\mu(t)}{t}\,dt \geqslant \frac{1}{4}\int_{\delta_p+\sigma_{p+1}}\frac{\mu(t)}{t}\,dt,$$

consequently

$$\int_0^{\pi}\left|\frac{\mu(t)\sin nt}{t}\right|dt \geqslant \frac{1}{4}\sum_{p=0}^{n-1}\int_{\delta_p+\sigma_{p+1}}\frac{\mu(t)}{t}\,dt = \frac{1}{4}\int_{\frac{\pi}{6n}}^{\pi+\frac{\pi}{6n}}\frac{\mu(t)}{t}\,dt,$$

and this magnitude tends to $+\infty$ as $n\to\infty$ due to the non-summability of $\mu(t)/t$ near $t=0$.

LEMMA 2. *Let $\mu(t)$ satisfy the conditions of Lemma 1. Then there exists a continuous $g(t)$, $|g(t)|\leqslant 1$ for which*

$$\overline{\lim_{n\to\infty}}\left|\int_0^{\pi} g(t)\,\mu(t)\frac{\sin nt}{t}\,dt\right| = +\infty.$$

To prove Lemma 2 it is sufficient to choose $\Phi_n(t,x)$ so that it satisfies the conditions of the lemma in § 52 Chapter I and

$$\Phi_n(t,0) = \mu(t)\frac{\sin nt}{t},\quad 0\leqslant t\leqslant\pi,$$

then we assume $x=0$ and take into account that it is possible to consider $|g(t)|\leqslant 1$ (see note at the end of the proof of the cited lemma).

Lemma 2 is proved.

Then to prove the theorem formulated on p. 302, taking $g(t)$ from Lemma 2, we assume that

$$f(t) = g(t)\,\mu(t)\quad\text{in}\quad(0,\pi)$$

and

$$f(-t) = f(t).$$

Then $f(t)$ is continuous, $f(0)=0$ (because we have assumed that $\mu(0)=0$), which means that

$$|f(t)-f(0)| = |f(t)| \leqslant \mu(t),$$

because $|g(t)|\leqslant 1$ and it remains to prove that the Fourier series of $f(t)$ diverges at $t=0$.

But since $f(t)$ is even we have

$$S_n(f, 0) = \frac{2}{\pi}\int_0^\pi f(t)\frac{\sin nt}{t}\,dt + o(1) = \frac{2}{\pi}\int_0^\pi g(t)\,\mu(t)\frac{\sin nt}{t}\,dt + o(1),$$

and we have seen that

$$\overline{\lim_{n\to\infty}}\left|\int_0^\pi g(t)\,\mu(t)\frac{\sin nt}{t}\,dt\right| = +\infty,$$

then the theorem is proved.

## § 5. The Salem test. Functions of Φ-bounded variation

Let us consider a continuous function $f(x)$. Let us prove the following theorem due to Salem[1]:

*Let $n$ be any odd integer. If the expression*

$$T_n(x) = \frac{f(x) - f\left(x + \frac{\pi}{n}\right)}{1} + \frac{f\left(x + 2\frac{\pi}{n}\right) - f\left(x + 3\frac{\pi}{n}\right)}{3} + \cdots$$

$$\cdots + \frac{f\left(x + \frac{(n-1)\pi}{n}\right) - f(x + \pi)}{n}, \tag{5.1}$$

*and also the expression for $Q_n(x)$, obtained by substituting $-\pi$ for $\pi$, tend to zero as $n \to \infty$ uniformly for $0 \leqslant x \leqslant 2\pi$, then $\sigma(f)$ converges uniformly.*

To prove this statement we recall that

$$S_n(x) - f(x) = \frac{1}{\pi}\int_0^\pi \varphi_x(t)\frac{\sin nt}{t}\,dt + o(1),$$

where $o(1)$ tends to zero uniformly and

$$\varphi_x(t) = f(x+t) + f(x-t) - 2f(x).$$

If we prove that under the conditions of our theorem the integrals

$$\int_0^\pi [f(x+t) - f(x)]\frac{\sin nt}{t}\,dt \tag{5.2}$$

and

$$\int_0^\pi [f(x-t) - f(x)]\frac{\sin nt}{t}\,dt, \tag{5.3}$$

converge uniformly to zero, then the theorem will be proved. Supposing that

$$\psi_x(t) = f(x+t) - f(x),$$

we will prove that the integral $\int_0^\pi [(\psi_x(t)\sin nt)/t]\,dt \to 0$ uniformly relative to $x$.

If we denote by $\omega(\delta, f)$ the modulus of continuity of our function $f(x)$, then

$$|\psi_x(t)| \leqslant \omega(\delta, f), \quad \text{if} \quad 0 \leqslant t \leqslant \delta,$$

and therefore

$$\left| \int_0^{\frac{\pi}{n}} \psi_x(t) \frac{\sin nt}{t}\, dt \right| \leqslant \pi\, \omega\left(\frac{\pi}{n}, f\right) = o(1) \tag{5.4}$$

uniformly with respect to $x$, whence it is clear that it is sufficient to consider the integral between the limits $\pi/n$ to $\pi$.

We have

$$I_n = \int_{\frac{\pi}{n}}^{\pi} \psi_x(t) \frac{\sin nt}{t}\, dt = \sum_{k=1}^{n-1} \int_{k\frac{\pi}{n}}^{(k+1)\frac{\pi}{n}} \psi_x(t) \frac{\sin nt}{t}\, dt$$

$$= \sum_{k=0}^{n-2} \int_{\frac{\pi}{n}}^{2\frac{\pi}{n}} \psi_x\left(t + k\frac{\pi}{n}\right) \frac{(-1)^k \sin nt}{t + k\dfrac{\pi}{n}}\, dt.$$

By change of variable $nt = u$, we find that

$$I_n = \sum_{k=0}^{n-2} \int_{\pi}^{2\pi} \psi_x\left(\frac{u + k\pi}{n}\right) (-1)^k \frac{\sin u}{u + k\pi}\, du.$$

Therefore, if we prove that

$$\sum_{n=0}^{n-2} \psi_x\left(\frac{u + k\pi}{n}\right) (-1)^k \frac{1}{u + k\pi} \tag{5.5}$$

tends to zero uniformly with respect to $x$ and with respect to $u$ for $\pi \leqslant x \leqslant 2\pi$, then we will have $I_n \to 0$ uniformly with respect to $x$ which combined with (5.4) proves that the integral (5.2) tends uniformly to zero.

In the sum (5.5) there are $(n-1)$ terms; if $n$ is odd, i.e. $(n-1)$ is even, we can combine them in pairs. If $n$ is even, then we add to this sum a term with index $k = n-1$; since $f(x)$ is continuous, then $|f(x)| \leqslant M$, where $M$ is some constant, and then $|\psi_x(t)| \leqslant 2M$ and the modulus of the additional term does not exceed $2M/n$ for $\pi \leqslant u \leqslant 2\pi$, i.e. it tends uniformly to zero. Thus, without affecting the generality, it is possible to confine ourselves to the case when $n$ is odd. Then the sum (5.5) can be rewritten in the form

$$\sum_{k=0}^{n-2}{}' \left[\psi_x\left(\frac{u+k\pi}{n}\right)\frac{1}{u+k\pi} - \psi_x\left(\frac{u+(k+1)\pi}{n}\right)\frac{1}{u+(k+1)\pi}\right], \tag{5.6}$$

where the sign $\sum'$ signifies that $k$ runs through even values only.

To estimate the sum (5.6) we note that

$$\psi_x\left(\frac{u+k\pi}{n}\right)\frac{1}{u+k\pi} - \psi_x\left(\frac{u+(k+1)\pi}{n}\right)\frac{1}{u+(k+1)\pi}$$
$$= \left[\psi_x\left(\frac{u+k\pi}{n}\right) - \psi_x\left(\frac{u+(k+1)\pi}{n}\right)\right]\frac{1}{u+k\pi}$$
$$+ \psi_x\left(\frac{u+(k+1)\pi}{n}\right)\left[\frac{1}{u+k\pi} - \frac{1}{u+(k+1)\pi}\right].$$

But

$$\left|\frac{1}{u+k\pi} - \frac{1}{u+(k+1)\pi}\right| < \frac{1}{(k+1)^2} \quad \text{for} \quad \pi \leqslant u \leqslant 2\pi;$$

also $|\psi_x(t)| \leqslant 2M$ for any $t$ and, finally, for $u \leqslant 2\pi$ we have

$$\left|\psi_x\left(\frac{u+(k+1)\pi}{n}\right)\right| \leqslant \omega\left(\frac{(k+3)\pi}{n}\right) \leqslant \omega\left(\frac{\pi}{\sqrt{n}}\right),$$

if $k+3 \leqslant \sqrt{n}$, and therefore, supposing $\nu = [\sqrt{n}-3]$ we find that

$$\left|\sum_{k=0}^{n-2}{}' \psi_x\left(\frac{u+(k+1)\pi}{n}\right)\left[\frac{1}{u+k\pi} - \frac{1}{u+(k+1)\pi}\right]\right|$$
$$\leqslant \omega\left(\frac{\pi}{\sqrt{n}}\right)\sum_{k=0}^{\nu}\frac{1}{(k+1)^2} + 2M\sum_{k=\nu+1}^{n-2}\frac{1}{(k+1)^2} = o(1),$$

because $\nu \to \infty$ as $n \to \infty$.

Thus, rejecting the quantity tending uniformly to zero, for the sum (5.6) we can substitute the sum

$$\sum_{k=0}^{n-2}{}' \left[\psi_x\left(\frac{u+k\pi}{n}\right) - \psi_x\left(\frac{u+(k+1)\pi}{n}\right)\right]\frac{1}{u+k\pi}. \tag{5.7}$$

We will make the following transformation, namely, we will substitute $1/(\pi+k\pi)$ for $1/(u+k\pi)$ : because

$$\left|\psi_x\left(\frac{u+k\pi}{n}\right) - \psi_x\left(\frac{u+(k+1)\pi}{n}\right)\right|$$
$$= \left|f\left(x+\frac{u+k\pi}{n}\right) - f\left(x+\frac{u+(k+1)\pi}{n}\right)\right| \leqslant \omega\left(\frac{\pi}{n}\right),$$

and

$$\left| \frac{1}{u + k\pi} - \frac{1}{(k + 1)\pi} \right| \leqslant \frac{1}{(k + 1)^2} \quad \text{for} \quad \pi \leqslant u \leqslant 2\pi,$$

we will achieve an error which does not exceed

$$\omega\left(\frac{\pi}{n}\right) \sum_{k=0}^{\infty} \frac{1}{(k + 1)^2} < C\omega\left(\frac{\pi}{n}\right),$$

where $C$ is an absolute constant, i.e. the error again tends uniformly to zero. But then the sum (5.7) is replaced by the expression

$$\frac{1}{\pi} \sum_{k=0}^{n-2}{}' \frac{\psi_x\left(\dfrac{u + k\pi}{n}\right) - \psi_x\left(\dfrac{u + (k + 1)\pi}{n}\right)}{k + 1},$$

i.e. by the expression

$$\frac{1}{\pi}\left[\frac{f\left(x + \dfrac{u}{n}\right) - f\left(x + \dfrac{u + \pi}{n}\right)}{1} + \frac{f\left(x + \dfrac{u + 2\pi}{n}\right) - f\left(x + \dfrac{u + 3\pi}{n}\right)}{3} + \cdots \right.$$

$$\left. \cdots + \frac{f\left(x + \dfrac{u + (n - 3)\pi}{n}\right) - f\left(x + \dfrac{u + (n - 2)\pi}{n}\right)}{(n - 2)}\right]. \tag{5.8}$$

If the following term is added to the expression (5.8)

$$\frac{f\left(x + \dfrac{u + (n - 1)\pi}{n}\right) - f(x + \pi)}{n},$$

the absolute magnitude of this term not exceeding $2M/n$, i.e. it tends uniformly to zero, then this expression becomes equal to $(1/\pi)\,T_n(x + u/n)$ where $T_n(x)$ is a function obeying the conditions of the theorem. But since it is given that $T_n(x)$ tends uniformly to zero as $n \to \infty$, then this is true for (5.8), which means that the integral of (5.8) tends uniformly to zero.

For the integral (5.3) $\psi_x(t)$ must be replaced by $\psi_x(-t)$, then all the argument is carried out in exactly the same way, as it has been assumed that, after $-\pi$ is substituted for $\pi$ in the expression for $T_n(x)$, the expression $Q_n(x)$ is obtained which again converges uniformly to zero.

The theorem is proved.

This test for uniform convergence can appear at a first glance to be hardly suitable for application. However, a number of interesting corollaries can be derived from it.

First we will prove that it includes both the Dini–Lipschitz test and the Jordan test. Indeed, if the Dini–Lipschitz test is fulfilled, then

$$\omega(\delta, f) \ln \frac{1}{\delta} = o(1)$$

which means that

$$\omega\left(\frac{\pi}{n}, f\right) \ln \frac{n}{\pi} = o(1).$$

But in the expressions for $T_n(x)$ and $Q_n(x)$ the modulus of every numerator does not exceed $\omega(\pi/n)$ and therefore

$$|T_n(x)| \leqslant \omega\left(\frac{\pi}{n}\right) \sum_{k=0}^{n} \frac{1}{k+1} = O(\ln n)\, \omega\left(\frac{\pi}{n}\right) = o(1)$$

and also

$$|Q_n(x)| = o(1),$$

whence it follows that $\sigma(f)$ converges uniformly.

As regards the Jordan test, it is possible to argue in the following way; first we choose a number $m$ such that $m \to \infty$ as $n \to \infty$, but

$$\omega\left(\frac{\pi}{n}\right) \ln m \to 0. \tag{5.9}$$

This can also be attained provided $m$ tends to infinity sufficiently slowly. Then the sum of $T_n(x)$ is divided into two terms: in the first sum the denominators range from 1 to $m$ and in the second sum are greater than or equal to $m + 1$. Then

$$|T_n(x)| \leqslant \omega\left(\frac{\pi}{n}\right) \sum_{k=0}^{m} \frac{1}{k+1} + \frac{V}{m+1},$$

where $V$ denotes the total variation of the function $f(x)$; by virtue of (5.9) $T_n(x)$ tends uniformly to zero.

We will now prove that the Salem test gives a considerably more general result then the Jordan test. We will introduce a definition.

DEFINITION. The function $f(x)$ is said to be *a function of $\Phi$-bounded variation in the interval* $[a, b]$ if the sum

$$\sum_i \Phi[\,|f(x_{i+1}) - f(x_i)|\,]$$

remains bounded however we choose the points of division $x_i$ in the interval $[a, b]$ (the classical case is $\Phi(t) = t$); here the function $\Phi(t)$ is assumed to be continuous and increasing for $t \geqslant 0$ and $\Phi(0) = 0$. This concept was introduced by L.C. Young[1].

We will not consider here the problem: under what conditions imposed on $\Phi(t)$ does the Fourier series for a function of $\Phi$-bounded variation converge uniformly? Salem investigated this problem in the work already cited [Salem[1], Chapter VI]. Here we will confine ourselves to a simple example.

Let

$$\Phi(t) = t^p \quad (p > 1).$$

Let us denote by $V_p[a, b]$ the upper bound of the quantities

$$\left\{\sum_i |f(x_{i+1}) - f(x_i)|^p\right\}^{1/p}.$$

It should be finite if $f(x)$ is of $\Phi$-bounded variation for $\Phi(t) = t^p$. It can be proved (in just the same way as it is proved that for a continuous function of bounded variation in $[a, b]$ the complete variation in the interval $[a, x]$ is a continuous function of $x$) that $V_p[a, t]$ is a continuous function of $x$ if $f(x)$ is continuous in $[a, b]$.

Let us prove that if $f(x)$ is continuous and $V_p(0, 2\pi)$ is finite, then $\sigma(f)$ converges uniformly. Let us suppose that $m = [\sqrt{n}] - 1$ and write

$$|T_n(x)| \leqslant \sum_{k=0}^{n} \left| f\left(x + k\frac{\pi}{n}\right) - f\left(x + (k+1)\frac{\pi}{n}\right) \right| \frac{1}{k+1}$$

$$= \sum_{k=0}^{m} \left| f\left(x + k\frac{\pi}{n}\right) - f\left(x + (k+1)\frac{\pi}{n}\right) \right| \frac{1}{k+1}$$

$$+ \sum_{k=m+1}^{n} \left| f\left(x + k\frac{\pi}{n}\right) - f\left(x + (k+1)\frac{\pi}{n}\right) \right| \frac{1}{k+1}.$$

Choosing $q$ so that $1/p + 1/q = 1$, we have

$$\sum_{k=0}^{m} \left| f\left(x + k\frac{\pi}{n}\right) - f\left(x + (k+1)\frac{\pi}{n}\right) \right| \frac{1}{k+1}$$

$$\leqslant \left\{ \sum_{k=0}^{m} \left| f\left(x + k\frac{\pi}{n}\right) - f\left(x + (k+1)\frac{\pi}{n}\right) \right|^p \right\}^{1/p} \left\{ \sum_{k=0}^{m} \frac{1}{(k+1)^q} \right\}^{1/q}$$

$$\leqslant C V_p\left(x, \frac{\pi}{\sqrt{n}}\right),$$

because $\sum_{k=0}^{\infty} 1/(k+1)^q$ converges. But $V_p\left(x, \pi/\sqrt{n}\right)$ tends to zero as $n \to \infty$.

Also

$$\sum_{k=m+1}^{n} \left| f\left(x + k\frac{\pi}{n}\right) - f\left(x + (k+1)\frac{\pi}{n}\right) \right| \frac{1}{k+1}$$

$$\leqslant \left\{ \sum_{k=m+1}^{n} \left| f\left(x + k\frac{\pi}{n}\right) - f\left(x + (k+1)\frac{\pi}{n}\right) \right|^p \right\}^{1/p} \left\{ \sum_{k=m+1}^{n} \frac{1}{(k+1)^q} \right\}^{1/q}$$

$$\leqslant V_p(0, 2\pi)\, o(1) = o(1)$$

again due to the convergence of $\sum 1/(k+1)^q$ and $m \to \infty$.

Thus $T_n(x)$ tends uniformly to zero; for $Q_n(x)$ the argument is just the same. Applying the Salem test, we see that $\sigma(f)$ converges uniformly.

## § 6. The Rogosinski identity

Before continuing with the study of new tests of uniform convergence for Fourier series, we will prove some general theorems concerning the convergence and summability of functional series and also introduce an identity derived by Rogosinski; later it will be extremely useful.

Let $\Phi(\alpha)$ be a continuous function possessing two continuous derivatives at $\alpha \geqslant 0$.

Let $\sum_{k=0}^{\infty} u_k(x)$ be an infinite series consisting of functions which are continuous over some interval $a \leqslant x \leqslant b$. We will assume that

$$t_n(x, \alpha) = \sum_{k=0}^{n} u_k(x)\, \Phi(k\alpha) \tag{6.1}$$

and prove the following theorems:

THEOREM 1. *If at a point x the series* $\sum u_k(x)$ *converges to* $S(x)$, *then for any constant A*

$$t_n(x, \alpha) \to S(x)\,\Phi(0) \quad as \quad n \to \infty$$

*uniformly relative to* $\alpha$ *for* $0 \leqslant \alpha \leqslant A/n$.

THEOREM 1′. *If the series* $\sum u_k(x)$ *converges to* $S(x)$ *uniformly for* $a \leqslant x \leqslant b$, *then*

$$t_n(x, \alpha) \to S(x)\,\Phi(0)$$

*uniformly for* $a \leqslant x \leqslant b$ *and* $0 \leqslant \alpha \leqslant A/n$.

THEOREM 2. *If at a point x the series* $\sum u_k(x)$ *is summable* $(C, 1)$ *to* $S(x)$, *then*

$$t_n(x, \alpha) - S(x)\,\Phi(0) = [S_n(x) - S(x)]\,\Phi(n\alpha) + R_n(x, \alpha), \tag{6.2}$$

*where*

$$R_n(x, \alpha) \to 0$$

*uniformly for* $0 \leqslant \alpha \leqslant A/n$.

THEOREM 2′. *If* $\sum u_k(x)$ *is summable* $(C, 1)$ *to* $S(x)$ *uniformly for* $a \leqslant x \leqslant b$, *then*

$$R_n(x, \alpha) \to 0$$

*uniformly for* $a \leqslant x \leqslant b$ *and* $0 \leqslant \alpha \leqslant A/n$.

In order to prove all these theorems we introduce first of all an identity. Let

$$\Delta_k(\alpha) = \Phi(k\alpha) - \Phi[(k+1)\alpha], \quad \Delta^2(k\alpha) = \Delta_k(\alpha) - \Delta_{k+1}(\alpha).$$

If $0 \leqslant \alpha \leqslant A/n$ where $A$ is a constant, then according to Lagrange's theorem we immediately obtain

$$\Delta_k(\alpha) = O\left(\frac{1}{n}\right); \quad \Delta_k^2(\alpha) = O\left(\frac{1}{n^2}\right) \tag{6.3}$$

uniformly for $k < n$.

Let us denote by $S_n(x)$ the partial sums and by $\sigma_n(x)$ the Cesàro sums of the series $\sum u_k(x)$. We will now prove that if $R_n(x, \alpha)$ is defined by the formula (6.2), then we have

$$R_n(x, \alpha) = \sum_{k=0}^{n-2} [\sigma_k(x) - S(x)]\,(k+1)\,\Delta_k^2(\alpha) + [\sigma_{n-1}(x) - S(x)]\, n\Delta_{n-1}(\alpha). \tag{6.4}$$

Indeed, on the basis of Abel's transformation we can write

$$t_n(x, \alpha) = \sum_{k=0}^{n-1} S_k(x)\Delta_k(\alpha) + S_n(x)\,\Phi(n\alpha).$$

Since

$$\Phi(0) = \sum_{k=0}^{n-1} \Delta_k(\alpha) + \Phi(n\alpha),$$

then, multiplying by $S(x)$, we find that

$$S(x)\,\Phi(0) = \sum_{k=0}^{n-1} \Delta_k(\alpha)\,S(x) + S(x)\,\Phi(n\alpha)$$

and, consequently,

$$t_n(x,\alpha) - S(x)\,\Phi(0) = \sum_{k=0}^{n-1} [S_k(x) - S(x)]\,\Delta_k(\alpha) + [S_n(x) - S(x)]\,\Phi(n\alpha). \quad (6.5)$$

Therefore from (6.2) and (6.5) we have

$$R_n(x,\alpha) = \sum_{k=0}^{n-1} [S_k(x) - S(x)]\,\Delta_k(\alpha).$$

Again applying Abel's transformation and noting that

$$\sum_{p=0}^{k} [S_p(x) - S(x)] = (k+1)\,[\sigma_k(x) - S(x)],$$

we find that

$$R_n(x,\alpha) = \sum_{k=0}^{n-2} [\sigma_k(x) - S(x)]\,(k+1)\,\Delta_k^2(\alpha) + [\sigma_{n-1}(x) - S(x)]\,n\,\Delta_{n-1}(\alpha),$$

and this is (6.4).

Now we will continue with the proof of the formulated theorems. We note first that it follows from formula (6.3) that

$$(k+1)\,\Delta_k^2(\alpha) = O\left(\frac{1}{n}\right) \quad \text{at} \quad 0 \leqslant \alpha \leqslant \frac{A}{n} \quad \text{and} \quad 0 \leqslant k \leqslant n-1,$$

$$n\Delta_{n-1}(\alpha) = O(1) \quad \text{at} \quad 0 \leqslant \alpha \leqslant \frac{A}{n},$$

and therefore we obtain from (6.4)

$$|R_n(x,\alpha)| = O\left(\frac{1}{n}\right) \sum_{k=0}^{n-2} |\sigma_k(x) - S(x)| + O(1)\,|\sigma_{n-1}(x) - S(x)|. \quad (6.6)$$

From this we readily derive Theorems 2 and 2′. Indeed, let $\varepsilon > 0$ be given. Under the conditions of Theorem 2 we have for sufficiently large $N$

$$|\sigma_n(x) - S(x)| < \varepsilon \quad \text{for} \quad n > N,$$

and under the conditions of Theorem 2′ this inequality holds uniformly in $[a, b]$. But from (6.6) we obtain

$$|R_n(x,\alpha)| = O\left(\frac{1}{n}\right) \sum_{k=0}^{N} |\sigma_n(x) - S(x)| + O\left(\frac{1}{n}\right) \sum_{k=N+1}^{n-2} |\sigma_k(x) - S(x)|$$
$$+ O(1)\,|\sigma_{n-1}(x) - S(x)|. \quad (6.7)$$

Since in the second sum in (6.7) the number of terms is less than $n$ but each of them is less than $\varepsilon$, then the whole of the second sum is less than $\varepsilon$; this is true also for the last term of formula (6.7); both these facts hold uniformly if we are under the conditions of Theorem 2′. It remains to consider the first sum. But the functions $u_n(x)$ are continuous, which means that $\sigma_n(x)$ are too (at $k = 0, 1, 2, \ldots, N$), and under the conditions of Theorem 2 this is also true for $S(x)$ in $[a, b]$. Therefore $C$ can be found such that

$$|\sigma_k(x) - S(x)| < C, \quad \begin{matrix} a \leqslant x \leqslant b, \\ k = 0, 1, \ldots, N \end{matrix}$$

(this is also true at the point $x$, if the conditions of Theorem 2 hold). From this it is clear that the first term of formula (6.7) does not exceed $C \cdot O(1/n) = o(1)$.

We have proved that under the conditions of Theorem 2 we have $R_n(x, \alpha) = o(1)$ and that this holds uniformly in $[a, b]$, if we have the condition of Theorem 2′, i.e. both these theorems are proved.

To prove Theorems 1 and 1′, it is sufficient to note that if the series converges to $S(x)$, then $\sigma_n(x) \to S(x)$ too, and then $R_n(x, \alpha) \to 0$, and according to what has been proved this holds uniformly in $[a, b]$, if $\sigma_n(x) \to S(x)$ uniformly, which in its turn should occur under the conditions of Theorem 1′. Therefore, from formula (6.2) due to $\Phi(\alpha)$ being bounded we see immediately that $t_n(x) - S(x)\Phi(0)$ tends to zero in the case of Theorem 1 and does so uniformly in the case of Theorem 1′. Thus all the theorems are proved.

We will now apply the results obtained to the important particular case, when the series under consideration is a trigonometric series, and $\cos\alpha$ plays the role of $\Phi(\alpha)$. Thus, let

$$u_0(x) = \frac{a_0}{2},$$

$$u_k(x) = a_k \cos kx + b_k \sin kx, \quad k = 1, 2, \ldots,$$

$$\Phi(\alpha) = \cos\alpha.$$

We now have the conditions under which the proved theorems can be applied. But in the case under consideration, as can be shown by a simple calculation,

$$t_n(x, \alpha) = \sum_{k=0}^{n} u_k(x) \cos k\alpha = \frac{1}{2} [S_n(x + \alpha) + S_n(x - \alpha)],$$

whence, applying formula (6.2) we find that

$$\frac{1}{2} [S_n(x + \alpha) + S_n(x - \alpha)] - S(x) = [S_n(x) - S(x)] \cos n\alpha + R_n(x, \alpha). \quad (6.8)$$

Formula (6.8) will be known as the *Rogosinski identity*. It is important to note that it follows from the theorems just proved that:

$R_n(x, \alpha) \to 0$ *uniformly relative to* $0 \leqslant \alpha \leqslant A/n$, *if* $\sigma_n(x) \to S(x)$ *and this holds uniformly for* $a \leqslant x \leqslant b$ *if* $\sigma_n(x) \to S(x)$ *uniformly for* $a \leqslant x \leqslant b$.

Rogosinski himself used this result to examine one method of summation (see Chapter VII, § 4), but his identity can be used to obtain a whole series of other interesting theorems. In particular, we apply it in the following section to the study of problems connected with the uniform convergence of a Fourier series.

## § 7. A test of uniform convergence, using the integrated series

Let $F(x)$ be a periodic function and

$$F(x) = \int_0^x f(t)\,dt.$$

The following theorems hold (see Salem[13]):

*If $f(x)$ is continuous and*

$$|S_n(F, x) - F(x)| = o\left(\frac{1}{n}\right) \tag{7.1}$$

*uniformly over $0 \leqslant x \leqslant 2\pi$, then $\sigma(f)$ converges uniformly in $[0, 2\pi]$.*

*If $f(x)$ is continuous in $[a, b]$ and*

$$|S_n(F, x) - F(x)| = o\left(\frac{1}{n}\right) \tag{7.2}$$

*uniformly in $[a, b]$, then for any $\varepsilon > 0$ the series $\sigma(f)$ converges uniformly in $[a + \varepsilon, b - \varepsilon]$.*

For brevity's sake, let us denote by $s_n(x)$ the partial sums of the series $\sigma(f)$ and by $S_n(x)$ the partial sums of the series $\sigma(F)$. If $f(x)$ is continuous everywhere, then $\sigma_n(x)$ tends to $f(x)$ uniformly over the whole interval $[0, 2\pi]$; if it is merely continuous in $[a, b]$, then $\sigma_n(x) \to f(x)$ uniformly in $(a + \varepsilon, b - \varepsilon)$ for any $\varepsilon > 0$. Therefore, applying Rogosinski's identity (see § 6) we see that

$$\frac{1}{2}[s_n(x + \alpha) + s_n(x - \alpha)] - f(x) = [s_n(x) - f(x)]\cos n\alpha + R_n(x, \alpha), \tag{7.3}$$

where $R_n(x, \alpha) \to 0$ uniformly for $0 \leqslant \alpha \leqslant A/n$ and uniformly for $0 \leqslant x \leqslant 2\pi$ in the first case, but uniformly in $(a + \varepsilon, b - \varepsilon)$ in the second case.

If we integrate the equality (7.3) with respect to $\alpha$ from 0 to $h$, where $h \leqslant A/n$, then we obtain

$$\frac{1}{2}[S_n(x + h) - S_n(x - h)] - hf(x) = [s_n(x) - f(x)]\frac{\sin nh}{h} + \int_0^h R_n(x, \alpha)\,d\alpha. \tag{7.4}$$

If $A/n < \varepsilon$, then due to (7.2)

$$\frac{1}{2}[S_n(x + h) - S_n(x - h)] = \frac{1}{2}[F(x + h) - F(x - h)] + o\left(\frac{1}{n}\right)$$

uniformly in $(a + \varepsilon, b - \varepsilon)$ (and this holds uniformly in $[0, 2\pi]$ if (7.1) is fulfilled).

On the other hand

$$\frac{1}{2}[F(x + h) - F(x - h)] = [f(x) + o(1)]\,h$$

also uniformly in $[0, 2\pi]$, if $f(x)$ is continuous everywhere, and uniformly in $(a + \varepsilon, b - \varepsilon)$ if $f(x)$ is continuous in $(a, b)$ and $h \leqslant A/n < \varepsilon$.

From this it follows that the left-hand side of formula (7.4) is $o(1/n) + o(h) = o(1/n)$, because $h = 0(1/n)$, which means that from (7.4)

$$[s_n(x) - f(x)]\frac{\sin nh}{h} + \int_0^h R_n(x, \alpha)\, d\alpha = o\left(\frac{1}{n}\right). \tag{7.5}$$

But, due to the properties of $R_n(x, \alpha)$ mentioned above, for any $\eta > 0$ it is possible to find $N$ such that

$$|R_n(x, \alpha)| < \eta \quad \text{for} \quad n > N$$

at $0 \leqslant x \leqslant 2\pi$ in the case of (7.1) and at $a + \varepsilon \leqslant x \leqslant b - \varepsilon$ in the case of (7.2). Consequently,

$$\left|\int_0^h R_n(x, \alpha)\, d\alpha\right| < \eta h < \eta \frac{A}{n} \tag{7.6}$$

uniformly for $0 \leqslant x \leqslant 2\pi$ or in $(a + \varepsilon, b - \varepsilon)$. Since $\eta$ can be taken as small as desired, then we conclude from (7.5) and (7.6) that

$$[s_n(x) - f(x)]\frac{\sin nh}{h} = o\left(\frac{1}{n}\right)$$

uniformly for $0 \leqslant x \leqslant 2\pi$ or for $a + \varepsilon \leqslant x \leqslant b - \varepsilon$.

Now supposing that $h = \pi/2n$, we find that

$$s_n(x) - f(x) = o(1)$$

uniformly in $[0, 2\pi]$ in the case of (7.1) and in $(a + \varepsilon, b - \varepsilon)$ in the case of (7.2) and both theorems are proved.

*Note.* The proofs of these theorems were given by Salem, but he himself remarked that the idea of integrating the Rogosinski identity is due Zygmund who applied this notion in another context.

## § 8. The generalization of the Dini–Lipschitz test (in the integral form)

We will prove the following theorem:

THEOREM. *If $f(x)$ is continuous and the condition*

$$\frac{1}{h}\int_0^h [f(x + t) - f(x - t)]\, dt = o\left(\frac{1}{\ln \frac{1}{h}}\right) \tag{8.1}$$

*is fulfilled uniformly in* $[0, 2\pi]$, *then* $\sigma(f)$ *converges uniformly in* $[0, 2\pi]$.

In this form this theorem was proved by Salem[13]; however, it is possible to formulate it somewhat differently, and then it takes the form in which it was proved by S.B. Stechkin†, namely:

† Stechkin obtained this theorem and described its proof in a report to the seminar on the theory of functions of a real variable in Moscow University in 1954 with reference to Salem's work.

*If $f(x)$ is continuous*

$$F(x) = \int_0^x f(t)\,dt$$

*and for a symmetrical modulus of smoothness*† *we have*

$$\omega_2(\delta, F) = o\left(\frac{\delta}{\ln\frac{1}{\delta}}\right),$$

*then $\sigma(f)$ converges uniformly.*

The equivalence of the two formulations immediately follows from

$$F(x+h) + F(x-h) - 2F(x) = \int_0^h [f(x+t) - f(x-t)]\,dt$$

and from the definition of the symmetrical modulus of smoothness.

We will now prove that if

$$\omega_2(\delta, F) = o\left(\frac{\delta}{\ln\frac{1}{\delta}}\right), \tag{8.2}$$

then for $R_n(F, x) = F(x) - S_n(x, F)$ we have

$$R_n(F, x) = o\left(\frac{1}{n}\right) \tag{8.3}$$

uniformly in $[0, 2\pi]$.

Indeed from formula (3.1) we have

$$|R_n(F, x)| \leqslant C E_n(F) \ln n,$$

where $C$ is a constant. But according to Jackson's theorem (see Appendix, § 7)

$$E_n(F) \leqslant C_1\, \omega_2\left(\frac{1}{n}, F\right), \tag{8.4}$$

where $C_1$ is again a constant. Therefore

$$|R_n(F, x)| = O\left(\ln n\, \omega_2\left(\frac{1}{n}\right)\right)$$

and in our case due to (8.2)

$$|R_n(F, x)| = O(\ln n)\, o\left(\frac{1}{n \ln n}\right) = o\left(\frac{1}{n}\right)$$

uniformly for $0 \leqslant x \leqslant 2\pi$. But then according to the theorem of the preceding section, supposing $R_n(f, x) = f(x) - S_n(x, f)$, we find that

$$|R_n(f, x)| = o(1)$$

uniformly relative to $x$ and the theorem is proved.

---

† See Introductory Material, § 25.

Without using the approximation theory, it is possible to prove the preceding theorem directly. This was done by Chereiskaya[1]†.

In the next section we will complete this theorem by considering the case when condition (8.1) is fulfilled not over the whole interval $[0, 2\pi]$ but only for somc interval $[a, b]$ contained in it. At the present moment we want to show why this theorem is a generalization of the Dini–Lipschitz test.

First of all it is clear that if the Dini–Lipschitz test is fulfilled, then from

$$|f(x+t)-f(x-t)| \leqslant 2\,\omega(h,f) \quad \text{for} \quad 0 \leqslant t \leqslant h$$

we find that

$$\frac{1}{h}\int_0^h |f(x+t)-f(x-t)|\,dt \leqslant 2\,\omega(h,f) = o\left(\frac{1}{\ln\frac{1}{h}}\right)$$

which means that condition (8.1) of the Salem–Stechkin theorem is fulfilled. But, on the other hand, condition (8.1) can be fulfilled without the function $f(x)$ satisfying the Dini–Lipschitz condition. In order to prove this, let us consider the following example (Salem writes that this example is due to Zygmund).

Let

$$f(x) = \sum_{n=1}^{\infty} \frac{\cos 2^n x}{n^{1+\alpha}}, \quad 0 < \alpha < 1. \tag{8.5}$$

It is clear that $f(x)$ is continuous, since the series converges absolutely and uniformly. We have

$$F(x) = \sum_{n=1}^{\infty} \frac{\sin 2^n x}{2^n n^{1+\alpha}}.$$

Let us prove that $F(x)$ possesses a modulus of smoothness $\omega_2(\delta, F)$ satisfying condition (8.1). Indeed,

$$F(x+h)+F(x-h)-2F(x) = -4\sum_{n=1}^{\infty} \frac{\sin^2(2^{n-1}h)}{2^n n^{1+\alpha}} \sin 2^n x.$$

We will choose $N$ such that

$$2^N \leqslant \frac{1}{h} < 2^{N+1}.$$

We have

$$|F(x+h)+F(x-h)-2F(x)| \leqslant 4\left[\sum_{n=1}^{N} \frac{\sin^2(2^{n-1}h)}{2^n n^{1+\alpha}} + \sum_{n=N+1}^{\infty} \frac{1}{2^n n^{1+\alpha}}\right]. \tag{8.6}$$

But

$$\sum_{N+1}^{\infty} \frac{1}{2^n n^{1+\alpha}} \leqslant \frac{1}{2^N N^{1+\alpha}} = O\left(\frac{h}{\left(\ln\frac{1}{h}\right)^{1+\alpha}}\right). \tag{8.7}$$

† A similar result was obtained by M. Satô. Later he also gave a generalization of this theorem (see Satô[1]).

We will prove that the first sum in (8.6) is of the same order. In fact, firstly,

$$\sum_{n=1}^{[N/2]} \frac{\sin^2(2^{n-1}h)}{2^n n^{1+\alpha}} \leqslant h^2 \sum_{n=1}^{[N/2]} \frac{2^{2n-2}}{2^n n^{1+\alpha}} = \frac{h^2}{4} \sum_{n=1}^{[N/2]} \frac{2^n}{n^{1+\alpha}} \tag{8.8}$$

$$< \frac{2^{N/2}h^2}{4} \sum_{n=1}^{\infty} \frac{1}{n^{1+\alpha}} = O(h^2 \cdot 2^{N/2}) = O(h^{3/2}) = o\left(\frac{h}{\left(\ln \frac{1}{h}\right)^{1+\alpha}}\right),$$

because $h^{1/2}(\ln 1/h)^{1+\alpha} = o(1)$; secondly

$$\sum_{n=[N/2]+1}^{N} \frac{\sin^2(2^{n-1}h)}{2^n n^{1+\alpha}} \leqslant \frac{h^2}{4} \sum_{n=[N/2]+1}^{N} \frac{2^n}{n^{1+\alpha}} \tag{8.9}$$

$$\leqslant \frac{h^2}{4\left(\frac{N}{2}\right)^{1+\alpha}} \sum_{1}^{N} 2^n = O\left(\frac{h^2 \cdot 2^N}{N^{1+\alpha}}\right) = O\left(\frac{h}{\left(\ln \frac{1}{h}\right)^{1+\alpha}}\right).$$

Combining (8.8) and (8.9) we see that the first sum on the right-hand side of (8.6) is of the same order as the second sum and finally

$$\omega_2(F, \delta) = O\left(\frac{\delta}{\left(\ln \frac{1}{\delta}\right)^{1+\alpha}}\right),$$

whence it is clear that condition (8.1) is fulfilled.

Now we want to show that the Dini–Lipschitz condition does not hold, i.e. that

$$\omega(\delta, f) \neq o\left(\frac{1}{\ln \frac{1}{\delta}}\right). \tag{8.10}$$

In order to prove this we note that S. B. Stechkin[2] proved that if

$$R_n(f) = \max_{0 \leqslant x \leqslant 2\pi} |f(x) - S_n(x)|,$$

then for a lacunary series in which $n_{k+1}/n_k > 1$ we have

$$E_n(f) > CR_n(f), \tag{8.11}$$

where $C$ is a constant depending only on $\lambda$.

In our case the series for $f(x)$ is lacunary. If we determine $N$ for a given $n$ from the inequality

$$2^N \leqslant n < 2^{N+1}, \tag{8.12}$$

then $S_n(x) = S_{2N}(x)$ for all $n$ satisfying (8.12). But we have

$$f(x) - S_{2N}(x) = f(x) - \sum_{k=1}^{N} \frac{\cos 2^k x}{k^{1+\alpha}} = \sum_{N+1}^{\infty} \frac{\cos 2^k x}{k^{1+\alpha}},$$

and therefore for all such $n$

$$R_n(f) = \max |f(x) - S_n(x)| \geqslant \sum_{N+1}^{\infty} \frac{1}{k^{1+\alpha}} > a\frac{1}{N^\alpha},$$

where $a > 0$ is a constant. By virtue of (8.11) it follows from this that

$$E_n(f) > C_1 \frac{1}{N^\alpha} \quad \text{for} \quad 2^N \leqslant n < 2^{N+1},$$

where $C_1$ is another constant, $C_1 > 0$. From Jackson's inequality it then follows that

$$\omega\left(\frac{1}{n}, f\right) > C_2 E_n(f) > C_3 \frac{1}{N^\alpha}.$$

Since $(N + 1) \ln 2 > \ln n$ due to (8.12), then

$$\omega\left(\frac{1}{n}, f\right) > C_4 \frac{1}{(\ln n)^\alpha}. \tag{8.13}$$

From this it follows that condition

$$\omega(\delta, f) = o\left(\frac{1}{\ln \frac{1}{\delta}}\right)$$

cannot be fulfilled, because it would result from it that

$$\omega\left(\frac{1}{n}, f\right) = o\left(\frac{1}{\ln n}\right),$$

which contradicts (8.13), because we have supposed that $\alpha < 1$.

Thus the Dini–Lipschitz condition is not fulfilled and our statement is proved.

## § 9. Uniform convergence over the interval [a, b]

In a number of cases it happens that some function $f(x)$ which is generally only summable appears to be continuous over some interval $[a, b]$ of length less than $2\pi$ and satisfies various additional conditions in that interval. Then the question can be asked: does its Fourier series converge uniformly over any interval $[a_1, b_1]$ lying entirely inside $[a, b]$ (if the function has discontinuities at the end points of the interval $[a, b]$, then uniform convergence over the whole of $[a, b]$ is of course not possible)?

Here it is often convenient to adopt the method of *extension of a function*†, which is carried out as follows: we set up a function $f_1(x)$ such that it coincides with $f(x)$ in $[a_1, b_1]$ and we extend it outside this interval so that as a result it possesses over the whole interval $[0, 2\pi]$ the "good" properties that it possesses in $[a, b]$. If this property is so "good" that due to it the series $\sigma(f_1)$ converges uniformly, then by virtue of the Riemann principle of localization (see Chapter I, § 33) the series $\sigma(f)$

† A number of interesting theorems referring to "extension of a function" can be found in a report by P.L. Ul'yanov[5].

will converge uniformly over any $(a + \varepsilon, b - \varepsilon)$ for $\varepsilon > 0$. Sometimes such an extension is not possible, but it is possible to take $f_1(x)$ to coincide with $f(x)$ in $(a + \varepsilon/2, b - \varepsilon/2)$ and to extend it so that the "good" property holds in $[0, 2\pi]$. After this we see that $\sigma(f_1)$ converges uniformly in $[0, 2\pi]$ and then $\sigma(f)$ converges uniformly in $(a + \varepsilon, b - \varepsilon)$.

How is it possible to "extend" a function whilst maintaining the given property? For this the idea is adopted which was first used by Riemann to prove his principle of localization: a function $\lambda(x)$ is set up which equals unity in $[a_1, b_1]$, equals zero

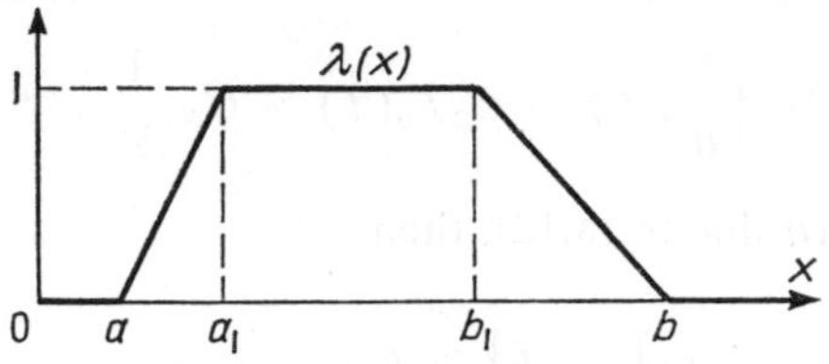


FIG. 16

outside $[a, b]$ and can be interpolated between $a$ and $a_1$, $b_1$ and $b$ either simply linearly (Fig. 16) or somewhat more precisely, if it is necessary to provide for the occurrence of derivatives up to a certain order (in particular, they should equal zero at the points $a$, $a_1$, $b_1$ and $b$). Then, supposing that

$$f_1(x) = \lambda(x) f(x).$$

it is found that $f_1(x)$ possesses the same properties in $[0, 2\pi]$ as $f(x)$ in $[a, b]$ (provided $\lambda(x)$ is chosen suitably).

Of course, this method requires special investigation in each individual case, since it is not possible to answer in a general way the question whether the $f_1(x)$ constructed in this manner will solve the problem set: everything depends on what property $f(x)$ possesses in $[a, b]$.

Here we will consider only one example to illustrate the method described; namely, we want to prove that the following theorem holds:

THEOREM. *If $f(x)$ is summable in $[0, 2\pi]$ and continuous in $[a, b]$, whilst*

$$\frac{1}{h}\int_0^h \{f(x+t) - f(x-t)\}\,dt = o\left(\frac{1}{\ln\frac{1}{h}}\right) \tag{9.1}$$

*uniformly relative to $x$ for $a \leqslant x \leqslant b$, then for any $\varepsilon > 0$ the series $\sigma(f)$ converges uniformly in $(a + \varepsilon, b - \varepsilon)$.*

This theorem, similarly to the theorem in § 8 was proved both by Stechkin (see footnote on p. 315) and by Salem[13]. The method of extension of a function was applied to a given case by Stechkin, then Salem produced a special proof for this case.

We will prove that if $f(x)$ satisfies the condition of the theorem, then it is possible to construct $f_1(x)$ such that it coincides with $f(x)$ in $(a + 2\varepsilon, b - 2\varepsilon)$ and that condition (9.1) is satisfied uniformly in $[0, 2\pi]$. For this, we set up $\lambda(x)$ such that:

$\lambda(x) = 1$ in $(a + 2\varepsilon, b - 2\varepsilon)$; $\lambda(x) = 0$ outside $(a + \varepsilon, b - \varepsilon)$; $\lambda(x)$ is interpolated linearly in $(a + \varepsilon, a + 2\varepsilon)$ and in $(b - 2\varepsilon, b - \varepsilon)$ (Fig. 17); and we suppose that

$$f_1(x) = f(x)\lambda(x).$$

Since $f(x)$ is continuous in $[a, b]$, then $f_1(x)$ is continuous everywhere in $[0, 2\pi]$. We have

$$f_1(x + t) - f_1(x - t) = f(x + t)\lambda(x + t) - f(x - t)\lambda(x - t)$$

$$= f(x + t)[\lambda(x + t) - \lambda(x - t)] + [f(x + t) - f(x - t)]\lambda(x - t). \qquad (9.2)$$

Let $x$ lie in $[0, a + \varepsilon/2]$ or in $[b - \varepsilon/2, 2\pi]$ and $|t| < \varepsilon/2$; then the first term on the right-hand side of (9.2) equals zero, since $\lambda(x + t) - \lambda(x - t) = 0$. If $x \in [a + \varepsilon/2, b - \varepsilon/2]$ and $|t| < \varepsilon/2$, then $f(x + t)$ is bounded due to $f(x)$ being continuous in $[a, b]$, whereas $\lambda(x)$ satisfies the Lipschitz condition of order 1, which means that $|\lambda(x + t) - \lambda(x - t)| < K|t|$ where $K$ is a constant. Combining both these results, we obtain

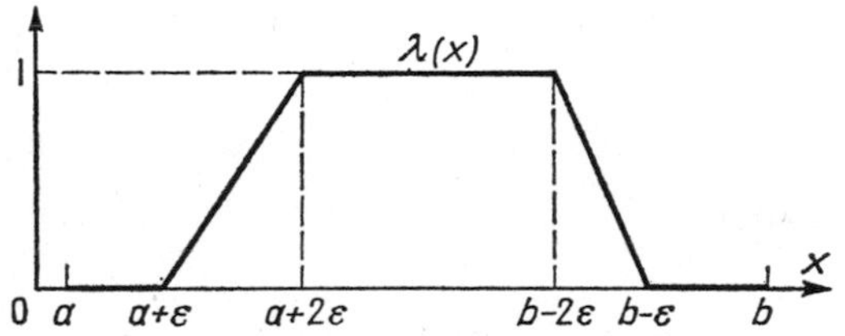


FIG. 17

$$|f(x + t)[\lambda(x + t) - \lambda(x - t)]| \leqslant K_1|t|$$

for $0 \leqslant x \leqslant 2\pi$ and $|t| < \varepsilon/2$, where $K_1$ is another constant. But then, taking $h \leqslant \varepsilon/2$, we find that

$$\left|\int_0^h [f_1(x + t) - f_1(x - t)]\,dt\right| \leqslant \left|\int_0^h \lambda(x - t)[f(x + t) - f(x - t)]\,dt\right| + O(h^2) \quad (9.3)$$

and thus everything reduces to the estimation of the integral

$$I(x) = \int_0^h \lambda(x - t)[f(x + t) - f(x - t)]\,dt.$$

If $x \in [0, a + \varepsilon/2]$ or $x \in [b - \varepsilon/2, 2\pi]$ and $|h| \leqslant \varepsilon/2$, then $I(x) = 0$, because $\lambda(x - t) = 0$. If $x \in [a + 3\varepsilon, b - 3\varepsilon]$ and $|h| \leqslant \varepsilon$, then $\lambda(x - t) = 1$ and then

$$I(x) = \int_0^h [f(x + t) - f(x - t)]\,dt = o\left(\frac{h}{\ln\frac{1}{h}}\right)$$

from the condition of the theorem.

If $x \in [a + \varepsilon/2, a + 3\varepsilon]$ and $|h| < \varepsilon/2$, then since $\lambda(x - t)$ decreases monotonically as $t$ increases, from the second mean value theorem, noting that $0 \leqslant \lambda(x) \leqslant 1$ everywhere, we have:

$$|I(x)| \leqslant \left| \lambda(x) \int_0^\xi [f(x+t) - f(x-t)]\, dt \right| = o\left(\frac{\xi}{\ln \frac{1}{\xi}}\right) = o\left(\frac{h}{\ln \frac{1}{h}}\right)$$

for $0 < \xi < h$.

We argue in a similar way for $x \in [b - 3\varepsilon, b - \varepsilon/2]$, in which case $\lambda(x - t)$ will be an increasing function with $t$ and we find that

$$|I(x)| = \left| \lambda(x - h) \int_\xi^h [f(x+t) - f(x-t)]\, dt \right| = o\left(\frac{h}{\ln \frac{1}{h}}\right),$$

because

$$\left| \int_\xi^h [f(x+t) - f(x-t)]\, dt \right|$$

$$= \left| \int_0^h [f(x+t) - f(x-t)]\, dt - \int_0^\xi [f(x+t) - f(x-t)]\, dt \right|$$

$$\leqslant o\left(\frac{h}{\ln \frac{1}{h}}\right) + o\left(\frac{\xi}{\ln \frac{1}{\xi}}\right) = o\left(\frac{h}{\ln \frac{1}{h}}\right).$$

Thus we have proved that for $f_1(x)$ condition (9.1) is satisfied uniformly for $0 \leqslant x \leqslant 2\pi$. This means that according to the theorem of § 8 we have: $\sigma(f_1)$ converges uniformly in $[0, 2\pi]$. But $f_1(x) = f(x)$ in $(a + 2\varepsilon, b - 2\varepsilon)$. This means that $\sigma(f)$ converges uniformly in $(a + 3\varepsilon, b - 3\varepsilon)$. Since $\varepsilon > 0$ is arbitrary, the theorem is proved.

COROLLARY. *If in some* $[a, b] \subset [0, 2\pi]$ *the Dini–Lipschitz test is fulfilled, i.e.*

$$f(x+h) - f(x) = o\left(\frac{1}{\ln \frac{1}{h}}\right) \tag{9.4}$$

*uniformly in* $[a, b]$, *then for any* $\varepsilon > 0$ *the series* $\sigma(f)$ *converges uniformly in* $(a + \varepsilon, b - \varepsilon)$.

Indeed, arguing in the same way as in § 8, we can prove that if (9.4) is fulfilled, then (9.1) is also fulfilled and it only remains to apply the theorem that has just been proved.

## § 10. The Satô test

We will now return to the question of convergence over the whole interval $[0, 2\pi]$. We have seen that tests exist which are expressed either only in terms of the coefficients of the series or only in terms of the properties of the function. We will prove a theorem due to Satô, from which tests of a combined type can be obtained, i.e. those which refer to both the properties of the function and the conditions imposed on the Fourier coefficients.

First, we introduce a definition.

DEFINITION. Let $\Phi(n)$ be a positive function of an integral argument $n$. *The function $f(x)$ belongs to the class $\Phi(n)$*, if

$$\Phi(n) \int_a^b f(x+t) \cos nt \, dt = O(1) \tag{10.1}$$

uniformly relative to $x, n, a, b$ for $b - a \leqslant 2\pi$.

The following theorem holds†.

SATO'S[1] THEOREM. *Let $f(x)$ belong to the class $\Phi(n)$ where $\Phi(n) = O(n)$ and $f(x)$ possesses a modulus of continuity $\omega(\delta)$. Then for any monotonically increasing $\Theta(n)$, where $1 \leqslant \Theta(n) \leqslant \Phi(n)$, three absolute constants, $A$, $B$ and $C$, are found for which*

$$|S_n(x) - f(x)| \leqslant \omega\left(\frac{1}{n}\right) \left[A \ln \Theta(n) + B \ln \frac{n}{\Phi(n)}\right] + \frac{C}{\Theta(n)}. \tag{10.2}$$

To prove this we note that (see (32.9) in Chapter I)

$$S_n(x) - f(x) = \frac{1}{\pi} \int_0^\pi [f(x+t) + f(x-t) - 2f(x)] \frac{\sin nt}{2 \operatorname{tg} \frac{t}{2}} dt + \varepsilon_n, \tag{10.3}$$

where

$$\varepsilon_n = O\left[\omega\left(\frac{\pi}{n}\right)\right] = O\left[\omega\left(\frac{1}{n}\right)\right]$$

(see Introductory Material, §25). Thus it is sufficient to prove that the modulus of the integral in (10.3) does not exceed the right-hand side of (10.2). But it is possible to prove this by first changing the lower limit of integration to $\pi/n$, since, supposing

$$\varphi_x(t) = f(x+t) + f(x-t) - 2f(x),$$

we have

$$\left| \int_0^{\pi/n} \varphi_x(t) \frac{\sin nt}{2 \operatorname{tg} \frac{t}{2}} dt \right| \leqslant 2\omega\left(\frac{\pi}{n}\right) n \frac{\pi}{n} = O\left[\omega\left(\frac{\pi}{n}\right)\right].$$

Thus, we will prove the existence of $A$, $B$ and $C$ such that

$$\left| \int_{\pi/n}^{\pi} \varphi_x(t) \frac{\sin nt}{2 \operatorname{tg} \frac{t}{2}} dt \right| \leqslant \omega\left(\frac{1}{n}\right) \left[A \ln \Theta(n) + B \ln \frac{n}{\Phi(n)}\right] + \frac{C}{\Theta(n)}. \tag{10.4}$$

† See also the work of Nash[1].

First of all, we write

$$\int_{\pi/n}^{\pi} \varphi_x(t) \frac{\sin nt}{2\,\mathrm{tg}\,\frac{t}{2}}\,dt = \sum_{k=1}^{n-1} \int_{k\frac{\pi}{n}}^{(k+1)\frac{\pi}{n}} \varphi_x(t) \frac{\sin nt}{2\,\mathrm{tg}\,\frac{t}{2}}\,dt = \sum_{k=1}^{n-1} I_k \tag{10.5}$$

and then combine the values $I_k$ in pairs in the same way as Salem did (see § 5). Since

$$I_k = \int_{\pi/n}^{2\frac{\pi}{n}} \varphi_x\left(t + \frac{k-1}{n}\pi\right) \frac{(-1)^{k-1}\sin nt}{2\,\mathrm{tg}\,\dfrac{t + \frac{k-1}{n}\pi}{2}}\,dt,$$

then it is possible to write for any odd $k$

$$I_k + I_{k+1} = \int_{\pi/n}^{2\frac{\pi}{n}} \varphi_x\left(t + \frac{k-1}{n}\pi\right) \left[\frac{1}{2\,\mathrm{tg}\,\dfrac{t + \frac{(k-1)}{n}\pi}{2}} - \frac{1}{2\,\mathrm{tg}\,\dfrac{t + \frac{k}{n}\pi}{2}}\right] \sin nt\,dt$$

$$+ \int_{\pi/n}^{2\frac{\pi}{n}} \left[\varphi_x\left(t + \frac{k-1}{n}\pi\right) - \varphi_x\left(t + \frac{k}{n}\pi\right)\right] \frac{1}{2\,\mathrm{tg}\,\dfrac{t + \frac{k}{n}\pi}{2}} \sin nt\,dt. \tag{10.6}$$

But due to the definition of $\varphi_x(t)$ we have for $\pi/n \leqslant t \leqslant 2\pi/n$

$$\left|\varphi_x\left(t + \frac{k-1}{n}\pi\right)\right| \leqslant 2\,\omega\left(\frac{k+1}{n}\pi\right) \leqslant 2\,(k+1)\,\omega\left(\frac{\pi}{n}\right) = O\left[k\,\omega\left(\frac{1}{n}\right)\right], \tag{10.7}$$

$$\left|\varphi_x\left(t + \frac{k-1}{n}\pi\right) - \varphi_x\left(t + \frac{k}{n}\pi\right)\right| \leqslant 2\,\omega\left(\frac{\pi}{n}\right) = O\left[\omega\left(\frac{1}{n}\right)\right]. \tag{10.8}$$

Moreover

$$\left|\frac{1}{2\,\mathrm{tg}\,\dfrac{t + \frac{k-1}{n}\pi}{2}} - \frac{1}{2\,\mathrm{tg}\,\dfrac{t + \frac{k}{n}\pi}{2}}\right| \leqslant \frac{\pi}{2}\,\frac{n}{k^2}, \tag{10.9}$$

and therefore from (10.6), (10.7), (10.8) and (10.9) we obtain

$$|I_k + I_{k+1}| = O\left[\frac{n}{k^2}\,\omega\left(\frac{1}{n}\right) k\,\frac{\pi}{n}\right] = O\left[\frac{1}{k}\,\omega\left(\frac{1}{n}\right)\right].$$

We denote by $q$ the highest odd number for which

$$q \leqslant \frac{(n-2)\,\Theta(n)}{\Phi(n)}.$$

Then $q \leqslant n - 2$ and

$$\sum_{k=1}^{q}{}' (I_k + I_{k+1}) = O\left[\omega\left(\frac{1}{n}\right) \sum_{k=1}^{q} \frac{1}{k}\right] = O\left[\omega\left(\frac{1}{n}\right) \ln q\right]$$

$$= O\left[\omega\left(\frac{1}{n}\right)\left\{\ln \frac{n}{\Phi(n)} + \ln \Theta(n)\right\}\right],$$

where the sign $\sum'$ indicates that $k$ runs through the odd numbers only. But

$$\sum_{k=1}^{q}{}' (I_k + I_{k+1}) = \int\limits_{\pi/n}^{(q+2)\frac{\pi}{n}} \varphi_x(t) \frac{\sin nt}{2\,\mathrm{tg}\,\frac{t}{2}}\,dt,$$

which means that it remains to prove that

$$I = \int\limits_{(q+2)\frac{\pi}{n}}^{\pi} \varphi_x(t) \frac{\sin nt}{2\,\mathrm{tg}\,\frac{t}{2}}\,dt = O\left[\frac{1}{\Theta(n)}\right],$$

and then the inequality (10.4) will be proved.

Supposing for brevity's sake that $\beta = (q+2)\,\pi/n$, we see from the definition of $q$ that $\beta \leqslant \pi$ and

$$\beta > \frac{\pi}{n}(n-2)\frac{\Theta(n)}{\Phi(n)} > \frac{\pi\,\Theta(n)}{2\,\Phi(n)} \quad \text{for} \quad n \geqslant 4. \tag{10.10}$$

Since $f(x)$ belongs to the class $\Phi(n)$, then

$$\left|\int\limits_{a}^{b} \varphi_x(t) \sin nt\,dt\right| = O\left[\frac{1}{\Phi(n)}\right] \tag{10.11}$$

for any $a, b$ and $x$. But from the second mean value theorem for some $\eta, \beta < \eta < \pi$, we have

$$I = \frac{1}{2\,\mathrm{tg}\,\frac{\beta}{2}} \int\limits_{\beta}^{\eta} \varphi_x(t) \sin nt\,dt,$$

whence by virtue of (10.10) and (10.11)

$$|I| \leqslant \frac{1}{\beta} O\left[\frac{1}{\Phi(n)}\right] = O\left(\frac{1}{\Theta(n)}\right) \quad (\text{for} \quad n \geqslant 4).$$

If $n < 4$, then the formula (10.4) is trivial, which means that the theorem is completely proved.

From this theorem we immediately obtain

COROLLARY 1. *Let $f(x)$ belong to the class $\Phi(n)$, where $\Phi(n) = O(n)$ and its modulus of continuity $\omega(\delta)$ satisfies the condition $\omega(1/n)\ln(n/\Phi(n)) \to 0$ as $n \to \infty$; moreover, for some monotonically increasing $\Theta(n)$ tending to infinity, let $\omega(1/n)\ln\Theta(n) \to 0$ as $n \to \infty$. Then the Fourier series of $f(x)$ converges to it uniformly.*

The Dini–Lipschitz test follows immediately from this. Indeed, it is sufficient to suppose that $\Phi(n) = \Theta(n) = \ln n$ in order to prove that as $\omega(1/n)\ln n \to 0$ the conditions formulated in Corollary 1 are fulfilled, and then uniform convergence occurs.

It can also be said that

COROLLARY 2. *If we have for the modulus of continuity of $f(x)$*

$$\omega\left(\frac{1}{n}\right) = o\left(\frac{1}{\ln\ln n}\right)$$

*and if*

$$\int_a^b f(x+t)\cos nt\,dt = O\left(\frac{\ln n}{n}\right),$$

*then Fourier series of $f(x)$ converges uniformly.*

Indeed, it is sufficient to suppose that $\Phi(n) = n/\ln n$ and $\Theta(n) = \ln n$.

## § 11. Concerning uniform convergence near every point of an interval

Let us note the validity of the following simple theorem:

THEOREM. *Let $f(x)$ possess the following property: for every point $x_0$ of the interval $[0, 2\pi]$ there is a neighbourhood $I_{x_0}$ and a function $g(x) = g_{x_0}(x)$ such that $f(x) = g(x)$ in $I_{x_0}$ and the Fourier series of $g(x)$ converges uniformly. Then the Fourier series of $f(x)$ converges uniformly.*

According to the Heine–Borel theorem we can find a finite number of points $x_1, x_2, \ldots, x_m$ such that the intervals $I_{x_1}, I_{x_2}, \ldots I_{x_m}$ overlap and cover the whole interval $[0, 2\pi]$. Let $I_{x_k} = (u_k, v_k)$. Without disturbing the generality it can be supposed that

$$u_k < v_{k-1} < u_{k+1} < v_k \quad (k = 1, 2, \ldots, m),$$

whilst $(u_{m+1}, v_{m+1}) \equiv (u_1, v_1) \pmod{2\pi}$.

Let $\lambda_k(x)$ be a continuous function of period $2\pi$, equal to 1 in $(v_{k-1}, u_{k+1})$, equal to 0 outside $(u_k, v_k)$ and linear in the intervals $(u_k, v_{k-1})$ and $(u_{k+1}, v_k)$. It is not difficult to see that

$$\lambda_1(x) + \lambda_2(x) + \cdots + \lambda_m(x) = 1.$$

It is clear that

$$\sigma(f) = \sigma[f(\lambda_1 + \cdots + \lambda_m)] = \sigma(f\lambda_1) + \cdots + \sigma(f\lambda_m),$$

therefore it is sufficient to prove the uniform convergence of every one of the series $\sigma(f\lambda_k)$. But from the definition of $\lambda_k(x)$ we have

$$\sigma(f\lambda_k) = \sigma[g_{x_k}\lambda_k],$$

and as regards $\sigma(g_{x_k})$ it has been assumed that this series converges uniformly.

If it is now noted that $\lambda_k(x)$ satisfies the Lipschitz condition of order 1, since it is a continuous broken function, then according to Steinhaus's theorem (see Chapter I, § 34) we see that $\sigma(g_{x_k}, \lambda_k)$ and $\lambda_k(x)\,\sigma(g_{x_k})$ are uniformly equi-convergent, which means that $\sigma(g_{x_k}, \lambda_k)$ converges uniformly. This concludes the proof.

## § 12. Concerning operations on functions to obtain uniformly convergent Fourier series

It is clear that if $f_1(x)$ and $f_2(x)$ are two functions with uniformly convergent Fourier series, then this also holds for their sum or difference. We will see in Chapter IX that in the case of absolute convergence the product of $f_1(x)$ with $f_2(x)$ also possesses an absolutely convergent Fourier series. In the case of uniform convergence this is not true; in § 23 we will see an example of a function $f(x)$ for which the Fourier series converges uniformly but the Fourier series of $f^2(x)$ diverges in a set of the power of the continuum. This example shows that if

$$\Phi(x) = g[f(x)],$$

where the series for $f(x)$ converges uniformly, then for $\Phi(x)$ this does not occur even in such a simple case as $g(u) = u^2$ (but for absolute convergence we have a positive result in the case of a sufficiently good $g(u)$, see Chapter IX, § 11).

Thus, it would appear that even an insignificant worsening of the function disturbs its property of having a uniformly convergent Fourier series. Moreover, it is interesting to show that it is possible by means of a carefully chosen monotonic transformation of the independent variable to convert any continuous function into one for which the Fourier series converges uniformly. We have in mind the following theorem derived by Bohr[1].

THEOREM. *Let $\Phi(t)$ be a continuous periodic function of period $2\pi$. Then there exists a strictly monotonic and continuous $t(\theta)$ such that*

$$f(\theta) = \Phi[t(\theta)]$$

*possesses an uniformly convergent Fourier series.*

We note that Pál[1] proved first a somewhat weaker theorem, that is, for any continuous $\Phi(t)$ he determined $t(\theta)$ having the properties given above so that the series for $f(\theta)$ was found to be uniformly convergent for $\delta \leqslant \theta \leqslant 2\pi - \delta$ for any $\delta > 0$. Then Bohr obtained the theorem formulated above.

Here we will describe not Bohr's proof but rather the proof due to Salem[10] as it is simpler and briefer. Just as for Paley's proof, it is based on Fejér's results derived from the theory of conformal transformations. First of all, we must state one of Fejér's[3] theorems:

FEJÉR'S THEOREM. *Let* $f(z) = \sum_{k=0}^{\infty} a_k z^k$ *be a power series convergent for* $|z| < 1$. *Let the function* $f(z)$ *be continuous for* $|z| \leqslant 1$. *We will assume that* $w = f(z)$ *is a single-valued function, which brings about the conformal transformation of the circle* $|z| < 1$ *into some finite region of the w-plane. Then the series* $\sum a_k z^k$ *converges uniformly on* $|z| = 1$ (*which means that it also converges uniformly for* $|z| \leqslant 1$).

We will first prove that if

$$f(z) = \sum_{k=0}^{\infty} a_k z^k,$$

where the series converges at $|z| < 1$, then the equality

$$\iint_{(C_r)} |f'(z)|^2 \, dx \, dy = \pi \sum_{k=1}^{\infty} k \, |a_k|^2 \, r^{2k}, \tag{12.1}$$

holds, where $0 \leqslant r < 1$ and the integration is carried out over the circle $C_r$ with radius $r$ and centre at the origin of the co-ordinates.

Indeed, changing to polar co-ordinates, we have

$$\iint_{(C_r)} |f'(z)|^2 \, dx \, dy = \int_0^r \varrho \, d\varrho \int_0^{2\pi} |f'(\varrho e^{i\varphi})|^2 \, d\varphi$$

$$= \int_0^r \varrho \, d\varrho \int_0^{2\pi} \left| \sum_{k=1}^{\infty} k a_k \varrho^{(k-1)} \, e^{i(k-1)\varphi} \right|^2 d\varphi$$

$$= 2\pi \int_0^r \varrho \left( \sum_{k=1}^{\infty} k^2 \, |a_k|^2 \, \varrho^{2k-2} \right) d\varrho = \pi \sum_{k=1}^{\infty} k \, |a_k|^2 \, r_k^{2k}.$$

Here all the operations are valid, since the function under the integral sign is non-negative, that is, it can be changed from a double integral to a repeated integral; moreover, series with positive terms are integrable. Thus (12.1) is proved.

Let us consider the case when $f(x)$ is continuous for $|z| \leqslant 1$ and $w = f(z)$ is a single-valued function giving conformal transformation of the circle $|z| < 1$ into some region of the $w$-plane then

$$\iint_{(C_r)} |f'(z)|^2 \, dx \, dy$$

defines the area $T_r$ of the form of the circle $(C_r)$ on the $w$-plane. But in this case $T_r$ should remain finite when $r \to 1$. This means that on the basis of (12.1) we have

$$\sum_{k=1}^{\infty} k \, |a_k|^2 < +\infty. \tag{12.2}$$

We will now show that the series $\sum_{k=0}^{\infty} a_k z^k$ on $|z| = 1$ is uniformly summable $(C, 1)$. Indeed, $f(z)$ is continuous in the circle $|z| \leqslant 1$, therefore $f(\varrho e^{i\varphi})$ tends uniformly to $f(e^{i\varphi})$ as $\varrho \to 1$. The same is true of their real and imaginary parts. Consequently, according to the theorem of Chapter I, § 60, the real and imaginary parts of the series $\sum_{k=0}^{\infty} a_k e^{ik\varphi}$ are Fourier series of continuous functions. Therefore they are uniformly summable by the method $(C, 1)$ which means that the series $\sum_{k=0}^{\infty} a_k e^{ik\varphi}$ is also uniformly summable by the method $(C, 1)$ to $f(e^{i\varphi})$.

Now from (12.2) and from the uniform $(C, 1)$ summability on the circle $|z| = 1$ we conclude from Fejér's lemma (see Appendix, § 12) that the series $\sum_{k=0}^{\infty} a_k z^k$ converges uniformly for $|z| = 1$ and Fejér's theorem is proved.

We will now continue with the proof of Bohr's theorem.

Let $\Phi(t)$ be a periodic function of period $2\pi$. Without disturbing the generality, it is possible to add a constant to $\Phi(t)$ so that

$$\int_0^{2\pi} \Phi(t)\, dt = 0.$$

In this case $\Phi(t)$ should become zero somewhere. Let this be at $t = 0$ (this can be achieved by displacement). Then $\Phi(0) = \Phi(2\pi) = 0$. Since $\int_0^{2\pi} \Phi(t)\, dt = 0$, then at least one value $a$ occurs $(0 < a < 2\pi)$, where $\Phi(a) = 0$.

We will assume first that in the open interval $(0, 2\pi)$ the point $a$ is the only point at which $\Phi(t)$ becomes zero. Then $\Phi(t)$ is essentially positive in one of the two intervals $(0, a)$ and $(a, 2\pi)$ and essentially negative in the other†. Let $\alpha(t)$ be any continuous function with period $2\pi$, such that $\alpha(0) = \alpha(2\pi) = 0$, whilst $\alpha(t)$ essentially increases in $(0, a)$ and essentially decreases in $(a, 2\pi)$. Then the equations

$$\left.\begin{aligned} x &= \alpha(t), \\ y &= \Phi(t) \end{aligned}\right\} \tag{12.3}$$

represent a simple closed Jordan curve. Let $w = f(z)$ be a single-valued function which causes conformal transformation of the circle $z < 1$ into a domain bounded by this curve (12.3). Such an $f(z)$ exists according to Riemann's theorem (see Appendix, § 6). From Carathéodory's theorem (see Appendix, § 6) the circumference of the circle transforms into the Jordan curve (12.3) uniquely and continuously. Let us consider $f(z)$ on $|z| = 1$, i.e. $z = e^{i\varphi}$. During the change in $\varphi$ from 0 to $2\pi$, it can be considered that $t(\varphi)$ changes from 0 to $2\pi$ continuously and essentially increasing (according to Carathéodory's theorem). If this is the case, then for the imaginary part of $f(e^{i\varphi})$ we have

$$y = \operatorname{Im} f(e^{i\varphi}) = \Phi[t(\varphi)],$$

where $t(\varphi)$ increases continuously and essentially. But according to the Fejér theorem just proved, if

$$f(z) = \sum a_k z^k,$$

then this series converges uniformly on $|z| = 1$. From this it follows that the Fourier series of $\Phi[t(\varphi)]$ converges uniformly and then the theorem is proved.

---

† We consider that $\Phi(t) \not\equiv 0$ (if the contrary were true, then the theorem is trivial).

We will now suppose that $a$ is not the only point in the open interval $(0, 2\pi)$ where $\Phi(t)$ becomes zero.

Let $M_1$ be the maximum of $|\Phi(t)|$ for $0 \leqslant t \leqslant a$ and let $t_1$ be a point in $(0, a)$ where $|\Phi(t_1)| = M_1$. Also let $M_2$ be the maximum of $|\Phi(t)|$ in $(a, 2\pi)$ and $t_2$ be a point in $(a, 2\pi)$ where $|\Phi(t_2)| = M_2$. Let us define the function $w(t)$ in the following way:

$$w(t) = \begin{cases} \max\limits_{0 \leqslant t' \leqslant t} |\Phi(t')| + \sin\left(\dfrac{\pi t}{a}\right) & \text{for} \quad 0 \leqslant t \leqslant t_1, \\ \max\limits_{0 \leqslant t' \leqslant a} |\Phi(t')| + \sin\left(\dfrac{\pi t}{a}\right) & \text{for} \quad t_1 \leqslant t \leqslant a \end{cases}$$

and similarly

$$w(t) = \begin{cases} -\max\limits_{a \leqslant t' \leqslant t} |\Phi(t')| - \sin\left[\dfrac{\pi(t-a)}{2\pi - a}\right] & \text{for} \quad a \leqslant t \leqslant t_2, \\ -\max\limits_{t \leqslant t' \leqslant 2\pi} |\Phi(t')| - \sin\left[\dfrac{\pi(t-a)}{2\pi - a}\right] & \text{for} \quad t_2 \leqslant t \leqslant 2\pi \end{cases}$$

and we will continue it periodically.

It is immediately evident that $w(t)$ is continuous and of bounded variation and that $\Phi_1(t) = \Phi(t) + w(t)$ over $[0 \leqslant t \leqslant 2\pi]$ and becomes zero only at $t = 0$, $t = a$, $t = 2\pi$ and that $\Phi_1(t)$ is essentially positive in the open interval $(0, a)$ and essentially negative in $(a, 2\pi)$. Therefore, by applying to it only the result that has just been obtained, we see that a monotonic $t(\theta)$ of the required form exists, for which the Fourier series of $\Phi_1[t(\theta)]$ converges uniformly over $[0 \leqslant t \leqslant 2\pi]$. But since $w(t)$ is continuous and of bounded variation, then the same result is valid for $\Phi(t)$ and the theorem is proved.

*Note.* There remains an unsolved problem set by N. N. Lusin: is it possible for any continuous $\Phi(t)$ to choose $t = t(\theta)$ which is not simply continuous and monotonic but is absolutely continuous and monotonic, such that for

$$f(\theta) = \Phi[t(\theta)]$$

the Fourier series converges uniformly?

N. N. Lusin also set another problem: is it possible for any continuous $\Phi(t)$ to choose a monotonic $t(\theta)$ so that the Fourier series of $f(\theta) = \Phi[t(\theta)]$ converges absolutely?

Neither of these problems has been solved.

The question can also be asked: is it impossible for every continuous $\Phi(x)$ to choose a continuous monotonic $F(y)$ so that the Fourier series for $F[\Phi(x)]$ converges uniformly?

## § 13. Concerning uniform convergence by rearrangement of the signs in the terms of the series

A problem can be defined as follows: a trigonometric series

$$\frac{a_0}{2} + \sum_{n=1}^{\infty} (a_n \cos nx + b_n \sin nx) \tag{13.1}$$

is given. Let us consider all those series

$$\frac{a_0}{2} + \sum_{n=1}^{\infty} \pm (a_n \cos nx + b_n \sin nx), \tag{13.2}$$

which can be derived from the given series by means of an arbitrary change in the signs of its terms. What conditions can be imposed on $a_n$ and $b_n$ to guarantee that any one of the series (13.2) be uniformly convergent?

An exhaustive answer to this question is given in the work by Salem and Zygmund[6]. In Chapter II, § 8, we have explained the meaning of the expression "nearly all the series" of the form (13.2). Using this explanation, Salem and Zygmund's theorem can be formulated thus:

THEOREM. *Let*

$$r_n = \sqrt{a_n^2 + b_n^2}, \qquad R_n = \sum_{k=n+1}^{\infty} r_k^2.$$

*If*

$$\sum_{n=1}^{\infty} \frac{\sqrt{R_n}}{n\sqrt{\ln n}} < +\infty, \tag{13.3}$$

*then nearly all the series* (13.2) *converge uniformly and consequently are Fourier series of continuous functions.*

*If $r_n$ decreases monotonically and if for some $p > 1$ we have $R_n (\ln n)^p \uparrow$, then the condition* (13.3) *is also necessary for nearly all the series* (13.2) *to be Fourier series of continuous functions.*

We will not give the proof of this theorem here, since it requires a large amount of auxiliary material.† We will merely show that as a simple corollary of this result the theorem is obtained, which was proved earlier by Paley and Zygmund[1], namely.

*If*

$$\sum_{n=1}^{\infty} (a_n^2 + b_n^2) \ln^{1+\varepsilon} n < +\infty, \quad \varepsilon > 0,$$

*then nearly all the series* (13.2) *converge uniformly.*

In fact, if the conditions of Paley and Zygmund's theorem are fulfilled we have

$$R_n = \sum_{n+1}^{\infty} (a_k^2 + b_k^2) \leqslant \frac{1}{\ln^{1+\varepsilon} n} \sum_{k=n+1}^{\infty} (a_k^2 + b_k^2) \ln^{1+\varepsilon} k = o\left(\frac{1}{\ln^{1+\varepsilon} n}\right)$$

and

$$\sum_{n=1}^{\infty} \frac{\sqrt{R_n}}{n\sqrt{\ln n}} < +\infty, \quad \text{because} \quad \sqrt{R_n} = O\left(\frac{1}{\ln^{1/2+\varepsilon/2} n}\right).$$

*The theorem ceases to be true if* $\varepsilon = 0$.

Indeed, it is sufficient to consider the series

$$\sum_{k=2}^{\infty} \pm \frac{\sin a^k x}{k \ln k},$$

† The proof is contained in the cited report by Salem and Zygmund[6] where there are also many other interesting results.

where $a$ is any integer provided that $a > 1$. It is clear that for this, supposing that $b_n = 0$, if $n \neq a^k$, $b_{a^k} = 1/(k \ln k)$, if $k = 2, 3, \ldots$, we have

$$\sum b_n^2 \ln n = \sum \frac{1}{k^2 \ln^2 k} \ln a^k = \ln a \sum \frac{1}{k \ln^2 k} < +\infty .$$

However, this series could not be uniformly convergent by any rearrangement of signs, since otherwise its sum would be a continuous function and then, because this series is lacunary, it should be absolutely convergent (see Chapter XI, § 6) which it is not, since

$$\sum_{k=2}^{\infty} \frac{1}{k \ln k} = +\infty .$$

## § 14. Extremal properties of some trigonometric polynomials

In the further study of the uniform convergence of trigonometric series, some auxiliary results are necessary, which are also interesting in themselves.

Let us set this problem: let the quantities $r_p \geqslant 0$ $(p = 1, 2, \ldots n)$ be given. Let us suppose that

$$f(x) = \sum_{p=1}^{n} r_p \cos(px - \alpha_p). \tag{14.1}$$

It is required to select the values $\alpha_p$ so that $\max |f(x)|$ will be a minimum.

As $x$ varies, then $|f(x)|$ will have a maximum value which is a positive and continuous function of $\alpha_p$; let us denote it by $M(\alpha_1, \ldots, \alpha_n)$. As $\alpha_p$ varies, then this function will have a minimum value $\mu$; we will try to estimate it from above. We will prove that

$$\mu < C \sqrt{\ln n} \sqrt{r_1^2 + r_2^2 + \cdots + r_n^2},$$

where $C$ is an absolute constant. For this purpose we will establish the validity of the lemma:

LEMMA. *Let*

$$f(x) = r_1 \cos(x - \alpha_1) + r_2 \cos(2x - \alpha_2) + \cdots + r_n \cos(nx - \alpha_n),$$

*where the values $r_p \geqslant 0$ are given. Then it is possible to choose the values $\alpha_p (p = 1, 2, \ldots, n)$ so that*

$$|f(x)| \leqslant C \sqrt{\ln n} \sqrt{r_1^2 + \cdots + r_n^2}, \tag{14.2}$$

*where $C$ is an absolute constant.*

This lemma can be proved by various methods (see, for example, Littlewood[1]; here we will give the proof by Salem[1]).

We note first of all that

$$\int_0^{2\pi} f^2(x)\, dx = \pi(r_1^2 + \cdots + r_n^2). \tag{14.3}$$

It is clear from this that

$$r_1^2 + \cdots + r_n^2 \leqslant 2M^2. \tag{14.4}$$

We will now consider the integral $I_k = \int_0^{2\pi} f^{2k}(x)\,dx$ for any positive integer $k$. If it is considered as a function of $\alpha_p^2$, then this function has a minimum and at the point where it is attained it is necessary that $\partial^2 I/\partial\alpha_p^2 \geqslant 0$ for $p = 1, 2, \dots n$. This inequality gives

$$\int_0^{2\pi} 2k(2k-1) f^{2k-2}(x)\, r_p^2 \sin^2(px - \alpha_p)\,dx - \int_0^{2\pi} 2k f^{2k-1}(x)\, r_p \cos(px - \alpha_p)\,dx \geqslant 0,$$

whence all the more so

$$\int_0^{2\pi} f^{2k-1}(x)\, r_p \cos(px - \alpha_p)\,dx \leqslant (2k-1)\, r_p^2 \int_0^{2\pi} f^{2k-2}(x)\,dx.$$

If such inequalities are derived for every $p = 1, 2, \dots, n$, then after combining them we obtain

$$\int_0^{2\pi} f^{2k}(x)\,dx \leqslant (2k-1)(r_1^2 + \cdots + r_n^2) \int_0^{2\pi} f^{2k-2}(x)\,dx. \tag{14.5}$$

But applying Hölder's inequality to the last integral we obtain

$$\int_0^{2\pi} f^{2k-2}(x)\,dx \leqslant (2\pi)^{1/k} \left\{\int_0^{2\pi} f^{2k}(x)\,dx\right\}^{\frac{k-1}{k}},$$

which on combination with the inequality (14.5) gives

$$\left(\int_0^{2\pi} f^{2k}(x)\,dx\right)^{1/k} \leqslant (2\pi)^{1/k}(2k-1)(r_1^2 + \cdots + r_n^2). \tag{14.6}$$

If we consider the function $|f(x)|$ for which the integral $I_k$ has a minimum value then it attains its maximum $M$ for at least one point $x_0$ and has the magnitude $M\lambda (0 < \lambda < 1)$ in at least two points $a$ and $b$, of which one point is to the left of $x_0$ and the other is to the right of $x_0$, whilst between them $|f|$ exceeds $M\lambda$ (this follows from the fact that $f(x)$ has a zero value in $[0, 2\pi]$). Then

$$2(M - M\lambda) < \int_a^b |f'(x)|\,dx < \sqrt{b-a}\left(\int_a^b [f'(x)]^2\,dx\right)^{1/2} < \sqrt{b-a}\,\pi\left(\sum_{p=1}^{n} p^2 r_p^2\right)^{1/2},$$

whence

$$b - a > \frac{4M^2(1-\lambda)^2}{\pi^2 \sum p^2 r_p^2}.$$

But due to (14.4) we have

$$b - a > \frac{2}{\pi^2}\,\frac{(1-\lambda)^2 \sum r_p^2}{\sum p^2 r_p^2},$$

and therefore

$$\int_0^{2\pi} f^{2k}(x)\,dx \geqslant \int_a^b f^{2k}(x)\,dx \geqslant (M\lambda)^{2k}(b-a) > (M\lambda)^{2k}\,\frac{2}{\pi^2}\,\frac{(1-\lambda)^2 \sum r_p^2}{\sum p^2 r_p^2}. \tag{14.7}$$

Since $\lambda$ here was still arbitrary, provided $0 < \lambda < 1$, we will select it so that $\lambda^{2k}(1 - \lambda)^2$ will be a maximum; for this we must take $\lambda = k/(k + 1)$.

Thus

$$\int_0^{2\pi} f^{2k}(x)\,dx \geqslant M^{2k}\left(\frac{k}{k+1}\right)^{2k} \frac{2}{\pi^2} \frac{\frac{1}{(k+1)^2}\sum r_p^2}{\sum p^2 r_p^2}. \tag{14.8}$$

Comparing the inequality (14.8) with the inequality (14.6) we find that

$$M^2 < Ak\left(\frac{\sum p^2 r_p^2}{\sum r_p^2}\right)^{1/k} (r_1^2 + \cdots + r_n^2), \tag{14.9}$$

where $A$ is an absolute constant.

If $k$ is chosen so that the right-hand side of (14.9) is a minimum, then we find that

$$M < B\sqrt{\ln\left(\frac{\sum p^2 r_p^2}{\sum r_p^2}\right)}\sqrt{r_1^2 + \cdots + r_n^2}$$

and a similar inequality holds even more so for $\mu = \min M$ ($B$ is an absolute constant). But since

$$\frac{\sum p^2 r_p^2}{\sum r_p^2} < n^2,$$

then, simplifying, we can write

$$\mu < C\sqrt{\ln n}\sqrt{r_1^2 + \cdots + r_n^2}, \tag{14.10}$$

where $C$ again is an absolute constant.

Thus, the lemma is proved.

As S. N. Bernstein[4] proved, the estimate (14.10) obtained cannot be bettered.

## § 15. The choice of arguments for given moduli of the terms of the series

In § 13 we considered the problem whether by the choice of the signs $\pm$ it was possible to make the series

$$\frac{a_0}{2} + \sum_{n=1}^{\infty} \pm (a_n \cos nx + b_n \sin nx)$$

uniformly convergent and consequently for it to be the Fourier series of a continuous function. The statement of this theorem by Zygmund and Salem was given then without proof; here we will take a closer look at this problem in solving a less difficult task, the solution being proved in detail.

The problem is set as follows: let the quantities $r_n \geqslant 0$ ($n = 1, 2, \ldots$) be given. It is required to choose $\alpha_n$ ($n = 1, 2, \ldots$) so that the series

$$\sum_{n=1}^{\infty} r_n \cos(nx - \alpha_n) \tag{15.1}$$

will be the Fourier series of a continuous function.

This question was first asked by Salem[1] and he gave his answer in the following form.

SALEM'S THEOREM. *If*

$$R_n = \sum_{k=n+1}^{\infty} r_k^2 \quad \text{and} \quad \sum_{n=1}^{\infty} \frac{\sqrt{R_n}}{n\sqrt{\ln n}} < +\infty, \tag{15.2}$$

*then it is always possible to choose the quantities* $\alpha_n$ *so that the series* (15.1) *is a Fourier series of a continuous function.*

Indeed, we will first prove that the integral values $n_k$ exist for which

$$\sum_{k=1}^{\infty} \sqrt{\ln n_{k+1}}\sqrt{R_{n_k}} < +\infty. \tag{15.3}$$

It is possible to take $n_k = 2^{2^k}$ for these values. In fact, starting from Cauchy's theorem (see Introductory Material, § 4), if $u_n \geq 0$ and $u_n \downarrow 0$, then the series $\sum u_n$ and $\sum 2^n u_{2^n}$ converge or diverge simultaneously. Therefore, if (15.2) is fulfilled, the series

$$\sum \frac{\sqrt{R_{2^n}}}{\sqrt{n}},$$

also converges and then, again applying Cauchy's theorem, we see that the series $\sum \sqrt{2^n}\sqrt{R_{2^{2^n}}}$ also converges, and this implies the convergence of (15.3) at $n_k = 2^{2^k}$.

Now we will suppose that

$$f_k(x) = \sum_{n_k+1}^{n_{k+1}} r_p \cos(px - \alpha_p), \quad k = 1, 2, \ldots$$

On the basis of the lemma in § 14 we can choose $\alpha_p$ ($p = n_k + 1, \ldots, n_{k+1}$) for any $k$ so that

$$|f_k(x)| < C\sqrt{\ln n_{k+1}}\sqrt{R_{n_k}},$$

and if this is so, then $\sum_{k=1}^{\infty} f_k(x)$ converges uniformly and therefore the function

$$f(x) = \sum_{p=1}^{\infty} r_p \cos(px - \alpha_p)$$

is continuous and this solves in a positive sense the question asked by Salem. The theorem is proved.

*Note.* Salem[1] also proved that his theorem cannot be bettered in any known sense. More exactly: if $R_n^0 \downarrow 0$, whilst $R_n^0 \ln n$ varies monotonically and $\sum \sqrt{R_n^0}/n\sqrt{\ln n} = +\infty$, then it is possible to set up the series $\sum_{p=1}^{\infty} r_p \cos(px - \alpha_p)$, for which $R_n \leq R_n^0$, but not for any choice of the values $\alpha_p$ is this series a Fourier series of a continuous function.

Salem also proved that if the values $r_n$ decrease sufficiently regularly, then no limitations can be imposed on the rate at which $r_n$ tends to zero and the necessary result is achieved by the selection of the arguments $\alpha_n$. More exactly: if $r_n \downarrow 0$ and $\{1/r_n\}$ is a concave sequence, then it is possible to choose $\alpha_n$ so that the series $\sum r_n \cos(nx - \alpha_n)$ is a Fourier series of a continuous function.

The question of whether a similar theorem holds for series of the type $\sum \pm r_n \cos nx$ remains unanswered.

## § 16. Concerning Fourier coefficients of continuous functions

The question arises: can anything be said concerning the rate at which the Fourier coefficients of continuous functions tend to zero?

It has been noted by Lebesgue that whatever kind of sequence of positive numbers $\varepsilon_n$ is taken, provided only that $\varepsilon_n \to 0$, it is possible to find a continuous function, for which for an infinite set of the values $n$ the moduli of the Fourier coefficients satisfy the condition

$$|a_n| + |b_n| \geqslant \varepsilon_n.$$

Indeed, it is sufficient to choose the values $n_k$ as increasing so rapidly that

$$\sum_{k=1}^{\infty} \varepsilon_{n_k} < +\infty$$

and to assume, for example, that

$$f(x) = \sum_{k=1}^{\infty} \varepsilon_{n_k} \cos n_k x.$$

It is clear that $f(x)$ is continuous and

$$|a_{n_k}| = \varepsilon_{n_k} \quad \text{for} \quad k = 1, 2, \ldots$$

The problem can also be put in this way: since for any $f(x) \in L^2$ we have $\sum (a_n^2 + b_n^2) < +\infty$, then this is true for any continuous $f(x)$. But, perhaps, it is possible to find an $\varepsilon > 0$ for every continuous $f(x)$ such that

$$\sum (|a_n|^{2-\varepsilon} + |b_n|^{2-\varepsilon}) < +\infty.$$

This question was asked by Carleman[1] and he himself replied in the negative. Moreover, he proved the following theorem.

CARLEMAN'S THEOREM. *There exists a continuous function $f(x)$ such that for any $\varepsilon > 0$ we have*

$$\sum (|a_n|^{2-\varepsilon} + |b_n|^{2-\varepsilon}) = +\infty,$$

*where $a_n$ and $b_n$ are its Fourier coefficients.*

We will not work through Carleman's proof here but will obtain his theorem from Salem's result described in § 15.

Let us supp ose that

$$r_n = \frac{1}{\sqrt{n}\,(\ln n)^{\beta}},$$

where $\beta > 1$. Then, supposing that

$$R_n = \sum_{p=n+1}^{\infty} r_p^2 = \sum_{p=n+1}^{\infty} \frac{1}{n(\ln n)^{2\beta}},$$

we see that

$$R_n = O\left(\frac{1}{(\ln n)^{2\beta-1}}\right),$$

and therefore

$$\sum_{n=1}^{\infty} \frac{\sqrt{R_n}}{n\sqrt{\ln n}} < +\infty.$$

But then according to Salem's theorem it is possible to choose the quantities $\alpha_n$ such that the series

$$\sum_{n=1}^{\infty} r_n \cos(nx - a_n)$$

is a Fourier series of a continuous function.

But since for this series

$$a_n^2 + b_n^2 = r_n^2 = \frac{1}{n(\ln n)^{2\beta}},$$

then

$$\sum r_n^{2-\varepsilon} = +\infty$$

for any $\varepsilon > 0$, whence the validity of Carleman's theorem follows.

Moreover, this example can serve as a proof of Banach's[1] theorem: *there exists a sequence $\varepsilon_n \to 0$ and a continuous function $f(x)$ for whose Fourier coefficients we have*

$$\sum_{n=1}^{\infty} (|a_n|^{2-\varepsilon_n} + |b_n|^{2-\varepsilon_n}) = +\infty.$$

In order to prove this, we take the function that has just been derived and choose $\varepsilon_n$ such that

$$\sum r_n^{2-\varepsilon_n} = +\infty.$$

Then our result will be proved. For convenience of estimation we shall write $2\varepsilon_n$ instead of $\varepsilon_n$. Since $r_n^2 = 1/n\,(\ln n)^{2\beta}$, then it is sufficient to choose $\varepsilon_n$ so that

$$\sum \frac{1}{n^{1-\varepsilon_n}(\ln n)^{2\beta(1-\varepsilon_n)}} = +\infty.$$

But it is known that this will occur, for example, if, starting from some $n_0$

$$\frac{n^{\varepsilon_n}}{(\ln n)^{2\beta}} > \frac{1}{\ln n},$$

i.e.

$$n^{\varepsilon_n} > (\ln n)^{2\beta-1} \quad \text{for} \quad n \geqslant n_0,$$

for which it is sufficient to take

$$\varepsilon_n \ln n > (2\beta - 1) \ln \ln n,$$

and this can be done by taking $\varepsilon_n = 1/\sqrt{\ln n}$.

Let us note that Banach obtained his theorem by operating on a result obtained in the same report which itself is of considerable interest. Namely, he proved that *if* $\{n_k\}$ *is any lacunary sequence and* $\alpha_k$ *and* $\beta_k$ *are any values, provided* $\sum(\alpha_k^2 + \beta_k^2) < +\infty$ *then it is always possible to find a continuous function for which* $a_{n_k} = \alpha_k$ *and* $b_{n_k} = \beta_k$ (i.e. at points given by a lacunary sequence the Fourier coefficients can be chosen as desired, provided only that the series of their squares converges†).

The proof of this proposition can be found in a book by Zygmund[A, 35], § 9.6, as well as in the author's own work.

Also, the following theorem due to Paley[3] should be noted.

PALEY'S THEOREM. *Whatever are the values* $d_n \geqslant 0, \sum d_n^2 = +\infty$, *it is possible to find a continuous* $f(x)$ *such that for its Fourier series*

$$\sum r_n \cos(nx - \alpha_n)$$

*we have*

$$\sum r_n d_n = +\infty.$$

Paley's theorem can be obtained as a corollary of the more general result derived by Orlicz[2]††.

ORLICZ'S THEOREM. *Let* $d_n \geqslant 0$ $(n = 1, 2, \ldots)$ *and* $\sum\limits_{n=1}^{\infty} d_n^2 = +\infty$. *Let* $\{\varphi_n(x)\}$ *be an orthogonal and normal system in* $[0, 1]$ *for which*

$$|\varphi_n(x)| \leqslant A \quad (n = 1, 2, \ldots). \tag{16.1}$$

*Then there exists a continuous function* $f(x)$ *for which the Fourier coefficients* $a_n$ *with respect to the system* $\{\varphi_n(x)\}$ *satisfy the condition*

$$\sum_{n=1}^{\infty} d_n |a_n| = +\infty. \tag{16.2}$$

In order to prove this theorem we will establish first the following lemma due to Orlicz[1].

LEMMA. *For some sequence* $f_n(x) \in L$ *let us suppose that for any* $n_1, n_2, \ldots, n_m$

$$\int_0^1 \left| \sum_{i=1}^{m} f_{n_i}(x) \right| dx < K, \tag{16.3}$$

*where* $K$ *is a constant. Then*

$$\sum_{j=1}^{\infty} f_j^2(x) \tag{16.4}$$

*converges almost everywhere in* $[0, 1]$.

*Proof.* Let us consider the sequence $r_n(t)$ of the Rademacher functions. We will show that it follows from (16.3) that

$$\int_0^1 \left| \sum_{j=1}^{m} f_j(x) r_j(t) \right| dx < 2K \quad (m = 1, 2, \ldots). \tag{16.5}$$

† Note yet another theorem due to Banach[1], namely: if $\alpha_k \to 0$ and $\beta_k \to 0$, then there always exists a summable function $f(x)$ for which $a_{n_k} = \alpha_k$ and $b_{n_k} = \beta_k$.

†† The two results were obtained independently and almost simultaneously.

Indeed, for any $t$ we have

$$\int_0^1 \left| \sum_{j=1}^{m} f_j(x) r_j(t) \right| dx = \int_0^1 \left| \sum_{j=1}^{m}{}' f_j(x) - \sum_{j=1}^{m}{}'' f_j(x) \right| dx$$

$$\leqslant \int_0^1 \left| \sum_i f_{n_i'}(x) \right| dx + \int_0^1 \left| \sum_i f_{n_i''}(x) \right| dx \leqslant 2K$$

(here all the values $j$ for which $r_j(t) = +1$ are denoted by $n_i'$ and the values $j$ for which $r_j(t) = -1$ by $n_i''$).

From the well-known relationship (see Khinchin[2] or Kaczmarz and Steinhaus[A.12], theorems[4,5,7]) we have for the Rademacher functions and any $c_j$

$$\left| \sum_{j=1}^{m} c_j^2 \right|^{1/2} \leqslant 8 \int_0^1 \left| \sum_{j=1}^{m} c_j r_j(t) \right| dt. \tag{16.6}$$

Supposing in (16.6) that $c_j = f_j(x)$ and integrating with respect to $x$, we obtain by virtue of (16.5)

$$\int_0^1 \left| \sum_{j=1}^{m} f_j^2(x) \right|^{1/2} dx \leqslant 8 \int_0^1 \left\{ \int_0^1 \left| \sum_{j=1}^{m} f_j(x) r_j(t) \right| dt \right\} dx$$

$$= 8 \int_0^1 \left\{ \int_0^1 \left| \sum_{j=1}^{m} f_j(x) r_j(t) \right| dx \right\} dt \leqslant 16\, K. \tag{16.7}$$

If the series (16.4) were to diverge in a set of positive measure, then it would be possible to find a set $E, mE > 0$, in which the series $\sum_{j=1}^{\infty} f_j^2(x)$ would diverge uniformly, i.e. it would be possible for any $A$ to take $m$ so large that $\sum_{j=1}^{\infty} f_j^2(x) > A$ for $x \in E$. But this contradicts (16.7) and therefore the lemma is proved.

Let us return to the proof of Orlicz's theorem. We will assume that the theorem is untrue. Then for any $f(x) \in C$ we have

$$\sum_{n=1}^{\infty} d_n |a_n| = C_1(f) < +\infty. \tag{16.8}$$

Let $n_1, n_2, \ldots n_k, \ldots$ be any sequence of natural numbers. From (16.8) it follows that

$$\sum_{k=1}^{\infty} d_{n_k} |a_{n_k}| < C_1(f).$$

But since

$$\sum_{k=1}^{m} d_{n_k} a_{n_k} = \int_0^1 f(t) \sum_{k=1}^{m} d_{n_k} \varphi_{n_k}(t)\, dt,$$

then we have for any $m$ and for any $n_k$

$$\left| \int_0^1 f(t) \left[ \sum_{k=1}^{m} d_{n_k} \varphi_{n_k}(t) \right] dt \right| \leqslant C_1(f).$$

Because this is true for any $f \in C$, then due to the lemma in Chapter I, § 52 we have

$$\overline{\lim_{m\to\infty}} \int_0^1 \left| \sum_{k=1}^{m} d_{n_k} \varphi_{n_k}(t) \right| dt < K < +\infty, \tag{16.9}$$

where $K$ is a constant, not dependent on $\{n_k\}$.

Let us suppose that $f_j(x) = d_j \varphi_j(x)$. Then it follows from (16.9): there exists a constant $K$ such that

$$\int_0^1 \left| \sum_{k=1}^{m} f_{n_k}(t) \right| dt < K.$$

But then according to Orlicz's lemma we have

$$\sum_{j=1}^{\infty} f_j^2(x)$$

converging almost everywhere, consequently

$$\sum_{j=1}^{\infty} d_j^2 \varphi_j^2(x)$$

converges almost everywhere. According to Yegorov's theorem for any $\varepsilon > 0$ it is possible to choose a set $P$, $mP > 1 - \varepsilon$, in which the convergence is uniform. Then

$$\sum_{j=1}^{\infty} d_j^2 \int_P \varphi_j^2(x)\, dx < +\infty.$$

But since by virtue of (16.1), if it is taken that $\varepsilon < 1/2A^2$, we obtain

$$\int_{CP} \varphi_j^2(x)\, dx \leqslant A^2 \varepsilon < \frac{1}{2},$$

whence

$$\int_P \varphi_j^2(x)\, dx > \frac{1}{2},$$

then $\sum_{j=1}^{\infty} d_j^2 < +\infty$ and this contradicts the conditions of the theorem.

As a corollary we obtain the theorem:

THEOREM. *If $\{\varphi_n(x)\}$ is any orthogonal system for which*

$$|\varphi_n(x)| \leqslant A,$$

*then a continuous $f(x)$ can be found for which the Fourier coefficients $a_n$ with respect to the system $\{\varphi_n(x)\}$ satisfy the condition*

$$\sum_{n=1}^{\infty} |a_n|^{2-\varepsilon} = +\infty$$

*for any $\varepsilon > 0$.*

Indeed, let us take $d_n = 1/\sqrt{n}$ and we will find according to Orlicz's theorem a continuous $f(x)$ such that

$$\sum_{n=1}^{\infty} d_n |a_n| = +\infty, \quad \text{i.e.} \quad \sum_{n=1}^{\infty} \frac{|a_n|}{\sqrt{n}} = +\infty.$$

Let $\varepsilon > 0$ be given.

We will define $r = 2 - \varepsilon$. Without disturbing the generality, it can be considered that $r > 1$. We find $r'$ such that $1/r + 1/r' = 1$. Then $r' > 2$ and

$$\sum_{n=1}^{\infty} \frac{|a_n|}{\sqrt{n}} \leqslant \left\{\sum_{n=1}^{\infty} \frac{1}{(\sqrt{n})^{r'}}\right\}^{1/r'} \left\{\sum_{n=1}^{\infty} |a_n|^r\right\}^{1/r} \leqslant C\left\{\sum_{n=1}^{\infty} |a_n|^r\right\}^{1/r}.$$

Since the left-hand side equals $+\infty$, then the right-hand side does also.

For the case of a trigonometric system this gives a new proof of Carleman's theorem.

Let us return to Paley's theorem.

We will say that $F(z) \in C$, if $F(z)$ is regular in the circle $|z| < 1$ and continuous in the closed circle $(z) \leqslant 1$. To prove this theorem, Paley established that if $d_n \geqslant 0$ and $\sum_{n=1}^{\infty} d_n^2 = +\infty$, then there exists $F(z) \in C$ such that

$$F(z) = \sum_{n=0}^{\infty} c_n z^n$$

and

$$\sum_{n=1}^{\infty} d_n |c_n| = +\infty.$$

S.B.Stechkin[11] examined a more general problem, namely: under what conditions imposed on a system of non-negative functions $\Phi_n$ does a function $F(z) \in C$ exist, for which

$$\sum_{n=1}^{\infty} \Phi_n(|c_n|) = +\infty?$$

In his work he used Paley's theorem (see Stechkin[10]) but obtained results which generalized both Paley's theorem and Carleman and Banach's theorem. Of the many statements proved by S.B.Stechkin, we note the following:

Let $d_n \geqslant 0$ and $0 < \varepsilon_n < 2$ $(n = 1, 2, \ldots)$. In order for $F(z) \in C$ to exist for which

$$\sum_{n=1}^{\infty} d_n^{\varepsilon_n} |c_n|^{2-\varepsilon_n} = +\infty,$$

it is necessary and sufficient that the series

$$\sum_{n=1}^{\infty} d_n^2 \eta^{1/\varepsilon_n}$$

diverges for any $\eta > 0$.

In particular, at $\varepsilon_n \geqslant \varepsilon > 0$ this condition is evidently equivalent to the divergence of the series $\sum d_n^2$.

## § 17. Concerning the singularities of Fourier series of continuous functions

Up until now we have examined those conditions under which the Fourier series of continuous functions are uniformly convergent. However, we already know (see Chapter I, §§ 44, 45) that it is possible to derive a Fourier series of a continuous function which is convergent everywhere but non-uniformly near a single point or is divergent at a single point. Now we want to strengthen these examples, i.e. to apply the method of "condensation of singularities" and thus show that the Fourier series of a continuous function can converge non-uniformly in any interval $(a, b)$ lying within $[0, 2\pi]$ and can also diverge both in denumerable everywhere-dense sets and in sets which are of the power of the continuum.

## § 18. A continuous function with a Fourier series non-uniformly convergent in any interval

Let us consider the continuous function $g(x)$ with a Fourier series which converges everywhere but non-uniformly near $x = 0$ (see Chapter I, § 44).

Let $r_1, r_2, \ldots, r_k, \ldots$ be all the rational points of the interval $[-\pi, \pi]$. We will choose positive $\varepsilon_k$ such that $\sum_{k=1}^{\infty} \varepsilon_k < 1$ and assume that

$$G(x) = \sum_{k=1}^{\infty} \varepsilon_k g(x - r_k). \tag{18.1}$$

The series (18.1) converges uniformly which means that $G(x)$ is continuous. Due to the uniform convergence of series (18.1) we have

$$S_n(G, x) = \sum_{k=1}^{\infty} \varepsilon_k S_n(g, x - r_k),$$

therefore

$$R_n(G, x) = S_n(G, x) - G(x) = \sum_{k=1}^{\infty} \varepsilon_k [S_n(g, x - r_k) - g(x - r_k)]$$

$$= \sum_{k=1}^{\infty} \varepsilon_k R_n(g, x - r_k). \tag{18.2}$$

Let $\eta > 0$ be given. We will choose $N$ so that

$$\sum_{N+1}^{\infty} \varepsilon_k < \eta.$$

Since according to formula (44.9), Chapter I,

$$|R_n(g, x - r_k)| \leqslant K, \tag{18.3}$$

then

$$\left| \sum_{N+1}^{\infty} \varepsilon_k R_n(g, x - r_k) \right| \leqslant K\eta. \tag{18.4}$$

On the other hand since the series for $g(x)$ converges at every point, then $R_n(g, x) \to 0$ as $n \to \infty$ and at any $x$; therefore

$$\sum_{k=1}^{N} \varepsilon_k R_n(g, x - r_k) \to 0 \quad \text{as} \quad n \to \infty. \tag{18.5}$$

From (18.4) and (18.5) it follows that

$$R_n(G, x) \to 0 \quad \text{as} \quad n \to \infty$$

also at any $x$, i.e. the Fourier series for $G(x)$ converges at every point.

We will now prove that it converges non-uniformly near every point $r_j (j = 1, 2, \ldots)$ and since their set is everywhere dense, this means non-uniformly over any interval $\Delta$ lying in $[-\pi, \pi]$, however small it is.

Let $r_j$ be fixed. We will surround it by an interval $\Delta$ so small that all the points $r_k$ for $k = 1, 2, \ldots N$, but $k \neq j$, are at a certain distance $\delta > 0$ from $\Delta$. Consequently, if $x \in \Delta$, then $|x - r_k| \geqslant \delta$ for $k = 1, 2, \ldots, N$ and $k \neq j$.

But since the series for $g(x)$ converges uniformly outside $(-\delta, \delta)$ for any $\delta > 0$, then this means that for any $k \neq j$, $k = 1, 2, \ldots, N$, we have

$$|R_n(g, x - r_k)| < \eta \quad \text{for} \quad x \in \Delta, \tag{18.6}$$

for every $n \geqslant n_0$ where $n_0$ depends only on $\eta$.

But from (18.2) we find that

$$R_n(G, x) = \varepsilon_j R_n(g, x - r_j) + \sum_{\substack{k=1 \\ k \neq j}}^{N'} \varepsilon_k R_n(g, x - r_k) + \sum_{N+1}^{\infty} \varepsilon_k R_n(g, x - r_j).$$

Therefore, for $x \in \Delta$ from (18.6) and (18.4)

$$|R_n(G, x)| \geqslant \varepsilon_j |R_n(g, x - r_j)| - \eta \sum_{k=1}^{N} \varepsilon_k - K\eta \geqslant \varepsilon_j |R_n(g, x - r_j)| - \eta(K + 1).$$

Since $\eta$ is at our disposal, we can choose it to be so small that

$$(K + 1)\eta < \frac{\varepsilon_j}{2}.$$

Now let $\nu_m$ and $x_m$ be the quantities entering into the inequality (44.10), Chapter I. Supposing that

$$\xi_m = r_j + x_m$$

for the $r_j$ chosen by us, we find that

$$|R_n(G, \xi_m)| \geqslant \varepsilon_j |R_n(g, x_m)| - \frac{\varepsilon_j}{2},$$

and since according to formula (44.10) of Chapter I

$$|R_{\nu_m}(g, x_m)| \geqslant 1 \quad (m = 1, 2, \ldots),$$

then

$$|R_{\nu_m}(G, \xi_m)| \geqslant \frac{\varepsilon_j}{2} \quad (m = 1, 2, \ldots). \tag{18.7}$$

Thus, we have found a sequence of quantities $\xi_m$, $\lim \xi_m = r_j$ (because $\lim x_m = 0$) such that (18.7) holds. This means that the Fourier series of $G(x)$ converges non-uniformly near $r_j$ and since this holds for any $j$, then the proof is concluded.

## § 19. Concerning a set of points of divergence for a trigonometric series

Before turning to the construction of Fourier series of continuous functions which are divergent in an everywhere dense set or in a set of the power of the continuum, we will prove some general theorems concerning the structure of a set of points of divergence for any series of continuous functions.

We will introduce a definition:

DEFINITION. The sequence of functions $f_n(x)$ will be known as *boundedly divergent* at the point $x_0$ if

$$-\infty < \underline{\lim} f_n(x_0) < \overline{\lim} f_n(x_0) < +\infty,$$

and *unboundedly divergent*, if

$$\overline{\lim} |f_n(x_0)| = +\infty.$$

We will say that the sequence diverges if it is not necessary to differentiate between the cases of bounded and unbounded divergence.

Let us prove a theorem.

THEOREM. *If the functions $f_n(x)$ are continuous in some interval $[a, b]$, then the set $E$ of points of unbounded divergence of the sequence $\{f_n(x)\}$ is a set of type $G_\delta$.*

*Proof.* Let us denote by $CE$ a set complementary to $E$. At every point $x_0 \in CE$ we have

$$\overline{\lim} |f_n(x_0)| < +\infty.$$

Let

$$F_n^{(k)} = E\{|f_n(x)| \leqslant K\}.$$

It is clear that $F_n^{(k)}$ is closed and therefore

$$F^{(k)} = \prod_{n=1}^{\infty} F_n^{(k)}$$

is also closed. But for $x_0 \in F^{(k)}$ all the $|f_n(x)|$ do not exceed $K$ and therefore $\overline{\lim} |f_n(x_0)| \leqslant K$, i.e. $x_0 \in CE$. Therefore, too

$$\sum_{k=1}^{\infty} F^{(k)} \subset CE.$$

But conversely $CE \subset \sum_{k=1}^{\infty} F^{(k)}$, since if $\overline{\lim}\, |f_n(x_0)| < +\infty$, then it is possible to find $k$ such that $|f_n(x_0)| \leqslant k$ for $n = 1, 2, \ldots$, i.e. if $x_0 \in CE$, then $x_0 \in F^{(k)}$ for some $k$. Thus, $CE = \sum_{k=1}^{\infty} F^{(k)}$, but every $F^{(k)}$ is closed, which means that $CE$ is a set of type $F_\sigma$ and therefore $E$ is a set of type $G_\delta$.

From this theorem we obtain

COROLLARY. *If a series of functions continuous in* $[a, b]$ *diverges unboundedly in a set which is everywhere dense in* $[a, b]$, *then the set of points of bounded divergence is of the power of the continuum in any interval belonging to* $[a, b]$.

Indeed, we have only just seen that the set $CE$, complementary to the set $E$ of points of unbounded divergence is a set of type $F_\sigma$, i.e.

$$CE = \sum_{k=1}^{\infty} F^{(k)},$$

where all $F^{(k)}$ are closed. But if one of the $F^{(k)}$ were anywhere dense, then it should contain an interval and this contradicts the fact that $E$ is everywhere dense.

This means that none of the $F^{(k)}$ are anywhere dense. But then $CE$ is a set of the first category, which means that $E$ is of the second category and therefore is of the power of the continuum in any interval lying within $[a, b]$ (see Appendix, § 5).

Later (Chapter V, § 22) we will be concerned with the construction of a set of points of divergence (without requiring unbounded divergence) for a series of continuous functions. Now in order not to disrupt the trend of the exposition, we will return to Fourier series of continuous functions.

## § 20. A continuous function with a Fourier series divergent in a set of the power of the continuum

Let us consider a function $f(x)$ defined by the series (45.2), Chapter I, where it is assumed that $n_k = a^{k^3}$. In the polynomial $Q_k(x)$ we substitute $k!\,x$ for the argument $x$, i.e. we consider the function

$$\Phi(x) = \sum_{k=1}^{\infty} \frac{1}{k^2} Q_k(k!x). \tag{20.1}$$

It is again continuous, since all the $Q_k(x)$ are all bounded (see Chapter I, formula (43.3)).

First of all we will note that if in the series (20.1) every cosine is considered as a separate term of the series, then it is a normal trigonometric series, i.e. in it all the cosines are arranged so that their orders increase. Indeed, since $Q_k(x) = Q(x, n_k)$ and we have seen that $n_k > 3n_{k-1}$, then all the more so is it true that $k!\,n_k > 3(k-1)!\,n_{k-1}$, i.e. the cosines entering into $Q_k(k!\,x)$ are not encountered in $Q_{k-1}((k-1)!\,x)$, and this is even more the case in the preceding terms. Hence, taking into account the uniform convergence of (20.1) we see that this is a Fourier series of $\Phi(x)$.

We will first prove that the series $\sigma(\Phi)$ diverges at all the points commensurable with $\pi$ and it has unbounded partial sums at them. Indeed, let

$$x = \pm \frac{p}{q}\pi.$$

Then, provided $k \geqslant q$, we will have

$$k!x \equiv 0 (\mathrm{mod}\, 2\pi).$$

But if we suppose that

$$l'_k = k!(2n_k - 1), \quad l''_k = 3n_{k-1}(k-1)!,$$

then, maintaining the notation of § 43 of Chapter I, we obtain

$$S_{l'_k}(\Phi, x) - S_{l''_k}(\Phi, x) = \frac{1}{k^2} P(k!x, n_k),$$

therefore at $k \geqslant q$

$$S_{l'_k}\left(\Phi, \frac{p}{q}\pi\right) - S_{l''_k}\left(\Phi, \frac{p}{q}\pi\right) = \frac{1}{k^2} P(0, n_k) > \frac{\ln n_k}{k^2} = k \ln a.$$

Thus at the point $x$ under consideration, we have

$$S_{l'_k}(\Phi, x) - S_{l''_k}(\Phi, x) > k \ln a$$

for all sufficiently large $k$. Hence it is clear that at this point the Fourier series of $\Phi(x)$ diverges and moreover possesses unbounded partial sums. We have defined this in the preceding section as unbounded divergence. Thus, the Fourier series of $\Phi(x)$ diverges unboundedly at all points commensurable with $\pi$, i.e. in a set everywhere dense in $[0, 2\pi]$ and therefore on the basis of the corollary to the theorem in the preceding section it diverges (and moreover unboundedly) in a set of the power of the continuum.

Up until now it has not been known whether it is possible to construct a continuous function in which the Fourier series diverges in a set of positive measure.

## § 21. Divergence in a given denumerable set

In the example of § 20, having established the divergence of a series in an everywhere dense set, we automatically obtained divergence in a set of the power of the continuum. This was the case too in a whole series of other examples derived by various authors, since they all proved unbounded divergence in an everywhere dense set and then (by virtue of the theorem in § 19) it was extended to a set of the second category.

Neder[1] asked the question: is it possible to construct a trigonometric series divergent in a given denumerable set and convergent everywhere outside it?

We will prove that the answer to this question is positive.

Let

$$x_1, x_2, \ldots, x_n, \ldots$$

be a given denumerable set in $(0, 2\pi)$. Let us take a continuous function $f(x)$ such that its Fourier series diverges at $x = 0$, converges at all the remaining points and possesses bounded partial sums. We constructed this function in Chapter I, § 45. Let $\varepsilon_n$ be positive quantities and $\sum \varepsilon_n < +\infty$. Let us assume that

$$F(x) = \sum \varepsilon_k f(x - x_k). \tag{21.1}$$

Since the series (21.1) converges uniformly, then $F(x)$ is continuous. We will prove first that its Fourier series diverges at every point $x_j$ $(j = 1, 2, \ldots)$.

Let $\varepsilon > 0$ be given. For the points $x_j$ under consideration let us choose $p$ so large that $p > j$ and

$$\sum_{k=p+1}^{\infty} \varepsilon_k < \varepsilon. \tag{21.2}$$

In Chapter I, § 45 we have seen that for the Fourier series of the function $f(x)$ there exist two sequences of integral numbers $\nu_m$ and $\mu_m$ for which

$$S_{\nu_m}(f, 0) - S_{\mu_m}(f, 0) > \ln a \quad (m = 1, 2, \ldots). \tag{21.3}$$

Since for any $n$ due to the uniform convergence of series (21.1) we have

$$S_n(F, x) = \sum_{k=1}^{\infty} \varepsilon_k S_n(f, x - x_k),$$

then

$$S_n(F, x_j) = \sum_{\substack{k=1\\k\neq j}}^{p}{}' \varepsilon_k S_n(f, x_j - x_k) + \varepsilon_j S_n(f, 0) + \sum_{k=p+1}^{\infty} \varepsilon_k S_n(f, x_j - x_k).$$

This means that

$$S_{\nu_m}(F, x_j) - S_{\mu_m}(F, x_j) = \sum_{\substack{k=1\\k\neq j}}^{p}{}' \varepsilon_k [S_{\nu_m}(f, x_j - x_k) - S_{\mu_m}(f, x_j - x_k)]$$
$$+ \varepsilon_j [S_{\nu_m}(f, 0) - S_{\mu_m}(f, 0)] + \sum_{p+1}^{\infty} \varepsilon_k [S_{\nu_m}(f, x_j - x_k)$$
$$- S_{\mu_m}(f, x_j - x_k)]. \tag{21.4}$$

We will recall that the partial sums for $f(x)$ are all bounded, i.e.

$$|S_n(f, x)| < A \quad n = 1, 2, \ldots, \quad -\pi \leqslant x \leqslant \pi. \tag{21.5}$$

Hence from (21.2) and (21.5) it follows that

$$\left| \sum_{p+1}^{\infty} \varepsilon_k [S_{\nu_m}(f, x_j - x_k) - S_{\mu_m}(f, x_j - x_k)] \right| < 2A\varepsilon. \tag{21.6}$$

Since the series for $f(x)$ converges everywhere apart from $x = 0$, then $S_n(f, x_j - x_k) \to f(x_j - x_k)$ as $n \to \infty$ for $k \neq j$ and $k = 1, 2, \ldots, p$. Hence it follows that $S_{\nu_m}(f, x_j - x_k) - S_{\mu_m}(f, x_j - x_k) \to 0$ at any $k \neq j$, $k \leqslant p$ and as $m \to \infty$. But then

$$\sum_{\substack{k=1\\k\neq j}}^{p}{}' \varepsilon_k [S_{\nu_m}(f, x_j - x_k) - S_{\mu_m}(f, x_j - x_k)] \to 0$$

as $m \to \infty$. Thus, for any $\eta > 0$ it is possible to take $m$ so large that

$$\left| \sum_{\substack{k=1 \\ k \neq j}}^{p}{}' \varepsilon_k [S_{\nu_m}(f, x_j - x_k) - S_{\mu_m}(f, x_j - x_k)] \right| < \eta. \tag{21.7}$$

If it is assumed that $\varepsilon$ is chosen so that $2A\varepsilon < \eta$, then from (21.3) – (21.7) we find that

$$S_{\nu_m}(F, x_j) - S_{\mu_m}(F, x_j) > \varepsilon_j \ln a - 2\eta > \frac{\varepsilon_j}{2} \ln a, \tag{21.8}$$

if $\eta$ is chosen so that $2\eta < (\varepsilon_j/2) \ln a$.

From formula (21.8) which is valid for all sufficiently large $m$, it follows that the Fourier series of $F(x)$ diverges at $x = x_j$, i.e. at all the points of the given denumerable set.

It is easily seen that if $\xi \in [0, 2\pi)$ and $\xi \neq x_j$ for any $j$, then the Fourier series of $F(x)$ converges at $x = \xi$. Indeed, maintaining the previous notation, we then have for any $n$ and $n + q$

$$|S_{n+q}(F, \xi) - S_n(F, \xi)| \leqslant \sum_{k=1}^{p} \varepsilon_k |S_{n+q}(f, \xi - x_k) - S_n(f, \xi - x_k)|$$
$$+ \sum_{p+1}^{\infty} \varepsilon_k |S_{n+q}(f, \xi - x_q) - S_n(f, \xi - x_k)|. \tag{21.9}$$

But every quantity in the first term of (21.9) can be made as small as desired for a sufficiently large $n$, because $\xi - x_k \neq 0$ $(k = 1, 2, \ldots, p)$, and therefore the Fourier series for $f$ converges at the point $\xi - x_k$, consequently the first term in (21.9) is $o(1)$ as $n \to \infty$ and the second does not exceed $2A\varepsilon < \eta$. Consequently, $S_{n+q}(F, \xi) - S_n(F, \xi)$ can be made as small as desired and the theorem is proved.

## § 22. Divergence in a set of the power of the continuum for bounded partial sums

In § 20 we constructed an example of the series $\sigma(f)$ for a continuous function divergent in a set of the power of the continuum. Its partial sums were not bounded. In § 21 we constructed a series with bounded partial sums which were however divergent in a given denumerable set.

A problem can be posed as follows: does a continuous function $f(x)$ exist in which $\sigma(f)$ diverges in a set of the power of the continuum, but nevertheless has bounded partial sums? A positive answer to this question is given in Tandori's[1] work†. Again the Fejér polynomial is used as a structural element.

Let us consider a sequence of points $x_k$, which we will choose later and let

$$F(x) = \sum_{k=1}^{\infty} \frac{1}{k^2} Q(x - x_k, n_k),$$

† Tandori notes that Zygmund[15] had already constructed an example of a bounded function with a Fourier series which was divergent in a set of the power of the continuum and which possessed bounded partial sums.

where as in the example of Chapter I, § 45,

$$n_k = a^{k^2}.$$

Here, as in the cited example, we evidently have

$$|S_n(F, x)| \leqslant B.$$

Since, repeating the argument which was given in § 45 of Chapter I, we see that

$$S_{\nu_m}(F, x) - S_{\mu_m}(F, x) = \frac{1}{m^2} P(x - x_m, n_m)$$

and

$$\frac{1}{m^2} P(0, n_m) > \ln a,$$

then it is possible to enclose the point $x_m$ by a small interval $I_m$, inside which due to the continuity of the polynomial $P(x, n_m)$ we will have

$$S_{\nu_m}(F, x) - S_{\mu_m}(F, x) > \frac{1}{2} \ln a, \quad x \in I_m. \tag{22.1}$$

We will now choose the points $x_m$ in the following way: we take $x_1$, $x_2$ and $x_3$ such that $I_2 \subset I_1$, $I_3 \subset I_1$ and the intervals $I_2$ and $I_3$ do not overlap: then $x_4$, $x_5$, $x_6$ and $x_7$ so that $I_4 \subset I_2$, $I_5 \subset I_2$ and $I_4$ does not overlap with $I_5$; also $I_6$ and $I_7$ do not overlap and $I_6 \subset I_3$, $I_7 \subset I_3$, and so on. All this can be achieved provided all the $I_m$ are taken to be sufficiently small.

It is clear that, continuing this process of dissection, we obtain a perfect set $P$, every set of which is contained in an infinite set of intervals of the type $I_m$. Because at every such point the inequality (22.1) holds for an infinite set of values of $m$, then at every point the Fourier series of $F(x)$ diverges and the proof of the theorem is concluded.

It is possible to strengthen the theorem by taking points of divergence such that their set is of the power of the continuum over any interval. For this the sequence $\{n_k\}$ is divided into a denumerable set of sequences $\{n_{i_k}\}$ $(i = 1, 2, \ldots)$. Then we enumerate all the binary intervals

$$\left(\frac{2\pi k}{2^n}, \frac{2\pi(k+1)}{2^n}\right), \quad n = 1, 2, \ldots, \quad k = 0, 1, \ldots, 2^n - 1$$

in the form of a single sequence $J_1, J_2, \ldots, J_l \ldots$. For any $l$ we construct in $J_l$ a perfect set $P_l$ with the help of the sequence $\{n_{l_k}\}$. It is clear that $E = \sum_{l=1}^{\infty} P_l$ is of the power of the continuum in any interval in $[0, 2\pi]$ whilst the Fourier series diverges at every point of the set $E$.

## § 23. Divergence for a series of $f^2(x)$

Let us denote by $S$ the class of continuous functions, the Fourier series of which converges. What can be said concerning operations which do not lead to functions outside this class?

Here it seems that, apart from the completely trivial fact that the operations of addition and subtraction keep the functions in class $S$, nothing positive can be said. The operation of multiplication already takes us out of this class. Moreover, the operation of multiplication leads to functions outside class $S$ even when the Fourier series of the multipliers converge uniformly.

Following Salem[7] we will give an example of a continuous function $f(x)$, the Fourier series of which converges uniformly, whilst the Fourier series of $f^2(x)$ diverges in a set of the power of the continuum.

Let the function $\omega(x)$ be defined in $-2\pi \leqslant x \leqslant 2\pi$ and possess the properties

(a) it is continuous, increasing and odd,

(b) $\omega(t)/t$ is non-summable in $(0, \pi)$ and is decreasing.

Let $r_1, r_2, \ldots, r_n, \ldots$ be a set of all the quantities of the form $r = 2\pi\,\alpha/\beta$, when the fraction $\alpha/\beta$ is proper and irreducible, $\alpha \neq 0$ and $\beta$ odd. It is clear that this set is everywhere dense in $(0, 2\pi)$.

Let us suppose that

$$\eta(x) = \sum_{k=1}^{\infty} \gamma_k \omega(x - r_k) \quad \text{in} \quad [0, 2\pi],$$

where the series $\sum \gamma_k < +\infty$ and all $\gamma_k > 0$. It is clear that $\eta(x)$ is continuous and increasing in $[0, 2\pi]$.

Let

$$\xi(x) = \eta(x) - \eta(0) - \frac{\eta(2\pi) - \eta(0)}{2\pi} x \quad \text{in} \quad [0, 2\pi]. \tag{23.1}$$

Then $\xi(x)$ is a continuous function of bounded variation in $[0, 2\pi]$ and $\xi(2\pi) = \xi(0) = 0$. If we require that $\xi(x + 2\pi) = \xi(x)$, then it will be everywhere continuous and of bounded variation. Therefore its Fourier series converges uniformly and also the Fourier series of $\xi^2(x)$, since it is also continuous and of bounded variation.

Also let

$$g(x) = \sum_{p=1}^{\infty} c_p \sin m_p x, \tag{23.2}$$

where $c_p > 0$ and $\sum c_p < +\infty$, whilst the numbers $m_p$ are integral; we will select them later.

It is clear that the Fourier series of $g(x)$ converges absolutely, therefore the Fourier series of $g^2(x)$ also possesses the same property, and consequently the series for $g^2(x)$ also converges uniformly.

We will now assume that

$$f(x) = \xi(x) + g(x)$$

and will prove that the Fourier series for $\xi(x)g(x)$ diverges at all the points $r_k$; then from

$$f^2(x) = \xi^2(x) + 2\xi(x)g(x) + g^2(x)$$

it will follow that the Fourier series of $f^2(x)$ diverges at all these points, because the series for $\xi^2(x)$ and $g^2(x)$ converge uniformly. Moreover, if we were to find that the partial sums of the Fourier series for $\xi(x)g(x)$ are unbounded at all the points $r_k$, then this will also be true of the series for $f^2(x)$ and then it will diverge in a set of the power of the continuum, because the set $\{r_k\}$ is everywhere dense (see the corollary to the theorem of § 19).

Thus, let us continue with the examination of the Fourier series for

$$\Phi(x) = \xi(x)g(x).$$

Denoting by $S_n(F, x)$ and $\bar{S}_n(F, x)$ the partial sums of the Fourier series of $F$ and its conjugate series, we have at the points $r_k$

$$S_n(\Phi, r_k) = \frac{1}{\pi}\int_0^\delta [\xi(r_k+t)g(r_k+t) + \xi(r_k-t)g(r_k-t)]\frac{\sin nt}{t}\,dt + o(1), \quad (23.3)$$

where $\delta$ can be taken as small as desired.

In particular, it is convenient for us to choose $\delta$ so that

$$\delta < \min(r_k, 2\pi - r_k).$$

Then neither $r_k - t$ nor $r_k + t$ for $0 < t < \delta$ go outside $(0, 2\pi)$.

Since the series (23.2) converges uniformly, then it is possible by substituting it for $g(x)$ in formula (23.3) to carry out the integration term by term, and this gives

$$\pi S_n(\Phi, r_k)$$
$$= \sum_{p=1}^{\infty} c_p \int_0^\delta [\xi(r_k+t)\sin m_p(r_k+t) + \xi(r_k-t)\sin m_p(r_k-t)]\frac{\sin nt}{t}\,dt + o(1).$$

Expanding the sines of the sum and difference, we find that

$$\pi S_n(\Phi, r_k) = \sum_{p=1}^{\infty} c_p \sin m_p r_k \int_0^\delta [\xi(r_k+t) + \xi(r_k-t)]\frac{\sin nt\cos m_p t}{t}\,dt$$
$$+ \sum_{p=1}^{\infty} c_p \cos m_p r_k \int_0^\delta [\xi(r_k+t) - \xi(r_k-t)]\frac{\sin nt\sin m_p t}{t}\,dt + o(1). \quad (23.4)$$

Since

$$\cos m_p t \sin nt = \frac{1}{2}[\sin(n+m_p)t + \sin(n-m_p)t],$$

then

$$\frac{1}{\pi}\int_0^\delta [\xi(r_k+t)+\xi(r_k-t)]\frac{\cos m_p t \sin nt}{t}\,dt$$

$$= \frac{1}{2}S_{n+m_p}(\xi, r_k) \pm \frac{1}{2}S_{|n-m_p|}(\xi, r_k) + o(1).$$

But $\xi(t)$ is a function of bounded variation, therefore the partial sums of its Fourier series are all bounded, which means that the first term on the right-hand side of formula (23.4) remains bounded as $n \to \infty$.

Let us now assume that $n = m_q$; we will have

$$\pi S_{m_q}(\Phi, r_k) = c_q \cos m_q r_k \int_0^\delta [\xi(r_k+t)-\xi(r_k-t)]\frac{\sin^2 m_q t}{t}\,dt$$

$$+ \sum_{p\neq q}{}' c_p \cos m_p r_k \int_0^\delta [\xi(r_k+t)-\xi(r_k-t)]\frac{\sin m_p t \sin m_q t}{t}\,dt + O(1). \quad (23.5)$$

But

$$\sin m_p t \sin m_q t = [1-\cos(m_p+m_q)t] - [1-\cos(m_p-m_q)t],$$

and therefore

$$-\frac{1}{\pi}\int_0^\delta [\xi(r_k+t)-\xi(r_k-t)]\frac{\sin m_p t \sin m_q t}{t}\,dt$$

$$= \frac{1}{2}\bar{S}_{m_p+m_q}(\xi, r_k) - \frac{1}{2}\bar{S}_{|m_p-m_q|}(\xi, r_k) + O(1),$$

since (see (32.14), Chapter I) we have for any bounded $f(x)$

$$\bar{S}_n(f, x) = -\frac{1}{\pi}\int_0^\delta [f(x+t)-f(x-t)]\frac{1-\cos nt}{t}\,dt + O(1),$$

where $\delta > 0$ is any value. But $\xi(t)$ is a function of bounded variation; which means that its Fourier coefficients are of the order $O(1/n)$ and therefore

$$|\bar{S}_{m_p+m_q}(\xi, r_k) - \bar{S}_{|m_p-m_q|}(\xi, r_k)| \leqslant C\sum_{|m_p-m_q|}^{m_p+m_q}\frac{1}{n} \leqslant C\ln\frac{m_p+m_q}{|m_p-m_q|}, \quad (23.6)$$

where $C$ is a constant.

Up until now we have not imposed any conditions on the integers $m_p$. We will now propose that they form a lacunary sequence. Then the expression on the right-hand side of formula (23.6) remains bounded. Indeed, let by definition $p < q$, then $m_p < m_q$, and if $m_{k+1}/m_k > \lambda$ $(k = 1, 2, \ldots)$, then

$$\frac{m_p + m_q}{m_q - m_p} = \frac{1 + \dfrac{m_p}{m_q}}{1 - \dfrac{m_p}{m_q}} < \frac{2}{1 - \dfrac{1}{\lambda}}.$$

Consequently the series on the right-hand side of formula (23.5) possesses a sum which is bounded with increase in $m_q$, i.e.

$$\pi S_{m_q}(\Phi, r_k) = c_q \cos m_q r_k \int_0^\delta [\xi(r_k + t) - \xi(r_k - t)] \frac{\sin^2 m_q t}{t} dt + O(1).$$

But since $\delta$ was chosen so that $r_k + t$ and $r_k - t$ do not go outside $[0, 2\pi]$, then according to formula (23.1)

$$\xi(r_k + t) - \xi(r_k - t) = \eta(r_k + t) - \eta(r_k - t) - \frac{\eta(2\pi) - \eta(0)}{\pi} t,$$

and therefore

$$\pi S_{m_q}(\Phi, r_k) = c_q \cos m_q r_k \int_0^\delta [\eta(r_k + t) - \eta(r_k - t)] \frac{\sin^2 m_q t}{t} dt + O(1).$$

But from the definition of $\eta(x)$ it follows that the expression in the brackets in the last integral is positive and greater than

$$\gamma_k[\omega(t) - \omega(-t)] = 2\gamma_k \omega(t),$$

therefore

$$|\pi S_{m_q}(\Phi, r_k)| > 2\gamma_k |\cos m_q r_k| \, c_q \int_0^\delta \frac{\omega(t) \sin^2 m_q t}{t} dt + O(1). \tag{23.7}$$

If we replace the integral in formula (23.7) by

$$\int_0^\pi \frac{\omega(t)}{t} \sin^2 m_q t \, dt, \tag{23.8}$$

then since $\omega(t)/t$ is summable in $(\delta, \pi)$, we replace the integral by a magnitude of order $O(1)$ and therefore

$$|\pi S_{m_q}(\Phi, r_k)| > 2\gamma_k |\cos m_q r_k| \, c_q \int_0^\pi \frac{\omega(t) \sin^2 m_q t}{t} dt + O(1), \tag{23.9}$$

where the term $O(1)$ varies with $r_k$ but not with $m_q$.

Due to the non-summability of $\omega(t)/t$ the integral (23.8) tends to $\infty$ as $q \to \infty$ (here the argument must follow that given in Lemma 1, § 4).

The lacunary sequence $\{m_q\}$ can be chosen as tending to infinity as rapidly as desired, and thanks to this it is possible for

$$c_q \int_0^\pi \frac{\omega(t)}{t} \sin^2 m_q t\, dt \to \infty \quad \text{as} \quad q \to \infty.$$

Then the left-hand side of the inequality (23.9) will tend to infinity provided $\cos m_q r_k$ does not tend to zero. However, thanks to our choice of $r_k$, this cannot occur, since

$$r_k = 2\pi \frac{\alpha}{\beta},$$

where $\beta$ is odd, and therefore for any integer $l$ we have

$$\left|(2l+1)\frac{\pi}{2} - m_q r_k\right| = \left|(2l+1)\frac{\pi}{2} - m_q 2\pi \frac{\alpha}{\beta}\right| = \pi \left|\frac{(2l+1)\beta - 4\alpha m_q}{2\beta}\right| \geqslant \frac{\pi}{2\beta}$$

(because an even value is subtracted from an odd, i.e. the modulus of the difference is not less than unity). Hence

$$|\cos m_q r_k| \geqslant \sin \frac{\pi}{2\beta} > \frac{1}{\beta}.$$

Thus

$$S_{m_q}(\Phi, r_k) \to \infty \quad \text{as} \quad q \to \infty,$$

i.e. the partial sums of the Fourier series for $\Phi(x)$ are not bounded at the points $r_k$, and this holds for all $r_k$. We have already seen that this is sufficient for the theorem to be proved.

## § 24. Sub-sequences of partial sums of Fourier series for continuous functions

D. Ye. Men'shov noticed the following circumstance. All the authors who constructed examples of continuous functions with somewhere divergent Fourier series usually proved the continuity itself of these functions by operating on the fact that their Fourier series possessed uniformly convergent sub-sequences of partial sums.

Therefore Men'shov asked the question: is it possible to find in the Fourier series of any continuous function a uniformly convergent subsequence of partial sums? But he himself gave a negative answer to this question. Moreover, he proved that *continuous functions exist for which any sub-sequence of the partial sums of their Fourier series diverges even if at only one point.*

Due to lack of space and in view of the complexity of the proof we refer the reader to the work by Men'shov[6].

Nevertheless, *it is possible to divide any continuous function into the sum of two continuous functions, the corresponding Fourier series for each of which contains a sub-sequence of partial sums which is uniformly convergent.*

This result, obtained by Men'shov in the same work, on the other hand, is very easy to prove and here we will give its proof.

Let

$$\varepsilon_1 = 1, \quad n_1 = 1, \quad T_1(x) \equiv 1.$$

We will construct by a recurrent method sequences of positive quantities $\varepsilon_j \to 0$, of integers $n_j$ monotonically increasing and of trigonometric polynomials $T_j(x)$ in the following way; if $\varepsilon_s$, $n_s$, $T_s(x)$ have already been defined for $s = 1, 2, \ldots, j-1$, then we choose $n_j$ so that

$$n_j > n_s \quad (1 \leqslant s \leqslant j-1),$$

$$n_j > v_s \quad (1 \leqslant s \leqslant j-1),$$

where $v_s$ is the order of the polynomial $T_s(x)$.

Let us assume that

$$\varepsilon_j = \frac{1}{2^j n_j}$$

and according to Bernstein's theorem choose a trigonometric polynomial $T_j(x)$ so that

$$|f(x) - T_j(x)| < \varepsilon_j \quad (-\pi \leqslant x \leqslant \pi), \tag{24.1}$$

where $f(x)$ is a given continuous function.

It is clear that the numbers $\{n_j\}$ increase monotonically and that $\varepsilon_j \to 0$ as $j \to \infty$. It is also clear that

$$f(x) = T_1(x) + [T_2(x) - T_1(x)] + \cdots + [T_j(x) - T_{j-1}(x)] + \cdots,$$

where the series converges uniformly because (24.1) is fulfilled.

We will assume that

$$\left.\begin{aligned} f_1(x) &= T_1(x) + [T_3(x) - T_2(x)] + \cdots + [T_{2j+1}(x) - T_{2j}(x)] + \cdots, \\ f_2(x) &= [T_2(x) - T_1(x)] + \cdots + [T_{2j}(x) - T_{2j-1}(x)] + \cdots \end{aligned}\right\}. \tag{24.2}$$

Since

$$|T_l(x) - T_{l-1}(x)| \leqslant |T_l(x) - f(x)| + |f(x) - T_{l-1}(x)|$$

$$< \varepsilon_l + \varepsilon_{l-1} < 2\varepsilon_{l-1} = \frac{1}{2^{l-2} n_{l-1}}, \tag{24.3}$$

then both the series (24.2) converge uniformly and therefore $f_1(x)$ and $f_2(x)$ are continuous. It is also clear that

$$f(x) = f_1(x) + f_2(x)$$

due to the very construction of these functions.

Let us assume that

$$m_k' = n_{2k}, \quad m_k'' = n_{2k+1}$$

and prove that

$$S_{m_k'}(f_1, x) \text{ converges uniformly to } f_1(x)$$

$$S_{m_k''}(f_2, x) \text{ converges uniformly to } f_2(x).$$

Due to the conditions imposed on the numbers $n_j$, we have

$$m'_k > v_s, \quad 1 \leqslant s \leqslant 2k - 1,$$

$$m''_k > v_s, \quad 1 \leqslant s \leqslant 2k.$$

Therefore

$$\left.\begin{aligned} S_{m'_k}(T_s, x) &= T_s(x), \quad 1 \leqslant s \leqslant 2k - 1, \\ S_{m''_k}(T_s, x) &= T_s(x), \quad 1 \leqslant s \leqslant 2k. \end{aligned}\right\} \tag{24.4}$$

We will assume that

$$\varphi_k^{(1)}(x) = T_1(x) + \sum_{j=1}^{k-1} [T_{2j+1}(x) - T_{2j}(x)], \quad R_k^{(1)}(x) = \sum_{j=k}^{\infty} [T_{2j+1}(x) - T_{2j}(x)],$$

$$\varphi_k^{(2)}(x) = \sum_{j=1}^{k} [T_{2j}(x) - T_{2j-1}(x)], \qquad R_k^{(2)}(x) = \sum_{j=k+1}^{\infty} [T_{2j}(x) - T_{2j-1}(x)].$$

Then

$$f_1(x) = \varphi_k^{(1)}(x) + R_k^{(1)}(x),$$

$$f_2(x) = \varphi_k^{(2)}(x) + R_k^{(2)}(x)$$

which means that

$$\left.\begin{aligned} S_{m'_k}(f_1) &= S_{m'_k}[\varphi_k^{(1)}] + S_{m'_k}[R_k^{(1)}], \\ S_{m''_k}(f_2) &= S_{m''_k}[\varphi_k^{(2)}] + S_{m''_k}[R_k^{(2)}]. \end{aligned}\right\} \tag{24.5}$$

But by virtue of (24.4) we have

$$\left.\begin{aligned} S_{m'_k}[\varphi_k^{(1)}] &= \varphi_k^{(1)}(x), \\ S_{m''_k}[\varphi_k^{(2)}] &= \varphi_k^{(2)}(x). \end{aligned}\right\} \tag{24.6}$$

Moreover

$$S_{m'_k}(R_k^{(1)}) = \frac{1}{\pi} \int_{-\pi}^{\pi} R_k^{(1)}(x + t) D_{m'_k}(t)\, dt,$$

$$S_{m''_k}(R_k^{(2)}) = \frac{1}{\pi} \int_{-\pi}^{\pi} R_k^{(2)}(x + t) D_{m''_k}(t)\, dt,$$

where $D_n(t)$ is a Dirichlet kernel.

Since due to (24.3)

$$|R_k^{(1)}(t)| \leqslant \sum_{j=k}^{\infty} |T_{2j+1} - T_{2j}| \leqslant \sum_{j=k}^{\infty} \frac{2}{2^{2j} n_{2j}} < \frac{1}{n_{2k}} \frac{2^{\frac{1}{2k-1}}}{1 - \frac{1}{4}} = \frac{8}{3} \frac{1}{n_{2k} 2^{2k}},$$

$$|D_n(t)| \leqslant n + \frac{1}{2} < 2n,$$

then

$$|S_{m'_k}(R_k^{(1)})| < \frac{1}{\pi} \frac{8}{3} \frac{2m'_k}{n_{2k} 2^{2k}} 2\pi = \frac{C}{2^{2k}},$$

since $m'_k = n_{2k}$ ($C$ is a constant).

This means that $S_{m_k}(R_k^{(1)}) \to 0$ as $k \to \infty$ and moreover uniformly; therefore we conclude from (24.5) and (24.6) that

$$S_{m_k'}(f_1) = \varphi_k^{(1)}(x) + o(1) \to f_1(x)$$

uniformly and it is also completely proved that

$$S_{m_k''}(f_2) \to f_2(x)$$

uniformly.

The proof is concluded.

## § 25. Resolution into the sum of two series convergent in sets of positive measure

In the preceding section we raised the question of the resolution of a continuous function into the sum of two functions possessing "better" Fourier series (namely, those for which there exists an uniformly convergent subsequence of partial sums).

Here we will prove another theorem of this kind, namely:

THEOREM. *Any function which is continuous in* $[0, 2\pi]$ *can be represented in the form of the sum of two functions, for each of which the Fourier series converges in a set of positive measure in any interval* $[a, b] \subset [0, 2\pi]$.

This fact follows immediately from the following theorem (see Bary[2]):

Any function which is continuous in $[a, b]$ can be resolved into the sum of two functions, each of which possesses a derivative in a set $E$ of positive measure in any interval $[\alpha, \beta]$ lying in $[a, b]$.

If it is recalled that at the point at which the function possesses a derivative, its Fourier series converges (see Chapter I, § 38), then we derive the required confirmation.

It should be noted that in the same work by Bary the following theorem was proved.

Any continuous function $F(x)$ can be represented in the form

$$F(x) = f_1[\varphi_1(x)] + f_2[\varphi_2(x)] + f_3[\varphi_3(x)], \tag{25.1}$$

where all the functions $f_i$ and $\varphi_i$ ($i = 1, 2, 3$) are absolutely continuous (the number of terms in the formula (25.1) cannot be reduced to two in the general case).

Thus, if it were possible to prove that any function of the form $f[\varphi(x)]$ where $f$ and $\varphi$ are absolutely continuous possesses a Fourier series convergent almost everywhere, then this would also be true for any continuous $F(x)$. However, the question of the validity of such a hypothesis remains open.

The study of functions which are superpositions of absolutely continuous functions can be reduced to the case when the external function $f$ is monotonic but the internal function $\varphi(x)$ satisfies the Lipschitz condition of order 1, since any superposition of two absolutely continuous functions can be represented in this form (see, for example, this same report by Bary[2] or the report by Bary and Men'shov[11]). This means that the Fourier series for $\varphi(x)$ not only converges uniformly but even absolutely (see Chapter IX, § 2). However, we are unable to derive anything relating to $f[\varphi(x)]$, only knowing that $f$ is monotonic and absolutely continuous.

## § 26. Problems

1. The Fourier series of a continuous (or bounded) function cannot converge to $+\infty$ at any one point of the interval $[0, 2\pi]$.

[Assume the opposite and use the properties of the arithmetic means (see § 48, Chapter I).]

2. There exists a function $f(x) \in C(0, 2\pi)$, the Fourier series of which converges absolutely for all $x \in [0, 2\pi]$ and $a_n(f) = o(1/n)$, $b_n(f) = o(1/n)$, and yet the function $f(x)$ is not of bounded variation in any interval $[a, b]$.

$$\left[\text{It is sufficient to take } f(x) = \sum_{n=1}^{\infty} \frac{1}{\sqrt{n\,2^n}} \cos 2^n x\,.\right]$$

3. Consider the functions $f_k(x) \in C(0, 2\pi)$ $(k = 1, 2, \ldots)$ such that

$$\frac{|a_0(f_k)|}{2} + \sum_{n=1}^{\infty} (|a_n(f_k)| + |b_n(f_k)| \leqslant D < \infty \quad (k = 1, 2, \ldots),$$

where $D$ is a constant. Then if

$$\lim_{k\to\infty} f_k(x) = F(x) \quad (-\infty < x < \infty),$$

the function $F(x)$ is continuous and its Fourier series converges absolutely for all $x \in [0, 2\pi]$.

A. BEURLING

4. Show that the Dini–Lipschitz test (see § 4) no longer holds if $o$ is replaced by $O$ in the equality (4.1).

G. FABER, H. LEBESGUE

5. Construct a function $f(x) \in C(0, 2\pi)$, the Fourier series of which diverges in a set of the power of the continuum but which after a rearrangement of the terms in the Fourier series becomes uniformly convergent in $[0, 2\pi]$.

S. B. STECHKIN

6. Prove that either all the Fourier series of continuous functions $f \in C(0, 2\pi)$ are convergent almost everywhere in $[0, 2\pi]$ or there exists a function $f_0(x) \in C(0, 2\pi)$, the Fourier series of which diverges almost everywhere in $[0, 2\pi]$.

[If a function $\varphi(x) \in C(0, 2\pi)$ exists, the Fourier series of which diverges in some set $E \subset [0, 2\pi]$ with $mE > 0$, then according to Men'shov's theorem (see § 24), a function $\varphi_0(x) \in C(0, 2\pi)$ exists, the Fourier series of which diverges in some set $E_0 \subset [0, 2\pi]$ with $mE_0 > 0$ and for some $n_k \uparrow \infty$ the sequence $S_{n_k}(x, \varphi_0)$ converges uniformly in $[0, 2\pi]$, i.e.

$$\| S_{n_k}(x, \varphi_0) - S_{n_i}(x, \varphi_0) \|_c \leqslant 1/2^\alpha \quad \text{for all} \quad k > i \geqslant i(\alpha).$$

Choosing sufficiently large values of $n_{k_\alpha}$ and $n_{i_\alpha}$ and also $N_\alpha$, we find that the function

$$f_0(x) = \sum_{\alpha=1}^{\infty} \alpha \, \{S_{n_{k_\alpha}}(N_\alpha x, \varphi_0) - S_{n_{i_\alpha}}(N_\alpha x, \varphi_0)\}$$

is the required one.]

7. Prove that whatever the sequence $w(n)\uparrow\infty$ is, a function $f(x)\in C(0, 2\pi)$ can be found with an absolutely convergent Fourier series and yet

$$\sum_{n=1}^{\infty}[a_n^2(f)+b_n^2(f)]\,\omega(n)=\infty.$$

$\left[\text{It is sufficient to take } f(x)=\sum_{k=1}^{\infty}\frac{1}{\sqrt{\omega(n_k)}}\cos n_k x \text{ where } n_k\uparrow\infty \text{ and } \omega(n_k)>2^k.\right]$

8. (i) For any set $E\subset(0, 2\pi)$ with $mE>0$ there exists a function $f(x)$ continuous in $E$ such that for any function $F(x)\in C(0, 2\pi)$ with $F(x)=f(x)$ for $x\in E$ the equality

$$\sum_{n=1}^{\infty}(|a_n(F)|^{2-\varepsilon}+|b_n(F)|^{2-\varepsilon})=\infty$$

holds for all $\varepsilon>0$.

(ii) A measurable set $E\subset[0, 2\pi]$ exists such that for any $\varepsilon>0$ the equality

$$\sum_{n=1}^{\infty}(|a_n(\varphi)|^{2-\varepsilon}+|b_n(\varphi)|^{2-\varepsilon})=\infty$$

holds, where $\varphi(x)$ is the characteristic function of the set $E$.

A. M. OLEVSKII

9. Let $n_k\uparrow\infty$ be some sequence of integers such that $\overline{\lim\limits_{k\to\infty}}\,(n_{k+1}-n_k)=\infty$. Then a trigonometric series

$$\frac{a_0}{2}+\sum_{n=1}^{\infty}(a_n\cos nx+b_n\sin nx),$$

exists for which the partial sums $S_{n_k}(x)$ converge uniformly in $[0, 2\pi-\varepsilon]$ for any given $\varepsilon\in(0, 1)$, although

$$\overline{\lim_{n\to\infty}}\sqrt{a_n^2+b_n^2}=\infty.$$

If $\overline{\lim\limits_{k\to\infty}}\,(n_{k+1}-n_k)<\infty$, then the statement formulated above is no longer valid (compare with the lemma of Chapter I, § 12 and with statement 19 of Chapter II, § 14).

S. B. STECHKIN, P. L. UL'YANOV

10. Functions $f(x)\in C(0, 2\pi)$ and $\varphi(x)\in(0, 2\pi)$ exist such that

$$|\varphi(x)-\varphi(y)|\leqslant|f(x)-|f(y)|\quad(\text{for all } x \text{ and } y)\qquad(26.1)$$

and at the same time the Fourier series of $f$ converges absolutely for all $x\in(-\infty, +\infty)$, whilst the Fourier series of $\varphi$ does not converge absolutely for nearly all $x\in(-\infty, +\infty)$.

(Compare with problem 14 (case $\alpha=1$) of Chapter V, § 24.)

11. Construct two functions $f(x)\in C(0, 2\pi)$ and $\varphi(x)\in C(0, 2\pi)$ which satisfy inequality (26.1) and yet the Fourier series of $f$ converges uniformly in $[0, 2\pi]$ whilst the Fourier series of $\varphi$ diverges in a set of the power of the continuum.

12. Construct a function $f(x)$ with $f(0) = f(\pi) = 0$ and continuous in $[0, \pi]$ such that the Fourier series of the function

$$F(x) = \begin{cases} f(x) & \text{for} \quad 0 \leqslant x \leqslant \pi \\ -f(-x) & \text{for} \quad -\pi \leqslant x \leqslant 0 \end{cases}$$

converges absolutely in $[-\pi, \pi]$, whilst the Fourier series of the function

$$\Phi(x) = \begin{cases} f(x) & \text{for} \quad 0 \leqslant x \leqslant \pi \\ f(-x) & \text{for} \quad -\pi \leqslant x \leqslant 0 \end{cases}$$

diverges at the point $x = 0$.

$\left[\text{The sum of the Lusin series } \sum_{n=1}^{\infty} \frac{1}{n^n} \sin n^{n^n} x \text{ can be taken for } f(x).\right]$

13. A function $f(x)$ with $f(0) = f(\pi) = 0$ which is continuous in $[0, \pi]$ exists such that the Fourier series of the function $\Phi(x)$ (see problem 12) converges absolutely for all $x \in [-\pi, \pi]$, whilst the Fourier series of the function $F(x)$ does not converge uniformly in $[-\pi, \pi]$.

$\left[\text{Assume that } f(x) = A + \sum_{n=1}^{\infty} \frac{1}{n^n} \cos 2n^{n^n} x, \text{ where } A = -\sum_{n=1}^{\infty} \frac{1}{n^n}.\right]$

14. Prove that a function $f(x) \in C(0, 2\pi)$ exists, the Fourier series of which converges uniformly in $[0, 2\pi]$, whilst the Fourier series of the function $|f(x)|$ diverges at some points.

$\left[\text{Take the function } \varphi(x) = \sum_{n=1}^{\infty} \frac{1}{n^n} \sin n^{n^n} x \text{ in } [0, \pi]\right]$ and construct a continuous function $\varphi_1(x)$ in $[0, \pi]$ with $\varphi_1(0) = \varphi_1(\pi) = 0$ such that $\varphi_1(x)$ increases in $[0, \pi/2]$, decreases in $[\pi/2, \pi]$ and $\varphi_1(x) \geqslant |\varphi(x)|$ for $0 \leqslant x \leqslant \pi$. Assuming that $f(x) = \varphi(x) + \varphi_1(x)$ for $0 \leqslant x \leqslant \pi$ and $f(x) = -f(-x)$ for $-\pi \leqslant x \leqslant 0$, we obtain the required example of the function $f$ (see also problem 12).]

15. If the function $f(x) \in V(0, 2\pi)$ and its Fourier series has the form

$$\sum_{k=1}^{\infty} (a_k \cos n_k x + b_k \sin n_k x),$$

where

$$\sum_{k=1}^{\infty} \frac{1}{\sqrt{k n_k}} < \infty,$$

then

$$\sum_{k=1}^{\infty} (|a_k| + |b_k|) < \infty.$$

S. B. STECHKIN[3]

16. No sequence of trigonometric polynomials $\{T_n(x)\}$ ($T_n(x)$ is of order not higher than $n$) exists which would form a basis in the space $C(0, 2\pi)$, i.e. for any function $f \in C(0, 2\pi)$ to be represented (in a unique way) in the form

$$f(x) = \sum_{n=1}^{\infty} c_n T_n(x),$$

where the latter series converges uniformly to $f(x)$ in $[0, 2\pi]$.

G. FABER, V. F. NIKOLAYEV, S. M. LOZINSKII, F. I. KHARSIHLADZE;
see also NATANSON, A22, pp. 672–678.

17. Prove that a sequence of trigonometric polynomials $\{T_{k_n}(x)\}$ exists which form a basis in the space $C(0, 2\pi)$ and

$$\lim_{n\to\infty} \frac{k_n}{n^{2+\varepsilon}} = 0$$

for any $\varepsilon > 0$.

[Consider a Schauder basis in the space $C(0, 2\pi)$ (see KACZMARZ and STEINHAUS, A 12, p. 63 of Russian translation) and $f_n(x)$ $(n = 0, 1, \ldots)$ with points of separation $2\pi k/2^m$. Assume that $k_n = n^2[\log^2 n]$. Let $T_{k_n}(x)$ be a trigonometric polynomial of the best (in the space $C(0, 2\pi)$) approximation for the function $f_n(x)$. Then $\|f_n - T_{k_n}\|_c = O(1/n \log^2 n)$ $(n \geqslant n_0)$. Next, apply to the systems $\{f_n\}$ and $\{T_{k_n}\}$ partly modified arguments from the Krein–Millman–Ruthman theorem (see A.12, p. 442 of the Russian translation), having selected the appropriate form for $n_0$ and the polynomials $T_{k_i}(x)$ with $0 \leqq i < n_0$.]

18. Let $k_n \uparrow \infty$ be a sequence of integers. The question is open as to the necessary and sufficient condition on the increase in $k_n$ for a sequence of trigonometric polynomials $\{T_{k_i}(x)\}$ to exist forming a basis in the space $C(0, 2\pi)$.

19. Consider a periodic (with period 1) function $\varphi(x) \in \mathrm{Lip}\,\alpha$ (i.e. $|\varphi(x) - \varphi(y)| \leqq B|x - y|^{\alpha}$) for some $\alpha \in (0, 1]$ and

$$\min_{x\in[0,1]} \varphi(x) = -1 < 1 = \max_{x\in[0,1]} \varphi(x).$$

Then if the real numbers $a$ and $b$ satisfy the inequalities

$$0 < a < 1/2 \quad \text{and} \quad a|b|^{\alpha} > 1 + \frac{2B}{1 - 2a},$$

the function

$$f(x) \equiv f_\varepsilon(x) \equiv \sum_{k=1}^{\infty} \varepsilon_k a^k \varphi(b^k x) \quad (-\infty < x < \infty)$$

does not possess a derivative at any point $x \in (-\infty, \infty)$ for any choice of the numerical sequence $\varepsilon \equiv \{\varepsilon_k\}$ where $\varepsilon_k = \pm 1$.

[The proof is basically the same as for the Weierstrass function $\sum_{k=1}^{\infty} a^k \cos 2\pi b^k x$.]

CHAPTER V

# CONVERGENCE AND DIVERGENCE OF A FOURIER SERIES IN A SET

## § 1. Introduction

We devote this chapter to the study of the convergence of a Fourier series in some set lying in $[0, 2\pi]$. Let us start by considering the conditions under which convergence almost everywhere occurs.

We will now define *the tests of the Weyl type* by those of the form: if $W(n)$ does not decrease monotonically and

$$\sum_{n=1}^{\infty}(a_n^2 + b_n^2)W(n) < +\infty, \tag{1.1}$$

then the series

$$\frac{a_0}{2} + \sum_{n=1}^{\infty}(a_n \cos nx + b_n \sin nx) \tag{1.2}$$

converges almost everywhere in $[0, 2\pi]$.

The name was proposed by N. N. Lusin because Weyl was the first to pay attention to tests of this type. Fatou[1] proved that $n$ can be used for $W(n)$, then Weyl[1] showed that it can be taken that $W(n) = \sqrt[3]{n}$; Hobson[1] obtained $W(n) = n^{\varepsilon}$ for any $\varepsilon > 0$; Plancherel[1] discovered that $W(n) = \ln^3 n$ could be used and Hardy[1] decreased this factor to $\ln^2 n$.

Such were the circumstances when Lusin wrote his dissertation[A.15]. He clearly emphasized that the more slowly the Weyl function grows, then the wider the class of series convergent almost everywhere satisfying this test becomes with subsequent strengthening of the convergence test. Therefore he insisted on the importance of the decrease in the factor due to Hardy. He expressed the hypothesis† that the Fourier series of any function with integrable squares converges and if this were true, then any increasing function would be a Weyl function. Lusin's hypothesis has not been confirmed up to now, nor has it been denied, although more than forty years have passed since it was expressed. As regards Hardy's factor, it was decreased to $\ln n$ in 1925 in the work by Kolmogorov and Seliverstov[1] and independently by Plessner[1]. It has not been possible yet to decrease the Weyl factor below $\ln n$, but it has also not been proved that such a decrease is impossible.

We begin the present chapter with the proof of the Kolmogorov–Seliverstov and Plessner theorem (§ 2).

† In Chapter VIII we will discuss what led Lusin to this hypothesis.

Plessner showed that the condition $\sum (a_n^2 + b_n^2) \ln n$ can be replaced by its equivalent condition

$$\int_0^{2\pi}\int_0^{2\pi} \frac{[f(x+t) - f(x-t)]^2}{t} \, dt\, dx < +\infty,$$

where $f(x)$ is the function for which $\sigma(f)$ is the Fourier series (see § 5). This convergence test for Fourier series of functions in $L^2$ was transposed by Marcinkiewicz to the case of functions in $L^p (1 \leqslant p \leqslant 2)$ (see § 8). In § 9 we will demonstrate other forms of the convergence test for Fourier series in $L^2$ and we will then transpose them (§ 10) to the case when it is not a matter of convergence almost everywhere in $[0, 2\pi]$ but only almost everywhere in some interval of length less than $2\pi$.

Returning to the problem of the behaviour of Fourier series for functions in $L^2$ over $[0, 2\pi]$, we will study the question of the connection between the increase in the Weyl factor and the existence of some almost everywhere convergent sub-sequence of partial sums of the Fourier series (§ 11).

In § 12 we tackle the same problem of convergence for functions in $L^2$ from a different viewpoint, namely, we study the sets of measure zero, in which the series $\sigma(f)$ can nevertheless diverge, if the coefficients of the Fourier series satisfy a condition of the type (1.1). The "denseness" or "rarefaction" of this set of zero measure varies with the growth of the Weyl function $W(n)$.

In §§ 13–16, rejecting the hypothesis that $f(x) \in L^2$ or of $f(x) \in L^p$ at $p > 1$, we will describe some tests, when $\sigma(f)$ converges almost everywhere or in a set of measure greater than zero. In § 17 it is proved that Fourier series exist which are divergent almost everywhere, and from the results if § 19 it follows that this is possible even when the series conjugate to the Fourier series is itself a Fourier series. In § 20, the construction of a Fourier series divergent at every point is given. The construction of this example is more complicated than the examples where divergence occurs almost everywhere (and therefore we describe their construction independently) but it is impossible to dispense with it if we wish to construct the example of a Fourier series convergent in a given set and divergent outside it (see § 22).

In § 21 we will answer the question: in what sense is it possible and in what sense is it impossible to speak of the transfer of the principle of localization from the case of an interval to the case of a set of positive measure?

Finally, concluding the chapter (§ 23) we produce some results demonstrating how important is the order in which the terms of the Fourier series are arranged in convergence problems.

## § 2. The Kolmogorov–Seliverstov and Plessner theorem

We will begin the study of the conditions under which the Fourier series converges almost everywhere with the following important theorem, derived simultaneously and independently by A.I. Plessner[1] on the one hand and A.N. Kolmogorov and G.A. Seliverstov[1] on the other.

THEOREM. *If*

$$\sum_{n=1}^{\infty} (a_n^2 + b_n^2) \ln n < +\infty,$$

*then the series*

$$\frac{a_0}{2} + \sum_{n=1}^{\infty} (a_n \cos nx + b_n \sin nx) \tag{2.1}$$

*converges almost everywhere.*

The proof worked through below is that due to Plessner. We will begin by establishing the following lemma:

LEMMA 1. *Let the sequence $f_1(x), f_2(x), \ldots, f_n(x), \ldots$ consist of summable functions, defined in the set $E$, $mE > 0$. For $n \geqslant m$ let*

$$\Phi_{mn} = \sup(f_m - f_m, f_{m+1} - f_m, \ldots, f_n - f_m),$$

$$\varphi_{mn} = \inf(f_m - f_m, f_{m+1} - f_m, \ldots, f_n - f_m)$$

*and*

$$J_{mn} = \int_E \Phi_{mn}(x)\,dx, \quad j_{mn} = \int_E \varphi_{mn}(x)\,dx.$$

*Let us suppose*

$$J_m = \lim_{n\to\infty} J_{mn}, \quad j_m = \lim_{n\to\infty} j_{mn}$$

(these limits exist because $\Phi_{mn}$ can only increase with increase in $n$ whilst $\varphi_{mn}$ can only decrease, which means that this is also true for $J_{mn}$ and $j_{mn}$).

*If*

$$\lim_{m\to\infty} J_m = 0 \quad \textit{and} \quad \lim_{m\to\infty} j_m = 0, \tag{2.2}$$

*then the sequence $f_n(x)$ converges to a finite limit almost everywhere in $E$.*

*Proof.* Let us assume that

$$\Phi_m(x) = \lim_{n\to\infty} \Phi_{mn}(x).$$

This limit exists since $\Phi_{mn}(x)$ can only increase with increase in $n$; it is clear that

$$J_m = \int_E \Phi_m(x)\,dx.$$

We will choose the numbers $m_k$ so that

$$0 \leqslant J_{m_k} < \frac{1}{2^k},$$

which is possible by virtue of (2.2). Then

$$\sum_{k=1}^{\infty} J_{m_k} < +\infty,$$

and therefore, since $\Phi_{m_k} \geqslant 0$ for all $x$, then

$$\sum_{k=1}^{\infty} \Phi_{m_k}(x) \tag{2.3}$$

converges almost everywhere in $E$ (see Introductory Material, § 14).

Let $x_0$ be a point of the set $\mathscr{E}$, $m\mathscr{E} = mE$, where the series (2.3) converges. Then $\Phi_{m_k}(x_0) \to 0$ as $k \to \infty$. This means that for any $\varepsilon$ it is possible to choose $k$ so that

$$0 \leqslant \Phi_{m_k}(x_0) < \varepsilon.$$

But since $\Phi_{mn}(x) \leqslant \Phi_m(x)$ for any $n > m$, then

$$0 \leqslant \Phi_{m_k n}(x_0) < \varepsilon, \quad n > m_k,$$

i.e.

$$f_n(x_0) - f_{m_k}(x_0) < \varepsilon, \quad n > m_k.$$

In a completely similar way, considering $\varphi_m(x) = \lim_{n\to\infty} \varphi_{mn}(x)$, we obtain

$$-\varepsilon < f_n(x_0) - f_{m_k}(x_0)$$

for any $x_0 \in \mathscr{E}_1$, where $\mathscr{E}_1$ is some set $m\mathscr{E}_1 = mE$. Consequently if $x_0 \in \mathscr{E}\mathscr{E}_1$, then

$$|f_n(x_0) - f_{m_k}(x_0)| < \varepsilon,$$

provided $m_k$ is sufficiently large and $n > m_k$ which means that the sequence converges at $x = x_0$. But $x_0$ is any point of $\mathscr{E}\mathscr{E}_1$, which means that the sequence converges almost everywhere in $E$. The lemma is proved.

We will continue with the proof of the Kolmogorov–Seliverstov Plessner theorem. Without restricting the generality, it is possible to suppose that and

$$a_0 = a_1 = b_1 = 0.$$

We will use Lemma 1, where the interval $[0, 2\pi]$ will play the part of the set $E$ and the partial sums $S_n(x)$ of the series (2.1) will play the part of the functions $f_n(x)$.

If we prove that

$$\left.\begin{aligned} 0 \leqslant J_{mn} &= \int_0^{2\pi} \Phi_{mn}(x)\,dx \leqslant K\sqrt{\sum_{k=m+1}^{n} (a_k^2 + b_k^2)\ln k}, \\ 0 \geqslant j_{mn} &= \int_0^{2\pi} \varphi_{mn}(x)\,dx \geqslant -K\sqrt{\sum_{k=m+1}^{n} (a_k^2 + b_k^2)\ln k}, \end{aligned}\right\} \tag{2.4}$$

where $K$ is an absolute constant, then the convergence of the series (2.1) will be established almost everywhere. We will confine ourselves to proving the first of the inequalities (2.4), the second being completely similar.

Also, since

$$\Phi_{mn} = \max(S_m - S_m, S_{m+1} - S_m, \ldots, S_n - S_m)$$

coincides with

$$\Phi_{1n} = \max(0, S_2 - S_1, \ldots, S_n - S_1) = \max(0, S_2, S_3, \ldots, S_n), \tag{2.5}$$

if it is assumed that $a_0 = a_1 = b_1 = \cdots = a_m = b_m = 0$, then it is sufficient to prove that

$$0 \leqslant \int_0^{2\pi} \Phi_{1n}(x)\,dx \leqslant K\sqrt{\sum_{k=1}^{n}(a_k^2 + b_k^2)\ln k}, \tag{2.6}$$

for (2.4) to be valid for any $m$. But if we examine formula (2.5) defining $\Phi_{1n}(x)$, then it becomes clear that for any $x$ the quantity $\Phi_{1n}(x)$ coincides with some $S_p(x)$ where $p = 1, 2, \ldots, n$. In other words, it is possible to write

$$\Phi_{1n}(x) = \sum_{k=2}^{p(x)}(a_k \cos kx + b_k \sin kx),$$

where the number of terms of the sum differs for different $x$ (therefore we denote it by $p(x)$), but $p(x)$ can only take the values $2, 3, \ldots, n$.

Thus, our theorem will be proved if the following proposition is proved:

LEMMA 2. *If $p(x)$ is an integral function which only takes one of the values* $1, 2, \ldots, n$, *for every $x$, then*†

$$I = \int_0^{2\pi}\left[\sum_{k=2}^{p(x)}(a_k \cos kx + b_k \sin kx)\right]dx \leqslant K\sqrt{\sum_{k=2}^{n}(a_k^2 + b_k^2)\ln k}. \tag{2.7}$$

To prove the validity of the inequality (2.7), let us consider the trigonometric polynomial

$$F_n(x) = \sum_{k=2}^{n}(a_k \cos kx + b_k \sin kx)\sqrt{\ln k}. \tag{2.8}$$

Since

$$a_k\sqrt{\ln k} = \frac{1}{\pi}\int_0^{2\pi} F_n(t)\cos kt\,dt, \quad b_k\sqrt{\ln k} = \frac{1}{\pi}\int_0^{2\pi} F_n(t)\sin kt\,dt,$$

then

$$\sum_{k=2}^{p(x)}(a_k \cos kx + b_k \sin kx) = \frac{1}{\pi}\int_0^{2\pi} F_n(t)\sum_{k=2}^{p(x)}\frac{\cos k(t-x)}{\sqrt{\ln k}}\,dt,$$

and therefore the expression $I$ on the left-hand side of the inequality (2.7), that we wish to prove, has the form

$$I = \int_0^{2\pi}\left\{\frac{1}{\pi}\int_0^{2\pi} F_n(t)\sum_{k=2}^{p(x)}\frac{\cos k(t-x)}{\sqrt{\ln k}}\,dt\right\}dx,$$

† For the case when $p(x) = 1$, it must be considered that

$$\sum_{k=2}^{p(x)} a_k \cos kx + b_k \sin kx = 0.$$

and, changing the order of the integration,

$$I = \int_0^{2\pi} \frac{1}{\pi} F_n(t) \left\{ \int_0^{2\pi} \sum_{k=2}^{p(x)} \frac{\cos k(t-x)}{\sqrt{\ln k}}\, dx \right\} dt.$$

Applying Bunyakovskii's inequality, we find

$$I^2 \leqslant \frac{1}{\pi^2} \int_0^{2\pi} F_n^2(t)\, dt \int_0^{2\pi} \left[ \int_0^{2\pi} \sum_{k=2}^{p(x)} \frac{\cos k(t-x)}{\sqrt{\ln k}}\, dx \right]^2 dt$$

and since by virtue of (2.8)

$$\frac{1}{\pi} \int_0^{2\pi} F_n^2(t)\, dt = \sum_{k=2}^{n} (a_k^2 + b_k^2) \ln k,$$

then the inequality (2.7) will be proved, if we prove that

$$J = \int_0^{2\pi} \left[ \int_0^{2\pi} \sum_{k=2}^{p(x)} \frac{\cos k(t-x)}{\sqrt{\ln k}}\, dx \right]^2 dt < C, \tag{2.9}$$

where $C$ is an absolute constant.

The integral $J$ on the left-hand side of the inequality (2.9) can be rewritten thus:

$$J = \int_0^{2\pi} \left[ \int_0^{2\pi} \sum_{k=2}^{p(x)} \frac{\cos k(t-x)}{\sqrt{\ln k}}\, dx \right] \left[ \int_0^{2\pi} \sum_{m=2}^{p(y)} \frac{\cos m(t-y)}{\sqrt{\ln m}}\, dy \right] dt$$

$$= \int_0^{2\pi} \int_0^{2\pi} \left\{ \left[ \int_0^{2\pi} \sum_{k=2}^{p(x)} \frac{\cos k(t-x)}{\sqrt{\ln k}} \sum_{m=2}^{p(y)} \frac{\cos m(t-y)}{\sqrt{\ln m}} \right] dt \right\} dx dy.$$

Since

$$\int_0^{2\pi} \cos k(t-x) \cos m(t-y)\, dt = 0,$$

if $m \neq k$ and

$$\int_0^{2\pi} \cos k(t-x) \cos k(t-y)\, dt = \pi \cos k(x-y),$$

then, denoting by $p(x, y)$ the least of the values $p(x)$ and $p(y)$ we have

$$J = \pi \int_0^{2\pi} \int_0^{2\pi} \sum_{k=2}^{p(x,y)} \frac{\cos k(x-y)}{\ln k}\, dx\, dy.$$

Let us denote by $E$ the set of points in the square $[0 \leqslant x \leqslant 2\pi]$, $[0 \leqslant y \leqslant 2\pi]$, where $p(x) \leqslant p(y)$, and its complementary set by $CE$. Then we have in $E$

$p(x, y) = p(x)$ and in $CE$ $p(x, y) = p(y)$ and

$$J = \pi \iint_E \sum_{k=2}^{p(x)} \frac{\cos k(x-y)}{\ln k} \, dx\, dy + \pi \iint_{CE} \sum_{k=2}^{p(y)} \frac{\cos k(x-y)}{\ln k} \, dx\, dy,$$

and therefore

$$J \leqslant \pi \iint_E \left| \sum_{k=2}^{p(x)} \frac{\cos k(x-y)}{\ln k} \right| dx\, dy + \pi \iint_{CE} \left| \sum_{k=2}^{p(y)} \frac{\cos k(x-y)}{\ln k} \right| dx\, dy$$

$$\leqslant \pi \int_0^{2\pi}\int_0^{2\pi} \left| \sum_{k=2}^{p(x)} \frac{\cos k(x-y)}{\ln k} \right| dx\, dy + \pi \int_0^{2\pi}\int_0^{2\pi} \left| \sum_{k=2}^{p(y)} \frac{\cos k(x-y)}{\ln k} \right| dx\, dy$$

$$= 2\pi \int_0^{2\pi}\int_0^{2\pi} \left| \sum_{k=2}^{p(y)} \frac{\cos k(x-y)}{\ln k} \right| dx\, dy, \tag{2.10}$$

since by interchanging the roles of $x$ and $y$ in the second row of (2.10) we see that the second integral coincides with the first. Since $p(y)$ already does not vary with $x$, then the inequality (2.10) includes the inequality (2.9), if we prove that for any $n$ we have

$$\int_0^{2\pi} \left| \sum_{k=2}^{n} \frac{\cos kx}{\ln k} \right| dx < M \quad (n = 1, 2, \ldots),$$

where $M$ is an absolute constant. But this fact was proved in Chapter I, § 30 (see 30.21). Thus the theorem is proved.

COROLLARY. *If $f(x) \in L^2$, then*

$$|S_n(x)| = o(\sqrt{\ln n}) \tag{2.11}$$

*almost everywhere.*

Let $f(x) \in L^2$ and

$$\sigma(f) = \frac{a_0}{2} + \sum_{n=1}^{\infty} (a_n \cos nx + b_n \sin nx).$$

According to the Kolmogorov–Seliverstov and Plessner theorem the series

$$\sum_{n=2}^{\infty} \frac{a_n \cos nx + b_n \sin nx}{\sqrt{\ln n}} \tag{2.12}$$

should converge almost everywhere since for its coefficients

$$\alpha_n = \frac{a_n}{\sqrt{\ln n}}, \quad \beta_n = \frac{b_n}{\sqrt{\ln n}}$$

the condition $\sum (\alpha_n^2 + \beta_n^2) \ln n < +\infty$ is fulfilled since $\sum (a_n^2 + b_n^2) < +\infty$.

Let $x_0$ be a point where the series (2.12) converges. Supposing that

$$u_n = a_n \cos nx_0 + b_n \sin nx_0, \quad l_n = \sqrt{\ln n} \tag{2.13}$$

and, applying Theorem 4 of § 25 in the Appendix, we see that

$$S_n(x_0) = o(\sqrt{\ln n}).$$

But since the series (2.12) converges almost everywhere, then for almost all the points of the interval (2.11) is fulfilled and the theorem is proved.

*Note.* We will recall that in Chapter I, § 50 it was proved for any summable $f$ that

$$S_n(x) = o(\ln n).$$

Now we will see that if $f \in L^2$, then this condition is strengthened: it is possible to replace $\ln n$ by $\sqrt{\ln n}$.

## § 3. A convergence test expressed by the first differences of the coefficients

The following simple note is due to Salem[1]: if for a trigonometric series

$$\frac{a_0}{2} + a_1 \cos x + \cdots + a_n \cos nx + \cdots, \tag{3.1}$$

which is not even a Fourier series, we have $a_n \to 0$, then it is possible to apply Abel's transformation to it which makes it possible to confirm for all points, apart from points of the type $x \equiv 0 \pmod{2\pi}$, the simultaneous convergence of this series and the series

$$(a_0 - a_1) \sin \frac{x}{2} + (a_1 - a_2) \sin 3\frac{x}{2} + \cdots + (a_n - a_{n+1}) \sin \frac{(2n+1)x}{2} + \cdots. \tag{3.2}$$

Therefore, if the series (3.1) converges almost everywhere, then the series (3.2) also converges and vice versa.

Hence, in particular, due to the theorem of § 2 it follows that if

$$\sum_{n=1}^{\infty} (a_n - a_{n+1})^2 \ln n < +\infty,$$

then the series (3.1) converges almost everywhere (this is true even if it is not a Fourier series).

The same argument holds for the series

$$\sum_{n=1}^{\infty} b_n \sin nx, \tag{3.3}$$

i.e. if $b_n \to 0$ and $\sum_{n=1}^{\infty} (b_n - b_{n+1})^2 \ln n < +\infty$, then the series (3.3) converges almost everywhere.

Finally, for the convergence almost everywhere of the general trigonometric series

$$\frac{a_0}{2} + \sum (a_n \cos nx + b_n \sin nx) = \sum \varrho_n \cos(nx - \alpha_n)$$

as $\varrho_n \to 0$ it is sufficient to have the convergence of

$$\sum [(a_n - a_{n+1})^2 + (b_n - b_{n+1})^2] \ln n,$$

and this is equivalent to the fulfilment of two conditions:

$$\left.\begin{array}{l}\sum (\varrho_n - \varrho_{n+1})^2 \ln n < +\infty, \\ \sum \varrho_n^2(\alpha_n - \alpha_{n+1})^2 \ln n < +\infty.\end{array}\right\} \tag{3.4}$$

This can, moreover, be expressed not quite precisely but only descriptively in the following way: here in the transfer from one term of the series to another "small" changes are made in the amplitudes $\varrho_n$ and the phases $\alpha_n$. If $M_n$ are points of a plane with coordinates $(a_n, b_n)$, then the Kolmogorov–Seliverstov and Plessner theorem asserts the convergence of the series almost everywhere if

$$\sum (\overline{OM_n})^2 \ln n < +\infty,$$

and the conditions (3.4) expressed by Salem signify that $\overline{OM_n} \to 0$ and

$$\sum (\overline{M_n M_{n+1}})^2 \ln n < +\infty.$$

These conditions can, in their turn, be replaced by others which include the second, third, etc. differences of the coefficients. See, for example, this report by Salem and also one by Dzhvarsheishvili[1].

## § 4. Convergence factors

We refer to the sequence of numbers $\{\mu_n\}$ as the *convergence factors* for a class of functions $\{f(x)\}$, if every time $f(x)$ belongs to the class under consideration and

$$\frac{a_0}{2} + \sum (a_n \cos nx + b_n \sin nx) \tag{4.1}$$

is its Fourier series, then the series

$$\frac{a_0}{2}\mu_0 + \sum (a_n \cos nx + b_n \sin nx)\mu_n \tag{4.2}$$

converges almost everywhere.

From the Kolmogorov–Seliverstov and Plessner theorem it immediately follows that *for functions belonging to the class $L^2$ the convergence factors are the numbers*

$$\mu_n = \frac{1}{\sqrt{\ln n}} \quad (n = 2, 3, \ldots)$$

($\mu_0$ and $\mu_1$ can be any values).

Indeed

$$\sum (a_n^2\mu_n^2 + b_n^2\mu_n^2) \ln n = \sum (a_n^2 + b_n^2) < +\infty,$$

if $f(x) \in L^2$, and it is sufficient to apply the Kolmogorov–Seliverstov and Plessner theorem to obtain the convergence of series (4.2) almost everywhere.

If $f(x) \in L$, then (see Chapter I, § 51) it is possible to use as convergence factors the numbers

$$\mu_n = \frac{1}{\ln n} \quad (n = 2, 3, \ldots).$$

## § 5. Other forms of the condition imposed in the Kolmogorov–Seliverstov and Plessner theorem

Following Plessner[1] we will prove that if

$$\sigma(f) = \frac{a_0}{2} + \sum_{n=1}^{\infty} (a_n \cos nx + b_n \sin nx),$$

then the conditions

$$\sum_{n=1}^{\infty} (a_n^2 + b_n^2) \ln n < +\infty, \tag{A}$$

$$\int_0^{2\pi}\int_0^{2\pi} \frac{[f(x+t) - f(x-t)]^2}{t} dt\, dx < +\infty, \tag{B}$$

$$\int_0^{2\pi}\int_0^{2\pi} \frac{[f(x+t) + f(x-t) - 2f(x)]^2}{t} dt\, dx < +\infty \tag{C}$$

are equivalent. After this it will be established that it can be asserted that *the series $\sigma(f)$ converges almost everywhere if $f(x)$ satisfies condition (B) or condition (C).*

In order to prove the equivalence of the relationships (A), (B) and (C), we will assume that

$$\psi(x, t) = f(x+t) - f(x-t); \quad \Psi(t) = \int_0^{2\pi} [\psi(x, t)]^2\, dx,$$

$$\varphi(x, t) = f(x+t) + f(x-t) - 2f(x); \quad \Phi(t) = \int_0^{2\pi} [\varphi(x, t)]^2\, dx.$$

It must be proved that if (A) is fulfilled, then the integrals

$$\int_0^{2\pi} \frac{\Psi(t)}{t} dt \quad \text{and} \quad \int_0^{2\pi} \frac{\Phi(t)}{t} dt$$

are finite and, conversely, if they are finite, then (A) holds.

We will work through the proof for $\Psi(t)$; for $\Phi(t)$ it is exactly similar.

If we expand $\psi(x, t)$ into a Fourier series with respect to the variable $x$, then

$$\psi(x, t) \sim \sum_{k=1}^{\infty} 2(b_k \cos kx - a_k \sin kx) \sin kt.$$

Therefore, on the basis of Parseval's equality

$$\Psi(t) = \int_0^{2\pi} \psi^2(x, t)\, dx = 4\pi \sum_{k=1}^{\infty} (a_k^2 + b_k^2) \sin^2 kt. \tag{5.1}$$

Let us assume that

$$\Psi_n(t) = 4\pi \sum_{k=1}^{\infty} (a_k^2 + b_k^2) \sin^2 kt.$$

Then it is clear that

$$\frac{\Psi_1(t)}{t} \leqslant \frac{\Psi_2(t)}{t} \leqslant \cdots \leqslant \frac{\Psi_n(t)}{t} \leqslant \cdots,$$

whilst all these functions are non-negative, integrable and

$$\lim_{n\to\infty} \frac{\Psi_n(t)}{t} = \frac{\Psi(t)}{t}.$$

Therefore, on the basis of the well-known theorem concerning the integration of increasing sequences of non-negative functions we conclude that

$$\int_0^{2\pi} \frac{\Psi(t)}{t}\, dt \tag{5.2}$$

is finite when and only when

$$\lim_{n\to\infty} \int_0^{2\pi} \frac{\Psi_n(t)}{t}\, dt$$

is finite. But since

$$\int_0^{2\pi} \frac{\Psi_n(t)}{t}\, dt = 4\pi \sum_{k=1}^{n} (a_k^2 + b_k^2) \int_0^{2\pi} \frac{\sin^2 kt}{t}\, dt,$$

then the existence of the integral (5.2) is equivalent to the convergence of the series

$$\sum_{k=1}^{\infty} (a_k^2 + b_k^2) \int_0^{2\pi} \frac{\sin^2 kt}{t}\, dt.$$

But it is clear that $\int_0^{2\pi} [(\sin^2 kt)/t]\, dt \sim \ln k$ and therefore the existence of the integral (5.2) or, what is just the same, the integral

$$\int_0^{2\pi}\int_0^{2\pi} \frac{[f(x+t) - f(x-t)]^2}{t}\, dt\, dx$$

is equivalent to the convergence of the series (A) and this is what was required to be proved.

## § 6. Corollaries of Plessner's theorem

(a) We have proved that for functions satisfying condition (A), the integrals (B) and (C) exist. But according to Fubini's theorem (see Introductory Material, § 18) from the existence of these double integrals it follows that *the integrals*

$$\int_0^{2\pi} \frac{[f(x+t)-f(x-t)]^2}{t}\,dt \tag{$\alpha$}$$

*and*

$$\int_0^{2\pi} \frac{[f(x+t)+f(x-t)-2f(x)]^2}{t}\,dt \tag{$\beta$}$$

*exist for almost all values of x* (*and are summable with respect to x in* $(0, 2\pi)$).

The fact of the existence of the integrals ($\alpha$) and ($\beta$) almost everywhere is indeed not trivial. In Chapter VIII, § 7 it will be proved that although

$$\int_0^{2\pi} \frac{f(x+t)-f(x-t)}{t}\,dt$$

exists almost everywhere not only for $f \in L^2$ but also for $f \in L$, however

$$\int_0^{2\pi} \frac{|f(x+t)-f(x-t)|}{t}\,dt$$

can be equal to $+\infty$ for all $x$, even for continuous $f(x)$ (see § 8 below); this could be proved too for

$$\int_0^{2\pi} \frac{|f(x+t)+f(x-t)-2f(x)|}{t}\,dt \quad \text{and for} \quad \int_0^{2\pi} \frac{f(x+t)+f(x-t)-2f(x)}{t}\,dt.$$

(b) We also note this corollary of Plessner's theorem:

*If*

$$\omega(\delta, f) = O\left(\frac{1}{\left(\ln \frac{1}{\delta}\right)^{\frac{1}{2}+\varepsilon}}\right), \tag{6.1}$$

*then the series* $\sigma(f)$ *converges almost everywhere.*

Indeed, in this case

$$f(x+t)-f(x) = O\left(\frac{1}{\left(\ln \frac{1}{|t|}\right)^{\frac{1}{2}+\varepsilon}}\right)$$

uniformly in $[0, 2\pi]$, i.e. (in the notation of § 5)

$$\psi^2(x, t) = O\left(\frac{1}{\left(\ln \frac{1}{|t|}\right)^{1+2\varepsilon}}\right)$$

uniformly in $[0, 2\pi]$, which means that

$$\int_0^{2\pi} \frac{\psi(t)}{t} dt < +\infty.$$

The same could be proved, supposing only that

$$\omega_2(\delta, f) = O\left(\frac{1}{\left(\ln \frac{1}{\delta}\right)^{\frac{1}{2}+\varepsilon}}\right)$$

and arguing for $\varphi^2(x, t)$ instead of $\psi^2(x, t)$.

The theorem† concerning the convergence almost everywhere of the series $\sigma(f)$, if $f(x)$ satisfies the condition (6.1) was proved here only because it is obtained immediately from Plessner's theorem. However, it should be noted that later Marcinkiewicz obtained a very much more general result, namely: if

$$\frac{1}{t}\int_0^t |f(x+t) - f(x)|\, dt = O\left(\frac{1}{\ln \frac{1}{t}}\right) \tag{6.2}$$

for $x \in E$, then $\sigma(f)$ converges almost everywhere in $E$ (see below, § 15).

It is appropriate to remark here that conditions of type (6.1) or (6.2) impose limitations on the behaviour of $f(x+t) - f(x)$ either uniformly in $[0, 2\pi]$ or in some set of measure greater than zero and permit deductions to be drawn concerning the behaviour of $\sigma(f)$ in the interval or in the set; this is completely analogous to the fact that the Dini–Lipschitz test

$$\omega(\delta, f) = o\left(\frac{1}{\ln \frac{1}{\delta}}\right)$$

and the more general Salem–Stechkin test (see Chapter IV, § 8)

$$\omega_2(\delta, F) = o\left(\frac{\delta}{\ln \frac{1}{\delta}}\right), \quad \text{where} \quad F(x) = \int_0^x f(t)\, dt,$$

permit the behaviour of a series to be judged over an entire interval or almost every-

† It was proved by Plessner.

where in it, but the condition

$$|f(x+t) - f(x)| = o\left(\frac{1}{\ln \frac{1}{t}}\right),$$

fulfilled at an individual point does not guarantee the convergence of $\sigma(f)$ at this point (see Chapter IV, § 4).

## § 7. Concerning the equivalence of some conditions expressed in terms of integrals and in terms of series

We have seen in § 5 that the existence of the integral

$$\int_0^{2\pi}\int_0^{2\pi} \frac{[f(x+t) - f(x-t)]^2}{t}\, dt\, dx < +\infty \tag{B}$$

and the convergence of the series

$$\sum_{n=1}^{\infty} (a_n^2 + b_n^2) \ln n < +\infty, \quad \text{where} \quad \sigma(f) = \frac{a_0}{2} + \sum (a_n \cos nx + b_n \sin nx), \tag{A}$$

are equivalent conditions. Both these conditions are sufficient for the almost everywhere convergence of the series $\sigma(f)$.

Generalizing Plessner's result concerning the equivalence of conditions (A) and (B), Ul'yanov[2] showed that if certain limitations which we will describe later are imposed on the function $\alpha(t)$ and it is supposed that

$$\omega(k) = \int_{2\pi/k}^{2\pi} \alpha(t)\, dt,$$

then the conditions

$$\int_0^{2\pi}\int_0^{2\pi} \alpha(t)\,[f(x+t) - f(x-t)]^2\, dt\, dx < +\infty \tag{7.1}$$

and

$$\sum_{k-1}^{\infty} (a_k^2 + b_k^2)\,\omega(k) < +\infty \tag{7.2}$$

are equivalent.

The following conditions can be those imposed on $\alpha(t)$:

(1) $\alpha(t)$ is non-negative and does not increase in $[0, 2\pi]$,

(2) $\int_0^{2\pi} \alpha(t)\, dt = +\infty$,

(3) there exists a constant $C$ such that for all sufficiently small $\delta$ we have

$$\frac{1}{\delta^2}\int_0^{\delta} t^2 \alpha(t)\, dt \leqslant C \int_{\delta}^{2\pi} \alpha(t)\, dt.$$

The last condition seems somewhat artificial (in contrast to the first two); its significance is that $\alpha(t)$ does not increase too quickly as $t \to 0$.

Let us prove that on fulfilling requirements (1), (2) and (3) conditions (7.1) and (7.2) are equally strong.

Due to Parseval's equality we have

$$\int_0^{2\pi} [f(x+t) - f(x-t)]^2 \, dt = 4\pi \sum_{k=1}^{\infty} (a_k^2 + b_k^2) \sin^2 kt.$$

Consequently

$$\int_0^{2\pi}\int_0^{2\pi} \alpha(t) [f(x+t) - f(x-t)]^2 \, dx\, dt = 4\pi \sum_{k=1}^{\infty} (a_k^2 + b_k^2) \int_0^{2\pi} \alpha(t) \sin^2 kt\, dt.$$

Thus it remains to prove that

$$\int_0^{2\pi} \alpha(t) \sin^2 kt\, dt \sim \omega(k) = \int_{2\pi/k}^{2\pi} \alpha(t)\, dt.$$

Due to condition (3), we have

$$\int_0^{2\pi} \alpha(t) \sin^2 kt\, dt = \int_0^{2\pi/k} \alpha(t) \sin^2 kt\, dt + \int_{2\pi/k}^{2\pi} \alpha(t) \sin^2 kt\, dt$$

$$\leqslant k^2 \int_0^{2\pi/k} \alpha(t)\, t^2\, dt + \int_{2\pi/k}^{2\pi} \alpha(t)\, dt \leqslant (4\pi^2 C + 1) \int_{2\pi/k}^{2\pi} \alpha(t)\, dt.$$

But

$$\int_0^{2\pi} \alpha(t) \sin^2 kt\, dt = \sum_{n=0}^{k-1} \int_{\frac{2\pi}{k} n}^{\frac{2\pi}{k}(n+1)} \alpha(t) \sin^2 kt\, dt$$

$$= \int_0^{2\pi/k} \sum_{n=0}^{k-1} \alpha\left(t + \frac{2\pi}{k} n\right) \sin^2 k \left(t + \frac{2\pi}{k} n\right) dt = \int_0^{2\pi/k} \sin^2 kt \left[\sum_{n=0}^{k-1} \alpha\left(t + \frac{2\pi}{k} n\right)\right] dt. \tag{7.3}$$

On the other hand

$$\int_{2\pi/k}^{2\pi} \alpha(t)\, dt = \sum_{n=1}^{k-1} \int_{\frac{2\pi}{k} n}^{\frac{2\pi}{k}(n+1)} \alpha(t)\, dt = \int_0^{2\pi/k} \sum_{n=1}^{k-1} \alpha\left(t + \frac{2\pi}{k} n\right) dt \leqslant \frac{2\pi}{k} \sum_{n=1}^{k-1} \alpha\left(\frac{2\pi}{k} n\right) \tag{7.4}$$

by virtue of the fact that $\alpha(t)$ does not increase. This means that for $0 \leqslant t \leqslant 2\pi/k$

$$\sum_{n=0}^{k-1} \alpha\left(t + \frac{2\pi}{k} n\right) \geqslant \sum_{n=0}^{k-1} \alpha\left(\frac{2\pi}{k} + \frac{2\pi}{k} n\right) = \sum_{n=0}^{k-1} \alpha\left[\frac{2\pi}{k}(n+1)\right]$$

$$= \sum_{n=1}^{k} \alpha\left(\frac{2\pi}{k} n\right) \geqslant \frac{k}{2\pi} \int_{2\pi/k}^{2\pi} \alpha(t)\, dt$$

due to (7.4). Therefore, from (7.3)

$$\int_0^{2\pi} \alpha(t)\sin^2 kt\,dt \geqslant \int_0^{2\pi/k} \sin^2 kt\,dt \frac{k}{2\pi} \int_{2\pi/k}^{2\pi} \alpha(t)\,dt = M \int_{2\pi/k}^{2\pi} \alpha(t)\,dt$$

$$\left(\text{where}\quad M = \frac{k}{2\pi} \int_0^{2\pi/k} \sin^2 kt\,dt = \frac{1}{2\pi}\int_0^{2\pi} \sin^2 u\,du = \frac{1}{2}\right).$$

Thus

$$\int_0^{2\pi} \alpha(t)\sin^2 kt\,dt \sim \int_{2\pi/k}^{2\pi} \alpha(t)\,dt,$$

and the theorem is proved.

In the particular case $\alpha(t) = 1/t$ all the conditions are satisfied and we revert to Plessner's theorem.

The meaning of Ul'yanov's theorem that has just been proved is that if it were possible to strengthen the Kolmogorov–Seliverstov and Plessner result, i.e. to obtain convergence of the Fourier series from the condition

$$\int_0^{2\pi}\int_0^{2\pi} \alpha(t)[f(x+t) - f(x-t)]^2\,dt\,dx < +\infty,$$

where $\alpha(t)$ as $t \to 0$ increases more slowly than $1/t$, then this would signify that the convergence of the Fourier series could be derived from the condition

$$\sum (a_k^2 + b_k^2)\omega(k) < +\infty,$$

where $\omega(k)$ increases more slowly than $\ln k$.

For example, the convergence of the integral

$$\int_0^{2\pi}\int_0^{2\pi} \frac{[f(x+t) - f(x-t)]^2}{t \ln \dfrac{1}{t}}\,dt\,dx < +\infty$$

is equivalent to the convergence of the series

$$\sum (a_k^2 + b_k^2) \ln\ln k < +\infty.$$

However, the question whether the additional condition is sufficient for the almost everywhere convergence of the Fourier series remains open.

As an appendix to the investigation described above concerning the equivalence of the convergence of series and integrals we will prove the following theorem due to Ul'yanov[9, 12]:

THEOREM. *If for some* $\varepsilon > 0$ *we have*

$$\omega(\delta, f) = O\left(\frac{1}{\left(\ln \dfrac{1}{\delta}\right)^{1+\varepsilon}}\right), \tag{7.5}$$

*then the series* $\sigma(f)$ *after re-arrangement of its terms converges almost everywhere in* $[0, 2\pi]$.

Orlicz† showed that if $a_k$ and $b_k$ are Fourier coefficients for $f(x)$, then for any $\varepsilon > 0$ from the convergence of the series

$$\sum_{n=1}^{\infty} (a_n^2 + b_n^2) \ln^{2+\varepsilon} n \tag{7.6}$$

it follows that $\sigma(f)$ converges almost everywhere for any re-arrangement of its terms. Therefore, it is sufficient for us to prove that condition (7.5) involves the convergence of series (7.6). But according to the preceding theorem due to Ul'yanov, supposing that

$$\alpha(t) = \frac{\left(\ln \frac{1}{t}\right)^{1+\varepsilon}}{t},$$

we see that the convergence of series (7.6) is equivalent to the convergence of the integral

$$\int_0^{2\pi}\int_0^{2\pi} \frac{\left(\ln \frac{1}{t}\right)^{1+\varepsilon}}{t} [f(x+t) - f(x-t)]^2 \, dx \, dt, \tag{7.7}$$

and since from (7.5)

$$[f(x+t) - f(x-t)]^2 = O\left(\frac{1}{\left(\ln \frac{1}{t}\right)^{2+2\varepsilon}}\right),$$

then the convergence of the integral (7.7) holds and the theorem is proved.

COROLLARY. *If* $f(\eta) \in \operatorname{Lip} \alpha \, (\alpha > 0)$, *then the series* $\sigma(f)$ *after any re-arrangement of its terms converges almost everywhere.*††

This immediately follows from the theorem just proved.

*Note.* We know that if

$$\omega(\delta, f) = o\left(\frac{1}{\ln \frac{1}{\delta}}\right),$$

then the series $\sigma(f)$ converges uniformly (the Dini–Lipschitz test).

In Ul'yanov's theorem just proved, a somewhat stronger limitation is imposed on the function $f(x)$, but then convergence almost everywhere of the series $\sigma(f)$ occurs after any re-arrangement of its terms.

---

† See Kaczmarz and Steinhaus[A.12], p. 198.

†† However, it should not converge absolutely if $\alpha \leqslant \frac{1}{2}$, as will be shown in Chapter IX, § 4. Therefore, a set of measure zero where it can diverge depends on the re-arrangement of terms made.

## § 8. A test of almost everywhere convergence for functions of $L^p(1 \leqslant p \leqslant 2)$

Marcinkiewicz[4] obtained an interesting generalization of Plessner's theorem when he proved the theorem:

THEOREM. *If* $1 \leqslant p \leqslant 2$ *and*

$$\int_0^{2\pi}\int_0^{2\pi} \frac{|f(x+t)-f(x-t)|^p}{t}\,dt\,dx < +\infty, \tag{8.1}$$

*then the Fourier series of* $f(x)$ *converges almost everywhere.*

For the case $p = 2$ this is Plessner's theorem. If $p = 1$, then our statement reduces to the Dini test (Chapter I, § 38).

Indeed, if (8.1) is fulfilled, then due to the periodicity of $f(x)$ and the oddness of the function under the integral sign in (8.1) we have

$$2\int_0^{2\pi}\int_0^{2\pi} \frac{|f(x+t)-f(x-t)|^p}{t}\,dt\,dx \geqslant \int_{-\pi}^{\pi} \frac{1}{|t|}\left\{\int_0^{2\pi} |f(x+t)-f(x-t)|^p\,dx\right\}dt$$

$$= \int_{-\pi}^{\pi} \frac{1}{|t|}\left\{\int_{-t}^{2\pi-t} |f(u+2t)-f(u)|^p\,du\right\}dt$$

$$= \int_{-\pi}^{\pi} \frac{1}{|t|}\left\{\int_0^{2\pi} |f(u+2t)-f(u)|^p\,du\right\}dt$$

$$= 2\int_0^{2\pi}\left\{\int_{-\pi}^{\pi} \frac{|f(u+2t)-f(u)|^p}{|2t|}\,dt\right\}du$$

$$= \int_0^{2\pi}\left\{\int_{-2\pi}^{2\pi} \frac{|f(u+v)-f(u)|^p}{|v|}\,dv\right\}du. \tag{8.2}$$

Here, changing the order of integration, we used Fubini's theorem (see Introductory Material, § 18); since it follows from (8.1) and (8.2) that

$$\int_0^{2\pi}\left\{\int_{-2\pi}^{2\pi} \left|\frac{f(u+v)-f(u)}{|v|}\right| dv\right\}du < +\infty,$$

then again from Fubini's theorem

$$\int_{-2\pi}^{2\pi} \left|\frac{f(u+v)-f(u)}{v}\right| dv < +\infty \tag{8.3}$$

for almost all $u \in [0, 2\pi]$, and then the Dini test is fulfilled for almost all $u$.

Thus, it remains to consider the case $1 < p < 2$.

Without disturbing the generality, it can be supposed that $f(x) \geqslant 0$, since, supposing that

$$f(x) = f_1(x) - f_2(x),$$

where $f_1(x) = f(x)$ for $f(x) \geqslant 0$, $f_1(x) = 0$ in the remaining cases, we see immediately that each of the non-negative functions $f_1(x)$ and $f_2(x)$ should satisfy condition (8.1).

We will denote by $A_n$, $B_n$ and $C_n$ the sets of points where, correspondingly,

$$f(x) \leqslant n, \quad n < f(x) \leqslant n+1, \quad f(x) > n+1$$

and by $C_x$ the set of points $t$ where $x + t \in C_n$ for $-\pi \leqslant t \leqslant \pi$ (here $n$ is fixed).

Let us assume that

$$\varphi(x) = \begin{cases} f(x) & \text{for } x \in A_n + B_n, \\ n+1 & \text{for } x \in C_n, \end{cases}$$

and let

$$\psi(x) = f(x) - \varphi(x).$$

We have already seen that (8.2) follows from (8.1) and this implies

$$\int_{-\pi}^{\pi} \frac{|f(x+t)-f(x)|^p}{t} dt < +\infty$$

almost everywhere in $[0, 2\pi]$ which means that this is all the more true almost everywhere in $A_n$. Then it is far more true that

$$\int_{C_x} \frac{|f(x+t)-f(x)|^p}{|t|} dt < +\infty \quad \text{almost everywhere in } A_n.$$

But if $x \in A_n$ and $t \in C_x$, then we have $|f(x+t) - f(x)| > 1$ and therefore it is all the more true that

$$\int_{C_x} \frac{|f(x+t)-f(x)|}{|t|} dt < +\infty \quad \text{almost everywhere in } A_n. \tag{8.4}$$

On the other hand, it is evident that

$$|\psi(x+t) - \psi(x)| \leqslant |f(x+t) - f(x)|$$

for $x \in A_n$ and $t \in C_x$. Therefore, from the inequality (8.4) we find that

$$\int_{C_x} \frac{|\psi(x+t)-\psi(x)|}{|t|} dt < +\infty \quad \text{almost everywhere in } A_n.$$

If $t$ does not lie in $C_x$, then $x+t$ does not lie in $C_n$ and then $\psi(x+t) = 0$; moreover, $\psi(x) = 0$ in $A_n$, which means that almost everywhere in $A_n$

$$\int_{-\pi}^{\pi} \frac{|\psi(x+t)-\psi(x)|}{|t|} dt = \int_{C_x} \frac{|\psi(x+t)-\psi(x)|}{|t|} dt < +\infty.$$

Then from the Dini test the Fourier series for $\psi(x)$ converges almost everywhere in $A_n$.

On the other hand, for all $x$ and $t$

$$|\varphi(x+t)-\varphi(x)| \leqslant |f(x+t)-f(x)|,$$

which means that if condition (8.1) is fulfilled for $f(x)$, then it is also fulfilled for $\varphi(x)$. But $\varphi(x)$ is bounded, therefore if condition (8.1) is fulfilled for $p<2$, then it is also true for $p=2$.

Thus,

$$\int_0^{2\pi}\int_0^{2\pi} \frac{|\varphi(x+t)-\varphi(x-t)|^2}{t}\,dt\,dx < +\infty,$$

and then according to Plessner's theorem, the Fourier series of $\varphi(x)$ converges almost everywhere. Since

$$f(x)=\varphi(x)+\psi(x),$$

then the Fourier series of $f(x)$ converges almost everywhere in $A_n$. Because this is true for any $n$ and $mA_n \to 2\pi$ as $n\to\infty$, then this series converges almost everywhere in $(-\pi,\pi)$ and hence the theorem is proved.

## § 9. Expression of the conditions of almost everywhere convergence in terms of the quadratic moduli of continuity and the best approximations

We already know (see § 2 and § 5) that if

$$\sigma(f)=\frac{a_0}{2}+\sum(a_n\cos nx+b_n\sin nx), \tag{9.1}$$

then the condition

$$\sum(a_n^2+b_n^2)\ln n < +\infty, \tag{9.2}$$

and also

$$\int_0^{2\pi}\int_0^{2\pi}\frac{[f(x+t)-f(x-t)]^2}{t}\,dt\,dx < +\infty \tag{9.3}$$

are sufficient for the convergence almost everywhere of the series (9.1) and in this case conditions (9.2) and (9.3) are equivalent.

Now, following Stechkin[6], we will prove several conditions equivalent to (9.2) and (9.3). These transformed conditions will be useful to obtain theorems referring to the convergence of the series $\sigma(f)$ not almost everywhere in $[-\pi,\pi]$ but almost everywhere in some interval $[a,b]$, $-\pi<a<b<\pi$.

We will define some notation. Let

$$\omega^{(2)}(\delta,f)=\sup_{0<h\leqslant\delta}\|\Delta_h f(x)\|_{L^2}=\sup_{0<h\leqslant\delta}\left\{\int_{-\pi}^{\pi}[f(x+h)-f(x-h)]^2\,dx\right\}^{1/2},$$

be the quadratic modulus of continuity; let

$$\omega_2^{(2)}(\delta,f)=\sup_{0<h\leqslant\delta}\|\Delta_h^2 f(x)\|_{L^2}=\sup_{0<h\leqslant\delta}\left\{\int_{-\pi}^{\pi}[f(x+2h)+f(x-2h)-2f(x)]^2\,dx\right\}^{1/2}$$

be the quadratic modulus of smoothness. Finally

$$R_{n+1}^{(2)}(f) = \|f(x) - S_n(x)\|_{L^2} = \left\{ \int_{-\pi}^{\pi} [f(x) - S_n(x)]^2 \, dx \right\}^{1/2},$$

where, as usual,

$$S_n(x) = \frac{a_0}{2} + \sum_{k=1}^{n} (a_k \cos kx + b_k \sin kx).$$

We will prove that conditions (9.2) and (9.3) are equivalent to each of the following conditions:

$$\sum_{n=1}^{\infty} \frac{1}{n} \{R_n^{(2)}(f)\}^2 < +\infty, \tag{9.4}$$

$$\sum_{n=1}^{\infty} \frac{1}{n} \left\{\omega_2^{(2)} \left(\frac{1}{n}, f\right)\right\}^2 < +\infty, \tag{9.5}$$

$$\sum_{n=1}^{\infty} \frac{1}{n} \left\{\omega^{(2)} \left(\frac{1}{n}, f\right)\right\}^2 < +\infty. \tag{9.6}$$

First it is necessary to know

LEMMA. *If $f(x) \in L^2 [-\pi, \pi]$, then*

$$\left[\omega^{(2)} \left(\frac{1}{n}, f\right)\right]^2 \leqslant \frac{8}{n^2} \sum_{k=1}^{n} k [R_k^{(2)} (f)]^2 \qquad (n = 1, 2, \ldots). \tag{9.7}$$

Indeed, by virtue of Parseval's equality,

$$\frac{1}{\pi} \int_{-\pi}^{\pi} [f(x + h) - f(x - h)]^2 \, dx = 4 \sum_{k=1}^{\infty} \varrho_k^2 \sin^2 kh$$

$$\leqslant 4 \left[\sum_{k=1}^{n} \varrho_k^2 \, k^2 h^2 + \sum_{k=n+1}^{\infty} \varrho_k^2\right] = 4 \left[h^2 \sum_{k=1}^{n} k^2 \varrho_k^2 + \sum_{k=n+1}^{\infty} \varrho_k^2\right],$$

where $\varrho_k^2 = a_k^2 + b_k^2$. Therefore

$$\left[\omega^{(2)} \left(\frac{1}{n}, f\right)\right]^2 = \sup_{0<h\leqslant 1/n} \int_{-\pi}^{\pi} |\Delta_h f(x)|^2 \, dx \leqslant 4\pi \left[\sum_{k=1}^{n} \left(\frac{k}{n} \varrho_k\right)^2 + \sum_{k=n+1}^{\infty} \varrho_k^2\right]$$

$$= \frac{4\pi}{n^2} \left\{1^2 \varrho_1^2 + 2^2 \varrho_2^2 + \cdots + n^2 \varrho_n^2 + n^2 \sum_{k=n+1}^{\infty} \varrho_k^2\right\}$$

$$= \frac{4\pi}{n^2} \sum_{k=1}^{n} (2k - 1) \sum_{m=k}^{n} \varrho_m^2 \leqslant \frac{8\pi}{n^2} \sum_{k=1}^{n} k \sum_{m=k}^{\infty} \varrho_m^2.$$

But

$$[R_{k+1}^{(2)}(f)] = \int_{-\pi}^{\pi} [f(x) - S_k(x)]^2 \, dx = \pi \sum_{m=k+1}^{\infty} \varrho_m^2, \tag{9.8}$$

which means that

$$\left[\omega^{(2)}\left(\frac{1}{n}, f\right)\right]^2 \leqslant \frac{8}{n^2}\sum_{k=1}^{n} k[R_k^{(2)}(f)]^2,$$

and the lemma is proved.

Let us return to the proof of the equivalence of all the conditions (9.2)–(9.6). Since

$$\sum_{k=1}^{n}\frac{1}{k} \sim \ln n,$$

then the convergence of series (9.2) is equivalent to the convergence of series

$$\sum_{n=1}^{\infty} \varrho_n^2 \sum_{k=1}^{n}\frac{1}{k}.$$

Since the terms of this series are non-negative, then it is possible to change the order of summation and to prove on the basis of (9.8) that this series can be rewritten in the form

$$\sum_{k=1}^{\infty}\frac{1}{k}\sum_{n=k}^{\infty}\varrho_n^2 = \frac{1}{\pi}\sum_{k=1}^{\infty}\frac{1}{k}[R_k^{(2)}(f)]^2,$$

and this is also series (9.4). Thus, (9.2) and (9.4) are equivalent; the equivalency of (9.2) and (9.3), as we have already said (see § 5), was proved by Plessner.

Now, on the basis of the just proved lemma, we see that

$$\sum_{n=1}^{\infty}\frac{1}{n}\left[\omega^{(2)}\left(\frac{1}{n}, f\right)\right]^2 \leqslant 8\sum_{n=1}^{\infty}\frac{1}{n^3}\sum_{k=1}^{n} k[R_k^{(2)}(f)]^2 = 8\sum_{k=1}^{\infty} k[R_k^{(2)}(f)]^2 \sum_{n=k}^{\infty}\frac{1}{n^3}$$

$$< C\sum_{k=1}^{\infty} k[R_k^{(2)}(f)]^2\frac{1}{k^2} = C\sum_{k=1}^{\infty}\frac{1}{k}[R_k^{(2)}(f)]^2,$$

and therefore the convergence of series (9.4) implies the convergence of series (9.6).

Since it is evident that

$$\omega_2^{(2)}\left(\frac{1}{n}, f\right) \leqslant 2\omega^{(2)}\left(\frac{1}{n}, f\right),$$

then the convergence of (9.6) implies the convergence of (9.5).

On the other hand, the convergence of (9.5) implies the convergence of (9.4); in fact, if we denote by $E_n^{(2)}(f)$ the best approximation to $f(x)$ by trigonometric polynomials of order not higher than $n$ in the metric space $L^2$, i.e.

$$E_n^{(2)}(f) = \min_{Tn}\left\{\int_{-\pi}^{\pi}[f(x) - T_n(x)]^2 dx\right\}^{1/2},$$

then since the minimum (see Chapter I, § 13) is attained here, when the partial sum of the Fourier series, i.e. $S_n(x)$ is taken as the polynomial $T_n(x)$, then

$$E_n^{(2)}(f) = R_{n+1}^{(2)}(f).$$

But according to Jackson's theorem for the space $L^2$ (see Appendix, § 7) we have

$$E_n^{(2)}(f) \leqslant C\omega_2^{(2)}\left(\frac{1}{n}, f\right).$$

Thus, the convergence of (9.5) implies the convergence of (9.4) and the equivalence of all the conditions (9.2)–(9.6) is proved.

## § 10. Tests of almost everywhere convergence in an interval of length less than $2\pi$

We will describe a number of theorems in which the conditions are considered for the Fourier series of some function to converge almost everywhere in an interval of length less than $2\pi$. Here again it is possible to use the method of "extension of a function" (see Chapter IV, § 9) in order to reduce this case to the case when the function possesses the required properties over the whole interval $[0, 2\pi]$.

To formulate the theorems we introduce some notation. Let us suppose that

$$\omega^{(2)}(\delta, f, a, b) = \sup_{0<h\leqslant\delta} \|\Delta_h f(x)\|_{(a,b)} = \sup_{0<h\leqslant\delta} \left\{\int_a^b [f(x+h) - f(x-h)]^2\, dx\right\}^{1/2},$$

$$\omega_2^{(2)}(\delta, f, a, b) = \sup_{0<h\leqslant\delta} \|\Delta_h^{(2)} f(x)\|_{(a,b)}$$

$$= \sup_{0<h\leqslant\delta} \left\{\int_a^b |f(x+h) + f(x-h) - 2f(x)|^2\, dx\right\}^{1/2}$$

and

$$R_{n+1}^{(2)}(f, a, b) = \left\{\int_a^b |f(x) - S_n(x)|^2\, dx\right\}^{1/2} \qquad (n = 1, 2, \ldots).$$

Of course for the definition of $\omega^{(2)}$ or $\omega_2^{(2)}$ it is necessary that $f(x) \in L^2$ not only in the interval $[a, b]$ but in some interval containing it, otherwise the integrals will not have any meaning; but $\omega_2^{(2)}(\delta, f, a', b')$ and $\omega^{(2)}(\delta, f, a', b')$, if $(a', b')$ is strictly within $(a, b)$ and $\delta$ is sufficiently small have meaning if $f(x) \in L^2$ in $[a, b]$.

With this notation Stechkin's[6] theorem will hold.

THEOREM. *If $f(x) \in L$ in $[0, 2\pi]$ and for any $(a', b')$, lying entirely within $[a, b]$, we have $f(x) \in L^2$ in $(a', b')$ and*

$$\sum_{n=1}^{\infty} \frac{1}{n} [R_n^{(2)}(f, a', b')]^2 < +\infty \tag{10.1}$$

*or*

$$\sum_{n=N}^{\infty} \frac{1}{n} \left[\omega_2^{(2)}\left(\frac{1}{n}, f, a', b'\right)\right]^2 < +\infty, \tag{10.2}$$

*or*

$$\sum_{n=N}^{\infty} \frac{1}{n} \left[\omega^{(2)}\left(\frac{1}{n}, f, a', b'\right)\right]^2 < +\infty, \tag{10.3}$$

*then the series $\sigma(f)$ converges almost everywhere in $(a, b)$.*

Note that for the series (10.2) and (10.3), the estimate must start not with $n=1$ but with some sufficiently large $N$ since $f(x) \in L^2$ only in $(a', b')$ but not in $(a, b)$ and therefore the integrals entering into the expression for $\omega^{(2)}$ and $\omega_2^{(2)}$ for small $n$ cannot have meaning; this has no effect on the convergence of the series $\sigma(f)$.

We will not give a proof of this theorem here but refer to the author's work; we note only that Stechkin had to "extend" the function from the interval $[a, b]$ to the interval $[0, 2\pi]$ so that quadratic modulus of continuity or quadratic modulus of smoothness, roughly speaking, maintains its order. After this, the theorems in § 9 could be used.

Also, we denote by $E_n^{(2)}(f, a, b)$ the best approximation in the metric $L^2$ for a function $f(x)$ in the interval $(a, b)$ then the following theorem holds (see Bary[91]):

THEOREM. *If $f(x) \in L$ in $[0, 2\pi]$ and if for any $(a', b')$ lying strictly within $(a, b)$, we have*

$$\sum_{n=1}^{\infty} \frac{[E_n^{(2)}(f, a', b')]^2}{n} < +\infty,$$

*then $\sigma(f)$ converges almost everywhere in $(a, b)$.*

Condition (B) of § 5 can also be transferred to the interval $[a, b]$, which was also done by Ul'yanov[11] in proving the theorem:

THEOREM. *Let $f(x) \in L\,[0, 2\pi]$ and $f(x) \in L^2(a', b')$ for any $(a', b') \subset (a, b) \subset [0, 2\pi]$. If for any $\varepsilon > 0$ $(\varepsilon < (b-a)/4)$ we have*

$$\int_{a+\varepsilon}^{b-\varepsilon} \int_0^{\varepsilon/2} \frac{|f(x+t) - f(x-t)|^2}{t}\, dt\, dx < A(\varepsilon) < +\infty, \tag{10.4}$$

*then the series $\sigma(f)$ converges almost everywhere in $(a, b)$.*

Ul'yanov proved this theorem for the case when $f(x) \in L^p (1 \leqslant p \leqslant 2)$ and $|f(x+t) - f(x-t)|^p$ is under the integral sign, but in the preceding formulation we confined ourselves to the case $p = 2$ in order to compare this theorem later with the remaining ones being discussed in this section.

In view of the fact that the proof here is not lengthy and is extremely simple, we will work it through completely.

*Proof.* Let $0 < \delta \leqslant \delta_0 = \min\{(b - a - 2\varepsilon)/4, \varepsilon\}$. Let us assume that $a_1 = a + \varepsilon$, $b_1 = b - \varepsilon$ and

$$\varphi(x) = \begin{cases} 1 & \text{for } x \in (a_1 + \delta, b_1 - \delta), \\ 0 & \text{for } x \in \left[0, a_1 + \dfrac{\delta}{2}\right] + \left[b_1 - \dfrac{\delta}{2}, 2\pi\right], \end{cases}$$

and interpolate $\varphi(x)$ linearly in the intervals $[a_1 + \delta/2, a_1 + \delta]$ and $[b_1 - \delta, b_1 - \delta/2]$; we will also expand it periodically. It is clear that $\varphi(x) \in \mathrm{Lip}\, 1$, more precisely that

$$|\varphi(x_2) - \varphi(x_1)| \leqslant K|x_2 - x_1|, \quad \text{where} \quad K = \frac{2}{\delta}. \tag{10.5}$$

Let us suppose that $F(x) = f(x)\varphi(x)$ and $F(x) = 0$, if $\varphi(x) = 0$. It is evident that $F(x) \in L^2\,[0, 2\pi]$. We will prove that

$$\int^{2\pi} \int^{2\pi} \frac{[F(x+t) - F(x-t)]^2}{t}\, dt\, dx < +\infty. \tag{10.6}$$

Since for any $\eta > 0$ it is evident that

$$\int_0^{2\pi}\int_\eta^{2\pi} \frac{[F(x+t)-F(x-t)]^2}{t}\,dt\,dx < +\infty,$$

then it is sufficient to prove that

$$I = \int_0^{2\pi}\int_0^{\delta/4} \frac{[F(x+t)-F(x-t)]^2}{t}\,dt\,dx < +\infty.$$

But $F(x) = 0$ for $x \in [0, a_1 + \delta/2] + [b_1 - \delta/2, 2\pi]$, therefore

$$I = \int_{a_1+\frac{\delta}{4}}^{a_1+2\delta}\int_0^{\delta/4} + \int_{a_1+2\delta}^{b_1-2\delta}\int_0^{\delta/4} + \int_{b_1-2\delta}^{b_1-\frac{\delta}{4}}\int_0^{\delta/4} \frac{[F(x+t)-F(x-t)]^2}{t}\,dt\,dx = I_1 + I_2 + I_3.$$

First let us estimate $I_2$; supposing under the conditions of the theorem $\varepsilon = 2\delta$, we see that

$$I_2 = \int_{a_1+2\delta}^{b_1-2\delta}\int_0^{\delta/4} \frac{[F(x+t)-F(x-t)]^2}{t}\,dt\,dx$$

$$= \int_{a_1+2\delta}^{b_1-2\delta}\int_0^{\delta/4} \frac{[f(x+t)-f(x-t)]^2}{t}\,dt\,dx \leqslant A(\varepsilon) < +\infty.$$

It remains to estimate $I_1$ and $I_3$. But it is evident from the course of the proof that the estimates for the integrals $I_1$ and $I_3$ are exactly similar. Let us consider, for example,

$$I_1 = \int_{a_1+\frac{\delta}{4}}^{a_1+2\delta}\int_0^{\delta/4} \frac{[F(x+t)-F(x-t)]^2}{t}\,dt\,dx.$$

Since $|\varphi(x)| \leqslant 1$ and (10.5) is satisfied, then we have

$$[F(x+t)-F(x-t)]^2 = [f(x+t)\varphi(x+t) - f(x-t)\,\varphi(x-t)]^2$$

$$= [f(x+t)\varphi(x+t) - f(x+t)\,\varphi(x-t) + f(x+t)\,\varphi(x-t)$$

$$- f(x-t)\,\varphi(x-t)]^2$$

$$\leqslant 2\,|f(x+t)|^2\,[\varphi(x+t)-\varphi(x-t)]^2 + 2[f(x+t)-f(x-t)]^2$$

$$\leqslant \frac{32t^2}{\delta^2}\,|f(x+t)|^2 + 2[f(x+t)-f(x-t)]^2.$$

From this it follows that

$$\frac{[F(x+t)-F(x-t)]^2}{t} \leqslant \frac{32}{\delta^2} t\,|f(x+t)|^2 + 2\frac{[f(x+t)-f(x-t)]^2}{t},$$

and therefore due to the choice of $\delta$, the condition $f \in L^2(a+\varepsilon, b-\varepsilon)$ and the inequality

$$I_1 \leqslant \frac{32}{\delta^2} \int\limits_{a_1+\frac{\delta}{4}}^{a_1+2\delta} \int\limits_0^{\delta/4} t\,|f(x-t)|^2\,dt\,dx + 2 \int\limits_{a_1+\frac{\delta}{4}}^{a_1+2\delta} \int\limits_0^{\delta/4} \frac{|f(x+t)-f(x-t)|^2}{t}\,dt\,dx < +\infty$$

we see that

$$\int\limits_0^{2\pi}\int\limits_0^{2\pi} \frac{[F(x+t)-F(x-t)]^2}{t}\,dt\,dx < +\infty,$$

and then according to Plessner's theorem the Fourier series of $F(x)$ converges almost everywhere in $[0, 2\pi]$. But for $x \in [a_1+\delta, b_1-\delta]$ we have $F(x) = f(x)$, which means that from Riemann's principle of localization for Fourier series $\sigma(f)$ converges almost everywhere in $[a_1+\delta, b_1-\delta]$, i.e. almost everywhere in $[a_1+2\varepsilon, b_1-2\varepsilon]$. But $\varepsilon > 0$ is arbitrary, therefore the Fourier series of $f(x)$ converges almost everywhere in $[a, b]$. The theorem is completely proved.

We have applied all the conditions given in § 9 to the case of the interval $[a, b]$, which are equivalent to the condition (9.2) occurring in the Kolmogorov–Seliverstov and Plessner theorem. As regards this condition (9.2) itself, i.e.

$$\sum (a_n^2 + b_n^2) \ln n < +\infty,$$

it can be shown that its transfer to the interval $[a, b]$ is not possible, since it makes no reference to the behaviour of the function in any interval. However, Ul'yanov stated quite correctly that this condition is contained in the Fourier coefficients themselves, and therefore the natural transfer of the Kolmogorov–Seliverstov and Plessner theorem from the interval $[0, 2\pi]$ to the interval $[a, b]$ gives this theorem.

THEOREM. *If $f(x) \in L\,[0, 2\pi]$ and $f(x) \in L^2\,[a, b]$, then from the condition*

$$\sum_{n=2}^{\infty} \left[ \left( \int_a^b f(x) \cos nx\,dx \right)^2 + \left( \int_a^b f(x) \sin nx\,dx \right)^2 \right] \ln n < +\infty \tag{10.7}$$

*the almost everywhere convergence in $[a, b]$ of the Fourier series for $f(x)$ follows.*

Indeed, supposing that

$$f_1(x) = \begin{cases} f(x) & \text{for } x \in [a, b], \\ 0 & \text{outside } [a, b], \end{cases}$$

we see that if $\alpha_k$ and $\beta_k$ are Fourier coefficients for $f_1(x)$, then the condition (10.7) signifies that

$$\sum_{n=2}^{\infty} (\alpha_n^2 + \beta_n^2) \ln n < +\infty,$$

and therefore the Fourier series of $f_1(x)$ converges almost everywhere. But then due to the principle of localization the Fourier series of $f(x)$ converges almost everywhere in $[a, b]$. The theorem is proved.

We will not dwell on the proof of the equivalence of all the sufficiency conditions introduced here for the convergence of a Fourier series almost everywhere in $[a, b]$, but will merely refer to the reports by Stechkin[6], Ul'yanov[1] and Bary[9], already cited.

We will also note that the problem of the transfer of the conditions of almost everywhere convergence to the case when the interval $[a, b]$ is concerned was studied by Alexits[1]. He first proved that the condition

$$\sum (a_n^2 + b_n^2) \ln n < +\infty$$

is equivalent to this condition: if there exists a positive monotonically increasing function $\lambda(x)$ for which

$$\int_0^\infty \frac{dx}{x\lambda(x)} < +\infty \quad \text{and} \quad \omega^{(2)}(\delta, f) = O\left(\frac{1}{\sqrt{\lambda\left(\frac{1}{\delta}\right)}}\right),$$

then, transferring to the case of the interval $[a, b]$, he obtained the theorem:

*If $f(x) \in L\,[0, 2\pi]$, $f(x) \in L^2\,[a, b]$ and*

$$\omega^{(2)}(\delta, f, a, b) = O\left(\frac{1}{\sqrt{\lambda\left(\frac{1}{\delta}\right)}}\right),$$

*where $\lambda(x)$ is positive, monotonically increases and satisfies the condition $\int_0^\infty [1/x\lambda(x)]\,dx < +\infty$, then the series $\sigma(f)$ converges almost everywhere in $[a, b]$.*

To end this section, we want to show that, using the conditions obtained for almost everywhere convergence in some interval, it is possible to strengthen somewhat the Kolmogorov–Seliverstov and Plessner result for the classical case of almost everywhere convergence.

In fact, if $f(x)$ does not belong to $L^2$ in $[0, 2\pi]$, then the Kolmogorov–Seliverstov and Plessner test cannot be applied. However, it is quite possible, for example, that in any interval $(a_k, b_k)$ adjacent to some closed set $F$ of measure zero, for any $(a', b')$ lying in $(a_k, b_k)$, the condition is fulfilled that

$$\sum_{n=1}^{\infty} \frac{1}{n} [R_n^{(2)}(f, a', b')]^2 < +\infty$$

(or any one which is equivalent to it). Then $\sigma(f)$ will converge almost everywhere in $(a_k, b_k)$ and because this holds for any $k$, then $\sigma(f)$ converges almost everywhere (since $mF = 0$). This note is due to Stechkin.

A similar note was made by Ul'yanov with reference to this theorem, formulated earlier (see Corollary 3 on p. 516 in Ul'yanov's report[11]). Generalizing Ul'yanov's idea, it is possible to formulate this corollary from the derived theorems:

*Let $f(x) \in L$ in $[0, 2\pi]$ and for almost any point $x_0$ in $[0, 2\pi]$ let there be a neighbourhood $\delta(x_0)$ and a function $\varphi(x) = \varphi(x, \delta(x_0))$ such that $f(x) \equiv \varphi(x, \delta(x_0))$*

*in* $\delta(x_0)$ *and the function* $\varphi(x)$ *satisfies in* $\delta(x_0)$ *one of the conditions guaranteeing almost everywhere convergence of its series* $\sigma(\varphi)$ *in this* $\delta$*; then the series* $\sigma(f)$ *converges almost everywhere in* $[0, 2\pi]$.

Some particular examples of such local conditions are those considered by Stechkin, Ul'yanov and Alexits.

## § 11. Indices of convergence

We know (see Chapter I, § 65) that if $f(x) \in L^2$, then for any lacunary sequence $\{n_k\}$ we have $S_{n_k}(x) \to f(x)$ almost everywhere.

On the other hand (see § 2), if

$$\sum (a_n^2 + b_n^2) \ln n < +\infty,$$

then

$$S_n(x) \to f(x) \quad \text{almost everywhere}$$

Salem[1] asked himself the following question: what can be said concerning the behaviour of the partial sums of the Fourier series for $f(x)$, if it is known for its coefficients that

$$\sum (a_n^2 + b_n^2)\, \omega(n) < +\infty, \tag{11.1}$$

where $\omega(n) \uparrow \infty$, but $\omega(n)$ increases more slowly than $\ln n$? To answer this question, he introduced the following definition:

DEFINITION. A sequence of integers $\{n_k\}$ is known as *a sequence of indices of convergence* for $f(x)$ if

$$S_{n_k}(x) \to f(x)$$

almost everywhere as $k \to \infty$.

Using this definition, he proved the following theorem:

THEOREM. *If* $\omega(n) \uparrow \infty$ *and* $\sum (a_n^2 + b_n^2)\, \omega(n) < +\infty$, *then a sequence* $\{n_k\}$ *can be found which varies only with* $\omega(n)$ *and not with* $f(x)$, *such that* $\{n_k\}$ *is the sequence of the indices of convergence for any* $f(x)$ *satisfying* (11.1).

Strictly speaking, it is not a question of searching for any sequence $\{n_k\}$ dependent only on $\omega(n)$ but for a sequence which increases as slowly as possible, otherwise a lacunary sequence could be used for $\{n_k\}$ in which case the problem would be solved immediately. Of course, the more rapidly $\omega(n)$ increases, then the greater the hope is that $\{n_k\}$ can be made to increase slowly.

We will describe the method that Salem used to obtain $\{n_k\}$ for a given $\omega(n)$.

First of all, as is also done in the proof of the Kolmogorov–Seliverstov and Plessner theorem, Salem gives an estimate for the integral

$$I = \int_0^{2\pi} S_{n(x)}(f)\, dx, \tag{11.2}$$

where $n(x)$ varies with $x$, but can only take the values $1, 2, \ldots, n$.

For brevity's sake, let us suppose that

$$A_p(x) = a_p \cos px + b_p \sin px \quad (p \geqslant 1)$$

and we will take $a_0 = 0$.

The function $S_{n(x)}(f)$ can be written in the form

$$S_{n(x)}(f) = \sum_{p=1}^{n} \psi_p A_p,$$

where

$$\psi_p(x) = \begin{cases} 1, & \text{if } \; p \leqslant n(x), \\ 0, & \text{if } \; p > n(x). \end{cases}$$

From this definition of the function $\psi_p(x)$ it follows that $\psi_p(x) \geqslant \psi_{p+1}(x)$. We have

$$I = \int_0^{2\pi} \left[ \sum_{p=1}^{n} \psi_p A_p \right] dx.$$

We have assumed that the series $\sum (a_n^2 + b_n^2)\,\omega(n)$ converges. This means that $F(x) \in L^2$ exists such that its Fourier series is $\sum (a_n \cos nx + b_n \sin nx)\sqrt{\omega(n)}$. Applying Abel's transformation, we find that

$$I = \int_0^{2\pi} \sum_{p=1}^{n} \frac{\psi_p}{\sqrt{\omega(p)}} A_p \sqrt{\omega(p)}\, dx = \int_0^{2\pi} \sum_{p=n}^{n} \Delta \left( \frac{\psi_p}{\sqrt{\omega_p}} \right) S_p(F)\, dx,$$

where $\Delta u_p = u_p - u_{p+1}$, if $p \neq n$ and $\Delta u_n = u_n$. We have

$$I = \int_0^{2\pi} \sum_{p=1}^{n} \frac{\Delta \psi_p S_p(F)}{\sqrt{\omega(p)}}\, dx + \sum_{p=1}^{n} \Delta \left( \frac{1}{\sqrt{\omega(p)}} \right) \int_0^{2\pi} \psi_{p+1} S_p(F)\, dx. \tag{11.3}$$

Since $|\psi_{p+1}(x)| \leqslant 1$, then

$$\left| \int_0^{2\pi} \psi_{p+1} S_p(F)\, dx \right| \leqslant \left( 2\pi \int_0^{2\pi} F^2\, dx \right)^{1/2},$$

moreover

$$\sum_{p=1}^{n} \Delta \left( \frac{1}{\sqrt{\omega(p)}} \right) \leqslant \frac{1}{\sqrt{\omega(1)}},$$

and therefore

$$|I| \leqslant \left| \int_0^{2\pi} \sum_{p=1}^{n} \frac{\Delta \psi_p S_p(F)}{\sqrt{\omega(p)}}\, dx \right| + \left( \frac{2\pi}{\omega(1)} \int_0^{2\pi} F^2(x)\, dx \right)^{1/2}. \tag{11.4}$$

Let us continue with the estimate of the integral

$$J = \int_0^{2\pi} \sum_{p=1}^{n} \frac{\Delta \psi_p S_p(F)}{\sqrt{\omega(p)}}\, dx. \tag{11.5}$$

It can be written in the form

$$J = \int_0^{2\pi} F(x)\left(\sum_{p=1}^{n} \frac{S_p(\Delta\psi_p)}{\sqrt{\omega(p)}}\right) dx.$$

Indeed, $\int_0^{2\pi} FS_p(\Delta\psi_p)\,dx = \int_0^{2\pi} \Delta\psi_p S_p(F)\,dx$, since each of these integrals by virtue of Parseval's equality is the $p$th partial sum of a series, the terms of which are the products of the coefficients of the Fourier series for $F$ and for $\Delta\psi_p$. We have

$$J^2 \leqslant \int_0^{2\pi} F^2\,dx \int_0^{2\pi}\left[\frac{S_1(\Delta\psi_1)}{\sqrt{\omega(1)}} + \cdots + \frac{S_n(\Delta\psi_n)}{\sqrt{\omega(n)}}\right]^2 dx = J_0 \int_0^{2\pi} F^2(x)\,dx. \quad (11.6)$$

We will examine the integral $J_0$. We have

$$J_0 = \int_0^{2\pi} \sum_{p=1}^{n} \frac{[S_p(\Delta\psi_p)]^2}{\omega(p)}\,dx + 2\int_0^{2\pi} \sum_{p<q} \frac{S_p(\Delta\psi_p)S_q(\Delta\psi_q)}{\sqrt{\omega(p)\,\omega(q)}}\,dx, \quad (11.7)$$

but

$$\sum_{p=1}^{n}\int_0^{2\pi} \frac{[S_p(\Delta\psi_p)]^2}{\omega(p)}\,dx \leqslant \sum_{p=1}^{n}\int_0^{2\pi} \frac{(\Delta\psi_p)^2}{\omega(p)}\,dx,$$

and since the sequence $\psi_p(x)$ is monotonically decreasing and moreover $\psi_p(x) = 1$ or $0$, then $(\Delta\psi_p)^2 = \Delta\psi_p$ and $\sum_{p=1}^{n}(\Delta\psi_p)^2 = \psi_1$; moreover, $\omega(p)$ monotonically increases, therefore for the first term of the right-hand side of equality (11.7) we find that

$$\int_0^{2\pi} \sum_{p=1}^{n} \frac{[S_p(\Delta\psi_p)]^2}{\omega(p)}\,dx \leqslant \frac{1}{\omega(1)}\int_0^{2\pi} \psi_1(x)\,dx < \frac{2\pi}{\omega(1)}. \quad (11.8)$$

Also we have

$$\sum_{q=p+1}^{n}\int_0^{2\pi} \frac{S_p(\Delta\psi_p)\,S_q(\Delta\psi_q)}{\sqrt{\omega(p)\omega(q)}}\,dx = \sum_{q=p+1}^{n}\int_0^{2\pi} \frac{S_p(\Delta\psi_p)\,\Delta\psi_q}{\sqrt{\omega(p)\,\omega(q)}}\,dx,$$

since

$$\int_0^{2\pi} S_p(\Delta\psi_p)\,\Delta\psi_q\,dx = \int_0^{2\pi} S_p(\Delta\psi_p)\,S_q(\Delta\psi_q)\,dx.$$

The latter equality follows from the fact that each of the integrals on the left-hand side, by virtue of Parseval's equality and the condition $p < q$, is the $p$th partial sum of the series consisting of the products of the Fourier coefficients for $S_p(\Delta\psi_p)$ and for $\Delta\psi_q$.

Therefore, we can write

$$\sum_{q=p+1}^{n}\int_{0}^{2\pi}\frac{S_p(\Delta\psi_p)\Delta\psi_q}{\sqrt{\omega(p)\,\omega(q)}}\,dx=\int_{0}^{2\pi}\frac{S_p(\Delta\psi_p)}{\sqrt{\omega(p)}}\sum_{q=p+1}^{n}\frac{\Delta\psi_q}{\sqrt{\omega(q)}}\,dx=\int_{0}^{2\pi}\frac{S_p(\Delta\psi_p)}{\omega(p)}\chi_p(x)\,dx,$$

if we have assumed that

$$\chi_p(x)=\sqrt{\omega(p)}\left[\frac{\Delta\psi_{p+1}}{\sqrt{\omega(p+1)}}+\cdots+\frac{\Delta\psi_n}{\sqrt{\omega(n)}}\right].$$

Again applying Parseval's formula, we prove that

$$\int_{0}^{2\pi}\frac{S_p(\Delta\psi_p)}{\omega(p)}\chi_p(x)\,dx=\int_{0}^{2\pi}\Delta\psi_p\frac{S_p(\chi_p)}{\omega(p)}\,dx.$$

Now let $k_p$ and $k_p'$ be two positive numbers which we will choose later but such that

$$\frac{1}{k_p}+\frac{1}{k_p'}=1.$$

Due to Young's inequality (see Introductory Material, § 8)

$$\Delta\psi_p\frac{|S_p(\chi_p)|}{\omega(p)}\leqslant\frac{1}{k_p}\left[\frac{|S_p(\chi_p)|}{\omega(p)}\right]^{k_p}+\frac{1}{k_p'}(\Delta\psi_p)^{k_p'}.$$

Consequently

$$\left|\sum_{p=1}^{n}\int_{0}^{2\pi}\Delta\psi_p\frac{S_p(\chi_p)}{\omega(p)}\,dx\right|\leqslant\sum_{p=1}^{n}\int_{0}^{2\pi}\frac{1}{k_p}\frac{|S_p(\chi_p)|^{k_p}}{[\omega(p)]^{k_p}}\,dx+\int_{0}^{2\pi}\psi_1(x)\,dx.$$

But for any $f\in L^p$ we have

$$\left(\int_{0}^{2\pi}|S_n(f)|^p\,dx\right)^{1/p}\leqslant A_p\left(\int_{0}^{2\pi}|f|^p\,dx\right)^{1/p},$$

where $A_p$ are constants dependent only on $p$, whilst for $p\geqslant 2$ we have $A_p<2p$ (see Chapter VIII, § 14).

If this is so, then by choosing $k_p\geqslant 2$ we can write

$$\int_{0}^{2\pi}|S_p(\chi_p)|^{k_p}\,dx\leqslant(4k_p)^{k_p}\int_{0}^{2\pi}(\chi_p)^{k_p}\,dx<2\pi(4k_p)^{k_p},$$

because, as is evident from the definition of $\chi_p(x)$, it is positive and less than unity.

Hence it follows that

$$\left|\sum_{p=1}^{n}\int_{0}^{2\pi}\Delta\psi_p\frac{S_p(\chi_p)}{\omega(p)}\,dx\right|<2\pi\sum_{p=1}^{n}\frac{1}{k_p}\left[\frac{4k_p}{\omega(p)}\right]^{k_p}+2\pi. \tag{11.9}$$

Here $k_p$ can be chosen as desired, provided only that $k_p\geqslant 2$.

In trying to make the right-hand side of (11.9) a minimum, we should find the minimum of the expression

$$\frac{1}{k_p}\left[\frac{4k_p}{\omega(p)}\right]^{k_p}.$$

But this requires the solution of the transcendental equation

$$4\frac{k_p e}{\omega(p)} = e^{1/k_p}.$$

If we assume that

$$k_p = \frac{\omega(p)}{4e}, \tag{11.10}$$

then this gives an approximate solution, because $\omega(p)\to\infty$. This choice is possible only at

$$\omega(p) \geqslant 8e,$$

which will occur provided $p$ is sufficiently large and $p \geqslant p_0$. Let us assume that

$$k_p = 2, \quad \text{if} \quad p < p_0,$$

and define $k_p$ according to the formula (11.10) for $p \geqslant p_0$. Then from (11.9) it follows that

$$\left|\sum_{p=1}^{n}\int_0^{2\pi} \Delta\psi_p \frac{S_p(\chi_p)}{\omega(p)}\,dx\right| \leqslant 2\pi\sum_{p=1}^{p_0}\frac{1}{2}\left[\frac{8}{\omega(p)}\right]^2 + 2\pi\sum_{p=p_0+1}^{n}\frac{4e}{\omega(p)}\left(\frac{1}{e}\right)^{\frac{\omega(p)}{4e}} + 2\pi. \tag{11.11}$$

From formula (11.4) and the expression of the integral $J$ in formula (11.5) it is immediately evident that on the left-hand side of the inequality (11.11) the quantity $p$ must take only those values which $n(x)$ can take in the integral $I$, since for other values we have $\Delta\psi_p = 0$. Therefore, if $n(x)$ only runs through the values occurring in some sequence $\{n_k\}$, the conditions under which the series

$$\sum_{k=1}^{\infty}\frac{1}{\omega(n_k)}\left(\frac{1}{e}\right)^{\frac{\omega(n_k)}{4e}}.$$

converges must be examined. Moreover, since the numbers $\omega(n_k)$ can be multiplied by any constant, without disturbing the convergence of the series $\sum (a_n^2 + b_n^2)\,\omega(n)$, the left-hand side of the inequality (11.11) remains bounded, provided the series

$$\sum_{k=1}^{\infty}\frac{1}{\omega(n_k)}\left(\frac{1}{A}\right)^{\omega(n_k)},$$

converges, where $A$ can be taken to be as large as desired. Consequently, on fulfilment of this condition, we will have

$$I < C\left(\int_0^{2\pi} F^2\,dx\right)^{1/2},$$

where $C$ depends on $\omega(n)$ but not on $f$. Hence, by the same method as was used in proving the Kolmogorov–Seliverstov and Plessner theorem, it is possible to conclude that $S_{n_k}(f)$ converges almost everywhere to $f(x)$.

Thus we obtain:

THEOREM. *If the series* $\sum (a_n^2 + b_n^2)\,\omega(n)$ *converges and if for the sequence* $\{n_k\}$ *it is possible to find a constant* $A$ *such that*

$$\sum_{k=1}^{\infty} \frac{1}{\omega(n_k)} \left(\frac{1}{A}\right)^{\omega(n_k)} < +\infty, \tag{11.12}$$

*then the sequence* $\{n_k\}$ *is a sequence of the indices of convergence.*

In particular, if $\omega(n) = \ln n$ and $n_k = k$ for $k \geqslant 2$, then

$$\sum_{k=2}^{\infty} \frac{1}{\ln k} \left(\frac{1}{A}\right)^{\ln k} < \sum_{k=1}^{\infty} \frac{1}{k^{\ln A}} < +\infty,$$

provided $A > \varepsilon$, and we revert to the Kolmogorov–Seliverstov and Plessner theorem.

If it is assumed, for example, that $\omega(n) = \sqrt{\ln n}$, then it is sufficient to take $n_k$ as increasing, as in $k^{\ln k}$, for the series (11.12) to be convergent. The growth of $k^{\ln k}$ is sufficiently rapid, but nevertheless very much slower than that of a lacunary sequence, because $k^{\ln k} = e^{(\ln k)^2}$.

Salem noted that if $\omega(n)$ increases very slowly and especially if $\omega(n) = \text{const}$, then this estimate does not give anything useful and, in particular, does not provide a theorem concerning lacunary sequences of the series $\sigma(f)$ for $f \in L^2$. However, in this case another simpler method can be applied and then a good estimate is obtained. For this we proceed in the following way.

Let us denote by $\sigma_n(f)$ the Fejér sum of order $n$ for the Fourier series of $f(x)$. If $\varrho_n^2 = a_n^2 + b_n^2$, then we have from Parseval's equality

$$\int_0^{2\pi} [S_n(f) - \sigma_n(f)]^2\,dx = \pi\,\frac{\varrho_1^2 + 2\varrho_2^2 + \cdots + n^2\varrho_n^2}{(n+1)^2}.$$

Let us consider the sequence $\{n_k\}$ for which

$$\sum_{k=1}^{\infty} \frac{\varrho_1^2 + 2\varrho_2^2 + \cdots + n_k^2\varrho_{n_k}^2}{n_k^2} < +\infty. \tag{11.13}$$

Then we will have

$$\sum_{k=1}^{\infty} \int_0^{2\pi} [S_{n_k}(f) - \sigma_{n_k}(f)]^2\,dx < +\infty,$$

i.e. almost everywhere $\sum_{k=1}^{\infty} [S_{n_k}(f) - \sigma_{n_k}(f)]^2 < +\infty$ and therefore it is all the more true that

$$S_{n_k}(f) - \sigma_{n_k}(f) \to 0$$

almost everywhere, whence it follows that $S_{n_k}(f) \to f$ almost everywhere. In this it is even not necessary that $f \in L^2$.

For example, if we assume only that $n\varrho_n^2 \to 0$ (although $f \bar{\in} L^2$), then it is possible to choose a sequence $n_k$ such that condition (11.13) is satisfied. Indeed, if $n\varrho_n^2 \to 0$, then we have

$$u_n = \frac{\varrho_1^2 + 2^2\varrho_2^2 + \cdots + n^2\varrho_n^2}{n^2} < \frac{1}{n}[1\varrho_1^2 + 2\varrho_2^2 + \cdots + n\varrho_n^2] \to 0,$$

as the arithmetic mean of the values tending to zero. Therefore it is possible to choose the values $n_k$ so that $\sum u_{n_k} < +\infty$ and consequently (11.13) is then fulfilled, which means that $\{n_k\}$ is a sequence of the indices of convergence.

Now let $f \in L^2$. Moreover, let

$$\sum \varrho_n^2 \omega(n) < +\infty.$$

We will prove that then (11.13) will be fulfilled, if

(a) $\dfrac{n^2}{\omega(n)} \uparrow$,

(b) $\dfrac{1}{n_k^2} + \dfrac{1}{n_{k+1}^2} + \cdots = O\left(\dfrac{\omega(n_k)}{n_k^2}\right)$.

In fact, supposing that $n_0 = 0$, the left-hand side of (11.13) can be written in the form

$$\sum_{k=1}^{\infty} \frac{\varrho_1^2 + 2^2\varrho_2^2 + \cdots + n_k^2\varrho_{n_k}^2}{n_k^2} = \sum_{k=1}^{\infty}\left(\sum_{j=n_{k-1}+1}^{n_k} j^2\varrho_j^2\right)\left(\frac{1}{n_k^2} + \frac{1}{n_{k+1}^2} + \cdots\right)$$

$$\leqslant C\sum_{k=1}^{\infty}\left(\sum_{j=n_{k-1}+1}^{n_k} j^2\varrho_j^2\right)\frac{\omega(n_k)}{n_k^2} < C\sum_{s=1}^{\infty}\varrho_s^2\omega(s),$$

since if $j \leqslant n_k$, then $j^2/\omega(j) \leqslant n_k^2/\omega(n_k)$ due to the hypothesis $n^2/\omega(n)\uparrow$. Thus, the fulfilment of condition (b) for a monotonic increase of $n^2/\omega(n)$ guarantees condition (11.13) and from what has been proved earlier leads to the conclusion that $\{n_k\}$ is a sequence of indices of convergence. Thus it is proved that:

THEOREM. *If $n^2/\omega(n)$ increases monotonically, then for all the functions satisfying condition*

$$\sum (a_n^2 + b_n^2)\,\omega(n) < +\infty,$$

*the sequence $\{n_k\}$ satisfying the condition*

$$\frac{1}{n_k^2} + \frac{1}{n_{k+1}^2} + \cdots = O\left(\frac{\omega(n_k)}{n_k^2}\right),$$

*is a sequence of indices of convergence.*

In particular, supposing that $\omega(n) = \text{const}$, we see that any lacunary sequence can be taken $\{n_k\}$ (and moreover even any sequence satisfying condition $(L)$, see Chapter I, § 65) and we find once more the theorem proved in Chapter I, § 65.

If $\omega(n)$ itself increases, then new results are obtained.

We now want to note that in the very definition of the sequence of indices of convergence no requirements were demanded of $f(x)$ apart from its summability. Here we have considered the functions $f(x) \in L^2$. But the indices of convergence can be studied for $f(x) \in L^p$ at $1 \leqslant p \leqslant 2$. We will describe some results obtained in this connection.

Littlewood and Paley[1] proved that if $f(x) \in L^p (p > 1)$ then the lacunary sequences are again sequences of indices of convergence (as in the case $p = 2$), but again at $p = 1$ this is untrue. Moreover, as Zygmund proved (see[A.35], § 10.33) the question of whether it is possible to find a sequence of indices of convergence which is completely independent of the function $f(x)$, i.e. which is applicable for all $f(x) \in L$, is answered in the negative. Indeed, as Zygmund noted (see[A.35], § 10.33), for any sequence $\{\lambda_k\}$ of positive numbers it is possible to find $f(x) \in L$ and a sequence $n_k$ such that $n_{k+1}/n_k > \lambda_k$ $(k = 1, 2, \ldots)$ and $S_{n_k}(x)$ diverges almost everywhere. This result can be obtained if the method by which the function with an almost everywhere divergent Fourier series is constructed in § 17 is closely studied.

Thus, it is impossible to find a sequence of indices of convergence, appropriate for all $f(x) \in L$. However, as Salem[1] proved, it is possible to find a sequence of indices of convergence which is general for all $f(x)$ with the same integral modulus of continuity. Namely, the theorem holds:

THEOREM. *For any summable $f(x)$ with integral modulus of continuity $\omega^{(1)}(\delta)$ the sequence of numbers $\{n_k\}$ for which*

$$\sum \omega^{(1)}\left(\frac{1}{n_k}\right) \left|\ln \omega^{(1)}\left(\frac{1}{n_k}\right)\right| < +\infty, \tag{11.14}$$

*is a sequence of indices of convergence.*

We will operate on the result which will be established in Chapter VIII, § 21: if $f(x) \in L$ and $p$ is any value, $0 < p < 1$, then

$$\int_0^{2\pi} |S_n(x)|^p \, dx < \frac{C}{1-p}\left(\int_0^{2\pi} |f(x)| \, dx\right)^p, \tag{11.15}$$

where $C$ is an absolute constant.

Let us consider the expression

$$B_n(x) = \frac{1}{2}\left[S_n\left(x + \frac{\pi}{2n}\right) + S_n\left(x - \frac{\pi}{2n}\right)\right].$$

In Chapter VII, § 4 it is proved that $B_n(x) \to f(x)$ almost everywhere as $n \to \infty$.

We have from (11.14) and (11.15)

$$\int_0^{2\pi} |S_n(x) - B_n(x)|^p \, dx$$

$$< \frac{C}{1-p}\left(\int_0^{2\pi}\left| f(x) - \frac{1}{2} f\left(x + \frac{\pi}{2n}\right) - \frac{1}{2} f\left(x - \frac{\pi}{2n}\right)\right| dx\right)^p.$$

But since

$$\omega^{(1)}(\delta) = \sup_{0 \leqslant h \leqslant \delta} \int_0^{2\pi} |f(x+h) - f(x)|\, dx,$$

then it immediately follows from this that

$$\int_0^{2\pi} |S_n(x) - B_n(x)|^p\, dx < \frac{C}{1-p}\left[\omega^{(1)}\left(\frac{\pi}{2n}\right)\right]^p \leqslant \frac{A}{1-p}\left[\omega^{(1)}\left(\frac{1}{n}\right)\right]^p, \quad (11.16)$$

where $A$ is some new constant, by virtue of the properties of the integral modulus of continuity.

Let us choose $p_n$ such that the right-hand side of the inequality (11.16) is a minimum; for this it must be taken that

$$p_n = 1 - \frac{1}{\left|\ln \omega^{(1)}\left(\frac{1}{n}\right)\right|}.$$

For this choice of $p_n$ we have

$$\int_0^{2\pi} |S_n(x) - B_n(x)|^{p_n}\, dx < A e\, \omega^{(1)}\left(\frac{1}{n}\right)\left|\ln \omega^{(1)}\left(\frac{1}{n}\right)\right|.$$

If we now take the values of $n_k$ satisfying (11.14), then

$$\sum_{k=1}^{\infty} \int_0^{2\pi} |S_{n_k}(x) - B_{n_k}(x)|^{p_{n_k}}\, dx < +\infty,$$

which means that $\sum_{k=1}^{\infty} |S_{n_k}(x) - B_{n_k}(x)|^{p_{n_k}}$ converges almost everywhere and, therefore, all the more so $|S_{n_k}(x) - B_{n_k}(x)|^{p_{n_k}} \to 0$ almost everywhere. From this it follows that $|S_{n_k}(x) - B_{n_k}(x)| \to 0$ almost everywhere, and since $B_n(x) \to f(x)$ almost everywhere, then $S_{n_k}(x) \to f(x)$ almost everywhere and the theorem is proved.

*Note.* Let us refer here to two reports by Zygmund, where the problem of the choice of the sub-sequence $n_k$ for which $S_{n_k}(x) \to f(x)$ was set out in a somewhat different form. Namely, Zygmund[10] proved first that for any $f(x) \in L^2$ it is possible for almost any $x$ to divide the natural series into two sequences $\{n_k\}$ and $\{m_k\}$ (the division, generally speaking, depends on the choice of the point $x$) so that $S_{n_k}(x) \to f(x)$ and the sequence $\{m_k\}$ satisfies the condition $\sum_{k=1}^{\infty} 1/m_k < +\infty$. Later (see Zygmund[11]) he generalized this result for functions $f(x) \in L^p$ $(p > 1)$ and noted that at $p = 1$ the theorem loses its force.

This result, as Zygmund himself noted, should be considered to be incomparable with the preceding results, because, there it was a matter of the sequences $\{n_k\}$ being sufficiently "rare" but nevertheless independent of the choice of the point, whereas in his case the choice of the sequence depends on the point, but this sequence is "very dense" $\left(\text{only the numbers } m_k \text{ for which } \sum_{k=1}^{\infty} 1/m_k < +\infty \text{ are omitted here}\right)$.

## § 12. The convex capacity of sets†

A number of authors paid attention to the following interesting question: if the series

$$\sum(a_n^2 + b_n^2)\, W(n) < +\infty,$$

where $W(n) \uparrow \infty$ converges, then what can be said concerning the set $E$ of the points of divergence of the series

$$\frac{a_0}{2} + \sum(a_n \cos nx + b_n \sin nx)?$$

We know (§ 2) that if $W(n)$ increases similarly to $\ln n$, and moreover more rapidly then $\ln n$, then $mE = 0$. However, the question arises whether it is not possible to improve on this statement concerning the measure of the set, knowing, for example, that $W(n)$ increases rapidly?

Here the idea is conceived that sets of measure zero should be classified and distinguished as "larger" and "smaller". This idea will also be considered by us later in Chapters XII, XIII and XIV. Here we will throw some light on it by introducing the concepts of the logarithmic capacity, $\alpha$-capacity and finally the convex capacity of sets.

Let us consider a system of all the sets $\{B\}$ which are Borel-measurable and lie in $[0, 2\pi]$.

We will define any non-negative completely additive function of sets as being of *measure* $\mu$ if it is definable in $\{B\}$ and normal, i.e. $\mu\,[0, 2\pi] = 1$. We will say that the *measure* $\mu$ *is concentrated in* $B$ and write $\mu \prec B$, if $\mu(B) = 1$, i.e. if

$$\int_B d\mu = \int_0^{2\pi} d\mu = 1.$$

De la Vallée-Poussin[3] introduced the concept of the logarithmic capacity of sets; this concept which was further studied in reports by Frostman[1], Nevanlinna[A.24] and other authors, appeared to be very useful. We will not show here how the magnitude of the logarithmic capacity of a set should be found, since it is not necessary to us; we only need to be able to distinguish whether the set possesses a logarithmic capacity which is positive or equal to zero. Therefore, we will remark only that de la Vallée-Poussin proposed the following.

DEFINITION 1. A Borel-measurable set $E$ is of *positive logarithmic capacity* if there exists a measure $\mu$ such that $\mu \prec E$ and the function

$$v(x, r) = \int_0^{2\pi} \ln \frac{1}{|e^{it} - re^{ix}|}\, d\mu \tag{12.1}$$

$(0 \leqslant r < 1)$ remains uniformly bounded with respect to $x$ as $r \to 1$.††

---

† It is recommended that this paragraph be read after §§ 19 and 20 of Chapter XIV.

†† With regard to the definition of an integral of the form $\int_0^{2\pi} f(x)\, d\mu$, see Appendix, § 8.

If for any $\mu \prec E$ the expression $v(x, r)$ is not uniformly bounded with respect to $x$ as $r \to 1$, then we will consider the logarithmic capacity of $E$ as being zero.

The connection between this concept and the question asked by us becomes clear, when we formulate the following theorem due to Beurling[1]:

BEURLING'S THEOREM. *If*

$$\sum_{n=1}^{\infty} (a_n^2 + b_n^2)\, n < +\infty,$$

*then the series*

$$\frac{a_0}{2} + \sum_{n=1}^{\infty} (a_n \cos nx + b_n \sin nx)$$

*can diverge only in a set, the logarithmic capacity of which equals zero.*

We will not work through the proof of this theorem, since it is obtained as the particular case of more general results.

Frostman and other authors studied too the concept of the $\alpha$-capacity of a set. We will confine ourselves here to distinguishing between the cases of positive $\alpha$-capacity and $\alpha$-capacity equal to zero, namely:

DEFINITION 2. A Borel-measurable set $E$ is of *positive* $\alpha$-capacity $(0 < \alpha < 1)$, if $\mu \prec E$ is found, for which the function

$$v(x, r) = \int_0^{2\pi} \frac{1}{|e^{it} - re^{ix}|^{\alpha}}\, d\mu \tag{12.2}$$

remains uniformly bounded with respect to $x$ as $r \to 1$.

If such a $\mu \prec E$, for which this condition is fulfilled, does not exist, then $E$ is of $\alpha$-capacity zero.†

With this definition, the following theorem holds:

THEOREM OF SALEM AND ZYGMUND[1]. *If*

$$\sum_{n=1}^{\infty} (a_n^2 + b_n^2)\, n^{a} < +\infty \quad (0 < \alpha < 1),$$

*then the trigonometric series*

$$\frac{a_0}{2} + \sum_{n=1}^{\infty} (a_n \cos nx + b_n \sin nx)$$

*can diverge only in a set in which the* $(1 - \alpha)$*-capacity equals zero.*

We will obtain this theorem later, just as the Beurling theorem, from a more general result.

Following Temko[1], we introduce the concept of the convex capacity of a set.

---

† In Chapter XII, § 9, Hausdorff's concept of the dimension of a set will be discussed. Let us note that Frostman studied the connection between the $\alpha$-capacity of a set and its dimension and proved: if the $\alpha$-capacity of a set $E$ is positive, then its Hausdorff dimension of order $\alpha$ is positive; if $E$ is of $\alpha$-capacity zero, then any closed subset of it possesses a Hausdorff dimension $\alpha + \varepsilon$ equal to zero for any $\varepsilon > 0$.

For this we will consider a sequence $\{\lambda_n\}$, possessing the properties: (1) $\lambda_n \to 0$ and (2) $\{\lambda_n\}$ is convex. It is known (see Chapter I, § 30) that then the function

$$Q(x) = \lambda_0 + \sum_{n=1}^{\infty} \lambda_n \cos nx, \tag{12.3}$$

definable by the series (12.3), which converges everywhere apart, perhaps, from the point $x = 0$, is a non-negative summable function. If this is so, then

$$Q(r, x) = \lambda_0 + \sum \lambda_n r^n \cos nx, \tag{12.4}$$

as the Poisson sum of $Q(x)$, satisfies the condition $Q(r, x) \geqslant 0$ for $0 \leqslant x \leqslant 2\pi$ and $0 \leqslant r < 1$. Let us give a definition proposed by Temko:

DEFINITION 3. The B-measurable set $E$ is of *positive convex capacity* relative to the sequence $\{\lambda_n\}$, if a measure $\mu \prec E$ exists for which the function

$$v(x, r) = \int_0^{2\pi} Q(r, x - t)\, d\mu(t) \tag{12.5}$$

remains uniformly bounded with respect to $x$ as $r \to 1$; here $Q(r, x)$ is defined by the formula (12.4).

In the case when this $\mu$ does not exist, then we say that the convex capacity of $E$ relative to $\{\lambda_n\}$ equals zero.

Let us show that *the logarithmic capacity and $\alpha$-capacity can be considered as particular cases of the convex capacity, if the sequence $\{\lambda_n\}$ is chosen correctly.*

Let us start with the logarithmic capacity; we have

$$v(x, r) = \int_0^{2\pi} \ln \frac{1}{|e^{it} - re^{ix}|}\, d\mu(t) = \int_0^{2\pi} \ln \frac{1}{|1 - re^{i(x-t)}|}\, d\mu(t).$$

Let us prove that this expression coincides with

$$v(x, r) = \int_0^{2\pi} Q(r, x - t)\, d\mu(t),$$

if $\{1/n\}$ is taken for the quantities $\{\lambda_n\}$ and $\lambda_0 = 0$, i.e. if we suppose that

$$Q(x) = \sum_{n=1}^{\infty} \frac{\cos nx}{n}.$$

In fact, then

$$Q(r, x) = \sum_{n=1}^{\infty} \frac{\cos nx}{n} r^n,$$

$$Q(r, x - t) = \sum_{n=1}^{\infty} \frac{\cos n(x - t)}{n} r^n = \operatorname{Re} \sum_{n=1}^{\infty} \frac{e^{in(x-t)} r^n}{n} = \operatorname{Re} \int_0^r \sum_{n=1}^{\infty} e^{in(x-t)} r^{n-1}\, dr$$

(here the term-by-term integration is valid, because $0 \leqslant r < 1$). But

$$\sum_{n=1}^{\infty} e^{in(x-t)} r^{n-1} = \frac{e^{i(x-t)}}{1 - re^{i(x-t)}} = -\frac{\frac{\partial}{\partial r}(1 - re^{i(x-t)})}{1 - re^{i(x-t)}},$$

and therefore

$$Q(r, x-t) = \operatorname{Re}\left\{-\int_0^r \frac{d(1-re^{i(x-t)})}{1-re^{i(x-t)}}\right\} = -\ln|1-re^{i(x-t)}| = \ln\frac{1}{|1-re^{i(x-t)}|},$$

and this is what had to be established.

Thus, *the logarithmic capacity of a set is positive, if its convex capacity relative to the sequence* $\{1/n\}$ *is positive and vice versa.*

Now, let us consider the case of $\alpha$-capacity. Here we can also write

$$v(x, r) = \int_0^{2\pi} \frac{d\mu(t)}{|e^{it} - re^{ix}|^\alpha} = \int_0^{2\pi} \frac{d\mu(t)}{|1 - re^{i(x-t)}|^\alpha}.$$

If the expression $[1 - re^{i(x-t)}]^{-\alpha}$ is expanded into a power series in powers of $r$, then we will have

$$[1 - re^{i(x-t)}]^{-\alpha} = 1 + \sum_{n=1}^{\infty} \gamma_n r^n e^{in(x-t)},$$

where

$$\gamma_n = \frac{\alpha(\alpha+1)\dots(\alpha+n-1)}{n!}. \tag{12.6}$$

It is clear that if $v(x, r)$ remains uniformly bounded as $r \to 1$, then this is true also for

$$\int_0^{2\pi} \operatorname{Re}\frac{1}{[1 - re^{i(x-t)}]^\alpha} d\mu(t).$$

But

$$\operatorname{Re}[1 - re^{i(x-t)}]^{-\alpha} = 1 + \sum_{n=1}^{\infty} \gamma_n r^n \cos n(x-t),$$

and therefore, supposing that

$$Q(x) = 1 + \sum_{n=1}^{\infty} \gamma_n \cos nx, \tag{12.7}$$

we see that

$$Q(r, x) = 1 + \sum \gamma_n r^n \cos nx$$

and

$$\int_0^{2\pi} Q(r, x-t)\, d\mu(t)$$

remains bounded uniformly with respect to $x$ as $r \to 1$, i.e. the set is of positive capacity relative to the sequence $\{\gamma_n\}$, whilst it is not difficult to estimate that $\Delta^2 \gamma_n \geqslant 0$, i.e. our sequence is convex.

On the other hand, if $Q(x)$ is defined by equation (12.7), where the values of $\gamma_n$ are given by formula (12.6), then, as we see, the real part of

$$I = \int_0^{2\pi} \frac{1}{(1 - re^{i(x-t)})^\alpha} d\mu$$

remains bounded uniformly with respect to $x$ as $r \to 1$. But since for any $r < 1$ and for any $\beta$ we have

$$1 - re^{i\beta} = |1 - re^{i\beta}|\, e^{i\theta},$$

where the argument $\theta$ of $(1 - re^{i\beta})$ lies between $-\pi/2$ and $\pi/2$, then

$$(1 - re^{i\beta})^{-\alpha} = |1 - re^{i\beta}|^{-\alpha}\, e^{-i\alpha\theta},$$

and therefore

$$\mathrm{Re}\,(1 - re^{i\beta})^{-\alpha} = |1 - re^{i\beta}|^{-\alpha} \cos\alpha\,\theta,$$

whilst $\cos\alpha\,\theta$ lies between $\cos\alpha\pi/2$ and 1.

From this it immediately follows that if the real part of the integral $I$ is uniformly bounded as $r \to 1$, then this is also true for $v(x, r)$, i.e. the $\alpha$-capacity of the set is then positive.

Thus, *a case of positive $\alpha$-capacity is a case of positive capacity relative to the sequence $\{\gamma_n\}$, definable by the formula* (12.6).

But it can be proved† (see Appendix, § 9) that

$$\gamma_n = C(\alpha)\frac{1}{n^{1-\alpha}}\left[1 + O\left(\frac{1}{n}\right)\right],$$

where $C(\alpha)$ is a constant depending only on $\alpha$ and since the series

$$\sum \frac{1}{n^{2-\alpha}} \cos nx$$

converges absolutely and uniformly for $0 \leqslant \alpha < 1$, then supposing that

$$Q^*(x) = \sum \frac{1}{n^{1-\alpha}} \cos nx,$$

we see that the function $Q(x)$ definable by equation (12.7) differs from $C(\alpha)\, Q^*(x)$ by the continuous function $\varphi(x)$, therefore for

$$\int_0^{2\pi} Q^*(r, x - t)\, d\mu(t)$$

uniform boundedness with respect to $x$ as $r \to 1$ occurs simultaneously with uniform boundedness of $\int_0^{2\pi} Q(r, x - t)\, d\mu(t)$. Hence we conclude:††

*The set $E$ is of positive $\alpha$-capacity when and only when it is of positive convex capacity relative to the sequence $\{1/n^{1-\alpha}\}$.*

This statement will be useful to us later.

---

† In § 9 of the Appendix the formula

$$A_n^\alpha = C(\alpha)\, n^\alpha + O(n^{\alpha-1}),$$

is obtained from which our statement also follows if it is noted that $A_n^{\alpha-1}$ coincides with $\gamma_n$.

†† The idea of comparing the series for $Q(x)$ and $Q^*(x)$ is taken from the above-cited report by Zygmund and Salem.

The cited reports of Beurling, Zygmund and Salem, and Temko contain a number of extremely interesting theorems concerning logarithmic capacity, $\alpha$-capacity and convex capacity. Although unable to describe these here, we will describe Temko's basic theorem, from which Beurling's theorem cited earlier and also the Zygmund and Salem theorem are obtained as corollaries. By modifying Temko's formulation somewhat, we will express this theorem in the following form:

THEOREM 1. *Let* $W(n) \uparrow \infty$ *and* $\sum 1/n W(n) < +\infty$. *If*

$$\sum (a_n^2 + b_n^2) W(n) < +\infty,$$

*then the trigonometric series*

$$\frac{a_0}{2} + (a_n \cos nx + b_n \sin nx)$$

*can diverge only in a set of convex capacity zero relative to the sequence* $\{\lambda_n\}$ *where*

$$\lambda_n = \sum_{k=n}^{\infty} \frac{1}{k W(k)}.$$

Both the proof of this theorem and the conclusion drawn by Beurling, and Zygmund and Salem from its results will be given a little later. In order to simplify the proof, we consider it appropriate to modify the concept of convex capacity and for this we introduce this definition.

DEFINITION 4. Set $E$ is of *generalized positive capacity* relative to the convex sequence $\{\lambda_n\}$, $\lambda_n \to 0$, if there exists a measure $\mu \prec E$ such that

$$v(r) = \int_0^{2\pi} \int_0^{2\pi} Q(r, x - y)\, d\mu(x)\, d\mu(y) \tag{12.8}$$

remains bounded as $r \to 1$. Here again

$$Q(r, t) = \sum_{n=0}^{\infty} \lambda_n r^n \cos nt.$$

It is clear that if $E$ is of positive convex capacity (in the Temko sense) relative to $\{\lambda_n\}$, then its generalized capacity relative to the same sequence is positive, because uniform boundedness with respect to $x$ for

$$\int_0^{2\pi} Q(r, x - t)\, d\mu(t)$$

involves even more so the boundedness of $v(r)$, definable by formula (12.8). The opposite is, however, not evident.†

From this it follows that if the theorem, analogous to Temko's theorem, except that the words "generalized convex capacity" are substituted for "convex capacity", is proved, then Temko's theorem will also be proved, since if divergence is possible

---

† Recently, Temko has proved that the definitions of convex capacity and generalized convex capacity are equivalent, if $n\Delta\lambda_n \downarrow$. This result has not been published yet. Thus, if this limitation on $\lambda_n$ is introduced, then using Definition 4 instead of Definition 3, we do not obtain stronger results, but the proof is considerably simplified.

only in a set of zero generalized convex capacity, then it is also possible in a set of zero convex capacity (in the Temko sense).

It is considerably simpler to operate with the generalized convex capacity since here the following simple theorem holds.†

THEOREM 2. *For the set E to be of positive generalized capacity relative to the convex sequence* $\{\lambda_n\}$, *it is necessary and sufficient that a measure* $\mu \prec E$ *exists such that*

$$\sum (\alpha_n^2 + \beta_n^2)\,\lambda_n < +\infty, \tag{12.9}$$

*where* $\alpha_n$ *and* $\beta_n$, *are the Fourier–Stieltjes coefficients for the measure* $\mu$, *i.e.*

$$\alpha_n = \frac{1}{\pi}\int_0^{2\pi} \cos nx\, d\mu; \quad \beta_n = \frac{1}{\pi}\int_0^{2\pi} \sin nx\, d\mu.$$

In fact, supposing that

$$Q(t) = \sum \lambda_n \cos nt; \quad Q(r, t) = \sum \lambda_n r^n \cos nt,$$

we know that $Q(r, t)$ is non-negative and continuous for $0 < r < 1$. We will estimate $v(r)$:

$$\begin{aligned}
v(r) &= \int_0^{2\pi}\int_0^{2\pi} Q(r, x-y)\, d\mu(x)\, d\mu(y)\\
&= \int_0^{2\pi}\left[\int_0^{2\pi} \sum_{n=1}^{\infty} \lambda_n r^n \cos n(x-y)\, d\mu(x)\right] d\mu(y)\\
&= \int_0^{2\pi}\left\{\sum_{n=1}^{\infty} \lambda_n r^n \left[\cos ny \int_0^{2\pi} \cos nx\, d\mu(x) + \sin ny \int_0^{2\pi} \sin nx\, d\mu(x)\right]\right\} d\mu(y)\\
&= \int_0^{2\pi}\left\{\sum_{n=1}^{\infty} \lambda_n r^n (\pi\alpha_n \cos ny + \pi\beta_n \sin ny)\right\} d\mu(y)\\
&= \pi \sum_{n=1}^{\infty} \lambda_n r^n \left[\alpha_n \int_0^{2\pi} \cos ny\, d\mu(y) + \beta_n \int_0^{2\pi} \sin ny\, d\mu(y)\right] = \pi^2 \sum_{n=1}^{\infty} \lambda_n r^n (\alpha_n^2 + \beta_n^2).
\end{aligned} \tag{12.10}$$

All the operations performed are valid, since for $r < 1$ the series under consideration converge uniformly, because the values $\{\lambda_n\}$ and also $\{|\alpha_n|\}$ and $\{|\beta_n|\}$ are all bounded.

It is now clear that if the generalized capacity is positive, then for some $\mu \prec E$ the left-hand side of (12.10) is bounded as $r \to 1$, which means that the right-hand side is also, and then

$$\sum_{n=1}^{\infty} (\alpha_n^2 + \beta_n^2)\,\lambda_n < +\infty.$$

If, on the other hand, this series converges, then the right-hand side of equation (12.10) is bounded as $r \to 1$, which means that the left-hand side is also, and then the generalized capacity is positive.

† In the cited report (Temko[11]) the necessity of condition (12.9) for the convex capacity of $E$ to be positive was proved. Recently, in a report by Temko, which is just being published, the theorem in the text is also proved.

The theorem is proved.†

COROLLARY 1. *If for two different convex sequences $\{\lambda_n\}$ and $\{\lambda'_n\}$ we have*

$$\lambda_n \sim \lambda'_n,$$

*then sets of generalized convex capacity zero will be the same for both sequences.*

We will use this statement below in the derivation of the Beurling and the Zygmund–Salem theorems from Temko's theorem.

COROLLARY 2. *If $\sum \lambda_n < +\infty$, then any B-set is of positive generalized capacity relative to $\{\lambda_n\}$.*

Indeed, for any normal measure $\mu$ we have

$$|\alpha_n| \leqslant \int_0^{2\pi} d\mu = 1, \quad |\beta_n| \leqslant \int_0^{2\pi} d\mu = 1,$$

and therefore

$$\sum_{n=1}^{\infty} (\alpha_n^2 + \lambda_n^2)\,\lambda_n < 2 \sum_{n=1}^{\infty} \beta_n < +\infty.$$

Therefore, in order to study sets of generalized convex capacity equal to zero, only the case when

$$\sum_{n=1}^{\infty} \lambda_n = +\infty.$$

must be considered. Finally, we have

COROLLARY 3. *Any B-measurable set $E$, $mE > 0$, is of positive generalized capacity†† relative to any convex sequences $\{\lambda_n\}$ where $\lambda_n \to 0$.*

Indeed, for any $\mathscr{E}$, $B$-measurable, let us suppose that

$$\mu(\mathscr{E}) = \frac{m(\mathscr{E} \cdot E)}{mE}.$$

It is clear that $\mu(\mathscr{E})$ is non-negative, completely additive, $\mu[0, 2\pi] = 1$ and $\mu(E) = 1$, i.e. $\mu \prec E$. If the characteristic function for the set $E$ is denoted by $\chi(x)$, then

$$\alpha_n = \frac{1}{\pi} \int_0^{2\pi} \cos nx \, d\mu = \frac{1}{\pi} \int_0^{2\pi} \chi(x) \cos nx \, dx,$$

$$\beta_n = \frac{1}{\pi} \int_0^{2\pi} \sin nx \, d\mu = \frac{1}{\pi} \int_0^{2\pi} \chi(x) \sin nx \, dx,$$

---

† From this it follows readily that if $E$ possesses a generalized convex capacity relative to $\{\lambda_n\}$ equal to zero, then any $E_1 \in E$ also possesses this property. Indeed if this were untrue, then $\mu \prec E_1$ could be found, such that for its Fourier–Stieltjes coefficients $\alpha_n$ and $\beta_n$ we would have

$$\sum_{n=1}^{\infty} (\alpha_n^2 + \beta_n^2)\,\lambda_n < +\infty. \tag{*}$$

But then for the same $\mu$ it can be said that $\mu \prec E$ and condition (*) is fulfilled, which means that $E$ possesses a positive generalized capacity relative to $\{\lambda_n\}$ which contradicts our hypothesis.

†† Temko proved this statement for the case of convex capacity, i.e. by using Definition 3.

i.e. the Fourier–Stieltjes coefficients for $\mu$ seem to be the Fourier coefficient of the bounded function $\chi(x)$. But if this is so, then

$$\sum(\alpha_n^2 + \beta_n^2) < +\infty,$$

and then for any $\lambda_n \to 0$ it is even more true that

$$\sum(\alpha_n^2 + \beta_n^2)\,\lambda_n < +\infty$$

which means that $E$ is of positive generalized capacity relative to $\{\lambda_n\}$.

But the significance of the concept of generalized capacity appears to be that, on the other hand, for any convex sequence $\{\lambda_n\}$ where $\lambda_n \to 0$ it is possible to construct a perfect set of zero measure which is of positive generalized convex capacity† relative to this sequence.

In order to prove this, we will operate on the following lemma, the proof of which is found in Chapter XIV, § 24.

LEMMA 1. *Let $\psi(n) \to 0$ and $\psi(n) \uparrow \infty$ as $n \to \infty$ but otherwise it is arbitrary. There exists a perfect set $P$, $mP = 0$, and a monotonic $F(x)$, constant in intervals adjacent to $P$, such that for*

$$\alpha_n = \frac{1}{\pi}\int_0^{2\pi} \cos nx\, dF, \quad \beta_n = \frac{1}{\pi}\int_0^{2\pi} \sin nx\, dF \tag{12.11}$$

*we have*

$$\sum_{k=1}^{n}(\alpha_k^2 + \beta_k^2) = O(\psi(n)). \tag{12.12}$$

(From the proof of the theorem in § 24 of Chapter XIV it is evident that this set is an $M$-set).

From this lemma it follows that

COROLLARY. *For any $\psi(n) \uparrow \infty$ a measure $\mu$ can be found such that $\mu \prec P$, $mP = 0$, and for*

$$\alpha_n = \frac{1}{\pi}\int_0^{2\pi} \cos nx\, d\mu, \quad \beta_n = \frac{1}{\pi}\int_0^{2\pi} \sin nx\, d\mu$$

*we have*

$$\sum_{k=1}^{\infty}(\alpha_k^2 + \beta_k^2) = O(\psi(n)).$$

Indeed, supposing for any interval

$$\mu(a, b) = F(b) - F(a),$$

where $F(x)$ is the function constructed in Lemma 1 and, requiring complete additivity of $\mu(E)$, we can define $\mu(E)$ in any Borel set, lying in $[0, 2\pi]$. In this case $\mu[0, 2\pi] = F(2\pi) - F(0) = 1$, $\mu \prec P$, and the necessary condition for the coefficients is fulfilled by virtue of the proved theorem.

† Temko proved a similar theorem for convex capacity (instead of generalized convex capacity); the proof worked through later is based on the same principle but is considerably shorter.

Now it is possible for us to prove the theorem:

THEOREM 3. *For any convex sequence* $\{\lambda_n\}$ *where* $\lambda_n \to 0$ *it is possible to find a perfect set* $P$, $mP = 0$, *such that the generalized capacity is positive relative to the sequence* $\{\lambda_n\}$.

First of all we will prove that it is possible to find a monotonic $\psi(n)$ such that

(1) $\sum \psi(n) \Delta \lambda_n < +\infty$,

(2) $\psi(n) \lambda_n = o(1)$.

Indeed, it is sufficient to take $\psi(n) = 1/\lambda_n^\alpha$ where $0 < \alpha < 1$. Since $\{\lambda_n\}$ is convex and $\lambda_n \to 0$, we have $\lambda_n \downarrow 0$, then $\psi(n) \uparrow \infty$. Since from $\lambda_n \downarrow 0$ it follows that $\Delta \lambda_n > 0$ and moreover $\sum \Delta \lambda_n < +\infty$, then according to the well-known theorem (see Appendix, § 25) the series

$$\sum \frac{\Delta \lambda_n}{R_{n-1}^a},$$

where $R_n = \sum_{k=n+1}^{\infty} \Delta \lambda_k = \lambda_{n+1}$, will also converge which means that the series

$$\sum \frac{\Delta \lambda_n}{\lambda_n^a} = \sum \Delta \lambda_n \psi(n)$$

converges and condition (1) is fulfilled. Moreover

$$\psi(n) \lambda_n = \lambda_n^{1-\alpha} \to 0 \quad \text{as} \quad n \to \infty,$$

and therefore condition (2) also holds.

On the basis of the corollary to Lemma 1 we can find $P$, $mP = 0$, and a measure $\mu$, such that $\mu \prec P$, and for

$$\alpha_n = \frac{1}{\pi} \int_0^{2\pi} \cos nx \, d\mu, \quad \beta_n = \frac{1}{\pi} \int_0^{2\pi} \sin nx \, d\mu$$

we have

$$\sum_{k=1}^{n} (\alpha_k^2 + \beta_k^2) = O(\psi(n)).$$

Then, as we will now show, the generalized capacity of $P$ relative to $\{\lambda_n\}$ will be positive.

In fact, supposing that

$$S_n = \sum_{k=1}^{n} (\alpha_k^2 + \beta_k^2),$$

we have

$$S_n = O(\psi(n))$$

and on the basis of Abel's transformation

$$\sum_{k=1}^{n} (\alpha_k^2 + \beta_k^2) \lambda_k = \sum_{k=1}^{n-1} S_k \Delta \lambda_k + S_n \lambda_n = O\left(\sum_{k=1}^{n-1} \psi(k) \Delta \lambda_k\right) + O(\psi(n) \lambda_n),$$

and since the series $\sum \psi(k)\,\Delta\lambda_k$ converges and $\psi(n)\,\lambda_n \to 0$, then

$$\sum_{k=1}^{\infty} (\alpha_k^2 + \beta_k^2)\,\lambda_k < +\infty,$$

and this also means (see Theorem 2) that the generalized capacity of $P$ relative to $\{\lambda_n\}$ is positive and the theorem is proved.

Before continuing with the proof of Temko's theorem, we will prove yet another lemma also appertaining to it:

LEMMA 2. *Let $\{\lambda_n\}$ be a convex sequence, for which $\lambda_n \to 0$, $n\Delta\lambda_n \downarrow 0$ and $\sum_{n=1}^{\infty} \lambda_n = +\infty$. Let us suppose that*

$$H(x) = \sum_{k=1}^{\infty} \lambda_k \cos kx. \tag{12.13}$$

*Let*

$$\gamma_n = n\Delta\lambda_n$$

*and*

$$\Gamma_n(x) = \sum_{k=1}^{n} \gamma_k \cos kx.$$

*Then for any $n$*

$$|\Gamma_n(x)| < A_1 H(x) + A_2, \quad 0 < x < 2\pi, \tag{12.14}$$

*where $A_1$ and $A_2$ are constants dependent only on $\{\lambda_n\}$.*

Let us note first of all that it follows from the conditions of the lemma that: $H(x)$ exists for all $x$, $0 < x < 2\pi$, it is non-negative and summable (see Chapter I, § 30). Moreover (see Chapter X, § 7) we have

$$H(x) \sim \int_1^{1/x} t\,\Delta\lambda(t)\,dt,$$

if $\lambda(n) = \lambda_n$ and $\lambda(t)$ is interpolated linearly between $\lambda(n)$ and $\lambda(n+1)$. The symbol $\sim$ signifies as usual the existence of two positive numbers $B$ and $C$ such that

$$B < \frac{\int_1^{1/x} t\,\Delta\lambda(t)\,dt}{H(x)} < C.$$

Now let $0 < x < 2\pi$ and $m = [1/x]$; then

$$\Gamma_n(x) = \sum_{k=1}^{m} \gamma_k \cos kx + \sum_{m+1}^{n} \gamma_k \cos kx = \Gamma_n^{(1)}(x) + \Gamma_n^{(2)}(x).$$

We have by virtue of $\Delta\lambda(t) \downarrow$

$$|\Gamma_n^{(1)}(x)| \leqslant \sum_{k=1}^{m} \gamma_k = \gamma_1 + \sum_{k=2}^{m} \frac{k}{k-1}(k-1)\,\Delta\lambda_k$$

$$< \gamma_1 + 2\sum_{k=2}^{m} \int_{k-1}^{k} t\,\Delta\lambda(t)\,dt < \gamma_1 + 2\int_1^{1/x} t\,\Delta\lambda(t)\,dt < \gamma_1 + 2CH(x).$$

Also for any $n$ at $x \neq 0$ from Abel's transformation

$$|\Gamma_n^{(2)}(x)| = \left|\sum_{m+1}^{n} \gamma_k \cos kx\right| = O\left(\frac{1}{x}\right)\gamma_{m+1},$$

and therefore

$$|\Gamma_n^{(2)}(x)| = O\left(\frac{1}{x}\right)\gamma_m = O\left(\frac{m\Delta\lambda_m}{x}\right) = O\left(\frac{1}{x^2}\Delta\lambda_m\right).$$

But since $\Delta\lambda(t)\downarrow$, then

$$\int_1^{1/x} t\Delta\lambda(t)\,dt \geqslant \int_1^{m} t\Delta\lambda(t)\,dt \geqslant \Delta\lambda_m \frac{t^2}{2}\Big|_1^m = O\left(\frac{1}{x^2}\Delta\lambda_m\right) - \frac{1}{2}\Delta\lambda_m,$$

therefore

$$|\Gamma_n^{(2)}(x)| < CH(x) + C_1$$

and consequently

$$|\Gamma_n(x)| < A_1 H(x) + A_2$$

and the theorem is proved.

From the proved lemma we obtain an important fact, which is the heart of Temko's theorem; in the same way as in the Kolmogorov–Seliverstov and Plessner theorem the inequality is proved.

$$\int_0^{2\pi}\left[\int_0^{2\pi}\sum_{k=2}^{n(x)}\frac{\cos k(x-t)}{\sqrt{\ln k}}\,dx\right]^2 dt \leqslant C,$$

where $n(x)$ takes any values $1, 2, \ldots, n$, and $C$ is an absolute constant as will be proved.

LEMMA 3. *Let*

$$W(n)\uparrow\infty,\quad \sum\frac{1}{nW(n)} < +\infty,$$

$$\lambda_n = \sum_{k=n}^{\infty}\frac{1}{kW(k)},\quad \textit{but}\quad \sum\lambda_n = +\infty.$$

*If for the quantities*

$$\alpha_n = \frac{1}{\pi}\int_0^{2\pi}\cos nx\,d\mu,\quad \beta_n = \frac{1}{\pi}\int_0^{2\pi}\sin nx\,d\mu \tag{12.15}$$

*we have*

$$\sum(\alpha_n^2+\beta_n^2)\lambda_n < +\infty, \tag{12.16}$$

*then for* $n(x) = 1, 2, \ldots, n$

$$J = \int_0^{2\pi}\left[\int_0^{2\pi}\sum_{k=1}^{n(x)}\frac{\cos k(x-t)}{\sqrt{W(k)}}\,d\mu(x)\right]^2 dt \leqslant C, \tag{12.17}$$

*where C is an absolute constant.*

First of all, we note that

$$\Delta\lambda_n = \frac{1}{n W(n)},$$

which means that

$$n\Delta\lambda_n = \frac{1}{W(n)} \downarrow 0$$

and

$$\Delta^2\lambda_n \geqslant 0,$$

therefore all the conditions of Lemma 2 are fulfilled.

Also we have

$$J = \int_0^{2\pi} \left\{ \int_0^{2\pi} \sum_{k=0}^{n(x)} \frac{\cos k(x-t)}{\sqrt{W(k)}}\, d\mu(x) \int_0^{2\pi} \sum_{m=1}^{n(y)} \frac{\cos m(y-t)}{\sqrt{W(m)}}\, d\mu(y) \right\} dt.$$

Changing the order of integration, we find that

$$J = \int_0^{2\pi}\int_0^{2\pi} \left\{ \int_0^{2\pi} \sum_{k=1}^{n(x)} \frac{\cos k(x-t)}{\sqrt{W(k)}} \sum_{m=1}^{n(y)} \frac{\cos m(y-t)}{\sqrt{W(m)}}\, dt \right\} d\mu(x)\, d\mu(y).$$

But (see the argument in the proof of the Kolmogorov–Seliverstov and Plessner theorem)

$$\int_0^{2\pi} \sum_{k=1}^{n(x)} \frac{\cos k(x-t)}{\sqrt{W(k)}} \sum_{m=1}^{n(y)} \frac{\cos m(y-t)}{\sqrt{W(m)}}\, dt = \pi \sum_{k=1}^{n(x,y)} \frac{\cos k(x-y)}{W(k)},$$

where $n(x, y) = \min(n(x), n(y))$. Therefore

$$J = \pi \int_0^{2\pi}\int_0^{2\pi} \sum_{k=1}^{n(x,y)} \frac{\cos k(x-y)}{W(k)}\, d\mu(x)\, d\mu(y).$$

Again, arguing just as in § 2, we see that

$$J \leqslant 2\pi \int_0^{2\pi}\int_0^{2\pi} \left| \sum_{k=1}^{n(y)} \frac{\cos k(x-y)}{W(k)} \right| d\mu(x)\, d\mu(y). \tag{12.18}$$

But we have already noted that the values $\{\lambda_n\}$ satisfy all the conditions of Lemma 2 and since the values of $\gamma_n$ in this lemma are now given by

$$\gamma_n = n\Delta\lambda_n = \frac{1}{W(n)},$$

then due to this lemma (see 12.14) we obtain for any $m$

$$\left| \sum_{k=1}^{m} \frac{\cos kt}{W(k)} \right| < A_1 H(t) + A_2, \tag{12.19}$$

where $A_1$ and $A_2$ are constants and $H(t)$ is defined by formula (12.13).

Now it is possible by applying formula (12.19) to write

$$\sum_{k=1}^{n(y)} \frac{\cos k(x-y)}{W(k)} < A_1 H(x-y) + A_2.$$

From this and from (12.18) we find

$$J \leqslant 2\pi \int_0^{2\pi}\int_0^{2\pi} [A_1 H(x-y) + A_2]\, d\mu(x)\, d\mu(y)$$

$$= 2\pi A_1 \int_0^{2\pi}\int_0^{2\pi} H(x-y)\, d\mu(x)\, d\mu(y) + 2\pi A_2, \qquad (12.20)$$

because $\int_0^{2\pi} d\mu(x) = 1$.

Since $H(t) = \sum \lambda_k \cos kt$ (see 12.13), then for $\alpha_n$ and $\beta_n$ definable by formula (12.15) we have

$$\int_0^{2\pi}\int_0^{2\pi} H(x-y)\, d\mu(x)\, d\mu(y) = \pi \sum_{n=1}^{\infty} (\alpha_n^2 + \beta_n^2)\lambda_n < +\infty. \qquad (12.21)$$

Here we must argue in the same way as in the proof of formula (12.10) and then pass to the limit as $r \to 1$ and operate on condition (12.16).

From (12.20) and (12.21) we obtain

$$J \leqslant C,$$

where $C$ is a constant and Lemma 3 is proved.

It is now possible to prove the basic theorem of this section, namely:

THEOREM. *Let $W(n) \uparrow \infty$ and $\sum 1/nW(n) < +\infty$. Let*

$$\lambda_n = \sum_{k=n}^{\infty} \frac{1}{kW(k)}. \qquad (12.22)$$

*If the series*

$$\sum (a_n^2 + b_n^2) W(n) < +\infty, \qquad (12.23)$$

*then the trigonometric series*

$$\frac{a_0}{2} + \sum_{n=1}^{\infty} (a_n \cos nx + b_n \sin nx) \qquad (12.24)$$

*converges everywhere, apart perhaps from the set $E$ in which the generalized convex capacity relative to $\{\lambda_n\}$ equals zero.*

We have already seen in the proof of Lemma 3 that $\{\lambda_n\}$ is convex. We have the right to suppose, moreover, that $W(n)$ increases not too quickly, or to be more precise, not so quickly that $\sum \lambda_n < +\infty$ (since we have seen that in the last case of sets of generalized capacity zero, this is indeed not so). Thus

$$\sum \lambda_n = +\infty.$$

Let us take $\psi(n) \uparrow \infty$ such that

$$\sum (a_n^2 + b_n^2) W(n)\psi(n) < +\infty.$$

This is always possible (see Appendix, § 25). Let

$$A_n = a_n \sqrt{\psi(n)}\,; \quad B_n = b_n \sqrt{\psi(n)}. \tag{12.25}$$

We then have

$$\sum (A_n^2 + B_n^2)\, W(n) < +\infty. \tag{12.26}$$

Let us consider the trigonometric series

$$\frac{A_0}{2} + \sum (A_n \cos nx + B_n \sin nx). \tag{12.27}$$

If $E$ is a set of points of divergence of the series (12.24), then the partial sums $S_n(x)$ of series (12.27) should be unbounded at every point (see Appendix, § 12, Corollary to Theorem 5), because $\psi(n) \uparrow \infty$. If we prove that the set of points where $S_n(x)$ are not bounded should be of generalized capacity zero relative to $\{\lambda_n\}$, then our theorem will be proved.†

Let us prove that this is untrue. Then according to Theorem 2, $\mu \prec E$ is found such that for the values

$$\alpha_n = \frac{1}{\pi}\int_0^{2\pi} \cos nx\, d\mu, \quad \beta_n = \frac{1}{\pi}\int_0^{2\pi} \sin nx\, d\mu$$

the condition

$$\sum (\alpha_n^2 + \beta_n^2)\, \lambda_n < +\infty. \tag{12.28}$$

will be fulfilled.

We will prove that for this $\mu$, if $n(x) = 1, 2, \ldots, n$, we have

$$\left|\int_0^{2\pi} S_{n_x}(\chi)\, d\mu\right| \leqslant C \sqrt{\sum_{k=1}^{n} (A_k^2 + B_k^2)\, W(k)}. \tag{12.29}$$

Here again the argument follows the same lines as in the Kolmogorov–Seliverstov and Plessner theorem.

Let us consider the function

$$F_n(x) = \sum_{k=1}^{n} (A_k \sqrt{W(k)} \cos kx + B_k \sqrt{W(k)} \sin kx).$$

Then

$$S_{n_x}(x) = \int_0^{2\pi} F_n(t) \sum_{k=1}^{n(x)} \frac{\cos k(x-t)}{\sqrt{W(k)}}\, dt,$$

and therefore

$$I = \int_0^{2\pi} S_{n_x}(x)\, d\mu = \int_0^{2\pi} \left\{ \int_0^{2\pi} F_n(t) \sum_{k=1}^{n(x)} \frac{\cos k(x-t)}{\sqrt{W(k)}}\, dt \right\} d\mu(x)$$

$$= \int_0^{2\pi} F_n(t) \left\{ \int_0^{2\pi} \sum_{k=1}^{n(x)} \frac{\cos k(x-t)}{\sqrt{W(k)}}\, d\mu(x) \right\} dt.$$

† Above (see the footnote to Theorem 2) we saw that part of a set of generalized capacity zero is itself of generalized capacity zero.

Consequently,

$$I^2 \leqslant \int_0^{2\pi} F_n^2(t)\,dt \int_0^{2\pi} \left[ \int_0^{2\pi} \sum_{k=1}^{n(x)} \frac{\cos k(x-t)}{\sqrt{W(k)}}\, d\mu(x) \right]^2 dt = J \int_0^{2\pi} F_n^2(t)\,dt,$$

where $J$ is the expression considered in Lemma 3, regarding which it was proved that it does not exceed the absolute constant $C$. But then

$$I^2 < C \int_0^{2\pi} F_n^2(t)\,dt = C\pi \sum_{k=1}^{n} (A_k^2 + B_k^2)\,W(k),$$

whence the validity of the inequality (12.29) follows.

Therefore, denoting as in the theorem of § 2

$$\Phi_{1n}(x) = \max\,\{S_1(x),\, S_2(x),\, \ldots,\, S_n(x)\},$$

we see that also

$$\left| \int_0^{2\pi} \Phi_{1n}(x)\,d\mu \right| \leqslant C \sqrt{\sum_{k=1}^{n} (A_k^2 + B_k^2)\,W(k)}\;.$$

Such an equality also holds for $\varphi_{1n}(x)$, if we suppose that

$$\varphi_{1n}(x) = \max\{-\,S_1(x),\, -\,S_2(x),\, \ldots,\, -\,S_n(x)\}.$$

Since the series (12.26) converges, then we have for any $n$

$$\left| \int_0^{2\pi} \Phi_{1n}(x)\,d\mu \right| \leqslant K, \qquad \left| \int_0^{2\pi} \varphi_{1n}(x)\,d\mu \right| \leqslant K, \tag{12.30}$$

where $K$ is an absolute constant. But $\mu \prec E$ and the sums $S_n(x)$ are not bounded at every point in the set $E$. This contradicts the conditions of (12.30) and the theorem is proved.

From this theorem, Beurling's theorem follows as a corollary, if it is supposed that $W(n) = n$, since then

$$\lambda_n = \sum_{k=n}^{\infty} \frac{1}{k^2} \sim \frac{1}{n}$$

which means that by virtue of Corollary 1 to Theorem 2 for

$$\sum (a_n^2 + b_n^2)n < +\infty$$

the trigonometric series can diverge only in a set of generalized convex capacity zero relative to $\{1/n\}$. But then, as we know, the logarithmic capacity of this set is also zero and Beurling's theorem is proved.

If we suppose that $W(n) = n^\alpha$, then

$$\lambda_n = \sum_{k=n}^{\infty} \frac{1}{k^{1+\alpha}} \sim \frac{1}{n^\alpha},$$

and therefore the trigonometric series with coefficients $a_n$, $b_n$, where $\sum (a_n^2 + b_n^2) n^\alpha < +\infty$ can diverge only in a set of generalized capacity zero relative to $\{1/n^\alpha\}$, i.e. $(1-\alpha)$-capacity zero; this is the Salem–Zygmund theorem.

*Note.* Unfortunately, for the case

$$\sum (a_n^2 + b_n^2) \ln n < +\infty$$

the theorem on convex capacity does not give any information, since the series

$$\sum \frac{1}{n \ln n}$$

diverges. But for the case

$$\sum (a_n^2 + b_n^2) (\ln n)^{1+\varepsilon},$$

where $\varepsilon > 0$ it is possible to derive the fact that the set of points of divergence is of generalized capacity zero relative to $\{\lambda_n\}$ where

$$\lambda_n = \sum_{k=n}^{\infty} \frac{1}{k(\ln k)^{1+\varepsilon}} \sim \frac{1}{(\ln n)^\varepsilon}.$$

We have considered it appropriate to study the question of convex capacity in detail here, because this concept is evidently useful in a number of problems concerning the theory of trigonometric series, where it is necessary to deal with the subtle properties of sets of measure zero. In particular, we find this is true whilst investigating absolute convergence (see Chapter XIII, § 10).

## § 13. A convergence test, using an integrated series†

In Chapter IV, § 7 the theorem was proved which stated that if $f(x)$ is continuous, $F(x)$ is its indefinite integral and

$$|S_n(x, F) - F(x)| = o\left(\frac{1}{n}\right)$$

uniformly in $[0, 2\pi]$, then also

$$|S_n(x, f) - f(x)| = o(1)$$

uniformly in $[0, 2\pi]$. Here we prove Salem's[13] theorem, which is similar but formulated in such a way that $f(x)$ is not assumed to be continuous although finite, so that the convergence will not be uniform; all the same it will occur almost everywhere. To be more precise we will prove the theorem:

THEOREM. *If $f(x)$ is summable, $F(x)$ is its indefinite integral and*

$$|S_n(x, F) - F(x)| = o\left(\frac{1}{n}\right) \tag{13.1}$$

† The result of this section depends on facts established in §§ 5 and 23 of Chapter VIII.

*in some set E* (uniformity not necessary), *then*

$$|S_n(x,f) - f(x)| = o(1)$$

*almost everywhere in E.*

*Proof*†. Let

$$\sum (a_n \cos nx + b_n \sin nx) \tag{13.2}$$

be $\sigma(f)$, then††

$$\sigma(F) = \sum \frac{-b_n \cos nx + a_n \sin nx}{n}. \tag{13.3}$$

Since the series (13.3) converges everywhere to $F(x)$, because $F(x)$ is absolutely continuous, then from condition (13.1) we conclude that

$$\sum_{k=n+1}^{\infty} \frac{-b_k \cos kx + a_k \sin kx}{k} = o\left(\frac{1}{n}\right)$$

almost everywhere in $E$.

The series conjugate to (13.2) has the form

$$\bar{\sigma}(f) = \sum (-b_k \cos kx + a_k \sin kx), \tag{13.4}$$

and according to the theorem of Chapter VIII, § 5 it should be summable $(C, 1)$ almost everywhere in $E$. Also, according to Theorem 4 of § 12 in the Appendix, if

$$\sum_{k=n+1}^{\infty} \frac{u_k}{k} = o\left(\frac{1}{n}\right)$$

and the series $\sum u_k$ is summable $(C, 1)$ then $\sum u_k$ converges. From this it immediately follows that the series (13.4) converges almost everywhere in $E$. Now let us apply Kuttner's theorem (Chapter VIII, § 23); if a trigonometric series converges in some set $E$, $mE > 0$, and its conjugate is summable $(C, 1)$ in $E$, then the conjugate series converges almost everywhere in $E$. This permits us to state that the convergence of $\bar{\sigma}(f)$ almost everywhere in $E$ implies the convergence almost everywhere in $E$ of $\sigma(f)$, and then our theorem is proved.

*Note.* The reverse statement also holds:

*If*

$$|S_n(x,f) - f(x)| = o(1) \quad \textit{in } E, \tag{13.5}$$

*then*

$$|S_n(x, F) - F(x)| = o\left(\frac{1}{n}\right) \quad \textit{almost everywhere in } E.$$

Indeed (13.5) signifies that $\sigma(f)$ converges almost everywhere in $E$; consequently, according to Kuttner's theorem, $\bar{\sigma}(f)$ also converges almost everywhere in $E$. This means that the series

$$\sum_{k=1}^{\infty} (-b_k \cos kx + a_k \sin kx) \quad \text{converges almost everywhere in } E,$$

† This proof is due to Zygmund and was described verbally by him to Salem.

†† We have assumed in series (13.2) that $a_0 = 0$, otherwise $F(x)$ would not be periodic.

and then from Theorem 3 in § 25 of the Appendix

$$\sum_{k=n+1}^{\infty} \frac{-b_k \cos kx + a_k \sin kx}{k} = o\left(\frac{1}{n}\right),$$

i.e.

$$|S_n(x, F) - F(x)| = o\left(\frac{1}{n}\right) \quad \text{almost everywhere in } E,$$

and the theorem is proved.

## § 14. The Salem test

In Chapter IV, § 8, a theorem was proved which was obtained simultaneously and independently by Salem and Stechkin; if

$$\frac{1}{h}\int_0^h [f(x+t) - f(x-t)]\,dt = o\left(\frac{1}{\ln \frac{1}{|h|}}\right) \tag{14.1}$$

uniformly for $a \leqslant x \leqslant b$ and if $f(x)$ is continuous in $(a, b)$, then $\sigma(f)$ converges in $(a+\varepsilon, b-\varepsilon)$ uniformly (here $\varepsilon > 0$ can be taken as any value).

Salem[13], rejecting the requirement of the continuity of $f(x)$, proves the following theorem:

THE SALEM THEOREM. *If*

$$\frac{1}{h}\int_0^h [f(x+t) - f(x-t)]\,dt = o\left(\frac{1}{\ln \frac{1}{|h|}}\right)$$

*uniformly in* $a \leqslant x \leqslant b$, *then* $\sigma(f)$ *converges almost everywhere in* $(a, b)$.

*Proof.* We assume that in the series $\sigma(f)$ the free term equals zero, since this does not decrease the generality of the argument. Then

$$F(x) = \int_0^x f(t)\,dt$$

will be periodic and from the condition (14.1) it immediately follows that

$$F(x+h) + F(x-h) - 2F(x) = o\left(\frac{h}{\ln \frac{1}{|h|}}\right) \tag{14.2}$$

uniformly in $(a, b)$. Because $F(x)$ is continuous, then from (14.2) it follows (see Chapter IV, § 9) that

$$|S_n(F, x) - F(x)| = o\left(\frac{1}{n}\right)$$

uniformly in $(a+\varepsilon, b-\varepsilon)$. On the basis of § 13 then

$$|S_n(f, x) - f(x)| = o(1)$$

almost everywhere in $(a+\varepsilon, b-\varepsilon)$. But since $\varepsilon > 0$ is arbitrary, then

$$S_n(f, x) - f(x) = o(1) \quad \text{almost everywhere in } (a, b),$$

and the theorem is proved.

## § 15. The Marcinkiewicz test

In the preceding theorem due to Salem (§ 14), condition (14.1) was assumed to be fulfilled over the whole interval $[a, b]$ (and, moreover, uniformly) and almost everywhere convergence was obtained in $[a, b]$. Marcinkiewicz[1] earlier considered some condition which was very similar to Salem's but he assumed it to be fulfilled in a set and obtained convergence almost everywhere in this set.

THE MARCINKIEWICZ THEOREM. *If*

$$\frac{1}{h}\int_0^h |f(x+u) - f(x)|\, du = O\left(\frac{1}{\ln \frac{1}{|h|}}\right) \tag{15.1}$$

*for* $x \in E$, $mE > 0$, *then* $\sigma(f)$ *converges almost everywhere in* $E$.

This theorem was known to Salem, however, he notes that his result cannot be obtained from the Marcinkiewicz theorem, since in the latter the expression $f(x+t) - f(x-t)$ under the integral sign is taken as its absolute magnitude.

The proof of Marcinkiewicz's theorem is based on two lemmas.

LEMMA 1. *Let* $P$ *be a perfect set in* $[0, 2\pi]$, $\Delta_n (n = 1, 2, \ldots)$ *its adjacent intervals,* $h(t)$ *be a non-negative function such that*

$$h(t) = 0 \quad \text{in} \quad P, \tag{15.2}$$

$$\frac{1}{\Delta_n}\int_{\Delta_n} h(t)\, dt < \frac{A}{\ln \frac{1}{\Delta_n}} \qquad (n = 1, 2, \ldots), \tag{15.3}$$

*where* $A$ *is a constant not dependent on* $n$; *then*

$$\int_0^{2\pi} \frac{h(t)}{|t-x|}\, dt < +\infty \quad \text{almost everywhere in } P. \tag{15.4}$$

*Proof.* Let us denote by $x_n$ the centre of the interval $\Delta_n$ and suppose that

$$\delta_n = \left(x_n - \frac{\Delta_n}{6},\quad x_n + \frac{\Delta_n}{6}\right).$$

Let us define the function $\psi(t)$ by the condition

$$\psi(t) = 3h[x_n + 3(t - x_n)] \quad \text{for} \quad t \in \delta_n$$

and

$$\psi(t) = 0 \quad \text{outside all} \quad \delta_n \quad (n = 1, 2, \ldots).$$

Let us denote by $\Phi(x)$ the characteristic function of the set $P$ and prove the convergence of the double integral

$$I = \int_0^{2\pi}\int_0^{2\pi} \Phi(x) \frac{\psi(t)}{|x-t|} dx\, dt. \tag{15.5}$$

Since $\psi(t) = 0$ outside all $\delta_n$, then

$$I = \sum \int_{\delta_n} \psi(t) \left( \int_0^{2\pi} \frac{\Phi(t)}{|x-t|} dx \right) dt = \sum \int_{\delta_n} \psi(t) \left( \int_P \frac{dx}{|x-t|} \right) dt. \tag{15.6}$$

But if $t \in \delta_n$ and $x \in P$, then $|x - t| \geqslant \frac{1}{3}\Delta_n$, and therefore

$$\int_P \frac{dx}{|x-t|} \leqslant 2 \int_{\Delta_n/3}^{2\pi} \frac{du}{u} = 2 \ln \frac{6\pi}{\Delta_n} = 2 \ln 6\pi + 2 \ln \frac{1}{\Delta_n} < 4 \ln \frac{1}{\Delta_n} \tag{15.7}$$

for all $n \geqslant n_0$, if $n_0$ is chosen so that $1/\Delta_n > 6\pi$ for all $n \geqslant n_0$.

Let us now note that

$$\int_{\delta_n} \psi(t)\, dt = 3 \int_{x_n - \Delta_n/6}^{x_n + \Delta_n/6} h[x_n + 3(t - x_n)]\, dt = \int_{x_n - \Delta_n/2}^{x_n + \Delta_n/2} h(u)\, du = \int_{\Delta_n} h(u)\, du, \tag{15.8}$$

and therefore on the basis of (15.3), (15.7) and (15.8)

$$\sum_{n=n_0}^{\infty} \int_{\delta_n} \psi(t) \left( \int_P \frac{dx}{|x-t|} \right) dt \leqslant 4 \sum_{n=n_0}^{\infty} \ln \frac{1}{\Delta_n} \int_{\Delta_n} h(u)\, du < 4A \sum_{n=1}^{\infty} \Delta_n < +\infty.$$

Comparing this with (15.6) we see that the double integral (15.5) has meaning.

From this, based on Fubini's well-known theorem, we immediately conclude that

$$\int_0^{2\pi} \frac{\psi(t)}{|x-t|} dt < +\infty \quad \text{almost everywhere in } P. \tag{15.9}$$

Let us prove that if $x_0$ is a point of density of the set $P$, then (15.9) implies (15.4). Indeed, from (15.9) it follows in any case that

$$\sum_{n=1}^{\infty} \int_{\delta_n} \frac{\psi(t)}{|x-t|} dt < +\infty.$$

If we assume, as in formula (15.8), $u = x_n + 3(t - x_n)$, then when $t$ passes through $\delta_n$, the argument $u$ passes through $\Delta_n$.

From

$$t - x = u - x - \tfrac{2}{3}(u - x_n)$$

we find $|t - x| < |u - x| (1 + \frac{2}{3} |(u - x_n)/(u - x)|)$. But because $x_0$ is a point of density for $P$, then $|(u - x_n)/(u - x)| \to 0$ as $|u - x| \to 0$, and therefore it is possible to make

$$|t - x| < |u - x| (1 + \varepsilon),$$

where $\varepsilon > 0$ is previously given (if only $t - x$ is sufficiently small). From this it follows that

$$\int_{\delta_n} \frac{\psi(t)}{|t - x|} dt \geqslant \frac{1}{1 + \varepsilon} \int_{\Delta_n} \frac{h(u)\, du}{|u - x|},$$

as only $\delta_n$ will be found in a sufficiently small neighbourhood of the point $x$, and therefore

$$\sum \int_{\Delta_n} \frac{h(u)\, du}{|u - x|} < + \infty .$$

Since $h(x) = 0$ outside all $\Delta_n$, then (15.4) is proved.

LEMMA 2. *Let $f(x)$ satisfy condition* (15.1) *at every point of $E$, $mE > 0$. Then there exists a perfect set $P$, contained in $E$, $mP > 0$, such that*

$$f(x) = g(x) + h(x), \tag{15.10}$$

*where*

$$|g(x + t) - g(x)| = O \frac{1}{\ln \dfrac{1}{|t|}} \tag{15.11}$$

*uniformly in* $(0, 2\pi)$, *then as*

$$h(x) = 0 \quad \textit{for} \quad x \in P$$

*and moreover*

$$\frac{1}{\Delta_n} \int_{\Delta_n} |h(t)|\, dt < \frac{A}{\ln \dfrac{1}{\Delta_n}} \quad (n = 1, 2, \ldots) \tag{15.12}$$

*for some constant $A$ and all adjacent intervals $\Delta_n$ of the set $P$.*

*Proof.* Let us denote by $E_n$ a subset of $E$ such that

$$\frac{1}{t} \int_0^t |f(x + u) - f(x)|\, du < \frac{n}{\ln \dfrac{1}{|t|}} \quad \text{for} \quad x \subset E_n \quad \text{and} \quad |t| < \frac{1}{n}. \tag{15.13}$$

It is clear that $E_1 \subset E_2 \subset \cdots \subset E_n \subset \cdots$ and $E = \sum E_n$, and therefore it is possible to find $n_0$ such that $mE_{n_0} > 0$. Let us suppose that $1/n_0 = \delta$, $n_0 = B$ and consider some perfect $P \in E_{n_0}$ of diameter less than $\delta$. Since $n_0$ can be taken as large as desired, then $\delta$ can be considered to be as small as desired.

Let $\mathscr{E}(x, t, M)$ be the aggregate of all the points $v$ of the interval $(x + t/3, x + t)$ for which

$$|f(v) - f(x)| \geqslant \frac{M}{\ln \dfrac{1}{|v - x|}} .$$

If $x \in P$ and $|t| < \delta$, then (15.13) holds and therefore

$$\frac{1}{t}\int_x^{x+t} |f(v) - f(x)|\, dv < \frac{B}{\ln \dfrac{1}{|t|}}.$$

But for the points $\mathscr{E}(x, t, M)$ we have $|v - x| > |t|/3$, which means that

$$\frac{1}{|t|} \frac{M}{\ln\left(\dfrac{1}{3}|t|\right)^{-1}} m\mathscr{E} \leqslant \frac{1}{|t|}\int_{\mathscr{E}} |f(v) - f(x)|\, dv < \frac{B}{\ln \dfrac{1}{|t|}},$$

whence

$$m\mathscr{E}\,(x, t, M) \leqslant \frac{B}{M} \frac{\ln \dfrac{1}{3}|t|}{\ln |t|} |t| \leqslant \frac{2B}{M}|t|,$$

if $\delta$, which also means $|t|$, is sufficiently small. If we take $M = 14B$, we obtain

$$m\mathscr{E}\,(x, t) = m\mathscr{E}(x, t, 14B) \leqslant \frac{|t|}{7}. \tag{15.14}$$

Now let $x < y$ be any two points of $P$. From (15.14) we find that

$$m\mathscr{E}(x, y - x) < \frac{1}{7}(y - x); \quad m\mathscr{E}(y, x - y) < \frac{1}{7}(y - x).$$

This means that in the interval $\{x + (y - x)/3, y - (y - x)/3\}$ a point $\xi$ can be found which does not enter either into $\xi(x, y - x)$ or into $\xi(y, y - x)$. Therefore

$$|f(\xi) - f(x)| \leqslant \frac{14B}{\ln \dfrac{1}{|\xi - x|}} \quad \text{and} \quad |f(\xi) - f(y)| \leqslant \frac{14B}{\ln \dfrac{1}{|\xi - y|}}.$$

From this

$$|f(x) - f(y)| \leqslant \frac{C}{\ln \dfrac{1}{|y - x|}}, \quad \text{where} \quad C = 28B.$$

We will denote by $g(x)$ the function which equals $f(x)$ in $P$ and is linear in adjacent intervals. It is easily seen that for this

$$|g(x + t) - g(x)| < \frac{3C}{\ln \dfrac{1}{|t|}} \quad \text{for} \quad |t| < \delta$$

and thus condition (15.11) is satisfied. Supposing that

$$h(x) = f(x) - g(x),$$

we see that $h(x) = 0$ in $P$ and it remains to prove (15.12).

Let $\Delta$ be one of the intervals adjacent to $P$ and $x$ be its left end-point. Since $x \in P$, then we have

$$\int_{\Delta} |h(t)|\,dt \leqslant \int_0^{\Delta} |f(x+t) - f(x)|\,dt + \int_0^{\Delta} |g(x+t) - g(x)|\,dt$$

$$< \Delta \frac{B}{\ln \frac{1}{\Delta}} + \Delta \frac{3C}{\ln \frac{1}{\Delta}} = A \frac{\Delta}{\ln \frac{1}{\Delta}},$$

where $A = B + 3C$, and the lemma is proved.

Now that these lemmas have been proved, let us continue with the proof of the theorem.

On the basis of Lemma 2 it is possible to divide $f(x)$ into a sum

$$f(x) = g(x) + h(x).$$

whilst $g(x)$ satisfies condition (15.11). But then

$$|g(x+t) - g(x-t)| = O\left(\frac{1}{\ln \frac{1}{|t|}}\right) \quad \text{uniformly in } (0, 2\pi)$$

which means that

$$\int_0^{\pi} \frac{[g(x+t) - g(x-t)]^2}{t}\,dt < +\infty,$$

and then it is all the more true that

$$\int_0^{2\pi}\int_0^{2\pi} \frac{[g(x+t) - g(x-t)]^2}{t}\,dt\,dx < +\infty.$$

But then according to Plessner's theorem (see § 5) the Fourier series for $g(x)$ converges almost everywhere.

On the other hand, since the function $|h(x)|$ satisfies the conditions of Lemma 1, then on the basis of this lemma the Dini test (see Chapter I, § 38) is fulfilled almost everywhere in $P$, and therefore its Fourier series converges almost everywhere in $P$. From this we conclude that the Fourier series of $f(x)$ also converges almost everywhere in $P$.

Since in any subset $\mathscr{E}$ of the set $E$, $m\mathscr{E} > 0$, there is a $P$ possessing this property, then it is clear that $\sigma(f)$ converges almost everywhere in $E$.

In § 18 it will be proved that this theorem in a sense cannot be strengthened.

## § 16. Convergence test expressed by the logarithmic measure of the set

Let us prove yet another convergence test of the series $\sigma(f)$ almost everywhere in $[0, 2\pi]$; it is interesting because it is expressed in a sense in terms of the structure of the function $f(x)$ and, in particular, gives an indication when the Fourier series of the characteristic function of a certain set converges almost everywhere. This test was derived by Kaidash[1].

First of all, let us introduce the concept of the logarithmic measure of a set.

Let us consider an arbitrary measurable set $E$. Let $\varepsilon > 0$ be given. Let us cover $E$ with a system of intervals $\delta_1, \delta_2, \ldots, \delta_n$, such that

$$\sum_{n=1}^{\infty} \delta_n < mE + \varepsilon,$$

and consider the value

$$\sum_{n=1}^{\infty} \delta_n \, |\ln \delta_n| \tag{16.1}$$

(it can also equal $+\infty$).

The lower bound of these quantities for the complete coverage of the set $E$, satisfying the given condition, is known as the logarithmic measure of the set $E$ correct to $\varepsilon$ and will be denoted by $L(E, \varepsilon)$. It is clear that when $\varepsilon$ is decreased, then the function $L(E, \varepsilon)$ can only increase and therefore there exists a limit

$$\lim_{\varepsilon \to 0} L(E, \varepsilon) = L(E),$$

which we call *the logarithmic measure of the set E*. The case $L(E) = +\infty$ is not excluded.

Our next aim is the proof of the theorem:

THEOREM. *Let $f(x)$ be non-negative and summable; let us suppose that*

$$E(l) = E\{f(x) > l\}$$

*and let $L[E(l)]$ be its logarithmic measure. If the function $\varphi(l) = L[E(l)]$ is summable in $0 \leqslant l < +\infty$, then the Fourier series for $f(x)$ converges almost everywhere.*

For the proof of this theorem some lemmas are necessary.

LEMMA 1. *Let G be an open set in* $[0, 2\pi]$.

*Let us arrange the intervals comprising it in descending order*

$$\delta_1 \geqslant \delta_2 \geqslant \cdots \geqslant \delta_n \geqslant \cdots$$

*and construct the series*

$$\sum_{n=1}^{\infty} \delta_n \, |\ln \delta_n| . \tag{16.2}$$

*If this series converges, then for the characteristic function $\psi(x)$ of the set G the Fourier series converges almost everywhere and the inequality holds*

$$\int_0^{2\pi}\!\!\int_0^{2\pi} \left| \frac{\psi(x+\alpha) + \psi(x-\alpha) - 2\psi(x)}{\alpha} \right| d\alpha \, dx \leqslant K \sum_{n=1}^{\infty} \delta_n \, |\ln \delta_n| , \tag{16.3}$$

*where K is an absolute constant.*

*Proof.* Let $\gamma > 0$ be any value; let us consider the integral

$$A(\gamma) = \int_0^{2\pi}\!\!\int_{\gamma}^{2\pi} |\psi(x+\alpha) - \psi(x)| \, \frac{d\alpha}{\alpha} \, dx . \tag{16.4}$$

We have

$$A(\gamma) = \int_{\gamma}^{2\pi} \frac{d\alpha}{\alpha} \int_{0}^{2\pi} |\psi(x+\alpha) - \psi(x)|\, dx = \int_{\gamma}^{2\pi} \frac{d\alpha}{\alpha} \int_{0}^{2\pi} [\psi(x+\alpha) - \psi(x)]^2\, dx,$$

since the function under the integral in the outer integral can take only the values 0 and 1. Therefore

$$A(\gamma) = \int_{\gamma}^{2\pi} \frac{d\alpha}{\alpha} \left\{ \int_{0}^{2\pi} \psi^2(x+\alpha)\, d\alpha - 2 \int_{0}^{2\pi} \psi(x+\alpha)\psi(x)\, dx + \int_{0}^{2\pi} \psi^2(x)\, dx \right\}$$

$$= \int_{\gamma}^{2\pi} \frac{d\alpha}{\alpha} \left\{ mG - 2 \int_{0}^{2\pi} \psi(x+\alpha)\psi(x)\, dx + mG \right\}$$

$$= 2 \int_{\gamma}^{2\pi} \left[ mG - \int_{0}^{2\pi} \psi(x+\alpha)\,\psi(x)\, dx \right] \frac{d\alpha}{\alpha}. \tag{16.5}$$

Let us denote by $N(\alpha)$ the number of all the intervals $\delta_n$ such that $\delta_n \geqslant \alpha$, and show that

$$\int_{0}^{2\pi} \psi(x+\alpha)\psi(x)\, dx \geqslant \sum_{\delta_n \geqslant \alpha} (\delta_n - \alpha) = \sum_{\delta_n \geqslant \alpha} \delta_n - N(\alpha)\alpha. \tag{16.6}$$

On any straight line $x + \alpha = c$ we have

$$\psi(x+\alpha) = \begin{cases} 0, & \text{if } \psi(c) = 0, \\ 1, & \text{if } \psi(c) = 1. \end{cases}$$

Thus, the set of points where $\psi(x+\alpha) = 1$ consists of parallel straight lines (Fig. 18) intersecting the abscissa axis in points belonging to the intervals $\delta_n$. The product $\psi(x)\,\psi(x+\alpha)$ will equal 1 at least in all the shaded right-angled triangles with base $\delta_n$ and height $\delta_n$. Let $\alpha_0$ be fixed. Let us consider the triangles which overlap the line $y = \alpha_0$. These will be the triangles for which $\delta_n > \alpha_0$. From this estimate (16.6) becomes clear geometrically.

Returning to formula (16.5) and substituting (16.6) we obtain

$$A(\gamma) \leqslant 2 \int_{\gamma}^{2\pi} \left[ mG - \sum_{\delta_n \geqslant \alpha} \delta_n + N(\alpha)\alpha \right] \frac{d\alpha}{\alpha}.$$

But since $mG = \sum \delta_n$, then

$$A(\gamma) \leqslant 2 \int_{\gamma}^{2\pi} \sum_{\delta_n < \alpha} \delta_n \frac{d\alpha}{\alpha} + 2 \int_{\gamma}^{2\pi} N(\alpha)\, d\alpha = A_1(\gamma) + A_2(\gamma). \tag{16.7}$$

We will first estimate the integral $A_2(\gamma)$; we have, using the notation $N(\gamma) = m$,

$$A_2(\gamma) = 2\int_{\gamma}^{2\pi} N(\alpha)\,d\alpha = 2[1(\delta_1 - \delta_2) + 2(\delta_2 - \delta_3) + \cdots + m(\delta_m - \gamma)]$$

$$= 2[\delta_1 + \cdots + \delta_m - m\gamma] \leqslant 2\sum_{n=1}^{\infty}\delta_n,$$

since it is clear that $N(\alpha) = k$, if $\delta_{k+1} < \alpha \leqslant \delta_k$ (Fig. 19).

Thus

$$A_2(\gamma) \leqslant 2\sum_{n=1}^{\infty}\delta_n. \tag{16.8}$$

Let us continue with the estimate of the integral $A_1(\gamma)$. If $\delta_{k+1} \leqslant \alpha \leqslant \delta_k$, then it is necessary in the function under the integral sign to take only those $\delta_n$, the index of which is greater than or equal to $k+1$, therefore (Fig. 20)

$$\frac{1}{2}A_1(\gamma) = \int_{\gamma}^{2\pi}\frac{d\alpha}{\alpha}\sum_{\delta_n<\alpha}\delta_n$$

$$= \int_{\delta_1}^{2\pi}\sum_{n=1}^{\infty}\delta_n\frac{d\alpha}{\alpha} + \int_{\delta_2}^{\delta_1}\sum_{2}^{\infty}\delta_n\frac{d\alpha}{\alpha} + \int_{\delta_3}^{\delta_2}\sum_{3}^{\infty}\delta_n\frac{d\alpha}{\alpha} + \cdots + \int_{\gamma}^{\delta_m}\sum_{m+1}^{\infty}\delta_n\frac{d\alpha}{\alpha}$$

$$= \sum_{n=1}^{\infty}\delta_n(\ln 2\pi - \ln\delta_1) + \sum_{n=2}^{\infty}\delta_n(\ln\delta_1 - \ln\delta_2) + \cdots + \sum_{n=m+1}^{\infty}\delta_n(\ln\delta_m - \ln\gamma)$$

$$= \ln 2\pi\sum_{n=1}^{\infty}\delta_n - \delta_1\ln\delta_1 - \delta_2\ln\delta_2 - \cdots - \delta_m\ln\delta_m - \ln\gamma\sum_{n=m+1}^{\infty}\delta_n$$

$$\leqslant \ln 2\pi\sum_{n=1}^{\infty}\delta_n + \sum_{n=1}^{\infty}\delta_n|\ln\delta_n| + \sum_{n=1}^{\infty}\delta_n|\ln\delta_n| \leqslant K\sum_{n=1}^{\infty}\delta_n|\ln\delta_n|, \tag{16.9}$$

where $K$ is a constant.

Combining (16.8) and (16.9) we find that

$$A(\gamma) \leqslant C\sum_{n=1}^{\infty}\delta_n|\ln\delta_n|, \tag{16.10}$$

where $C$ is a constant.

In exactly the same way we find the integral

$$\int_0^{2\pi}\int_{\gamma}^{2\pi}\frac{|\psi(x-\alpha) - \psi(x)|}{\alpha}\,d\alpha\,dx \leqslant C_1\sum_{n=1}^{\infty}\delta_n|\ln\delta_n|. \tag{16.11}$$

Therefore, combining them together, we find

$$\int_0^{2\pi}\int_{\gamma}^{2\pi}\frac{|\psi(x+\alpha) + \psi(x-\alpha) - 2\psi(x)|}{\alpha}\,d\alpha\,dx \leqslant C_2\sum_{n=1}^{\infty}\delta_n|\ln\delta_n|. \tag{16.12}$$

Since the right-hand side of the inequality (16.12) does not depend on $\gamma$, then this means that the integral

$$\int_0^{2\pi}\int_\gamma^{2\pi} \frac{|\psi(x+\alpha)+\psi(x-\alpha)-2\psi(x)|}{\alpha}\,d\alpha\,dx$$

remains bounded as $\gamma \to 0$ and formula (16.3) is true. But the function under the integral sign is non-negative. From this it follows that it is Lebesgue-integrable in the square $(0 \leqslant \alpha \leqslant 2\pi,\ 0 \leqslant x \leqslant 2\pi)$. Then from Fubini's theorem it follows that the integral

$$\int_0^{2\pi} \frac{|\psi(x+\alpha)+\psi(x-\alpha)-2\psi(x)|}{\alpha}\,d\alpha$$

exists and is finite for nearly all values of $x$.

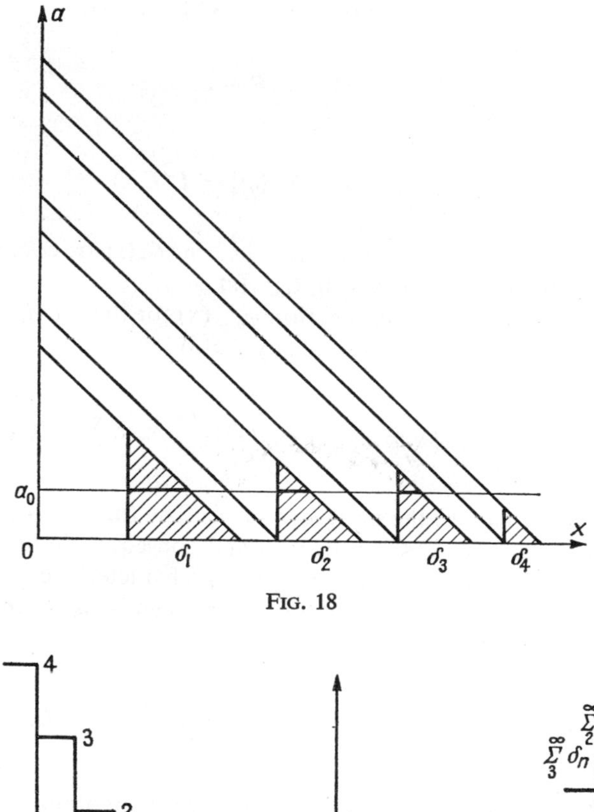


FIG. 18

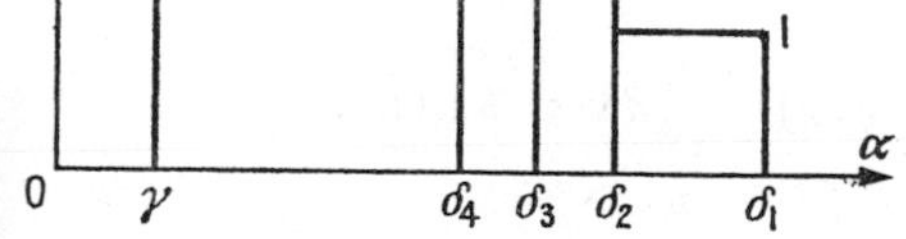


FIG. 19

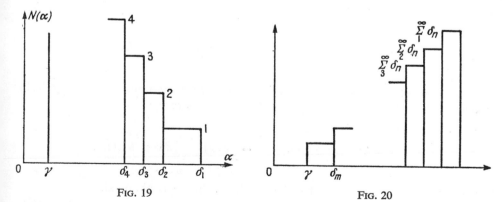

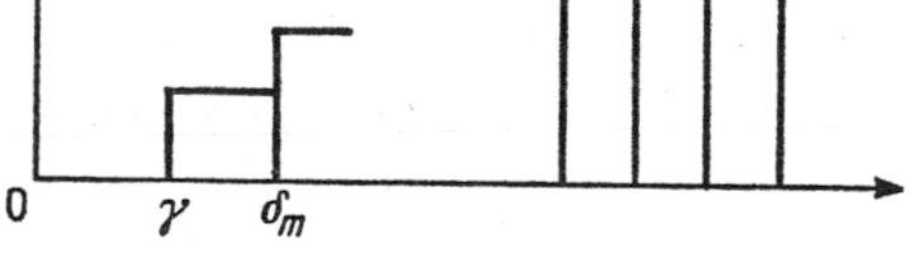


FIG. 20

Applying the Dini test, we can say that at every point where this integral exists, the Fourier series of $\psi(x)$ converges. Consequently, it converges almost everywhere and the lemma is completely proved.

LEMMA 2. *Let E be a set of finite logarithmic measure. Then the Fourier series for its characteristic function $\psi(x)$ converges almost everywhere and the estimate*

$$\int_0^{2\pi}\int_0^{2\pi} |\psi(x+\alpha)+\psi(x-\alpha)-2\psi(x)|\frac{d\alpha}{\alpha}dx \leqslant KL(E),$$

*holds, where $L(E)$ is the logarithmic measure and K is a constant.*

*Proof.* From the definition of logarithmic measure it follows that $L(E) = \lim L(E, \varepsilon)$ where $L(E, \varepsilon)$ is the logarithmic measure correct to $\varepsilon$. If $\varepsilon$ is fixed, then we can choose a sequence of the coverings $G_n(\varepsilon)$ for the set $E$

$$G_n(\varepsilon) = \{\delta_1^{(n)}(\varepsilon), \delta_2^{(n)}(\varepsilon), \ldots, \delta_k^{(n)}(\varepsilon), \ldots\}$$

such that

$$\sum_{k=1}^{\infty} \delta_k^n(\varepsilon) < mE + \varepsilon,$$

whilst

$$\lim_{n\to\infty} \sum_{k=1}^{\infty} \delta_k^{(n)}(\varepsilon)\,|\ln \delta_k^{(n)}(\varepsilon)| = L(E, \varepsilon).$$

We will suppose that the intervals of the $n$th covering $G_n(\varepsilon)$ are completely contained in the intervals of the $(n-1)$th covering $G_{n-1}(\varepsilon)$.

Let us consider the characteristic function $\psi_{n,\varepsilon}(x)$ for the set $G_n(\varepsilon)$ and apply to it the estimate from Lemma 1. We have for any $\gamma > 0$

$$\int_0^{2\pi}\int_\gamma^{2\pi} |\psi_{n,\varepsilon}(x+\alpha)+\psi_{n,\varepsilon}(x-\alpha)-2\psi_{n,\varepsilon}(x)|\frac{d\alpha}{\alpha} \leqslant K\sum \delta_k^{(n)}(\varepsilon)\,|\ln \delta_k^{(n)}(\varepsilon)|.$$

Keeping $\gamma$ fixed, we pass to the limit as $n \to \infty$, The function $\psi_{n,\varepsilon}(x)$ tends to the limit $\psi_\varepsilon(x)$ as $n \to \infty$, since $G_n(\varepsilon) \subset G_{n-1}(\varepsilon)$ and consequently for every $x$ we have $\psi_{n-1,\varepsilon}(x) \geqslant \psi_{n,\varepsilon}(x)$. The function $\psi_\varepsilon(x)$ is again the characteristic function of a certain set. Passage to the limit as $n \to \infty$ under the integral sign is valid, since all $\psi_{n,\varepsilon}(x)$ are all bounded (for any $\varepsilon$). Therefore

$$\int_0^{2\pi}\int_\gamma^{2\pi} |\psi_\varepsilon(x+\alpha)+\psi_\varepsilon(x-\alpha)-2\psi_\varepsilon(x)|\frac{d\alpha}{\alpha}dx \leqslant KL(E, \varepsilon).$$

If we now let $\varepsilon \to 0$, then the functions $\psi_\varepsilon(x)$ will tend almost everywhere to the function $\psi(x)$, characteristic for the set $E$, and therefore

$$\int_0^{2\pi}\int_\gamma^{2\pi} |\psi(x+\alpha)+\psi(x-\alpha)-2\psi(x)|\frac{d\alpha}{\alpha}dx \leqslant KL(E).$$

Letting $\gamma$ tend to zero, we see that the required estimate is obtained.

Repeating the argument with reference to the Dini test, given in the proof of Lemma 1, we prove that the Fourier series of $\psi(x)$ converges almost everywhere and Lemma 2 is proved.

Finally, let us note yet another obvious lemma.

LEMMA 3. *If $f(x) \geqslant 0$ and finite almost everywhere, $\psi(x, l)$ is the characteristic function for the set $E(l)$, where*

$$E(l) = E\{f(x) > l\},$$

*then for almost all $x$*

$$f(x) = \int_0^\infty \psi(x, l)\, dl.$$

Indeed, for all the points $(x, l)$ for which $f(x) \leqslant l$, we have $\psi(x, l) = 0$ and if $f(x) > l$, then $\psi(x, l) = 1$. Therefore, if $x$ is fixed and $f(x)$ is finite, then $\psi(x, l)$ possesses only one point of discontinuity in the interval $(0, \infty)$ and is bounded and measurable, which means that it is integrable in $(0, \infty)$. Moreover, it is clear that the length of this interval, in which $\psi(x) = 1$ coincides with the magnitude of the ordinate $f(x)$ of our function, whence it follows that

$$\int_0^\infty \psi(x, l)\, dl = \int_0^{f(x)} 1 \cdot dl = f(x),$$

and this is what was required to be proved.

PROOF OF THE THEOREM. Let us estimate the second integral, applying Lemma 3:

$$\int_0^{2\pi}\int_\gamma^{2\pi} |f(x+\alpha) + f(x-\alpha) - 2f(x)| \frac{d\alpha}{\alpha}\, dx$$

$$= \int_0^{2\pi}\int_\gamma^{2\pi} \left| \int_0^\infty \{\psi(x+\alpha, l) + \psi(x-\alpha, l) - 2\psi(x, l)\}\, dl \right| \frac{d\alpha}{\alpha}\, dx$$

$$\leqslant \int_0^{2\pi}\int_\gamma^{2\pi}\int_0^\infty |\psi(x+\alpha, l) + \psi(x-\alpha, l) - 2\psi(x, l)|\, dl \frac{d\alpha}{\alpha}\, dx.$$

Since under the integral sign there is an absolutely integrable function with respect to the three variables $x, l, \alpha$ and $\alpha > \gamma$, then it is possible to change the order of integration. As a result of the re-arrangement we obtain

$$\int_0^{2\pi}\int_\gamma^{2\pi} |f(x+\alpha) + f(x-\alpha) - 2f(x)| \frac{d\alpha}{\alpha}\, dx$$

$$\leqslant \int_0^\infty \left\{ \int_0^{2\pi}\int_\gamma^{2\pi} |\psi(x+\alpha, l) + \psi(x-\alpha, l) - 2\psi(x, l)| \frac{d\alpha}{\alpha}\, dx \right\} dl.$$

For the double integral in the curly brackets we can use the estimate of Lemma 2 and this gives

$$\int_0^{2\pi}\int_\gamma^{2\pi} |f(x+\alpha)+f(x-\alpha)-2f(x)| \frac{d\alpha}{\alpha}\, dx$$

$$\leqslant \int_0^\infty KL[E(l)]\, dl = K\int_0^\infty \varphi(l)\, dl. \tag{16.13}$$

According to the condition of the theorem the function $\varphi(l) = L[E(l)]$ is summable over $0 \leqslant l < \infty$. This means that the right-hand side of (16.13) is finite, whilst it does not depend on $\gamma$. From this it follows that

$$\int_0^{2\pi}\int_0^{2\pi} |f(x+\alpha)+f(x-\alpha)-2f(x)| \frac{d\alpha}{\alpha}\, dx < +\infty.$$

Consequently, there exists almost everywhere

$$\int_0^{2\pi} |f(x+\alpha)+f(x-\alpha)-2f(x)| \frac{d\alpha}{\alpha}$$

and by virtue of the Dini test the Fourier series of $f(x)$ converges almost everywhere. The theorem is proved.

COROLLARY. *If $f(x)$ is non-negative, continuous or even if upper semi-continuous, and if the region*

$$E_l = \sum_{n=1}^{\infty} \delta_n(l),$$

*is composed of intervals in which $f(x) > l$, such that*

$$\int_0^M \sum \delta_n(l)\, |\ln \delta_n(l)|\, dl$$

*converges (where $M$ is the upper bound of $f(x)$ in $[0, 2\pi]$), then the Fourier series for $f(x)$ converges almost everywhere.*

Indeed, in this case $E_1$ is of logarithmic measure equal to $\sum \delta_n(l)\,|\ln \delta_n(l)|$ and the condition expressed is the requirement of the summability of this logarithmic measure.

We note that since the problem of the convergence almost everywhere of the series $\sigma(f)$ is not resolved for the case when $f(x) \in L^2$ or even for the case when $f(x)$ is bounded, then great interest is aroused, in particular, by the question: when does the Fourier series converge almost everywhere for the characteristic function $f(x)$ of some set $E$? In the work by G. V. Tolstov[2] one special case was considered when this occurs. Namely, if $P$ is a perfect set and $\delta_1, \delta_2, \ldots, \delta_n, \ldots$ its adjacent intervals arranged in decreasing order of their length, then in the case when they decrease at the rate of a geometric progression, the series $\sigma(f)$ converges almost everywhere, it $f(x)$ is characteristic for $P$.

Let us prove that Tolstov's theorem follows from Kaidash's results.
In fact, if $\delta_n$ decreases at the rate of a geometric progression, i.e.

$$\delta_n = O\left(\frac{1}{a^n}\right), \quad \text{where} \quad a > 1,$$

then

$$\sum \delta_n |\ln \delta_n| = O\left(\sum \frac{n}{a^n}\right) < +\infty,$$

and then the set $G = CP$ is of finite logarithmic measure. Therefore, according to Lemma 2 for the characteristic function $\varphi(x)$ of the set $G$ the series $\sigma(\varphi)$ converges almost everywhere and it also converges almost everywhere for $\sigma(f)$, since $f(x) + \varphi(x) = 1$.

*Note*†. If $\psi(x)$ is the characteristic function of some set, then the integrals

$$\int_0^{2\pi}\int_0^{2\pi} \frac{|\psi(x+\alpha) + \psi(x-\alpha) - 2\psi(x)|}{\alpha}\, d\alpha\, dx \tag{16.14}$$

and

$$\int_0^{2\pi}\int_0^{2\pi} \frac{[\psi(x+\alpha) + \psi(x-\alpha) - 2\psi(x)]^2}{\alpha}\, d\alpha\, dx \tag{16.15}$$

exist or do not exist simultaneously, since at every point $x$ the expressions $|\psi(x+\alpha) + \psi(x-\alpha) - 2\psi(x)|$ and $[\psi(x+\alpha) + \psi(x-\alpha) - 2\psi(x)]^2$ are either simultaneously equal to zero or simultaneously equal to 1, or the first equals 2 and the second equals 4. On the other hand (see § 5) the existence of the integral (16.15) is equivalent to the condition

$$\sum (a_n^2 + b_n^2) \ln n < +\infty,$$

if $a_n$ and $b_n$ are the Fourier coefficients for $\psi(x)$. From this it follows that it is possible to derive these corollaries from Lemmas 1 and 2.

(1) If $\psi(x)$ is the characteristic function of some open set and if for its adjacent intervals $\delta_n$ (arranged in decreasing order) the series $\sum \delta_n |\ln \delta_n| < +\infty$, then for the characteristic function of this set the Fourier series satisfies the condition

$$\sum (a_n^2 + b_n^2) \ln n < +\infty$$

(and consequently converges almost everywhere).

(2) The same conclusion concerning a Fourier series is valid, if $\psi(x)$ is a characteristic function of the set with finite logarithmic measure.

† This note is due to P. L. Ul'yanov.

## § 17. Fourier series, almost everywhere divergent

We want to prove that Fourier series exist which are divergent almost everywhere†. The first example of this kind was constructed by Kolmogorov[1]. In his example the partial sums of the series were almost everywhere not bounded.

Later, Marcinkiewicz[1] constructed a function in which the Fourier series diverges almost everywhere but the partial sums are bounded.

Since in the proofs of the existence of such functions there are many general factors, it is first appropriate to prove a lemma, which is then suitable for the construction of both the required examples. Condition 3 of this lemma is necessary only for the Marcinkiewicz example: for the Kolmogorov example it is sufficient for the conditions 1, 2 and 4 to be satisfied.

LEMMA. *There exists a sequence of functions $\varphi_n(x)$, satisfying the conditions:*

1. $$\varphi_n(x) \geqslant 0; \quad \int_0^{2\pi} \varphi_n(x)\,dx = 2 \quad (n = 1, 2, \ldots).$$

2. *Any $\varphi_n(x)$ is a function of bounded variation.*

3. *There exists a constant $A$ such that*

$$|S_p(x, \varphi_n)| < A \ln n \quad (p = 1, 2, \ldots)$$

*for all $x \in H_n$, where*

$$\lim_{n\to\infty} mH_n = 2\pi.$$

4. *For any $\varepsilon > 0$ there exists $\alpha > 0$ and an integer $N$ such that for any $n > N$ there is a set $\mathscr{E}_n$, for which*

(a) $m\,\mathscr{E}_n > 2\pi - \varepsilon$,

(b) *for any $x \in \mathscr{E}_n$ there is a $p_x$ such that $|S_{p_x}(x, \varphi_n)| > \alpha \ln n$,*

(c) $n \leqslant p_x \leqslant m_n$ *where $m_n$ depends only on $n$, but not on $\varepsilon$.*

For the proof of the lemma we assume that

$$A_k = k\frac{4\pi}{2n+1}$$

$$(k = 1, 2, \ldots, n).$$

Let

$$\lambda_1 = 1, \lambda_2, \ldots, \lambda_n, \ldots$$

be an increasing sequence of odd numbers, which we will choose later. Let

$$m_1 = n, \quad 2m_k + 1 = \lambda_k(2n+1) \quad (k = 2, \ldots, n).$$

---

† Apart from those given here, a proof of the existence of such series is also given in § 19. It is briefer but it is less clear geometrically.

We will assume that

$$\Delta_k = \left(A_k - \frac{1}{m_k^2}, A_k + \frac{1}{m_k^2}\right) \quad (k = 1, 2, \ldots, n).$$

It is clear that the intervals $\Delta_k$ do not overlap.

Let

$$\varphi_n(x) = \begin{cases} \dfrac{m_k^2}{n} & \text{in } \Delta_k \quad (k = 1, 2, \ldots, n), \\ 0 & \text{outside all } \Delta_k. \end{cases}$$

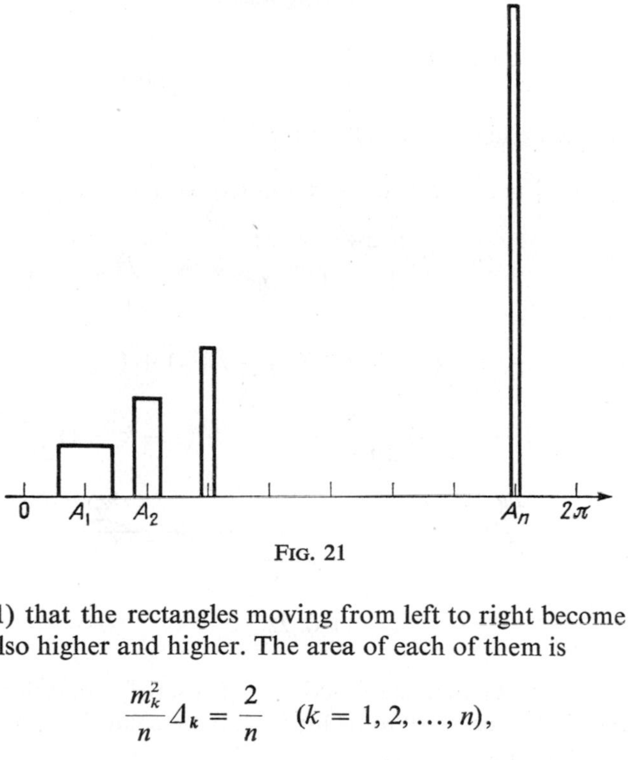


FIG. 21

We see (Fig. 21) that the rectangles moving from left to right become narrower and narrower but also higher and higher. The area of each of them is

$$\frac{m_k^2}{n}\Delta_k = \frac{2}{n} \quad (k = 1, 2, \ldots, n),$$

and therefore

$$\int_0^{2\pi} \varphi_n(x)\,dx = \sum_{k=1}^{n} \int_{\Delta_k} \varphi_n(x)\,dx = n\frac{2}{n} = 2.$$

From the construction it is evident that $\varphi_n(x) \geqslant 0$ and $\varphi_n(x)$ is of bounded variation; this means that conditions 1 and 2 are fulfilled.

For $n \geqslant 2$ let

$$d_k = \left[A_k + \frac{1}{n\ln n}, A_{k+1} - \frac{1}{n\ln n}\right] \quad (k = 1, 2, \ldots, n-1)$$

and

$$H_n = \sum_{k=1}^{n-1} d_k.$$

It is clear that

$$mH_n = (n-1)\left[\frac{4\pi}{2n+1} - \frac{2}{n\ln n}\right] \to 2\pi \quad \text{as} \quad n \to \infty.$$

We want to estimate for $x \in H_n$ the partial sum $S_p(x, \varphi_n)$ for any $p$. For this purpose we first note that for any $k$ we have

$$m_k \geqslant \lambda_k n \geqslant n,$$

and therefore the intervals $d_k$ (Fig. 22) not only do not overlap $\Delta_j$ (for any $k$ and $j$) but if $x \in d_k$ and $t \in \Delta_j$, then always for $n \geqslant 2$

$$|t - x| \geqslant \frac{1}{n\ln n} - \frac{1}{n^2} > \frac{1}{2n\ln n}. \tag{17.1}$$

Moreover, for $j < k$ we have for $t \in \Delta_j$ and $x \in d_k$

$$|t - x| = x - t = (x - A_k) + (A_k - A_j) + (A_j - t)$$

$$> (k-j)\frac{4\pi}{2n+1} - \frac{1}{n^2} > (k-j)\frac{2\pi}{2n+1}, \tag{17.2}$$

and for $j > k + 1$

$$|t - x| = t - x = (t - A_j) + (A_j - A_{k+1}) + (A_{k+1} - x)$$

$$> (j-k-1)\frac{4\pi}{2n+1} - \frac{1}{n^2} > (j-k-1)\frac{2\pi}{2n+1}. \tag{17.3}$$

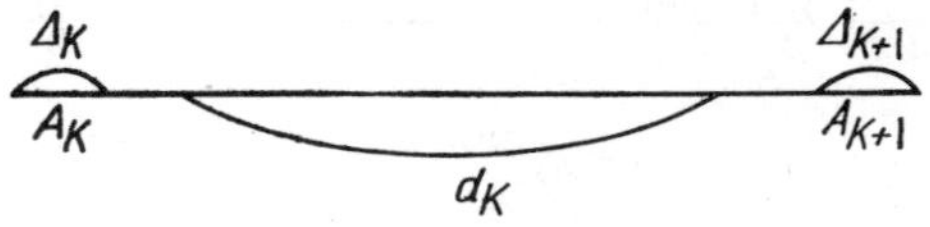


FIG. 22

Our purpose is to prove that the functions $\varphi_n(x)$ satisfy conditions 3 and 4. The inequality (17.1) will be necessary to us for both these conditions. Now let us return to the proof for the fulfilment of 3.

We want to estimate for $x \in d_k$ the expression

$$S_p(x, \varphi_n) = \frac{1}{\pi}\int_0^{2\pi} \varphi_n(t)\frac{\sin\left(p + \frac{1}{2}\right)(t - x)}{2\sin\frac{t-x}{2}}\,dt. \tag{17.4}$$

Instead of this it is sufficient to estimate

$$\tilde{S}_p(x, \varphi_n) = \frac{1}{\pi}\int_0^{2\pi} \varphi_n(t)\frac{\sin p(t - x)}{t - x}\,dt, \tag{17.5}$$

since

$$|S_p(x, \varphi_n) - \tilde{S}_p(x, \varphi_n)| \leqslant C, \tag{17.6}$$

where $C$ does not depend on $n$, because $\int_0^{2\pi} \varphi_n(t)\,dt = 2$ (see Chapter I, § 32).

But

$$|\tilde{S}_p(x, \varphi_n)| \leqslant \frac{1}{\pi}\int_0^{2\pi} \varphi_n(t)\frac{1}{|t-x|}\,dt = \sum_{j=1}^{n}\frac{1}{\pi}\int_{\Delta_j} \varphi_n(t)\frac{1}{|t-x|}\,dt. \tag{17.7}$$

On the basis of

$$\int_{\Delta_j} \varphi_n(t)\,dt = \frac{2}{n} \quad (j = 1, 2, \dots, n)$$

from the formulae (17.1)–(17.3), if $x \in d_k$, we find for $j = k$ and $j = k+1$ that

$$\int_{\Delta_j} \varphi_n(t)\frac{1}{|t-x|}\,dt \leqslant 2n\frac{2}{n}\ln n = 4\ln n,$$

then

$$\int_{\Delta_j} \varphi_n(t)\frac{1}{|t-x|}\,dt \leqslant \begin{cases} \dfrac{2n+1}{2\pi}\,\dfrac{1}{k-j}\,\dfrac{2}{n} < \dfrac{2}{k-j} & \text{for } j < k, \\[2ex] \dfrac{2n+1}{2\pi}\,\dfrac{1}{j-k-1}\,\dfrac{2}{n} < \dfrac{2}{j-k-1} & \text{for } j > k+1, \end{cases}$$

and therefore, from (17.7)

$$|\tilde{S}_p(x, \varphi_n)| \leqslant \sum_{j=1}^{k-1}\frac{2}{k-j} + 8\ln n + \sum_{j=k+2}^{n}\frac{2}{j-k-1}$$

$$= \left[8\ln n + 2\sum_{j=1}^{k-1}\frac{1}{j} + 2\sum_{j=1}^{n-k-1}\frac{1}{j}\right] < 12\ln n, \tag{17.8}$$

since each of the sums in the square brackets does not exceed $\sum_{1}^{n} 1/j < \ln n$.

From (17.6) and (17.18) it follows that for $x \in d_k$

$$|S_p(x, \varphi_n)| < A\ln n, \tag{17.9}$$

where $A$ is a constant. But $H_n = \sum_{k=1}^{n-1} d_k$, and therefore (17.9) holds for any $x \in H_n$, which means that condition 3 of the lemma is fulfilled.

To prove 4 we recall that the numbers $m_k$ in the definition of $\varphi_n(x)$ were not then defined. Let us assume that we allowed $\lambda_1 < \lambda_2 < \cdots < \lambda_{k-1}$ and in the same way we defined $m_1 < m_2 < \cdots < m_{k-1}$. We can choose $m_k$ so large that

$$\left|\frac{1}{\pi}\int_{\sum_{j=1}^{k-1}\Delta_j} \varphi_n(t)D_{m_k}(t-x)\,dt\right| < 1 \quad (k \geqslant 2) \tag{17.10}$$

for all $x \in d_{k-1}$. Indeed, by virtue of (17.1) the function $\dfrac{\varphi_n(t)}{2\sin[(t-x)/2]}$ is bounded for every $\Delta_s$ and therefore the integral

$$\int_{\Delta_j} \frac{\varphi_n(t)}{2\sin\dfrac{t-x}{2}} \sin\left(m_k + \frac{1}{2}\right)(t-x)\,dt$$

can be made as small as desired on increase of $m_k$ (see Chapter I, § 19).

Having chosen $m_k$ so that (17.10) is satisfied, we have now determined by induction all the quantities $m_1, m_2, \ldots, m_n$. We will begin by estimating $S_{m_k}(x, \varphi_n)$ for $x \in d_k$.

Since the Dirichlet kernel $D_n(t) = \frac{1}{2} + \cos t + \cdots + \cos nt$, then it is evident that for any $t$

$$|D_n'(t)| \leqslant n^2.$$

Therefore, according to the Lagrange theorem for $t \in \Delta_j$

$$|D_{m_k}(t-x) - D_{m_k}(A_j - x)| \leqslant m_k^2 \frac{1}{m_j^2} \leqslant 1 \quad \text{for} \quad j \geqslant k,$$

which means that for $j \geqslant k$

$$\left| \frac{1}{\pi} \int_{\Delta_j} \varphi_n(t) D_{m_k}(t-x)\,dt - \frac{1}{\pi} \int_{\Delta_j} \varphi_n(t) D_{m_k}(A_j - x)\,dt \right| \leqslant \frac{1}{\pi} \int_{\Delta_j} \varphi_n(t)\,dt = \frac{2}{n\pi}.$$

Consequently for $x \in d_{k-1}$

$$\frac{1}{\pi} \int_{\sum_{j=k}^{n} \Delta_j} \varphi_n(t) D_{m_k}(t-x)\,dt = \frac{1}{\pi} \int_{\sum_{j=k}^{n} \Delta_j} \varphi_n(t) D_{m_k}(A_j - x)\,dt + O(1). \tag{17.11}$$

But

$$D_{m_k}(A_j - x) = \frac{\sin\left(m_k + \dfrac{1}{2}\right)(A_j - x)}{2\sin\dfrac{A_j - x}{2}} = \frac{\sin(2m_k+1)\left(j\dfrac{2\pi}{2n+1} - \dfrac{x}{2}\right)}{2\sin\dfrac{A_j - x}{2}}$$

$$= -\frac{\sin(2m_k+1)\dfrac{x}{2}}{2\sin\dfrac{A_j - x}{2}},$$

because $(2m_k + 1) = (2n+1)\lambda_k$ where $\lambda_k$ is an integer.

Let us note that for $j \geqslant k$ we have $A_j - x \geqslant 0$, moreover, $A_j - x < 2\pi$, therefore the denominator is positive which means that

$$\sum_{j=k}^{n} D_{m_k}(A_j - x) = -\sin(2m_k+1)\frac{x}{2} \sum_{j=k}^{n} \frac{1}{2\sin\dfrac{A_j - x}{2}}, \tag{17.12}$$

where the sum is positive. We have, moreover,

$$A_j - x \leqslant A_j - A_{k-1} = (j-k+1)\frac{4\pi}{2n+1},$$

and therefore

$$\left|\sum_{j=k}^{n} D_{m_k}(A_j - x)\right| \geqslant \left|\sin(2m_k+1)\frac{x}{2}\right| \frac{2n+1}{4\pi} \sum_{j=k}^{n} \frac{1}{j-k+1}.$$

From (17.11) and (17.12), considering $\int_{\Delta_j} \varphi_n(t)\,dt = 2/n$, we find that

$$\left|\frac{1}{\pi}\int_{\sum_{j=k}^{n}\Delta_k} \varphi_n(t) D_{m_k}(t-x)\,dt\right|$$

$$\geqslant \frac{1}{\pi}\frac{2n+1}{4\pi}\frac{2}{n}\left|\sin(2m_k+1)\frac{x}{2}\right| \sum_{j=k}^{n}\frac{1}{j-k+1} + O(1)$$

$$> \frac{1}{\pi^2}\left|\sin(2m_k+1)\frac{x}{2}\right| \sum_{j=k}^{n}\frac{1}{j-k+1} + O(1). \tag{17.13}$$

Up until now we have assumed that $k$ is arbitrary. Now we will consider only those $k$ for which

$$k < n - \sqrt{n}$$

or

$$n - k > \sqrt{n}. \tag{17.14}$$

For these $k$ we have

$$\sum_{j=k}^{n}\frac{1}{j-k+1} = \sum_{1}^{n-k+1}\frac{1}{j} > \ln\sqrt{n} = \frac{1}{2}\ln n, \tag{17.15}$$

and therefore from (17.13) and (17.15)

$$\left|\frac{1}{\pi}\int_{\sum_{j=k}^{n}\Delta_j} \varphi_n(t) D_{m_k}(t-x)\,dt\right| \geqslant \frac{1}{2\pi^2}\ln n\left|\sin(2m_k+1)\frac{x}{2}\right| + O(1) \tag{17.16}$$

for $x \in d_{k-1}$ and $k$, satisfying (17.14).

Noting that

$$S_{m_k}(x, \varphi_n) = \frac{1}{\pi}\int_{\sum_{j=1}^{n}\Delta_j} \varphi_n(t)\, D_{m_k}(t-x)\,dt,$$

we find from (17.10) and (17.16) for $x \in d_{k-1}$ and $2 \leqslant k < n - \sqrt{n}$ that

$$\left|S_{m_k}(x, \varphi_n)\right| > \frac{1}{2\pi^2}\ln n\left|\sin(2m_k+1)\frac{x}{2}\right| + O(1). \tag{17.17}$$

Let $\delta > 0$ be given. Let us denote by $G_{k-1}(\delta)$ the set of all $x \in d_{k-1}$, for which

$$\left|\sin(2m_k + 1)\frac{x}{2}\right| < \delta. \tag{17.18}$$

Let us show that for

$$G(\delta) = \sum_{k=1}^{n-1} G_k(\delta)$$

we have

$$mG(\delta) = O(\delta).$$

Indeed, if $x \in d_{k-1}$, then

$$\frac{A_{k-1}}{2} < \frac{x}{2} < \frac{A_k}{2},$$

i.e.

$$(k-1)\frac{2\pi}{2n+1} < \frac{x}{2} < k\frac{2\pi}{2n+1}.$$

But $2m_k + 1 = \lambda_k(2n+1)$, therefore

$$\left|\sin(2m_k+1)\frac{x}{2}\right| = \left|\sin\lambda_k(2n+1)\left(\frac{x}{2} - (k-1)\frac{2\pi}{2n+1}\right)\right|$$

and it is sufficient to study the behaviour of

$$|\sin\lambda_k(2n+1)t| \quad \text{for} \quad 0 < t < \frac{2\pi}{2n+1}$$

or

$$|\sin\lambda_k u| \quad \text{for} \quad 0 < u < 2\pi.$$

But the set of all $u$ for which $|\sin\lambda_k u| < \delta$ consists of $4\lambda_k$ intervals (Fig. 23), the length of each of which is easily seen to be $\dfrac{\arcsin\delta}{\lambda_k}$, and therefore the overall sum of their lengths equals $4\arcsin\delta$. This means that the set of those $t$ of $(0, 2\pi)$, where $|\sin\lambda_k(2n+1)t| < \delta$ is of measure $4\arcsin\delta$, but the set of those $x$, where (17.18) is fulfilled, is consequently of measure less than $\dfrac{8\arcsin\delta}{2n+1} < \dfrac{4\arcsin\delta}{n}$.

From this, it is even more true that

$$mG_{k-1}(\delta) < \frac{4\arcsin\delta}{n}$$

and

$$mG < 4\arcsin\delta = O(\delta).$$

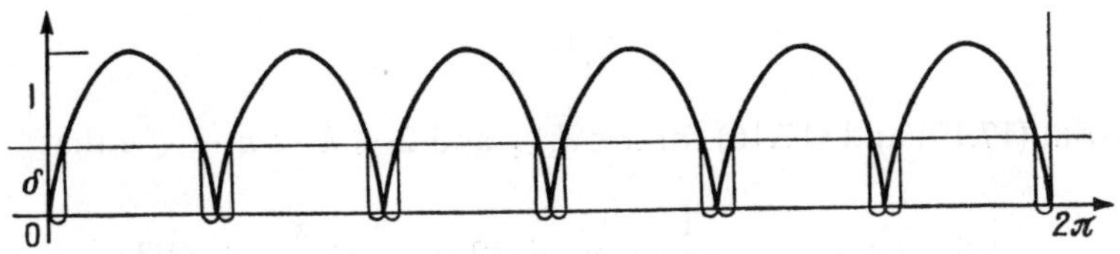


FIG. 23

Let us note that if $x \bar{\in} G$, but $x \in d_k$, then

$$\left| \sin(2m_k + 1)\frac{x}{2} \right| \geqslant \delta. \tag{17.19}$$

Combining (17.19) and (17.17) we see that for $x \in d_k$, $x \bar{\in} G$ and $k \leqslant n - \sqrt{n}$ we have

$$|S_{m_k}(x, \varphi_n)| \geqslant \frac{\delta}{2\pi^2} \ln n - O(1). \tag{17.20}$$

Let us suppose that $E_n = \sum_{k=1}^{[n-\sqrt{n}]-1} d_k$ and $\mathscr{E}_n = [CG(\delta)]\, E_n$, where $CG(\delta)$ is a set of points $x \in [0, 2\pi]$ and $x \bar{\in} G(\delta)$. We have

$$mE_n = ([n - \sqrt{n}] - 1)\left(\frac{4\pi}{2n+1} - \frac{2}{n \ln n}\right) \to 2\pi \quad \text{as} \quad n \to \infty.$$

Therefore

$$m\mathscr{E}_n \geqslant 2\pi - o(1) - O(\delta),$$

i.e.

$$m\mathscr{E}_n > 2\pi - \varepsilon,$$

if $\delta$ is chosen correctly and $n > N$ where $N$ is sufficiently large.

But if $x \in \mathscr{E}_n$, then $x \in E_n$ which means that a $k$ can be found for it such that $x \in d_{k-1}$ and $k \leqslant n - \sqrt{n}$, moreover, $x \bar{\in} G$, therefore (17.20) is true for it, whilst $m_1 \leqslant m_k \leqslant m_n$. Therefore, recalling that $m_1 = n$, we can assert that for any $x \in \mathscr{E}_n$ there is a $p_x$, $n \leqslant p_x \leqslant m_n$, such that

$$|S_{p_x}(x, \varphi_n)| \geqslant \frac{\delta}{2\pi^2} \ln n - O(1),$$

whilst

$$m\mathscr{E}_n > 2\pi - \varepsilon \quad \text{for} \quad n > N.$$

If we assume $N$ to be sufficiently large, then

$$\frac{\delta}{2\pi} \ln n - O(1) > \frac{\delta}{4\pi^2} \ln n \quad \text{at} \quad n > N$$

and, denoting $\alpha = \delta/4\pi^2$, we can write

$$|S_{p_x}(x, \varphi_n)| > \alpha \ln n \quad \text{for} \quad n > N.$$

We see that 4 is fulfilled and the theorem is completely proved.

For the construction of the examples of Kolmogorov and Marcinkiewicz we now consider the functions $\varphi_n(x)$ entering into the preceding lemma, and we choose the sequence of integers

$$n_1 < n_2 < \cdots < n_k < \cdots,$$

satisfying a number of conditions which will be formulated below, but in any case

(a) $$\sum_{k=1}^{\infty} \frac{1}{\sqrt{\ln n_k}} < +\infty.$$

After this the functions

$$\Phi(x) = \sum_{k=1}^{\infty} \frac{\varphi_{n_k}(x)}{\sqrt{\ln n_k}} \tag{17.21}$$

and

$$F(x) = \sum_{k=1}^{\infty} \frac{\varphi_{n_k}(x)}{\ln n_k} \tag{17.22}$$

will be definable almost everywhere and summable, since

$$\sum_{k=1}^{\infty} \frac{\int_0^{2\pi} \varphi_{n_k}(x)\,dx}{\sqrt{\ln n_k}} = 2\sum_{k=1}^{\infty} \frac{1}{\sqrt{\ln n_k}} < +\infty$$

(this is all the more true, if $\ln n_k$ is in the denominator) and it remains to apply Lebesgue's theorem (see Introductory Material, § 14).

Let us show that by an intelligent choice of the numbers $\{n_k\}$ the functions $\Phi(x)$ and $F(x)$ possess almost everywhere divergent Fourier series, whilst for $\Phi(x)$ we have

$$\overline{\lim_{n\to\infty}} |S_n(x, \Phi)| = +\infty \quad \text{almost everywhere,} \tag{17.23}$$

and for $F(x)$

$$\overline{\lim_{n\to\infty}} |S_n(x, F)| < +\infty \quad \text{almost everywhere.} \tag{17.24}$$

We will construct the numbers $\{n_k\}$ by induction compared with some other sequence

$$q_1 < q_2 < \cdots < q_k < \cdots.$$

First of all, we assume that

$$n_1 = q_1 = 1.$$

Also, supposing that

$$n_1 < n_2 < \cdots < n_{k-1},$$

$$q_1 < q_2 < \cdots < q_{k-1}$$

have already been constructed, we choose $q_k > q_{k-1}$ so that for $i = 1, 2, \ldots, k-1$ we have in the set $P_k$, $mP_k > 2\pi - 1/2^k$, the inequality

(b) $$|S_p(x, \varphi_{n_i}) - \varphi_{n_i}(x)| < \frac{1}{k} \quad \text{for} \quad p \geqslant q_k.$$

This is possible since all $\varphi_n(x)$ are of bounded variation, which means that their Fourier series converge to them everywhere, apart from points of discontinuity, and therefore $P_k$ can be chosen according to Yegorov's theorem.

After $q_k$ has been defined thus, we find $n_k$ such that

(c) $$\sqrt{\ln n_k} \geqslant 2^k m_{n_i} \quad (i = 1, 2, \ldots, k-1)$$

(where the numbers $m_n$ are taken from the condition 4 of the lemma) and, moreover,

(d) $$\sqrt{\ln n_k} \geqslant 2^k q_k.$$

Thus, by induction, we determine all the $n_k$ and all the $q_k$. Since $m_n \geqslant n > 1$, then in any case (a) follows from (c) and therefore the functions $\Phi(x)$ and $F(x)$ are now completely defined.

Let us prove that their Fourier series diverge almost everywhere, whilst the conditions (17.23) and (17.24) are satisfied.

Let us denote by $M$ the set of those $x$ for which the series (17.21) converges to $\Phi(x)$, but the series (17.22) converges to $F(x)$, and, moreover, $\Phi(x)$ and $F(x)$ are finite. We have

$$mM = 2\pi.$$

Let us suppose that

$$P = \underline{\lim}_{n\to\infty} P_k,$$

where the sets $P_k$ are defined in condition (b). We have

$$mP = 2\pi.$$

Let $\varepsilon > 0$ be given. Let us consider the sets $\mathscr{E}_n$ defined in condition 4 of the lemma, and let

$$\mathscr{E} = \overline{\lim_{k\to\infty}}\, \mathscr{E}_{n_k}.$$

Since

$$m\,\mathscr{E}_n > 2\pi - \varepsilon$$

for all sufficiently large values of $n$, then

$$m\,\mathscr{E} \geqslant 2\pi - \varepsilon.$$

Finally, let

$$E = \mathscr{E} PM.$$

Then

$$mE > 2\pi - \varepsilon.$$

Let us prove that $\sigma(\Phi)$ diverges at every point of $E$, and $\sigma(F)$ almost everywhere in $E$; since $\varepsilon$ is arbitrary, then it will follow that they diverge almost everywhere.

Let us note that series with positive terms can be integrated term by term; this is true, if we multiply all the terms of the series by a function which changes its sign only a finite number of times in the interval of integration; but the Dirichlet kernel possesses this property and therefore

$$S_p(x, \Phi) = \frac{1}{\pi}\int_0^{2\pi} \Phi(t) D_p(t-x)\, dt$$

$$= \sum_{k=1}^{\infty} \frac{1}{\sqrt{\ln n_k}} \frac{1}{\pi}\int_0^{2\pi} \varphi_{n_k}(t) D_p(t-x)\, dt = \sum_{k=1}^{\infty} \frac{1}{\sqrt{\ln n_k}} S_p(x, \varphi_{n_k})$$

and similarly

$$S_p(x, F) = \sum_{k=1}^{\infty} \frac{1}{\ln n_k} S_p(x, \varphi_{n_k}).$$

Let $\eta > 0$ be given. If $x \in E$, then $x \in M$ which means that it is possible to take $k$ so large that

$$\left| \sum_{j=1}^{k-1} \frac{1}{\sqrt{\ln n_j}} \varphi_{n_j}(x) - \Phi(x) \right| < \eta \tag{17.25}$$

and

$$\left| \sum_{j=1}^{k-1} \frac{1}{\ln n_j} \varphi_{n_j}(x) - F(x) \right| < \eta. \tag{17.26}$$

But $x \in E$, which means that $x \in P$, and therefore $x \in P_k$ for $k \geqslant k_0$, consequently, for this $x$

$$|S_p(x, \varphi_{n_i}) - \varphi_{n_i}(x)| < \frac{1}{k} \quad \text{for} \quad p \geqslant q_k$$

(for $i = 1, 2, \ldots, k-1$). From this it follows that for $p \geqslant q_k$ we have

$$\left| \sum_{j=1}^{k-1} \frac{1}{\sqrt{\ln n_j}} S_p(x, \varphi_{n_j}) - \sum_{j=1}^{k-1} \frac{1}{\sqrt{\ln n_j}} \varphi_{n_j}(x) \right| < \frac{1}{k} \sum_{j=1}^{k-1} \frac{1}{\sqrt{\ln n_j}} < \frac{1}{k}, \tag{17.27}$$

since from (c) in any case

$$\sum_{k=1}^{\infty} \frac{1}{\sqrt{\ln n_k}} < \sum_{k=1}^{\infty} \frac{1}{2^k} = 1.$$

From (17.25) and (17.27) it follows that

$$\left| \sum_{j=1}^{k-1} \frac{1}{\sqrt{\ln n_j}} S_p(x, \varphi_{n_j}) - \Phi(x) \right| < \eta + \frac{1}{k}, \quad \text{if} \quad p \geqslant q_k \quad \text{and} \quad x \in E. \tag{17.28}$$

In exactly the same way we have

$$\left| \sum_{j=1}^{k-1} \frac{1}{\ln n_j} S_p(x, \varphi_{n_j}) - F(x) \right| < \eta + \frac{1}{k} \quad \text{for} \quad x \in E \quad \text{and} \quad p \geqslant q_k. \tag{17.29}$$

Let us note that from (d) it follows that it is even more true that $n_k > q_k$, and therefore the inequalities (17.28) and (17.29) in any case hold, if $p \geqslant n_k$.

Now we note that if $x \in E$, then $x \in \mathscr{E}_{n_k}$ for an infinite set of values of $k$; consequently on the basis of condition 4 of the lemma there is a $p_x$, $n_k \leqslant p_x \leqslant m_{n_k}$ such that

$$|S_{p_x}(x, \varphi_{n_k})| > \alpha \ln n_k. \tag{17.30}$$

Let us then write

$$S_{p_x}(x, \Phi) - \Phi(x) = \sum_{j=1}^{k-1} \frac{1}{\sqrt{\ln n_j}} S_{p_x}(x, \varphi_{n_j}) - \Phi(x)$$

$$+ \frac{1}{\sqrt{\ln n_k}} S_{p_x}(x, \varphi_{n_k}) + \sum_{j=k+1}^{\infty} \frac{1}{\sqrt{\ln n_j}} S_{p_x}(x, \varphi_{n_j}). \tag{17.31}$$

We have

$$|S_{p_x}(x, \varphi_{n_j})| \leqslant (p_x + 1) \int_0^{2\pi} \varphi_{n_j}(t)\, dt = 2(p_x + 1) < 4p_x \leqslant 4m_{n_k},$$

and therefore by virtue of condition (c) imposed on $n_k$

$$\left|\sum_{j=k+1}^{\infty} \frac{1}{\sqrt{\ln n_j}} S_{p_x}(x, \varphi_{n_j})\right| \leqslant 4m_{n_k} \sum_{j=k+1}^{\infty} \frac{1}{\sqrt{\ln n_j}} \leqslant 4 \sum_{j=k+1}^{\infty} \frac{1}{2^j} = \frac{1}{2^{k-2}}. \quad (17.32)$$

Then from (17.28), (17.30), (17.31) and (17.32), we find that

$$|S_{p_x}(x, \Phi) - \Phi(x)| \geqslant \alpha\sqrt{\ln n_k} - \eta - \frac{1}{k} - \frac{1}{2^{k-2}} \geqslant 2\alpha - \eta - o(1),$$

and since $\eta$ is arbitrarily small, then the right-hand side can be made as large as desired with increase in $k$.

But since for any $x \in E$ this relationship holds for an infinite set of values $k$ and $p_x \geqslant n_k$, then for $x \in E$

$$\overline{\lim_{n\to\infty}} |S_n(x, \Phi)| = +\infty.$$

The divergence in $E$ of the series $\sigma(\varphi)$ follows from this, and due to

$$mE > 2\pi - \varepsilon$$

and the fact that $\varepsilon$ is arbitrary, the relationship (17.23) holds almost everywhere.

For the proof of the divergence of the series $\sigma(F)$ in $E$ we argue thus: we also have

$$S_{p_x}(x, F) - F(x) = \sum_{j=1}^{k-1} \frac{1}{\ln n_j} S_{p_x}(x, \varphi_{n_j}) - F(x)$$
$$+ \frac{1}{\ln n_k} S_{p_x}(x, \varphi_{n_k}) + \sum_{j=k+1}^{\infty} \frac{1}{\ln n_j} S_{p_x}(x, \varphi_{n_j}). \quad (17.33)$$

From (17.32) it is immediately evident that

$$\left|\sum_{j=k+1}^{\infty} \frac{1}{\ln n_j} S_{p_x}(x, \varphi_{n_j})\right| \leqslant \frac{1}{2^{k-2}}. \quad (17.34)$$

From (17.33), (17.29), (17.30) and (17.34) we find that

$$|S_{p_x}(x, F) - F(x)| \geqslant \alpha - \eta - \frac{1}{k} - \frac{1}{2^{k-2}} > \frac{\alpha}{3}, \quad (17.35)$$

if we take $\eta < \alpha/3$ and $k$ so large that $2/k < \alpha/3$.

Thus, for $x \in E$ there is an infinite set of values $p_x$ for which (17.35) holds. Meanwhile, if the Fourier series of any function converges in a set of positive measure, then it converges to it almost everywhere in this set. This means that from (17.35) the divergence of $\sigma(F)$ almost everywhere in $E$ holds, which means almost everywhere in $[0, 2\pi]$.

It remains for us to prove that

$$\overline{\lim_{n\to\infty}} |S_n(x, F)| < +\infty$$

almost everywhere. For this purpose we assume that

$$H = \varliminf_{k\to\infty} H_{n_k},$$

where the sets $H_n$ are taken from condition 3 of the lemma. We have

$$mH = 2\pi,$$

since $n_k$ increase very quickly (see condition (d) of the lemma). Let us suppose that

$$E^* = HPM$$

and prove that condition (17.24) holds for any $x \in E^*$, i.e. almost everywhere.

Indeed, let $x \in E^*$. Let $p$ be any integer. Let us find $k$ such that

$$q_k \leqslant p < q_{k+1}.$$

We have

$$|S_p(x, F)| \leqslant \left|\sum_{j=1}^{k-1} \frac{S_p(x, \varphi_{n_j})}{\ln n_j}\right| + \left|\frac{S_p(x, \varphi_{n_k})}{\ln n_k}\right| + \left|\sum_{j=k+1}^{\infty} \frac{S_p(x, \varphi_{n_j})}{\ln n_j}\right|. \tag{17.36}$$

But due to (17.29) and $p \geqslant q_k$ at sufficiently large $k$ we will have

$$\left|\sum_{j=1}^{k-1} \frac{S_p(x, \varphi_{n_j})}{\ln n_j}\right| \leqslant F(x) + \eta = \frac{1}{k} \quad \text{for} \quad x \in E. \tag{17.37}$$

By virtue of condition 3 of the lemma

$$\left|\frac{S_p(x, \varphi_{n_k})}{\ln n_k}\right| < A \quad \text{for} \quad x \in H_{n_k}, \tag{17.38}$$

which means that this will also hold for $x \in E^*$ for sufficiently large $k$. Finally

$$\left|\sum_{j=k+1}^{\infty} \frac{1}{\ln n_j} S_p(x, \varphi_{n_j})\right| \leqslant 4q_{k+1} \sum_{j=k+1}^{\infty} \frac{1}{\ln n_j} \leqslant 4q_{k+1} \sum_{j=k+1}^{\infty} \frac{1}{2^j q_j} < \frac{1}{2^{k-2}}, \tag{17.39}$$

since $q_j \geqslant q_{k+1}$ for $j \geqslant k+1$.

Combining (17.36), (17.37), (17.38) and (17.39) we find that

$$|S_p(x, F)| \leqslant F(x) + \eta + \frac{1}{k} + A + \frac{1}{2^{k-2}} < +\infty \quad \text{for} \quad p \geqslant p_0(x)$$

for any $x \in E^*$ and the proof is concluded.

*Note.* We have obtained for the functions $\Phi(x)$ the equality

$$\overline{\lim_{n\to\infty}} |S_n(x, \Phi)| = +\infty \quad \text{almost everywhere.}$$

The question arises whether it is possible to construct a $f(x)$ for which

$$\lim_{n\to\infty} S_n(x, f) = +\infty \quad \text{almost everywhere.}$$

It seems that this is impossible. Moreover, we will prove in Chapter XV, §4 that if for the Fourier series we have

$$\overline{\lim} S_n(x) = +\infty$$

in some $E$, $mE > 0$, then almost everywhere in it

$$\underline{\lim}_{n\to\infty} S_n(x) = -\infty.$$

## § 18. The impossibility of strengthening the Marcinkiewicz test

The results of the preceding section permit us to prove that the theorem of § 15 in a sense cannot be strengthened. Namely, the following theorem due to Marcinkiewicz[1] holds.

THEOREM. *Let $\omega(t)$ be a positive, even function, which is non-decreasing in some* $(0, \delta)$ $(0 < \delta \leqslant \frac{1}{3})$ *and such that*

$$\lim_{t\to 0} \omega(t) = 0, \quad \lim_{t\to 0} \omega(t) \ln \frac{1}{|t|} = +\infty. \tag{18.1}$$

*Then there exists a function $f(x)$ for which*

$$\frac{1}{t}\int_0^t |f(x+u) - f(x)|\, du = O[\omega(t)] \tag{18.2}$$

*almost everywhere in* $[0, 2\pi]$ *and yet its Fourier series diverges almost everywhere.*

Let us assume that

$$\varphi(t) = \omega(t) \ln \frac{1}{|t|} \quad (0 \leqslant t \leqslant \delta). \tag{18.3}$$

Then from (18.1) it follows that $\varphi(t) \to +\infty$ as $t \to 0$.

If we suppose that

$$\varphi_1(t) = \min_{0<\tau\leqslant t} \varphi(\tau),$$

then $\varphi_1(t)$ can also decrease in $(0, \delta)$, $\varphi_1(t) \leqslant \varphi(t)$ and

$$\lim_{t\to 0} \varphi_1(t) = +\infty.$$

If we denote

$$\omega_1(t) = \frac{\varphi_1(t)}{\ln \dfrac{1}{|t|}},$$

then it is clear that $\omega_1(t) \leqslant \omega(t)$ and

$$\lim_{t\to 0} \omega_1(t) \ln \frac{1}{|t|} = +\infty. \tag{18.4}$$

Let us prove that for any $\alpha$, $0 \leqslant \alpha \leqslant 1$, the inequality holds

$$\alpha\omega_1(t) \leqslant \omega_1(\alpha t) \quad \text{for} \quad 0 \leqslant t \leqslant \delta. \tag{18.5}$$

In fact, the function $t \ln(1/t)$ increases monotonically in $(0, \delta)$ and $\varphi_1(t)$ decreases monotonically. Therefore, the function

$$\frac{\omega_1(t)}{t} = \frac{\varphi_1(t)}{t \ln \dfrac{1}{t}}$$

decreases monotonically in $(0, \delta)$, i.e.

$$\frac{\omega_1(t_1)}{t_1} > \frac{\omega_1(t_2)}{t_2} \quad \text{for} \quad 0 < t_1 < t_2 \leqslant \delta. \tag{18.6}$$

From (18.6) it follows that

$$\alpha\omega_1(t) = \alpha t \frac{\omega_1(t)}{t} < \alpha t \frac{\omega_1(\alpha t)}{\alpha t} = \omega_1(\alpha t),$$

i.e. (18.5) is valid.

Since from (18.4) it follows that

$$\lim_{n\to\infty} \omega_1\left(\frac{1}{n}\right) \ln n = +\infty,$$

then supposing that

$$\varepsilon_n^2 = \frac{1}{\omega_1\left(\dfrac{1}{n}\right) \ln n}, \tag{18.7}$$

we have $\lim\limits_{n\to\infty} \varepsilon_n = 0$. But since $\omega_1(1/n) \to 0$ it can be taken that

$$\frac{1}{\sqrt{\ln n}} \leqslant \varepsilon_n \leqslant 1 \quad \text{for} \quad n \geqslant n_0. \tag{18.8}$$

Let us define

$$f_n(x) = \frac{\varphi_n(x)}{\ln n},$$

where $\varphi_n(x)$ are functions from the lemma of § 17. We have already proved that if the numbers $n_k$ are chosen so that conditions (a), (b), (c) and (d) are satisfied (see the construction of the Kolmogorov and Marcinkiewicz examples, p. 437), then the function

$$f(x) = \sum_{k=1}^{\infty} f_{n_k}(x)$$

possesses an almost everywhere divergent Fourier series.

If we require that, apart from these conditions, the numbers $n_k$ satisfy an additional condition too, namely, that

(e) $$\varepsilon_{n_k} < \frac{1}{4^{k+2}} \quad \text{and} \quad n_1 \geqslant n_0,$$

and this is possible since $\varepsilon \to 0$, then the function $f(x)$ will satisfy the conditions of our theorem.

In order to prove this, if the divergence of $\sigma(f)$ almost everywhere is already proved, it is sufficient to prove that $f(x)$ satisfies condition (18.2).

For this purpose, maintaining the notation of § 17, let us consider the set

$$D_n = \sum_{k=1}^{n-1}\left[A_k + \frac{\sqrt{\varepsilon_n}}{n}, A_{k+1} - \frac{\sqrt{\varepsilon_n}}{n}\right].$$

It is clear that its measure is greater than $2\pi - 2\sqrt{\varepsilon_n} - 3\pi/n$ and therefore

$$mD_{n_k} = 2\pi - 2\sqrt{\varepsilon_{n_k}} - \frac{3\pi}{n_k} > 2\pi - \frac{1}{2^k}$$

due to (d) and (e). Let $\varepsilon > 0$ be given. It is possible to find $p$ such that $1/2^{p-1} < \varepsilon$ and then, supposing that

$$D(\varepsilon) = \prod_{k=p+1}^{\infty} D_{n_k},$$

we have

$$mD(\varepsilon) > 2\pi - \varepsilon.$$

Since all the functions $f_{n_k}(x)$ consist of a finite number of steps, then it is possible to cover the points of discontinuity of $f_{n_1}(x), \ldots, f_{n_p}(x)$ by a system of a finite number of intervals of total length less than $\varepsilon$, and then the remaining set $B(\varepsilon)$ consists of a finite number of intervals, in each of which all the $f_{n_i}(x)$ are constructed for $i = 1, 2, \ldots, p$.

Let us prove that in the set

$$A(\varepsilon) = D(\varepsilon)B(\varepsilon)$$

the function $f(x)$ satisfies condition (18.2). Since

$$mA(\varepsilon) \geqslant 2\pi - 2\varepsilon,$$

and $\varepsilon$ is arbitrary, then it will follow that (18.2) holds almost everywhere.

Let us first estimate for $x_0 \in D_n (n \geqslant n_0)$ the integral

$$\frac{1}{u}\int_0^u |f_n(x_0 + t) - f_n(x_0)|\, dt.$$

Because $x_0 \in D_n$, then a $k$ can be found such that

$$x_0 \in \left[A_k + \frac{\sqrt{\varepsilon_n}}{n}, A_{k+1} - \frac{\sqrt{\varepsilon_n}}{n}\right].$$

According to the construction, $\varphi_n(x)$ equals zero outside any

$$\left(A_j - \frac{1}{m_j^2}, A_j + \frac{1}{m_j^2}\right) \quad (j = 1, 2, \ldots, n),$$

therefore it is evident that (see (18.8))

$$\frac{1}{u}\int_0^u |f_n(x_0+t)-f_n(x_0)|\,dt = 0 \quad \text{for} \quad 0<|u|<\frac{\sqrt{\varepsilon_n}}{2n}.$$

If $\sqrt{\varepsilon_n}/2n \leqslant |u| \leqslant 1/n$, then $f_n(x_0) = 0$ and due to (18.7)

$$\left|\frac{1}{u}\int_0^u |f_n(x_0+t)-f_n(x_0)|\,dt\right| = \left|\frac{1}{u}\int_0^u f_n(x_0+t)\,dt\right|$$

$$\leqslant \frac{1}{|u|}\,\frac{2}{n}\,\frac{1}{\ln n} \leqslant \frac{2n}{\sqrt{\varepsilon_n}}\,\frac{2}{n}\,\varepsilon_n^2\omega_1\left(\frac{1}{n}\right) = 4\varepsilon_n\sqrt{\varepsilon_n}\,\omega_1\left(\frac{1}{n}\right).$$

But from (18.5) and (18.8)

$$\varepsilon_n\sqrt{\varepsilon_n}\,\omega_1\left(\frac{1}{n}\right) \leqslant 2\varepsilon_n\omega_1\left(\frac{\sqrt{\varepsilon_n}}{2n}\right) \leqslant 2\varepsilon_n\omega\left(\frac{\sqrt{\varepsilon_n}}{2n}\right) \leqslant 2\varepsilon_n\omega(u),$$

and therefore

$$\left|\frac{1}{u}\int_0^u |f_n(x_0+t)-f_n(x_0)|\,dt\right| \leqslant 8\varepsilon_n\omega(u). \tag{18.9}$$

Arguing in just the same way, if $\frac{m}{n} \leqslant |u| < \frac{m+1}{n}$ $(m = 1, 2, \ldots, n-1)$ we find that

$$\left|\frac{1}{u}\int_0^u |f_n(x_0+t)-f_n(x_0)|\,dt\right| = \left|\frac{1}{u}\int_0^u f_n(x_0+t)\,dt\right|$$

$$\leqslant \frac{1}{|u|}\,\frac{2(m+1)}{n}\,\frac{1}{\ln n} \leqslant \frac{n}{m}\,\frac{2(m+1)}{n}\,\varepsilon_n^2\omega_1\left(\frac{1}{n}\right) \leqslant 4\varepsilon_n^2\omega(u),$$

i.e. (18.9) is even more true.

From this it follows that for any $x_0 \in D_n$ we have

$$\left|\frac{1}{u}\int_0^u |f_n(x_0+t)-f_n(x_0)|\,dt\right| \leqslant 8\varepsilon_n\omega(u) \quad \text{for} \quad 0 \leqslant |u| \leqslant 1,$$

and therefore for $x_0 \in D_n$ due to (e)

$$\left|\frac{1}{u}\int_0^u |f_{n_k}(x_0+t)-f_{n_k}(x_0)|\,dt\right| \leqslant 8\varepsilon_{n_k}\omega(u) < \frac{1}{4^{k-1}}\,\omega(u). \tag{18.10}$$

Now let $x_0 \in A(\varepsilon)$. We will write

$$f(x_0) = \sum_{k=1}^{p} f_{n_k}(x_0) + \sum_{p+1}^{\infty} f_{n_k}(x_0) = F_1(x_0) + F_2(x_0). \tag{18.11}$$

Since $x_0 \in A(\varepsilon)$, then $x_0 \in D(\varepsilon)$, i.e. $x_0 \in D_{n_k}$ for $k \geqslant p+1$, therefore due to (18.10) we have for $0 \leqslant |u| \leqslant 1$

$$\left|\frac{1}{u}\int_0^u |F_2(x_0+t) - F_2(x_0)|\,dt\right| \leqslant \sum_{k=p+1}^{\infty} \left|\frac{1}{u}\int_0^u f_{n_k}(x_0+t) - f_{n_k}(x_0)\,dt\right|$$

$$\leqslant \sum_{k=p+1}^{\infty} \frac{1}{4^{k-1}}\,\omega(u) = \frac{\omega(u)}{3\cdot 4^{p-1}} < \varepsilon^2\,\omega(u) \tag{18.12}$$

from the choice of the value $p$.

But $x_0 \in A(\varepsilon)$ which means that $x_0 \in B(\varepsilon)$ and therefore any one of $f_{n_k}(x)$ $(k = 1, 2, \ldots, p)$ is constructed in some small neighbourhood of the point $x_0$, i.e.

$$\frac{1}{u}\int_0^u |f_{n_k}(x_0+t) - f_{n_k}(t)|\,dt = 0 \quad (k = 1, 2, \ldots, p),$$

provided $u$ is sufficiently small. Hence

$$\frac{1}{u}\int_0^u |F_1(x_0+t) - F_1(x_0)|\,dt = 0. \tag{18.13}$$

Combining (18.12) and (18.13) we see that for sufficiently small $u$

$$\left|\frac{1}{u}\int_0^u |f(x_0+t) - f(x_0)|\,dt\right| \leqslant \omega(u)$$

and this holds for all $x \in A(\varepsilon)$. This means that for every $x_0 \in A(\varepsilon)$ it is possible to find a constant $C_{x_0}$ (dependent on $x_0$) such that

$$\left|\frac{1}{u}\int_0^u |f(x_0+t) - f(x_0)|\,dt\right| \leqslant C_{x_0}\omega(u)$$

for all $u$ in $[0, 2\pi]$, i.e. at the point $x_0$ (18.2) is valid. This concludes the proof of the theorem.

## § 19. Concerning the series conjugate to an almost everywhere divergent Fourier series

The question arises: are the series $\bar{\sigma}(\Phi)$ and $\bar{\sigma}(F)$, where $\Phi(x)$ and $F(x)$ are the functions constructed in § 17, Fourier series? We will show that the answer to this question in both cases is in the negative.

To prove this, we note the functions $\Phi(x)$ and $F(x)$ are non-negative. But according to M. Riesz's[1] theorem, which will be proved in Chapter VIII, if for a non-negative function $\psi(x)$ the series $\bar{\sigma}(\psi)$ is a Fourier series, then

$$\psi(x)\ln^+\psi(x) \in L. \tag{19.1}$$

($\ln^+ x$ signifies a function coinciding with $\ln x$, if $\ln x \geqslant 0$, and equal to zero if $\ln x < 0$).

Let us prove that for $\Phi(x)$ and $F(x)$ the condition of (19.1) does not hold. It is sufficient to prove this for $F(x)$, since $\Phi(x) \geqslant F(x)$ almost everywhere because all the terms of series (17.21) are greater than the corresponding terms of series (17.22).

Now note that

$$F(x)\ln^+ F(x) \geqslant \sum_{k=1}^{N} \frac{\varphi_{n_k}(x)\ln^+ F(x)}{\ln n_k} \qquad \text{for any } N.$$

It is all the more true that

$$F(x)\ln^+ F(x) \geqslant \sum_{k=1}^{N} \frac{\varphi_{n_k}(x)}{\ln n_k}\ln^+ \frac{\varphi_{n_k}(x)}{\ln n_k} \qquad \text{for any } N.$$

But for any $n$ we have (noting that $m_j \geqslant n$)

$$\int_0^{2\pi} \frac{\varphi_n(x)}{\ln n}\ln^+\frac{\varphi_n(x)}{\ln n}\,dx = \frac{1}{\ln n}\sum_{j=1}^{n}\int_{\Delta_j}\frac{m_j^2}{n}\ln^+\frac{m_j^2}{n\ln n}\,dx$$

$$= \frac{1}{\ln n}\sum_{j=1}^{n}\frac{m_j^2}{n}\ln^+\frac{m_j^2}{n\ln n}\,\frac{2}{m_j^2} = \frac{2}{n\ln n}\sum_{j=1}^{n}\ln^+\frac{m_j^2}{n\ln n}$$

$$\geqslant \frac{2}{n\ln n}\,n\ln\frac{n}{\ln n} = 2\,\frac{\ln n - \ln\ln n}{\ln n} \to 2 \quad \text{as} \quad n \to \infty,$$

whence it is clear that

$$\int_0^{2\pi} F(x)\ln^+ F(x)\,dx = +\infty,$$

i.e. $F(x)\ln^+ F(x)$ is non-summable.

*Note.* From what has been proved it follows immediately that for any $p > 1$ we have

$$F(x) \bar{\in} L^p \quad \text{and} \quad \Phi(x) \bar{\in} L^p.$$

Thus, neither the Kolmogorov example nor the Marcinkiewicz example decides the question of the existence of a Fourier series divergent almost everywhere and for which $f(x) \in L^p$ at $p > 1$ (in particular, the problem remains open for a function with integrable square, which we have already mentioned in the introduction to this chapter).

We have proved that neither the Kolmogorov example nor the Marcinkiewicz example gives the answer to the question: can the conjugate series $\bar{\sigma}(f)$ to a series $\sigma(f)$ divergent almost everywhere also be a Fourier series? It seems that this question is nevertheless resolved in a positive sense.

This result was noted by Sunouchi[3]. As a matter of fact it was contained in Hardy and Rogosinski's book[A. 10]. Wishing to prove Kolmogorov's theorem concerning the existence of a function with a Fourier series divergent almost everywhere, they constructed this function in a different way to Kolmogorov's method; Sunouchi whilst analysing their argument proved that for the function $f(x)$ constructed by them the series $\bar{\sigma}(f)$ is itself a Fourier series.

In order to construct this function, we prove the lemma:

LEMMA. *There exists a sequence of trigonometric polynomials $T_n(x)$ possessing the properties*

(a) $T_n(x) \geqslant 0$,

(b) $\frac{1}{\pi}\int_{-\pi}^{\pi} T_n(x)\,dx = 1$,

(c) *for every $T_n$ there corresponds a set $E_n$, $mE_n \to 2\pi$ as $n \to \infty$, such that for any $x \in E_n$ a $k_x$ can be found for which*

$$|S_{k_x}(x, T_n)| > M_n$$

*and $M_n \to \infty$ as $n \to 0$.*

This lemma plays the same role as the lemma of § 17, but here the functions $\varphi_n(x)$ which were discontinuous have been replaced by trigonometric polynomials.

To prove the lemma we suppose in the same way as in the lemma of § 17 that

$$A_j = \frac{4\pi j}{2n+1} \quad (0 \leqslant j \leqslant n),$$

and once more let $m_0, m_1, \ldots, m_n$ be integral values such that $2m_j + 1$ is divisible by $2n + 1$ ($j = 1, 2, \ldots, n$) but, moreover, we suppose that

$$m_0 \geqslant n^4 \quad \text{and} \quad m_{j+1} > 2m_j.$$

We assume that

$$T_n(x) = \frac{1}{n+1}\{F_{m_0}(x - A_0) + F_{m_1}(x - A_1) + \cdots + F_{m_n}(x - A_n)\},$$

where $F_m$ is a Fejér kernel. Let us prove that the trigonometric polynomials $T_n(x)$ satisfy the conditions of the lemma.

Indeed, $T_n(x) \geqslant 0$, since the Fejér kernels are non-negative and because in the Fejér kernels the free term equals $\frac{1}{2}$, then

$$\frac{1}{\pi}\int_{-\pi}^{\pi} T_n(x)\,dx = 1.$$

Thus, conditions (a) and (b) are satisfied.

Let $m_j \leqslant k \leqslant m_{j+1}$. Then

$$S_k(x, T_n) = \frac{1}{n+1}\left[\sum_{l=0}^{j} F_{m_l}(x - A_l) + \sum_{l=j+1}^{n}\left\{\frac{1}{2} + \sum_{r=1}^{k}\frac{m_l + 1 - r}{m_l + 1}\cos r(x - A_l\right\}\right].$$

Indeed, for $m_l$ at $l \leqslant j$ the partial sum of the first $k$ terms of the Fourier series of $F_{m_l}$ simply coincides with the same polynomial $F_{m_l}$; for the remaining $F_{m_l}$ we express them by cosines in the usual way and take the first $k$ terms of this expansion.

If we now divide each of the terms of the last sum into two, using the fact that

$$m_l + 1 - r = k + 1 - r + m_l - k,$$

and denoting the Dirichlet kernel, as usual, by $D_k(u)$, then

$$\frac{1}{2} + \sum_{r=1}^{k} \frac{m_l + 1 - r}{m_l + 1} \cos r(x - A_l)$$

$$= \frac{1}{2} + \frac{k+1}{m_l+1} \sum_{r=1}^{k} \frac{k+1-r}{k+1} \cos r(x - A_l) + \frac{m_l - k}{m_l + 1} \sum_{i=1}^{k} \cos r(x - A_l)$$

$$= \frac{1}{2} + \frac{k+1}{m_l+1} \left[F_k(x - \mathrm{A}_l) - \frac{1}{2}\right] + \frac{m_l - k}{m_l + 1} \left[D_k(x - A_l) - \frac{1}{2}\right]$$

$$= \frac{k+1}{m_l+1} F_k(x - A_l) + \frac{m_l - k}{m_l + 1} D_k(x - A_l).$$

Consequently

$$S_k(x, T_n) = \frac{1}{n+1} \sum_{l=0}^{j} F_{m_l}(x - A_l) + \frac{1}{n+1} \sum_{l=j+1}^{n} \frac{k+1}{m_l+1} F_k(x - A_l)$$

$$+ \frac{1}{n+1} \sum_{l=j+1}^{n} \frac{m_l - k}{m_l + 1} D_k(x - A_l) = S_1 + S_2 + S_3. \tag{19.2}$$

This identity holds for $m_j \leqslant k \leqslant m_{j+1}$ and we will use it for $k = m_j$.

Let us consider $S_{m_j}(x, T_n)$ in the interval $I_j(A_j + 1/n^2, A_{j+1} - 1/n^2)$. If $x \in I_j$, then for any $l$, even for $l = j$, we have $|x - A_l| \geqslant 1/n^2 \geqslant 1/\sqrt{m_l}$, since $n^4 \leqslant m_0$. But if $t \neq 0$, then $F_m(t) = 0(1/mt^2)$ (see Chapter I, § 47), which means that

$$F_{m_l}(x - A_l) = O\left(\frac{1}{m_l\,|x - A_l|^2}\right) = O(1).$$

From this it follows that the terms of the form $F_{m_l}(x - A_l)$ which are encountered in $S_1$ and $S_2$ are bounded and since for $k = m_j$ and $l \geqslant j + 1$ we also have $\dfrac{k+1}{m_l+1} \leqslant 1$, then we come to the conclusion that the sums $S_1$ and $S_2$ are themselves bounded. Thus

$$|S_{m_j}(x, T_n)| > |S_3| - H \quad \text{for} \quad x \in I_j,$$

where $H$ is a bounded quantity.

We now note that since $2m_j + 1$ is divisible by $2n + 1$, then

$$D_{m_j}(x - A_l) = \frac{\sin\left(m_j + \frac{1}{2}\right)(x - A_l)}{2 \sin \frac{x - A_l}{2}} = \frac{\sin(2m_j + 1)\frac{x}{2}}{2 \sin \frac{x - A_l}{2}} = -\frac{\sin(2m_j + 1)\frac{x}{2}}{2 \sin \frac{A_l - x}{2}}$$

which means that

$$S_3 = -\sin(2m_j + 1)\frac{x}{2} \frac{1}{n+1} \sum_{l=j+1}^{n} \frac{m_l - m_j}{m_l + 1} \frac{1}{2 \sin \frac{A_l - x}{2}}.$$

The terms in the last sum are all positive, therefore

$$\frac{1}{2\sin\dfrac{A_l - x}{2}} > \frac{1}{A_l - x} \geqslant \frac{1}{A_l - A_j} = \frac{2n+1}{(l-j)\,4\pi}.$$

Moreover, from $m_{j+1} > 2m_j$ it follows that $(m_l - m_j)/(m_l + 1) \geqslant \frac{1}{2}$ for $l \geqslant j+1$ and therefore

$$|S_3| \geqslant \left|\sin(2m_j + 1)\frac{x}{2}\right| \frac{1}{2(n+1)} \frac{2n+1}{4\pi} \sum_{l=j+1}^{n} \frac{1}{l-j}$$

$$\geqslant \frac{1}{8\pi}\ln(n-j)\left|\sin(2m_j+1)\frac{x}{2}\right|.$$

If we only consider those values $j$ for which $j \leqslant n - \sqrt{n}$, then for them

$$|S_3| \geqslant \frac{1}{16\pi}\ln n\left|\sin(2m_j+1)\frac{x}{2}\right|.$$

Let us denote by $E_n$ the set of those $x$ for which $x \in I_j$ at $j \leqslant n - \sqrt{n}$ and

$$\left|\sin(2m_j+1)\frac{x}{2}\right| \geqslant \frac{1}{\sqrt{\ln n}}. \tag{19.3}$$

It is clear that for them

$$|S_3| \geqslant \frac{1}{16\pi}\sqrt{\ln n}$$

and consequently

$$|S_{m_j}(x, T_n)| > \frac{\sqrt{\ln n}}{16\pi} - H = M_n, \tag{19.4}$$

where $M_n \to \infty$ as $n \to \infty$. But the sum of the lengths of the intervals $I_j$ at $j \leqslant n - \sqrt{n}$ is of the order

$$\left(n - \sqrt{n}\right)\left(\frac{4\pi}{2n+1} - \frac{2}{n^2}\right) \to 2\pi \quad \text{as} \quad n \to \infty,$$

and if the points at which the inequality (19.3) is broken are discarded from these intervals, then, as we have seen in proving the lemma of § 17, we are only discarding a set of measure not exceeding $4 \arcsin(1/\sqrt{\ln n}) = o(1)$, therefore

$$mE_n \to 2\pi \quad \text{as} \quad m \to \infty,$$

and the lemma is proved.

Let us return to the construction of a function $f(x)$ with Fourier series divergent almost everywhere but such that $\bar{\sigma}(f)$ is also a Fourier series.

Let us choose the sequence $n_k$ so that

$$\sum \frac{1}{\sqrt{M_{n_k}}} < +\infty. \tag{19.5}$$

Since $T_n(x)$ is a trigonometric polynomial of order $m_n$, then it is possible to write

$$T_{n_k}(x) = \sum_{\nu=-m_{n_k}}^{m_{n_k}} c_\nu^{(k)} e^{i\nu x}$$

(writing the polynomial in the exponential form). If we choose the numbers $\nu_k$ so that

$$\nu_1 > m_{n_1}, \nu_2 > \nu_1 + m_{n_1} + m_{n_2}, \ldots, \nu_k > \nu_{k-1} + m_{n_{k-1}} + m_{n_k}, \ldots,$$

then the trigonometric polynomials

$$P_{n_k}(x) = \frac{e^{i\nu_k x}}{\sqrt{M_{n_k}}} \sum_{\nu=-m_{n_k}}^{m_{n_k}} c_\nu^{(k)} e^{i\nu x} = \frac{1}{\sqrt{M_{n_k}}} \sum_{\nu=-m_{n_k}}^{m_{n_k}} c_\nu^{(k)} e^{i(\nu+\nu_k)x}$$

have the property that at $j \neq k$ the polynomials $P_{n_k}$ and $P_{n_j}$ do not possess similar terms. Since

$$\int_0^{2\pi} |P_{n_k}(x)|\, dx = \frac{1}{\sqrt{M_{n_k}}} \int_0^{2\pi} T_{n_k}(x)\, dx = \frac{\pi}{\sqrt{M_{n_k}}},$$

then from (19.5)

$$\sum_{k=1}^{\infty} \int_0^{2\pi} |P_{n_k}(x)|\, dx < +\infty, \tag{19.6}$$

and therefore the function

$$F(x) = \sum_{k=1}^{\infty} P_{n_k}(x) \tag{19.7}$$

is definable almost everywhere and summable. Its values will be complex numbers. Supposing

$$F(x) = f(x) + ig(x),$$

we will prove that $f(x)$ is the required function.

For this we note first of all that in the series (19.7) the terms are arranged in ascending order of the exponents $e^{i\nu x}$. Expressing every $P_{n_k}$ in the expanded form we obtain the series

$$\sum_{k=1}^{\infty} P_{n_k}(x) = \sum_{\nu=0}^{\nu=+\infty} \gamma_\nu e^{i\nu x}, \tag{19.8}$$

which is easily seen to be a complex Fourier series of $F(x)$. In fact, because (19.6) converges, then term-by-term integration after multiplying by $e^{-i\nu x}$ is allowed, thence it is clear that

$$\frac{1}{2\pi} \int_0^{2\pi} F(x)\, e^{-i\nu x}\, dx = \gamma_\nu.$$

From this it follows immediately that the functions $f(x)$ and $g(x)$ are summable, whilst $\sigma(f)$ and $\sigma(g)$ are the real and imaginary parts of the series (19.8).

Now let us prove that the series (19.8) diverges almost everywhere. For this we take the set $E_{n_k}$ of the preceding lemma; let

$$E = \overline{\lim_{k\to\infty}}\, E_{n_k}.$$

It is clear that

$$mE = 2\pi.$$

Let $x_0 \in E$, then $x_0 \in E_{n_k}$ for an infinite set of values of $k$. Since for any $p$ it can be said concerning $S_p(x, T_n)$ that it is part of the polynomial $T_n$, then the lemma states that for $x_0 \in E_{n_k}$ part of the polynomial $T_{n_k}$ is found to possess a modulus exceeding $M_{n_k}$. But this part is certainly encountered in the series (19.8), because all the $T_{n_k}(k)$ which are only divisible by $\sqrt{M_{n_k}}$ figure in it. This means that in the series (19.8) are found those parts of

$$\sum_{\alpha}^{\beta_k} \gamma_\nu e^{i\nu x},$$

for which

$$\left|\sum_{\alpha_k}^{\beta_k} \gamma_\nu e^{i\nu x}\right| > \sqrt{M_{n_k}},$$

whilst this is true for an infinite set of values of $k$. Therefore, the series diverges for any $x_0 \in E$, i.e. almost everywhere.

If one of the series $\sigma(f)$ or $\sigma(g)$ should converge in some set of positive measure, then the other would also converge in it almost everywhere. This will be proved in Chapter VIII, § 23. Then the series (19.8) which has the form $\sigma(f) + i\sigma(g)$ would also converge in a set of measure greater than zero. But we have proved that this is impossible. Thus, $\sigma(f)$ and $\sigma(g)$ diverge almost everywhere, and the theorem is proved.

*Note*†. The question arises: why is $\bar{\sigma}(f)$ a Fourier series in this example, whilst this was not so in the Kolmogorov and Marcinkiewicz examples?

If instead of multiplying all the polynomials $T_{n_k}(x)$ by the factor $e^{i\nu_k x}$, we had simply taken

$$\psi(x) = \sum_{k=1}^{\infty} \frac{T_{n_k}(x)}{\sqrt{M_{n_k}}},$$

then we would again have obtained the function $\psi(x) \geqslant 0$. We will prove that we have $\psi(x) \ln^+\psi(x) \bar{\in} L$.

Indeed, for any $k$ we have

$$\psi(x) \ln^+ \psi(x) \geqslant \frac{T_{n_k}(x)}{\sqrt{M_{n_k}}} \ln^+ \frac{T_{n_k}(x)}{\sqrt{M_{n_k}}}.$$

From formula (19.4) we immediately see that

$$M_n \sim \sqrt{\ln n}.$$

† This note is due to Ul'yanov[8].

Therefore it is sufficient to prove that

$$\int_0^{2\pi} \frac{T_n(x)}{(\ln n)^{1/4}} \ln^+ \frac{T_n(x)}{(\ln n)^{1/4}}\, dx \to \infty \quad \text{as} \quad n \to \infty.$$

But for $\pi/2n \leqslant x \leqslant \pi/n$ we have for the Fejér kernel

$$F_n(x) = \frac{1}{2(n+1)} \left( \frac{\sin(n+1)\frac{x}{2}}{\sin\frac{x}{2}} \right)^2 \geqslant Cn,$$

where $C$ is a positive constant. Therefore

$$\int_0^{2\pi} T_n(x) \ln^+ \frac{T_n(x)}{(\ln n)^{1/4}}\, dx = \sum_{i=0}^{n} \frac{1}{n+1} \int_0^{2\pi} F_{m_i}(x - A_i) \ln^+ \frac{T_n(x)}{(\ln n)^{1/4}}\, dx$$

$$\geqslant \sum_{i=0}^{n} \frac{1}{n+1} \int_{A_i+\frac{\pi}{2m_i}}^{A_i+\frac{\pi}{m_i}} F_{m_i}(x - A_i) \ln^+ \frac{F_{m_j}(x - A_i)}{(n+1)(\ln n)^{1/4}}\, dx$$

$$\geqslant C \frac{1}{n+1} \sum_{i=0}^{n} \int_{A_i+\frac{\pi}{2m_i}}^{A_i+\frac{\pi}{m_i}} m_i \ln \frac{Cm_i}{(n+1)(\ln n)} \geqslant C_1 \ln n,$$

where $C_1$ is another constant; here we operated on the fact that $m_i > n^4$.

Consequently,

$$\int_0^{2\pi} \frac{T_n(x)}{(\ln n)^{1/4}} \ln^+ \frac{T_n(x)}{(\ln n)^{1/4}}\, dx \geqslant C_1 (\ln n)^{3/4}.$$

If this is so then it is known that $\bar{\sigma}(\psi)$ for $\psi(x)$ is not a Fourier series. But in the Hardy and Rogosinski example the polynomials $T_{n_k}(x)$ were multiplied by the factor $e^{i\nu_k x}$ so that the $F(x)$ was obtained not by a positive function but by a complex one in which the real and imaginary parts assume both positive and negative values. Thus, interference of the positive and negative values was obtained which produced the required effect.

## § 20. A Fourier series, divergent at every point

In the examples of the preceding section the Fourier series was divergent almost everywhere. If we want to secure divergence at every point† then it is possible to base it on the same idea, but it is necessary to correct the auxiliary functions which we will use.

First of all we will strengthen the lemma of the preceding section thus:

LEMMA. *There exists a sequence of trigonometric polynomials $f_n(x)$ possessing the properties*

(a) $f_n(x) \geqslant 0$,

(b) $\frac{1}{\pi}\int_{-\pi}^{\pi} f_n(x)\,dx = 1, \quad n = 1, 2, \ldots,$

(c) *if $\nu_n$ is the order of the polynomial $f_n(x)$, then there can be found numbers $\lambda_n \to \infty$, numbers $M_n \to \infty$, sets $E_n$*

$$E_1 \subset E_2 \subset \cdots \subset E_n \subset \ldots, \quad [0, 2\pi] = \sum_{n=1}^{\infty} E_n$$

*and for every point $x \in E_n$ there exists an integer $k_x$ such that $\lambda_n \leqslant k_x \leqslant \nu_n$ and*

$$S_{k_x}(x, f_n) > M_n.$$

Thus the properties of the polynomials $f_n(x)$ are the same as for the polynomials $T_n(x)$ in the lemma of § 19 but the sets $E_n$ fill the whole interval $[0, 2\pi]$.

We will show first that if this lemma is proved, then there exists a function $f(x)$ with an everywhere divergent Fourier series, whilst for all $x$ we have unbounded divergence, i.e.

$$\overline{\lim_{n\to\infty}} |S_n(x, f)| = +\infty.$$

In order to construct this function, we will proceed in the same way as in § 17, i.e. we will choose the numbers $n_k$ to increase sufficiently rapidly and suppose that

$$f(x) = \sum_{k=1}^{\infty} \frac{f_{n_k}(x)}{\sqrt{M_{n_k}}}. \tag{20.1}$$

First of all we can consider $n_k$ to be taken so that

$$M_{n_k} > 4M_{n_{k-1}}, \tag{20.2}$$

† The existence of a function with a Fourier series divergent at every point was discovered by Kolmogorov. But in his note[3] (containing only two pages) only the properties were given of those trigonometric polynomials from which this function is constructed. A more detailed description of the whole proof was given by Zygmund ([A.35], § 8.4), who noted that his construction was communicated to him by Kolmogorov.

Here we will adhere basically to Zygmund's proof, only we will give a more detailed exposition and will replace No. 8.404 by a new argument which appears simpler to us.

then the series $\sum 1/\sqrt{M_{n_k}}$ converges: therefore due to property (b) series (20.1) converges almost everywhere and defines the summable function $f(x)$. If we take $n_1 = 1$ and construct $n_m$ recurrently so that

$$\lambda_{n_m} < \nu_{n_{m-1}}, \tag{20.3}$$

$$\sqrt{M_{n_m}} > \nu_{n_{m-1}}, \tag{20.4}$$

then, as we will now show, the Fourier series of $f(x)$ will diverge everywhere.

Indeed, we have, if $x \in E_{n_m}$,

$$S_{k_x}(x, f) = \sum_{j=1}^{m-1} \frac{1}{\sqrt{M_{n_j}}} S_{k_x}(x, f_{n_j}) + \frac{1}{\sqrt{M_{n_m}}} S_{k_x}(x, f_{n_m})$$

$$+ \sum_{j=m+1}^{\infty} \frac{1}{\sqrt{M_{n_j}}} S_{k_x}(x, f_{n_j}). \tag{20.5}$$

Due to the choice of the numbers $k_x$ we have from property (c)

$$\frac{1}{\sqrt{M_{n_m}}} S_{k_x}(x, f_{n_m}) > \frac{M_{n_m}}{\sqrt{M_{n_m}}} = \sqrt{M_{n_m}}. \tag{20.6}$$

On the other hand, since $k_x \geqslant \lambda_{n_m} > \nu_{n_{m-1}}$ due to (20.3), then $k_x$ exceeds the orders of all the $f_{n_j}$ found in the first sum, which means that $S_{k_x}(x, f_{n_j}) = f_{n_j}(x)$ for $j = 1, 2, \ldots, m-1$, and since all the $f_{n_j}(x) \geqslant 0$, then the whole of the first sum in (20.5) is non-negative.

We now note that for any $j$

$$|S_{k_x}(x, f_{n_j})| \leqslant \frac{(2k_x + 1)}{\pi} \int_0^{2\pi} f_{n_j}(x)\, dx \leqslant (2\nu_{n_m} + 1) < 3\nu_{n_m},$$

and therefore

$$\left| \sum_{j=m+1}^{\infty} \frac{1}{\sqrt{M_{n_j}}} S_{k_x}(x, f_{n_j}) \right| \leqslant 3\nu_{n_m} \sum_{j=m+1}^{\infty} \frac{1}{\sqrt{M_{n_j}}} \leqslant \frac{3\nu_{n_m}}{\sqrt{M_{n_{m+1}}}} \sum_{j=0}^{\infty} \frac{1}{2^j} < 6, \tag{20.7}$$

since $\sqrt{M_{n_s}} > 2\sqrt{M_{n_{s-1}}}$ due to (20.2) for any $s$ and $\sqrt{M_{n_{m+1}}} > \nu_{n_m}$ due to the choice of the numbers $n_m$ (see (20.4)).

Combining (20.5), (20.6) and (20.7) we see that

$$S_{k_x}(x, f) \geqslant \sqrt{M_{n_m}} - 6.$$

Since any point $x$ belongs to the set $E_{n_m}$, provided $m$ is sufficiently great (due to the property (c)), then we see that for any $x$

$$\overline{\lim_{n \to \infty}} |S_n(x, f)| = +\infty$$

and the theorem is proved.

Thus, we have reduced the matter to the lemma and it is obvious that this is the central part of the whole proof.

The construction of the polynomials $f_n(x)$ will differ from the construction of the polynomials $T_n(x)$ in two details; as we have no right to lose a single point, we cannot discard the set where $\sin(k_x + \frac{1}{2})x$ is small (as was done in the lemma of § 19). Therefore, the number $k_x$ must be chosen more precisely. Moreover, it will be impossible to discard those intervals which surround the "danger" points $A_i$ in the preceding construction; to correct the position we add to the polynomial $T_n(x)$ some non-negative polynomial $\tau_n(x)$ which for some $m$ will have sufficiently large partial sums $S_m(x, \tau_n)$ in these intervals and, on the other hand, since $\tau_n(x) \geqslant 0$, does not spoil the behaviour of $T_n(x)$ where the sums $S_{k_x}(x, T_n)$ were large. Now we will express this general idea in a precise form.

To simplify the numerical calculation, instead of the points $A_i$ at which is constructed the polynomial $T_n(x)$ in the lemma of § 19, we consider the points

$$x_l = \frac{2\pi}{n} l \qquad (l = 0, 1, \dots, n)$$

and we again assume that

$$T_n(x) = \frac{1}{n+1} \sum_{l=0}^{n} F_{m_l}(x - x_l),$$

where $F_m$ is a Fejér kernel. The numbers $m_0 < m_1 < \cdots < m_n$ are integral values which we shall choose later, but we will assume that $m_{j+1} > 2m_j$ $(j = 0, 1, \dots, n-1)$. Just as in the lemma of § 19 we can for any $k$, provided $m_j \leqslant k < \frac{1}{2} m_{j+1}$, write

$$S_k(x, T_n) = \frac{1}{n+1} \sum_{l=0}^{j} F_{m_l}(x - x_l) + \frac{1}{n+1} \sum_{l=j+1}^{n} \frac{k+1}{m_l+1} F_k(x - x_l)$$
$$+ \frac{1}{n+1} \sum_{l=j+1}^{n} \frac{m_l - k}{m_l + 1} D_k(x - x_l). \tag{20.8}$$

Since the Fejér polynomials are all non-negative, then for any $x$

$$S_k(x, T_n) \geqslant \frac{1}{n+1} \sum_{l=j+1}^{n} \frac{m_l - k}{m_l + 1} D_k(x - x_l).$$

Because

$$D_k(t) = \frac{\sin\left(k + \dfrac{1}{2}\right)t}{2\sin\dfrac{t}{2}} = \frac{\sin kt}{t} + \varphi_k(t),$$

where $|\varphi_k(t)| < C$ for any $k$ and $t \in [0, 2\pi]$ (see Chapter I, § 32) then

$$S_k(x, T_n) \geqslant \frac{1}{n+1} \sum_{l=j+1}^{n} \frac{m_l - k}{m_l + 1} \frac{\sin k(x - x_l)}{x - x_l} - O(1). \tag{20.9}$$

We now assume that $k = \varrho n$ where $\varrho$ is an integer. Then

$$\sin k(x - x_l) = \sin\left(kx - \varrho n \frac{2\pi}{n} l\right) = \sin kx$$

and

$$\sum_{l=j+1}^{n}\left(\frac{m_l-k}{m_l+1}\right)\frac{\sin k(x-x_l)}{x-x_l} = -\sin kx \sum_{l=j+1}^{n}\left(\frac{m_l-k}{m_l+1}\right)\frac{1}{x_l-x}. \qquad (20.10)$$

We surround by an interval of length $2\delta$ all the points $x_l$ and, moreover, all the centres of the intervals between them, i.e. we discard from $[0, 2\pi]$ all the intervals $I_l$ of the form

$$I_l = \left(l\frac{\pi}{n} - \delta, l\frac{\pi}{n} + \delta\right), \quad l = 0, 1, \ldots, 2n-1.$$

Here $\delta$ is a number which we will choose later, but in any case it will be $o(1/n)$. Let us denote

$$\sigma_l = \left[l\frac{\pi}{n} + \delta, (l+1)\frac{\pi}{n} - \delta\right], \quad l = 0, 1, \ldots, 2n-1.$$

It is clear that any point of $[0, 2\pi]$ falls either in one of $I_l$ or in one of $\sigma_l$.

Let $x \in \sigma_{2j}$ or $x \in \sigma_{2j+1}$. Then we will apply to it formula (20.9), that is, for this value of $j$. Because

$$x \leqslant (2j+2)\frac{\pi}{n} - \delta = x_{j+1} - \delta,$$

then for $l \geqslant j+1$ we have $x_l - x > 0$; moreover, for $l \geqslant j+1$ we have

$$\frac{m_l-k}{m_l+1} = \frac{1-\dfrac{k}{m_l}}{1+\dfrac{1}{m_l}} > \frac{1}{4} \qquad (20.11)$$

because $k < \frac{1}{2} m_{j+1}$; therefore, if for the $x$ under consideration and for some $k_x$ we have

$$-\sin k_x x \geqslant \frac{1}{2}, \qquad (20.12)$$

then from (20.9), (20.10) and (20.11) we find that

$$S_{k_x}(x, T_n) \geqslant \frac{1}{8(n+1)} \sum_{l=j+1}^{n} \frac{1}{x_l - x} - O(1),$$

where the sum is positive; after this, noting that $x > x_j$, we can write

$$\begin{aligned} S_{k_x}(x, T_n) &\geqslant \frac{1}{8(n+1)} \sum_{l=j+1}^{n} \frac{1}{x_l - x_j} - O(1) \\ &= \frac{n}{16\pi(n+1)} \sum_{l=j+1}^{n} \frac{1}{l-j} - O(1) > \frac{1}{32\pi} \sum_{s=1}^{n-j} \frac{1}{s} - O(1) - C\ln(n-j), \end{aligned}$$

where $C$ is a constant. Thus, if $j \leqslant n - \sqrt{n}$, we obtain

$$S_{k_x}(x, T_n) > C \ln \sqrt{n} = C_1 \ln n. \qquad (20.13)$$

Thus, if $j \leqslant n - \sqrt{n}$ and if for every $x \in \sigma_{2j}$ and for every $x \in \sigma_{2j+1}$ it is possible to find its $k_x$ satisfying the conditions

($\alpha$) $m_j \leqslant k_x < \frac{1}{2} m_{j+1}$,

($\beta$) $k_x$ divisible by $n$,

($\gamma$) $-\sin k_x x \geqslant \frac{1}{2}$,

then for any such $x$ we will have (20.13).

For the present we assume that for a reasonable choice of the values $m_j$ it is possible to find such $k_x$ and we will conclude the proof of the lemma, and then return to this point.

Let us consider the polynomial

$$\tau_n(x) = F_n[2nx],$$

where $F_n$ is the Fejér polynomial of the $n$th order. It is clear that the order of the polynomial $\tau_n(x)$ equals $2n^2$; it is non-negative and satisfies the condition

$$\frac{1}{\pi}\int_0^{2\pi} \tau_n(x)\,dx = 1. \tag{20.14}$$

We have for any integer $l$

$$\tau_n\left(l\frac{\pi}{n}\right) = F_n(0) = \frac{1}{n+1}\sum_{k=0}^{n} D_k(0) > \frac{1}{n+1}\sum_{k=0}^{n} k = \frac{n}{2}.$$

Moreover, since $|F_n'(x)| \leqslant n^2$ for all $x$, then $|\tau_n'(x)| < 2n^3$. From this it follows that if we assume that $\delta = 1/8n^4$, then for $x \in I_l$ we have

$$\left|\tau_n(x) - \tau_n\left(l\frac{\pi}{n}\right)\right| < \delta 2n^3 \leqslant \frac{1}{n},$$

whence

$$\tau_n(x) > \frac{n}{4} \quad \text{for} \quad x \in I_l \quad (l = 0, 1, \ldots, 2n). \tag{20.15}$$

We assume that $m_0 = 2n^2$. From $|D_{m_0}'(x)| \leqslant m_0^2$ and $D_{m_0} = m_0 + \frac{1}{2}$, it follows that for $-\delta \leqslant x \leqslant \delta$

$$|D_{m_0}(x) - D_{m_0}(0)| \leqslant m_0^2\delta < 4n^4\frac{1}{8n^4} = \frac{1}{2},$$

and therefore, in any case already

$$D_{m_0}(x) > 1 \quad \text{for} \quad -\delta \leqslant x \leqslant \delta. \tag{20.16}$$

Thus, if we take $\delta = 1/8n^4$, then both the inequalities (20.15) and (20.16) will be satisfied.

We have assumed that $m_0 = 2n^2$; now let

$$f_n(x) = \frac{1}{2}[T_n(x) + \tau_n(x)],$$

where the numbers $m_1, m_2, \ldots, m_n$ are at present at our disposal. Since (20.14) holds and also $(1/\pi)\int_0^{2\pi} T_n(x)dx = 1$, then condition (b) of the lemma for the polynomials $f_n(x)$ is fulfilled; moreover, it is evident that they are non-negative.

It is clear that the order of the polynomial $f_n(x)$ is $m_n$, because such is the order of $T_n(x)$, but the order of $\tau_n(x)$ is $2n^2 = m_0 < m_n$. Therefore, supposing $\lambda_n = m_0 = 2n^2$ and $\nu_n = m_n$, we see that if $k_x$ satisfy condition $\alpha$), then

$$\lambda_n \leqslant k_x < \nu_n,$$

as was required in the lemma, whilst $\lambda_n \to \infty$.

Because $k_x \geqslant \lambda_n = m_0$ and the order of $\tau_n(x)$ is $m_0$, then

$$S_{k_x}(\tau_n) = \tau_n(x) \geqslant 0,$$

which means that

$$S_{k_x}(f_n) = \frac{1}{2}S_{k_x}(T_n) + \frac{1}{2}S_{k_x}(\tau_n) \geqslant \frac{C_1}{2}\ln n = C_2 \ln n \tag{20.17}$$

by virtue of (20.13) for all $x \in \sigma_{2j}$ and $x \in \sigma_{2j+1}$ at $j \leqslant n - \sqrt{n}$.

We will now prove that for $x \in I_l$ $(l = 0, 1, \ldots, 2n)$ we have

$$S_{m_0}(x, f_n) > C\ln n, \tag{20.18}$$

where $C$ is some positive constant.

Indeed, supposing in formula (20.8) $j = 0$ and $k = m_0$ we have

$$S_{m_0}(x, T_n) = \frac{1}{n+1}\sum_{l=0}^{n}\frac{m_0+1}{m_l+1}F_{m_0}(x - x_l) + \frac{1}{n+1}\sum_{l=1}^{n}\frac{m_l - m_0}{m_l+1}D_{m_0}(x - x_l).$$

Since all the Fejér polynomials are non-negative, then

$$S_{m_0}(x, T_n) \geqslant \frac{1}{n+1}\sum_{l=1}^{n}\frac{m_l - m_0}{m_l+1}D_{m_0}(x - x_l). \tag{20.19}$$

Let $x \in I_m$, i.e.

$$m\frac{\pi}{n} - \delta \leqslant x \leqslant m\frac{\pi}{n} + \delta. \tag{20.20}$$

If $m$ is even, let $m = 2j$, then $m\pi/n = 2j\pi/n = x_j$ which means that

$$|x - x_j| < \delta.$$

Then due to the choice of $\delta$ it follows from (20.16) that, discarding the term $l = j$ from formula (20.19), we only strengthen the inequality, i.e. at $m = 2j$ it follows from (20.19) that

$$S_{m_0}(x, T_n) \geqslant \frac{1}{n+1}\sum_{l=1}^{n}{}'\frac{m_l - m_0}{m_l+1}D_{m_0}(x - x_l) \geqslant -\frac{1}{n+1}\sum_{l=1}^{n}{}'|D_{m_0}(x - x_l)|, \tag{20.21}$$

where the sign $\sum'$ indicates that $l = j$ is excluded, which signifies that no argument of the terms of the sums in (20.21) can equal zero. But noting that for $0 < u < \pi$

$$|D_n(u)| \leqslant \frac{\pi}{|u|},$$

we have

$$S_{m_0}(x, T_n) \geqslant -\frac{\pi}{(n+1)} \sum_{l=1}^{n}{}' \frac{1}{|x - x_l|}.$$

Because $x$ differs from $2j\pi/n$ by a magnitude of order $0\,(1/n^4)$, then

$$S_{m_0}(x, T_n) \geqslant -C_3 \frac{1}{n+1} \sum_{l=1}^{n}{}' \frac{1}{\left|2j\frac{\pi}{n} - l\frac{2\pi}{n}\right|} = -C_4 \sum_{l=1}^{n}{}' \frac{1}{|j - l|} > -C_5 \ln n, \tag{20.22}$$

where $C_1, C_2, \ldots$ are positive constants.

If $m$ is odd, $m = 2j + 1$, then it is not necessary to discard any terms from (20.19). But noting again that

$$S_{m_0}(x, T_n) \geqslant -\frac{\pi}{(n+1)} \sum_{l=1}^{n} \frac{1}{|x - x_l|}$$

and that $x$ differs from $(2j+1)\,\pi/n$ by a magnitude of order $O\,(1/n^4)$ we see that

$$S_{m_0}(x, T_n) \geqslant -C_6 \frac{1}{n+1} \sum_{l=1}^{n} \frac{1}{\left|(2j+1)\frac{\pi}{n} - l\frac{2\pi}{n}\right|}$$

$$> -C_7 \sum_{l=1}^{n} \frac{1}{|2j + 1 - 2l|} > -C_8 \ln n. \tag{20.23}$$

Thus, from formulae (20.22) and (20.23) we see that for any $x \in I_m$ $(m = 0, 1, \ldots, 2n)$ we have

$$S_{m_0}(x, T_n) > -C_9 \ln n, \tag{20.24}$$

where $C_9 = \max(C_5, C_8)$.

We now note that since $m_0$ is the order of the polynomial $\tau_n(x)$, then

$$S_{m_0}(x, \tau_n) = \tau_n(x).$$

But if $x \in I_m$, then by virtue of (20.15) we have

$$\tau_n(x) > \frac{n}{4},$$

and therefore

$$S_{m_0}(x, \tau_n) > \frac{n}{4} \tag{20.25}$$

in all $I_m$, and then from (20.24) and (20.25)

$$S_{m_0}(x, f_n) > \frac{n}{8} - \frac{C_9}{2} \ln n > C_{10} n,$$

and this is also formula (20.18), which we wished to prove.

Let us now denote by $E_n$ the interval $\left[0, \frac{2\pi}{n}(n - \sqrt{n})\right]$. It is clear that

$$E_1 \subset E_2 \subset \cdots \subset E_n \subset \cdots \quad \text{and} \quad [0, 2\pi] = \sum_{n=1}^{\infty} E_n.$$

If $x \in E_n$, then either $x \in I_m$ for some $m$, or $x \in \sigma_m$, whilst this index $m$ is such that if $m = 2j$ or $m = 2j+1$, then $j \leqslant n - \sqrt{n}$. Therefore, for this $x$ either a $k_x$ is found according to formula (20.17) such that

$$S_{k_x}(x, f_n) > C_2 \ln n,$$

or according to formula (20.18) we have

$$S_{m_0}(x, f_n) > C \ln n.$$

In any case for any $x \in E_n$ a $k_x$ is found such that

$$m_0 \leqslant k_x < m_n$$

and

$$S_{k_x}(x, f_n) > M_n, \quad \text{where} \quad M_n \to \infty,$$

and the lemma is proved, apart from the point which was mentioned on p. 459.

It remains for us to prove that if $m_0$ is chosen, then it is possible to choose the numbers $m_k$ $(k = 1, 2, \ldots, n)$ so that

(1) $m_0 < m_1 < \cdots < m_n$,

(2) for every $x \in \sigma_{2j}$ and $x \in \sigma_{2j+1}$ a $k_x$ is found such that $k_x$ is divisible by $n$,

$$m_j \leqslant k_x < \frac{1}{2} m_{j+1}$$

and

$$-\sin k_x x \geqslant \frac{1}{2}.$$

We will reduce the possibility of such a definition of the numbers $m_j$ to a problem of numerical theory.

First of all we note that if $x \in \sigma_{2j}$, then

$$x = x_j + \theta \frac{2\pi}{n},$$

and if $x \in \sigma_{2j+1}$, then

$$x = x_{j+1} - \theta \frac{2\pi}{n},$$

where in both cases

$$\delta \leqslant \theta \frac{2\pi}{n} < \frac{\pi}{n} - \delta,$$

i.e.

$$\frac{n\delta}{2\pi} \leqslant \theta \leqslant \frac{1}{2} - \frac{n\delta}{2\pi},$$

and denoting $\eta = n\delta/2\pi = 1/16\pi n^3$ we see that

$$\eta \leqslant \theta \leqslant \frac{1}{2} - \eta, \tag{20.26}$$

where $\eta$ is a positive constant dependent only on $n$ and not on $x$.

If $k_x$ is divisible by $n$, then $k_x = \varrho n$, where $\varrho$ is an integer, therefore

$$-\sin k_x x = \begin{cases} -\sin \varrho n \left(x_j + \theta \dfrac{2\pi}{n}\right) & \text{for} \quad x \in \sigma_{2j}, \\ -\sin \varrho n \left(x_{j+1} - \theta \dfrac{2\pi}{n}\right) & \text{for} \quad x \in \sigma_{2j+1}. \end{cases}$$

In both cases $\varrho n x_j$ and $\varrho n x_{j+1}$ are multiples of $2\pi$, and therefore

$$-\sin k_x x = \begin{cases} -\sin \varrho n \theta \dfrac{2\pi}{n} = -\sin 2\pi\varrho\theta & \text{for} \quad x \in \sigma_{2j}, \\ \sin \varrho n \theta \dfrac{2\pi}{n} = \sin 2\pi\varrho\theta & \text{for} \quad x \in \sigma_{2j+1}. \end{cases}$$

Thus, if $\theta$ is given satisfying condition (20.26), then it must be known how to find integer $\varrho_1$ and $\varrho_2$ such that

$$-\sin 2\pi\varrho_1\theta \geqslant \frac{1}{2}, \quad \text{and also} \quad \sin 2\pi\varrho_2\theta \geqslant \frac{1}{2},$$

in other words, that

$$\frac{7}{12} \leqslant (\varrho_1\theta) \leqslant \frac{11}{12} \quad \text{and} \quad \frac{1}{12} \leqslant (\varrho_2\theta) \leqslant \frac{5}{12},$$

where $(x)$ signifies the fractional part of the number $x$.

We will prove that, whatever $N$ is, it is always possible to find $\varrho_1$ and $\varrho_2$ such that

$$N \leqslant \varrho_1 \leqslant M,$$
$$N \leqslant \varrho_2 \leqslant M,$$

where $M$ is a constant dependent only on $\eta$.

Let us assume first that

$$\eta \leqslant \theta \leqslant \frac{1}{3}.$$

Then, since ${}^{11}/_{12} - {}^{7}/_{12} = {}^{1}/_{3}$ and ${}^{5}/_{12} - {}^{1}/_{12} = {}^{1}/_{3}$, the values $(\theta)$, $(2\theta)$, $(3\theta)$, ..., $(m\theta)$, ... differ from one another by a distance not greater than the length of each of the intervals $[{}^{1}/_{12}, {}^{5}/_{12}]$ or $[{}^{7}/_{12}, {}^{11}/_{12}]$; therefore, permitting $\varrho$ to pass successively through all the integers from $N$ to $N + M$, where $M = [1/\eta] + 1$, we can find such $\varrho_1$ and $\varrho_2$ as are necessary to us.

If $\frac{1}{3} \leqslant \theta \leqslant \frac{1}{2} - \eta$, then $\frac{2}{3} \leqslant 2\theta \leqslant 1 - 2\eta$; supposing $\theta_0 = 1 - 2\theta$, we see that

$$2\eta \leqslant \theta_0 \leqslant \frac{1}{3},$$

and therefore it is possible, as in the preceding case, to find $\varrho_1$ and $\varrho_2$ such that

$$-\sin 2\pi\varrho_1\theta_0 \geqslant \frac{1}{2} \quad \text{and} \quad \sin 2\pi\varrho_2\theta_0 \geqslant \frac{1}{2},$$

and therefore

$$-\sin 2\pi\varrho_1(1-2\theta) \geqslant \frac{1}{2} \quad \text{and} \quad \sin 2\pi\varrho_2(1-2\theta) \geqslant \frac{1}{2},$$

whence

$$\sin 2\pi\varrho_1 2\theta \geqslant \frac{1}{2} \quad \text{and} \quad -\sin 2\pi\varrho_2 2\theta \geqslant \frac{1}{2}.$$

Supposing that

$$\varrho_1^* = 2\varrho_2 \quad \text{and} \quad \varrho_2^* = 2\varrho_1,$$

we see that the required values of $\varrho$ are found for $\theta$, whilst again

$$\varrho_1^* \geqslant N, \quad \varrho_2^* \geqslant N$$

and

$$\varrho_1^* \leqslant M_1, \quad \varrho_2^* \leqslant M_1, \quad \text{where} \quad M_1 = 2M.$$

Now the last step remains: the construction of the values $m_i$. Since $m_0$ is already defined, we suppose that $m_0 < m_1 < \cdots < m_j$ are already known and we will define $m_{j+1}$. We already know how to define $k_x$ for every $x \in \sigma_{2j}$ and $x \in \sigma_{2j+1}$ such that

$$-\sin k_x x \geqslant \frac{1}{2},$$

whilst $k_x = \varrho n$ where $\varrho$ can be made larger than the given number $N$ and less than $N + M$, where $M$ depends only on $n$. Therefore, if $N$ is taken so that $nN \geqslant m_j$, we will have $k_x \geqslant m_j$ for all such $x$.

If now we choose $m_{j+1}$ so that $(N + M)n < \frac{1}{2} m_{j+1}$, then we see that

$$k_x = \varrho n < (N+m)\,n < \frac{1}{2} m_{j+1},$$

and the latter is the inequality which had to be established.

Thus, the proof of the lemma is concluded and with it the whole theorem.

*Note.* In the constructed example of an everywhere divergent Fourier series we have unbounded divergence at every point, i.e.

$$\overline{\lim}\, |S_n(x,f)| = +\infty.$$

Up until now, it is not known whether it is possible to construct an everywhere divergent Fourier series, for which at every point

$$\overline{\lim}\, |S_n(x,f)| < +\infty.$$

Marcinkiewicz[1] noted that if such series exist, then bounded functions also exist with almost everywhere divergent Fourier series. The proof can be found in a report by Ul'yanov[8] (theorem 12). However, not only for bounded functions but also for functions with integrable square it has not yet been possible to construct such series, and the problem of their existence is considered to be one of the most difficult in the theory of Fourier series.

## § 21. Concerning the principle of localization for sets

We know (see Chapter I, § 33) that if two functions $f_1(x)$ and $f_2(x)$ coincide in some interval $[a, b]$, then at any point outside it the series $\sigma(f_1)$ and $\sigma(f_2)$ behave identically, i.e. converge or diverge simultaneously.

The question arises whether it would not be possible to transfer this theorem to a set, even if in a somewhat weakened form; namely, whether it would not be possible to assert that if $f_1(x) = f_2(x)$ in $E$, $mE > 0$, then the series $\sigma(f_1)$ and $\sigma(f_2)$ behave identically almost everywhere in $E$.

The answer to this question appears to be in the negative, if some additional restrictions are not imposed on the function and on the set.

To prove this, it is sufficient to prove that for a reasonable choice of the values $\{n_k\}$ entering into the construction of the function $\Phi(x)$ in the Kolmogorov example (see § 17), for any $\varepsilon > 0$ the set $E$ of those points, where $\Phi(x) \neq 0$, can be constructed such that $mE < \varepsilon$. Indeed, the functions $\varphi_n(x)$, constructed in § 17, possess this property that $\varphi_n(x) = 0$ everywhere apart from the intervals $\Delta_1, \Delta_2, \dots, \Delta_n$, the length of each of these intervals is $2/m_k^2$, and since $m_k \geqslant \lambda_k n$, where $\lambda_k \geqslant 1$, then

$$m(\Delta_k) < \frac{2}{n^2} \quad (k = 1, 2, \dots, n),$$

and therefore the set $E_n$ of those $x$ where $\varphi_n(x) \neq 0$ is of measure

$$mE_n < \frac{2}{n}.$$

But

$$\Phi(x) = \sum_{k=1}^{\infty} \frac{1}{\sqrt{n_k}} \varphi_{n_k}(x).$$

Therefore, the function $\Phi(x)$ can be different from zero only when one of $\varphi_{n_k}(x) \neq 0$, which means that $E = E\{\Phi(x) \neq 0\} \subset \sum_{k=1}^{\infty} E_{n_k}$, and therefore

$$mE < 2 \sum_{k=1}^{\infty} \frac{1}{n_k}.$$

Since the values $n_k$ are at our disposal, they can be made such that the condition $\sum_{k=1}^{\infty} 1/n^k < \varepsilon/2$ is fulfilled and then

$$\Phi(x) = 0 \quad \text{in} \quad CE, \; mCE > 2\pi - \varepsilon.$$

It is not less true that $\sigma(f)$ diverges almost everywhere.

This example shows that the principle of localization does not hold for sets.

However, in § 19 we have seen that the function $\Phi(x)$ is non-summable for any power $p > 1$. If we only consider functions of $L^p (p > 1)$, then, as we will see, for corresponding limitations imposed on the set, the principle of localization appears to be valid.† This result due to G.P.Tolstov[2] will now be described. He proved it for the case $p = 2$ but the proof is readily extended to the case $f(x) \in L^p$, provided $p > 1$.

Thus we will prove the theorem:

THEOREM. *For any* $\mu$, $0 < \mu < 2\pi$, *there exists a perfect nowhere-dense set* $P$, $mP = \mu$, *such that if the functions* $f_1(x)$ *and* $f_2(x)$ *of* $L^p (p > 1)$ *coincide in* $P$, *then their Fourier series are equi-convergent*†† *almost everywhere in* $P$.

In order to prove this statement, we require another auxiliary lemma, referring to points of density.

For any set $\mathscr{E}$ and interval $(\alpha, \beta)$ we will denote by $\mathscr{E}(\alpha, \beta)$ that part of $\mathscr{E}$ which falls in $(\alpha, \beta)$.

As is known for any set $E$ of positive measure almost all its points are points of density, which means that for nearly all $x \in E$ we have

$$\lim_{h\to 0} \frac{mE(x, x+h)}{|h|} = 1.$$

Denoting, as usual, the set complementary to $E$ by $CE$, it is possible to describe this relationship in the form

$$\lim_{h\to 0} \frac{mCE(x, x+h)}{|h|} = 0. \tag{21.1}$$

Tolstoi shows that by choosing the set intelligibly it is possible to arrange that for its points the term on the left-hand side of (21.1) tends to zero as rapidly as we wish. To be more precise, we have this

LEMMA. *Let* $\varphi(h)$ *be any function definable in some interval* $0 \leqslant h \leqslant h_0$ *positive, monotonic and* $\lim_{h\to 0} \varphi(h) = 0$; *let* $[a, b]$ *be any interval. If* $0 < \mu < b - a$, *then there exists a perfect, nowhere-dense set* $P$, $mP = \mu$, *such that for almost all* $x \in P$ *we have*

$$\frac{mCP(x, x+h)}{|h|} < \varphi(|h|), \tag{21.2}$$

*if* $|h| < \delta$ ($\delta$, *generally speaking, depends on* $x$).

*Proof.* Without upsetting the generality, it is possible to suppose that $\varphi(h_0) < 1$. Let us assume that

$$\left.\begin{aligned} \mu_1 &= \frac{1}{2} h_0 \varphi(h_0), \\ \mu_n &= \frac{1}{2} \mu_{n-1} \varphi(\mu_{n-1}), \quad n \geqslant 2. \end{aligned}\right\} \tag{21.3}$$

It is clear that

$$\sum_{n=1}^{\infty} \mu_n < +\infty, \quad \sum_{n=k}^{\infty} \mu_n < 2\mu_k.$$

† The question of whether this will be true for $f(x) \in L^p$ without additional limitations on the set remains open.

†† The term "equi-convergent" was introduced in Chapter I, § 33.

Let us denote by $N$ the smallest integer for which

$$\sum_{n=N}^{\infty} \mu_n < (b - a) - \mu$$

(these values exist because $b - a > \mu$ and the series $\sum \mu_n$ converges).

Let us suppose that

$$u_1 = u_2 = \cdots = u_N = \frac{b - a - \mu - \sum\limits_{n=N+1}^{\infty} \mu_n}{N},$$

$$u_n = \mu_n \quad \text{for} \quad n > N.$$

It is clear that

$$\sum_{n=1}^{\infty} u_n = b - a - \mu.$$

We will remove from $[a, b]$ a system of intervals $(a_n, b_n)$ such that $b_n - a_n = u_n$; we require that these intervals do not possess common endpoints and that the perfect set $P$ remaining after their separation is nowhere-dense. Otherwise, they are arbitrary. It is clear that $mP = \mu$. Let us prove that this set satisfies the conditions of the lemma.

To prove this, we will combine with each interval $(a_n, b_n)$ an interval $\sigma_n'$ to the left

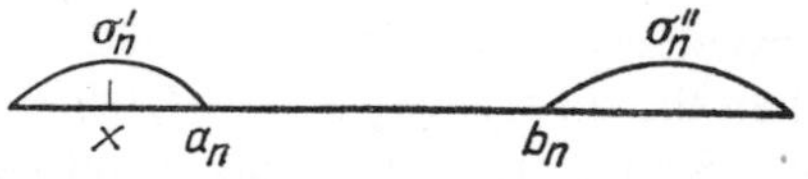


FIG. 24

and an interval $\sigma_n''$ to the right, both of length $\mu_{n-1}$ (Fig. 24). Since the sum of the lengths of the combined intervals forms a convergent series, then the set $E$ of points falling in an infinite set of such intervals is of measure zero.† Therefore, almost all the points of $P$ do not enter into $E$. Let us consider any point $x \in P$, not belonging to $E$ and not a point of the first kind for $P$; we will prove that the inequality (21.2) holds for it, if $|h|$ is sufficiently small, then the proof of the lemma will be concluded.

Let $h > 0$ (the proof for $h < 0$ is exactly the same). We will divide all the intervals $(a_n, b_n)$ into two types: the interval $(a_n, b_n)$ will belong to the first type, if $\sigma_n'$ (with the same index $n$) contains the point $x$; all the remainder will be of the second type. For any $x$ there is only a finite number of intervals of the first type; moreover, $x$ does not coincide with $a_n$, $b_n$ for any $n$. Therefore, having chosen $h$ less than the distance from $x$ to any of $(a_n, b_n)$ of the first type, we see that between $x$ and $x + h$ there is not a single point belonging to any interval of the first type. We choose $h$ thus. Now we note that if between $x$ and $x + h$ there is a point $\xi$ of some interval $(a_n, b_n)$ of the second type, then $x + h > \xi \geqslant a_n$, but $x$ does not enter into $\sigma_n'$, which means that $x < a_n - \mu_{n-1}$, whence $h \geqslant \mu_{n-1}$. Therefore, if $k$ is the least index of the interval of the second type possessing a point between $x$ and $x + h$, then from the relationship

† According to the well-known theorem, if $\Sigma m\mathscr{E}_n < +\infty$, then for $\mathscr{E} = \overline{\lim}\, \mathscr{E}_n$ we have $m\mathscr{E} = 0$ (see Introductory Material, § 12).

$\mu_{k-1} \leqslant h$ it follows that $k \to \infty$ as $h \to 0$. It is possible to choose $h$ to be sufficiently small for $k > N$, then $b_n - a_n = \mu_n$ for all $n \geqslant k$. But in this case

$$\frac{mCP(x, x+h)}{h} = \frac{m\left[(x, x+h)\sum\limits_{n=k}^{\infty}(a_n, b_n)\right]}{h} \leqslant \frac{\sum\limits_{n=k}^{\infty}\mu_n}{\mu_{k-1}} < \frac{2\mu_k}{\mu_{k-1}}$$
$$= \varphi(\mu_{k-1}) \leqslant \varphi(h)$$

due to (21.3) and the fact that $\varphi(h)$ is monotonic, which means that the lemma is proved.

Let us return to proving the theorem. Let $f_1(x)$ and $f_2(x)$ both belong to $L^p (p > 1)$. Let us define $q$ from the condition

$$\frac{1}{p} + \frac{1}{q} = 1,$$

and let $0 < \mu < 2\pi$. We will construct on the basis of the lemma a perfect, nowhere-dense set $P$, $mP = \mu$, such that for $\alpha > 0$

$$\frac{mCP(x, x+h)}{|h|} \leqslant \frac{|h|^{q-1}}{(|\ln|h||)^{q+\alpha}} \tag{21.4}$$

almost everywhere in $P$, provided $|h|$ is sufficiently small.

If $f_1(x) = f_2(x)$ in $P$, then the difference $f_1(x) - f_2(x) = 0$ in $P$. If we prove that from $f(x) = 0$ in $P$ it follows that $\sigma(f)$ converges to zero almost everywhere in $P$, then the theorem will be proved.

We will prove that if $\delta$ is sufficiently small, then at any point $x$ where (21.4) is fulfilled we will have

$$\int\limits_0^\delta \frac{|f(x \pm h) - f(x)|}{h} dh < +\infty. \tag{21.5}$$

Then applying the Dini test we see that $\sigma(f)$ converges at this point $x$, which means that $\sigma(f)$ will converge almost everywhere in $P$. The fact that it should converge to zero follows from $f(x) = 0$ in $P$ and from the fact that if the series $\sigma(\psi)$ converges in some set of positive measure, then it does so to $\psi(x)$ almost everywhere in this set (see Chapter I, § 48).

To prove (21.5) we will consider the expression $|f(x+h) - f(x)|$; the argument will be exactly similar for $|f(x-h) - f(x)|$.

Thus, let us consider

$$\int\limits_0^\delta \frac{|f(x+h) - f(x)|}{h} dh = \int\limits_x^{x+\delta} \left|\frac{f(y) - f(x)}{y - x}\right| dy.$$

Without upsetting the generality, it is possible to take $\delta < 1$ and to divide the interval $(x, x+\delta)$ into a sum of intervals of the form $(x + \delta^{n+1}, x + \delta^n)$ $(n = 1, 2, \ldots)$.

Let us denote for brevity's sake the part $CP$, lying in $(x + \delta^{n+1}, x + \delta^n)$ by $A_n$. Since $f(x) = 0$ in $P$, then

$$\int_{x+\delta^{n+1}}^{x+\delta^n} \left| \frac{|f(y) - f(x)|}{y - x} \right| dy = \int_{A_n} \frac{|f(y)|}{|y - x|} dy.$$

Applying Hölder's inequality, we find that

$$\int_{A_n} \frac{|f(y)|}{|y - x|} dy \leqslant \left\{ \int_{A_n} |f(y)|^p \, dy \right\}^{1/p} \left\{ \int_{A_n} \frac{dy}{|y - x|^q} \right\}^{1/q}$$

$$\leqslant M \left\{ \int_{A_n} \frac{dy}{|y - x|^q} \right\}^{1/q}, \qquad (21.6)$$

where $M = \left\{ \int_0^{2\pi} |f(y)|^p dy \right\}^{1/p}$. But $|y - x|^q \geqslant \delta^{(n+1)q}$, and therefore based on (21.4)

$$\int_{A_n} \frac{dy}{|y - x|^n} \leqslant \frac{mCP(x, x + \delta^n)}{\delta^{(n+1)q}} \leqslant \frac{\delta^{nq}}{\delta^{(n+1)q} (n\,|\ln \delta|)^{q+\alpha}} = \frac{C}{n^{q+\alpha}},$$

where $C$ depends only on $\delta$ and not on $n$, and then

$$\left( \int_{A_n} \frac{dy}{|y - x|^q} \right)^{1/q} \leqslant \frac{C^{1/q}}{n^{1+\frac{\alpha}{q}}},$$

and from (21.6) we obtain

$$\int_0^{\delta} \frac{|f(x + h) - f(x)|}{h} dh \leqslant M \sum_{n=1}^{\infty} \int_{A_n} \frac{|f(y)|}{|y - x|} dy \leqslant MC^{1/q} \sum_{n=1}^{\infty} \frac{1}{n^{1+\frac{\alpha}{q}}} < +\infty,$$

which concludes the proof of the theorem.

If $p = 1$, then the theorem ceases to be true. Indeed, if we operate on a result due to D.E. Men'shov which will be proved in Chapter VI, then it is possible to state further that: whatever the perfect nowhere-dense set $P$, it is possible to construct two summable functions $f_1(x)$ and $f_2(x)$ such that $f_1(x) = f_2(x)$ in $P$ and the Fourier series of $f_1(x)$ diverges almost everywhere in $[0, 2\pi]$, whilst the Fourier series of $f_2(x)$ converges almost everywhere in $[0, 2\pi]$. This result immediately follows from the existence of almost everywhere divergent Fourier series (see § 17) and from Men'shov's theorem (see Chapter VI, § 7); *for any summable $f(x)$ and for any perfect nowhere-dense set $P$ it is possible to find a summable $g(x)$ such that $g(x) = f(x)$ in $P$, yet the Fourier series of $g(x)$ converges almost everywhere.*

## § 22. Concerning the convergence of a Fourier series in a given set and its divergence outside it

We will pose the problem thus; let a set $E$ be given; under what conditions does a Fourier series exist which is convergent in $E$ and divergent in its complement $CE$?

First of all we note a number of cases where the solution of the problem is already known to us or can obtained readily. If $E$ coincides with the whole interval, then the solution is trivial; if $E$ is empty, i.e. $CE$ coincides with the whole interval, then the solution is given by the example constructed in § 20.

The case when $E$ is an interval of length less than $2\pi$ was considered by Steinhaus[2]; we will not discuss this, as it is possible to obtain the required result from a more general theorem due to Rajchman[1]: for any closed set $F$ it is possible to construct a trigonometric series convergent everywhere in $F$ and divergent everywhere in its complement. Rajchman, it is true, did not provide for his series being a Fourier series, simply adding to his argument a few words stating that it is possible to prove that the theorem is also true for a Fourier series.

For the proof of Rajchman's theorem we first construct a function $\Phi(x)$ for which the Fourier series diverges at every point (see § 20). Let

$$\sigma(\Phi) = \frac{a_0}{2} + \sum_{n=1}^{\infty} (a_n \cos nx + b_n \sin nx). \tag{22.1}$$

Let us also construct the function $\lambda(x)$ so that it equals zero in $F$, that it is positive in every interval $(\alpha_n, \beta_n)$ adjacent to $F$ and that it is continuous together with its derivatives up to the third order. For this it is sufficient, for example, to suppose that

$$\lambda_n(x) = \begin{cases} (x - \alpha_n)^4 (\beta_n - x)^4 & \text{in } (\alpha_n, \beta_n),\ n = 1, 2, \ldots, \\ 0 & \text{in } F \end{cases}$$

and

$$\lambda(x) = \sum_{n=1}^{\infty} \frac{1}{n^2} \lambda_n(x).$$

If

$$\lambda(x) = \gamma_0 + \sum (\gamma_n \cos nx + \delta_n \sin nx), \tag{22.2}$$

then

$$f(x) = \Phi(x)\, \lambda(x)$$

possesses a Fourier series which converges to zero at every point of $F$ and diverges at every point outside $F$; this follows from the fact that this Fourier series can be considered as the product of the series (22.1) and (22.2) of which the second possesses coefficients of the order $O(1/n^3)$ and converges to zero at every point of $F$; moreover, since $\lambda(x) \neq 0$ outside $F$, then the product diverges, since the series (22.1) diverges. All these results follow from the theorem concerning "the formal product" of two trigonometric series, since in the given case the formal product is transformed into the real product (see Chapter I, § 71).

Thus, Rajchman's theorem is proved, which means that for the case when $E$ is closed (in particular, when $E$ is an interval) the problem set is solved in the affirmative.

Before going any further we note that the problem posed at the beginning of this section must be solved differently, depending on whether we simply want to obtain divergence in $E$ or unbounded divergence, i.e. the fulfilment of the condition

$$\overline{\lim}\, |S_n(x)| = +\infty.$$

We have seen (see Chapter IV, § 19) that the set of points where the series of continuous functions diverges unboundedly is always a set of the type $G_\delta$, i.e. its complement is of the type $F_\sigma$.

Thus, it is possible to pose the question thus: does there exist for any set $E$ of type $F_\sigma$ a trigonometric series convergent everywhere in $E$ and unboundedly divergent everywhere in $CE$? And, in particular, does a Fourier series exist possessing this property?

An answer in the affirmative was given to the first question by S.B. Stechkin[4], operating on the results of Herzog and Piranian[1], who constructed a power series which was convergent in a given $E$ of type $F_\sigma$ lying on the circle of convergence and unboundedly divergent in $CE$.

But Stechkin did not aim at constructing a Fourier series satisfying the same conditions.

Later, Zeller answered the question concerning the Fourier series in the affirmative, that is, Zeller[1] proved the following theorem:

THEOREM. *Whatever is the set $E \subset [0, 2\pi]$ of type $F_\sigma$, it is possible to find a Fourier series which converges at every point of $E$ and is unboundedly divergent at every point of its complement $CE = [0, 2\pi] - E$.*

First of all, we require the following

LEMMA. *Let $[a, b]$ be an arbitrary interval, provided that $[a, b] \subset (0, 2\pi)$, and $[c, d] \subset (a, b)$; if $\varepsilon > 0$ is any positive value and $N$ is as large as desired, then there exists a trigonometric polynomial*

$$T_\varepsilon(x) = \sum_{k=p}^{q} (a_k \cos kx + b_k \sin kx),$$

*for which $q > p \geqslant N$ and the conditions are satisfied that;*

$$(1) \int_0^{2\pi} |T_\varepsilon(x)|\, dx < \varepsilon, \tag{22.3}$$

$$(2)\ |S_k(x, T_\varepsilon)| < \varepsilon,\ x \in [0, 2\pi] - [a, b],\quad k = 1, 2, \ldots, \tag{22.4}$$

(3) *for any $x \in [c, d]$ an index $k_x$ is found such that*

$$|S_{k_x}(x, T_\varepsilon)| > \frac{1}{\varepsilon}. \tag{22.5}$$

PROOF OF THE LEMMA. We know (see § 20) that a function $f(x)$ exists for which $\sigma(f)$ diverges unboundedly for every $x$ of $[0, 2\pi]$. Let us suppose that

$$f_1(x) = \begin{cases} f(x) & \text{for } x \in [c, d], \\ 0 & \text{for } x \in [0, 2\pi] - [c, d]. \end{cases}$$

From Riemann's principle of localization the series $\sigma(f)$ diverges unboundedly for $x \in [c, d]$ and converges for $x \in [0, 2\pi] - [c, d]$. We cannot say what happens at the points $c$ and $d$ themselves. If it appears that $\sigma(f_1)$ diverges unboundedly at them, then we suppose that

$$\varphi(x) = f_1(x).$$

If $\sigma(f_1)$ is not unboundedly divergent at one of these points or at both of them, then we assume that

$$\varphi(x) = f_1(x) + \tau(x),$$

where $\tau(x)$ is a continuous function for which $\sigma(\tau)$ diverges unboundedly at $c$ or at $d$ or at both these points (according to what we require) and converges everywhere at the remaining points. Moreover, we require that $\tau(x) = 0$ for $[0, 2\pi] - (c, d)$. The construction of such a function is possible (see Chapter I, § 46).

Thus we obtain $\varphi(x)$ such that it satisfies the conditions $\varphi(x) = 0$ at $x \in [0, 2\pi] - [c, d]$ and $\sigma(\varphi)$ diverges unboundedly in $[c, d]$. Multiplying $\varphi(x)$ by any constant $\lambda$, we obtain the function $\psi(x) = \lambda\varphi(x)$, for which again $\psi(x) = 0$ for $x \in [0, 2\pi] - [c, d]$ and $\sigma(\psi)$ diverges unboundedly in $[c, d]$. But thanks to the possibility of taking $\lambda$ as desired, we can make $\int_0^{2\pi} |\psi(x)|\, dx$ as we wish and, in particular,

$$\int_0^{2\pi} |\psi(x)|\, dx < \frac{\varepsilon\delta}{2^{16} N}, \tag{22.6}$$

where $\delta = \min[c - a, b - d, 1, a, 2\pi - b]$.

Since $\sigma(\psi)$ diverges unboundedly in $[c, d]$, then for any $x \in [c, d]$ and for any $M$ we find an index $n_x \geqslant N$ such that

$$|S_{n_x}(x, \psi)| > M. \tag{22.7}$$

In particular, this will be true for $M > 1/\varepsilon + \varepsilon$.

But $S_{n_x}(t, \psi)$ is a continuous function of $t$ for fixed $n_x$, which means that it is possible to find $\eta_x$ such that

$$|S_{n_x}(t, \psi)| > \frac{1}{\varepsilon} + \varepsilon \quad \text{for } x - \eta_x < t < x + \eta_x.$$

Thus, every point $x$ of the interval $[c, d]$ can be covered by the interval $(x - \eta_x, x + \eta_x)$, in which (22.7) is true. According to the Heine–Borel lemma it is possible to find a finite number of such intervals covering the whole of $[c, d]$. This means that it is possible to find $L$ such that for any $x \in [c, d]$ there exists an $n_x$, $N \leqslant n_x \leqslant L$, such that (22.7) holds for it.

We see that the function $\psi(x)$ possesses, figuratively speaking, a "small" integral (see (22.6)), "large" partial sums in $[c, d]$ (see (22.7)) and equals zero outside $[c, d]$ which means that this is all the more true outside $[a, b]$. We now show that it is possible to express it approximately by a trigonometric polynomial which thanks to the given properties of $\psi(x)$ satisfies all the requirements of the lemma.

First we find a function $\alpha(x)$ which is periodic and continuous, its derivative $\alpha'(x)$ also being periodic and continuous, such that $\alpha(x) = 0$ for $x \in [0, 2\pi] - [c, d]$ and

$$\int_0^{2\pi} |\psi(x) - \alpha(x)|\, dx < \frac{\varepsilon\delta}{2^{16}L}. \tag{22.8}$$

Because $\int_0^{2\pi} \alpha'(x)\, dx = \alpha(2\pi) - \alpha(0) = 0$, the free term in the series $\sigma(\alpha')$ equals zero, which means that it is possible to approximate to it within any degree of accuracy by means of a trigonometric polynomial $\beta(x)$ with free term equal to zero; for example, the Fejér sum of order $m$ for the series $\sigma(\alpha')$, where $m$ is taken sufficiently large. In this it is possible, without upsetting the generality, to consider $m \geqslant L$.

Let

$$|\alpha'(x) - \beta(x)| < \frac{\varepsilon\delta}{2^{16}L}, \qquad 0 \leqslant x \leqslant 2\pi. \tag{22.9}$$

Since $\beta(x)$ possesses a free term equal to zero, then supposing that

$$\gamma(x) = \int_0^x \beta(t)\, dt, \tag{22.10}$$

we see that $\gamma(x)$ is also a trigonometric polynomial; let

$$\gamma(x) = \sum_{k=0}^{m} (a_k \cos kx + b_k \sin kx), \quad m \geqslant L.$$

Let us prove that the polynomial

$$T_\varepsilon(x) = \sum_{k=N}^{m} (a_k \cos kx + b_k \sin kx)$$

satisfies all the conditions of the lemma.

For this, we note first of all that for $x \in [0, 2\pi] - [c, d]$ we have $\alpha(x) = 0$, which means that $\alpha'(x) = 0$ also and therefore it follows from (22.9) that

$$|\gamma'(x)| = |\beta(x)| < \frac{\varepsilon\delta}{2^{16}L} \quad \text{in } [0, 2\pi] - [c, d]. \tag{22.11}$$

Moreover, from (22.9) and (22.10)

$$|\alpha(x) - \gamma(x)| \leqslant \int_0^x |\alpha'(t) - \beta(t)|\, dt \leqslant 2\pi \frac{\varepsilon\delta}{2^{16}L} < \frac{\varepsilon\delta}{2^{13}L}, \tag{22.12}$$

whence

$$|\gamma(x)| \leqslant \frac{\varepsilon\delta}{2^{13}L} \quad \text{for} \quad x \in [0, 2\pi] - [c, d], \tag{22.13}$$

since then $\alpha(x) = 0$. Also from (22.12)

$$\int_0^{2\pi} |\alpha(t) - \gamma(t)|\, dt \leqslant \frac{\varepsilon\delta}{2^{13}L} 2\pi < \frac{\varepsilon\delta}{2^{10}L}. \tag{22.14}$$

Combining (22.8) and (22.14) we find that

$$\int_0^{2\pi} |\psi(t) - \gamma(t)|\, dt \leqslant \frac{\varepsilon\delta}{2^{16}L} + \frac{\varepsilon\delta}{2^{10}L} < \frac{\varepsilon\delta}{2^{9}L}. \tag{22.15}$$

If it is now taken into account that $L > N$ and if (22.15) and (22.6) are compared, then we obtain

$$\int_0^{2\pi} |\gamma(t)|\, dt < \frac{\varepsilon\delta}{2^{16}N} + \frac{\varepsilon\delta}{2^{9}N} < \frac{\varepsilon\delta}{2^{8}N}. \tag{22.16}$$

We now note that

$$T_\varepsilon(x) = \gamma(x) - \sum_{k=0}^{N-1} (a_k \cos kx + b_k \sin kx) = \gamma(x) - S_{N-1}(x, \gamma), \tag{22.17}$$

and since

$$S_{N-1}(x, \gamma) < (2N - 1) \int_0^{2\pi} |\gamma(x)|\, dx < \frac{\varepsilon}{2^7}, \tag{22.18}$$

then

$$|T_\varepsilon(x)| \leqslant |\gamma(x)| + \frac{\varepsilon}{2^7}$$

and consequently

$$\int_0^{2\pi} |T_\varepsilon(x)|\, dx \leqslant \int_0^{2\pi} |\gamma(x)|\, dx + \frac{\varepsilon}{2^7} 2\pi < \frac{\varepsilon}{2^8 N} + \frac{\varepsilon}{2^4} < \frac{\varepsilon}{2^3},$$

which means that all the more so

$$\int_0^{2\pi} |T_\varepsilon(x)|\, dx < \varepsilon$$

and, consequently, condition (1) which should be satisfied by the polynomial $T_\varepsilon(x)$ is satisfied.

In order to prove that condition (2) also holds, we first estimate $S_n(x, \gamma)$ for all $n$ and for $x \in [0, 2\pi] - [a, b]$.

We have

$$S_n(x, \gamma) = \frac{1}{\pi} \int_0^{2\pi} \gamma(t)\, D_n(t - x)\, dt = \frac{1}{\pi} \int_{x-\delta}^{2\pi+(x-\delta)} \gamma(t)\, D_n(x - t)\, dt$$

$$= \frac{1}{\pi} \int_{x-\delta}^{x+\delta} \gamma(t)\, D_n(x - t)\, dt + \frac{1}{\pi} \int_{x+\delta}^{2\pi+x-\delta} \gamma(t)\, D_n(x - t)\, dt = I_1(x) + I_2(x). \tag{22.19}$$

Since

$$\int_0^t D_n(u)\,du = \frac{t}{2} + \sum_{k=1}^{n} \frac{\sin kt}{k},$$

and

$$\left| \sum_{k=1}^{n} \frac{\sin kt}{k} \right| \leqslant \pi + 2$$

(see Chapter I, § 30) then

$$\left| \int_{t_1}^{t_2} D_n(u)\,du \right| \leqslant \pi + 2(\pi + 2) < 2^4 \quad \text{for} \quad 0 \leqslant t_1 \leqslant t_2 \leqslant 2\pi, \tag{22.20}$$

and, therefore, carrying out integration by parts for $I_1(x)$ we find from (22.11) and (22.13) that

$$|I_1(x)| = \left| \frac{1}{\pi} \gamma(t) \int_{x-\delta}^{t} D_n(t-x)\,dt \Bigg|_{x-\delta}^{x+\delta} - \frac{1}{\pi} \int_{x-\delta}^{x+\delta} \gamma'(t) \left( \int_{x-\delta}^{t} D_n(u-x)\,du \right) dt \right|$$

$$\leqslant \frac{1}{\pi} \frac{2\varepsilon\delta}{2^{13}L} 2^4 + \frac{1}{\pi} \frac{\varepsilon\delta}{2^{16}L} 2^4\, 2\delta < \frac{\varepsilon}{\pi 2^8 L} + \frac{\varepsilon}{2^{12}L} < \frac{\varepsilon}{2^9}. \tag{22.21}$$

Here we have the right to use (22.11) and (22.13), since for $x \in [0, 2\pi] - [a, b]$ and for $\delta = \min[a, c-a, b-d, 2\pi - b]$ for $x - \delta \leqslant t \leqslant x + \delta$ the point $t \bar{\in} [c, d]$.

Also we have due to (22.16)

$$|I_2(x)| = \left| \frac{1}{\pi} \int_{x+\delta}^{2\pi+(x-\delta)} \gamma(t) \frac{\sin\left(n + \frac{1}{2}\right)(t-x)}{2 \sin \frac{t-x}{2}}\,dt \right| \leqslant \frac{1}{2\pi \sin \frac{\delta}{2}} \int_0^{2\pi} |\gamma(t)|\,dt$$

$$< \frac{1}{2\delta} \frac{\varepsilon\delta}{2^8 N} < \frac{\varepsilon}{2^9 N} < \frac{\varepsilon}{2^9}, \tag{22.22}$$

and therefore from (22.19), (22.21) and (22.22)

$$|S_n(x, \gamma)| < \frac{\varepsilon}{2^8} \quad \text{for} \quad x \in [0, 2\pi] - [a, b]. \tag{22.23}$$

Let us continue with the estimate of $S_n(x, T_\varepsilon)$. If $n \leqslant N - 1$, then $S_n(x, T_\varepsilon) \equiv 0$, because in the polynomial $T_\varepsilon(x)$ the coefficients $a_k$ and $b_k$ equal zero at $k \leqslant N - 1$. If $n > N - 1$, then from (22.17) it is evident that

$$S_n(x, T_\varepsilon) = S_n(x, \gamma) - S_{N-1}(x, \gamma),$$

and therefore due to (22.23) and (22.18)

$$|S_n(x, T_\varepsilon)| \leqslant |S_n(x, \gamma) - S_{N-1}(x, \gamma)| \leqslant \frac{\varepsilon}{2^8} + \frac{\varepsilon}{2^7} < \frac{\varepsilon}{2^6} \quad \text{in} \quad [0, 2\pi] - [a, b],$$

i.e. condition (2) is also fulfilled.

Let us return to condition (3). Let $x \in [c, d]$. Due to (22.7) for this $x$ there is found an $n_x$, $N \leqslant n_x \leqslant L$, such that

$$|S_{n_x}(x, \psi)| > \frac{1}{\varepsilon} + \varepsilon.$$

But

$$|S_{n_x}(x, \gamma)| \geqslant |S_{n_x}(x, \psi)| - |S_{n_x}(x, \gamma - \psi)|, \tag{22.24}$$

and due to (22.15)

$$S_{n_x}(x, \gamma - \psi)| \leqslant (2n_x + 1)\frac{1}{\pi}\int_0^{2\pi} |\gamma - \psi|\, dt \leqslant (2L + 1)\frac{1}{\pi}\frac{\varepsilon\delta}{2^9 L} < \frac{\varepsilon}{2^9}, \tag{22.25}$$

which means that from (22.24) and (22.25)

$$|S_{n_x}(x, \gamma)| > \frac{1}{\varepsilon} + \varepsilon - \frac{\varepsilon}{2^9}.$$

Finally, from (22.17) due to $n_x \geqslant N$ and (22.18)

$$|S_{n_x}(T_\varepsilon)| > |S_{n_x}(x, \gamma)| - |S_{N-1}(x, \gamma)| > \frac{1}{\varepsilon} + \varepsilon - \frac{\varepsilon}{2^9} - \frac{\varepsilon}{2^7} > \frac{1}{\varepsilon},$$

which also means that condition (3) is fulfilled.

The lemma is completely proved.

Let us continue with the proof of the Zeller theorem. Let $E$ be a given set of type $F_\sigma$. If $E$ is an empty set, then the problem is solved by Kolmogorov's example (see § 20). If $E$ were to contain one point then it is possible to transfer it to the origin of

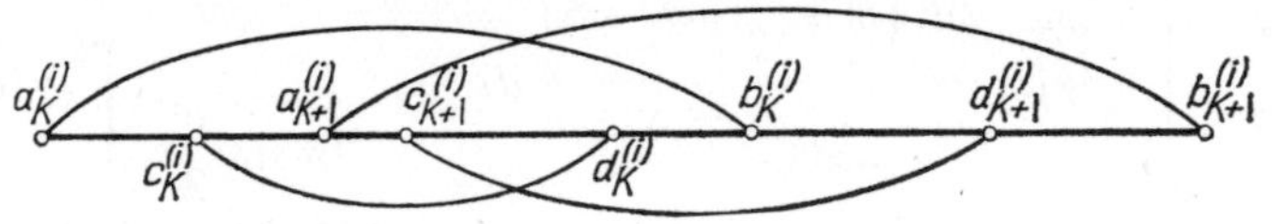


FIG. 25

the coordinates. Then $CE \subset (0, 2\pi)$. Since $CE$ is of type $G_\delta$, then, without upsetting the generality, it is possible to consider it as composed of open sets $G_i$ which satisfy the condition

$$G_1 \supset G_2 \supset \cdots \supset G_i \supset \cdots.$$

Thus, let $CE = \prod_{n=1}^{\infty} G_i$ where the sets $G_i$ satisfy this requirement.

Every open set is the sum of not more than a denumerable set of intervals. Any interval can be represented in the form of a sum of a denumerable set of sub-intervals, whilst it is possible to choose them so that any point of the interval belongs to not more than two such sub-intervals. Therefore, every $G_i$ can be represented in the form of a sum of a denumerable set of sub-intervals $[a_k^{(i)}, b_k^{(i)}]$ $(k = 1, 2, \ldots)$ whilst any point $x \in G_i$ belongs to not more than two such sub-intervals.

Inside every such $[a_k^{(i)}, b_k^{(i)}]$ we locate a sub-interval $[c_k^{(i)}, d_k^{(i)}]$ choosing it so that every point $x \in G_i$ falls without fail into some $[c_k^{(i)}, d_k^{(i)}]$, but not into more than two such sub-intervals (Fig. 25).

If this is so, then arranging all the $[a_k^{(i)}, b_k^{(i)}]$ into one sequence, say simply $[a_j, b_j]$ $(j = 1, 2, \ldots)$, and the $[c_k^{(i)}, d_k^{(i)}]$ contained in them into the sequence $[c_j, d_j]$ (the enumeration for $[c, d]$ is carried out according to the same rule as for $[a, b]$, so that $[c_j, d_j] \subset (a_j, b_j)$) we see that any point of $CE$ belongs to an infinite set $[c_j, d_j]$, but on the other hand any point $x \in E$, due to $G_i$ being enclosed in one another, cannot enter into an infinite set $G_i$ (otherwise it would enter into $CE$), and then it can belong only to a finite value of $[a_j, b_j]$, i.e. if $x \in E$, then $x \bar{\in} [a_j, b_j]$ for all sufficiently large $j$.

Now we will apply our lemma. For any $j$ it is possible to find a trigonometric polynomial $T_j(x)$ for which

$$(1) \int_0^{2\pi} |T_j(x)|\, dx < \frac{1}{2^j},$$

$$(2)\ |S_k(x, T_j)| < \frac{1}{2^j} \quad \text{for} \quad x \in [0, 2\pi] - [a_j, b_j],\ k = 1, 2, \ldots,$$

(3) for any $x \in [c_j, d_j]$ an index $k_x$ is found such that

$$|S_{k_x}(x, T_j)| > 2^j.$$

Moreover, we require nothing of the polynomial $T_1(x)$, but the remaining $T_j(x)$ are constructed recurrently thus: when the polynomial $T_{j-1}(x)$ is already found and consequently its power $m_{j-1}$ is known, $T_j(x)$ must be chosen so that its coefficients differing from zero possess indices exceeding $m_{j-1}$ (i.e. the role $N$ in our lemma should be played by the value $m_{j-1} + 1$).

Let us now construct the series

$$\sum_{j=1}^{\infty} T_j(x).$$

It should converge almost everywhere to some summable function $f(x)$, because

$$\sum_{j=1}^{\infty} \int_0^{2\pi} |T_j(x)|\, dx < \sum_{j=1}^{\infty} \frac{1}{2^j} < +\infty.$$

Let us denote by $T$ the series which is obtained from $\sum_{j=1}^{\infty} T_j(x)$, if the order of the terms is maintained, but every term in any polynomial $T_j(x)$ is considered as a separate term of the series $T$ (and not grouped, by combining them in the polynomial $T_j(x)$).

Due to the choice of polynomials $T_j(x)$ the series $T$ is a normal trigonometric series (i.e. in it every $\cos kx$ and $\sin kx$ is encountered not more than once) and it is easy to prove that it is a Fourier series of $f(x)$ (the argument is the same as in the construction of the divergent series in the example of § 19).

Therefore the convergence or divergence of the Fourier series of $f(x)$ at any point is determined by the convergence or divergence of the series $T$ at this point. We will show that it converges at every point of $E$ and diverges unboundedly at every point of $CE$.

Indeed, let $x \in E$, which means that $x \bar{\in} CE$. Therefore $i(x)$ is found such that $x \bar{\in} [a_j, b_j]$ for all $j > i(x)$. But then due to the construction of the polynomials $T_j(x)$ we have

$$|S_k(x, T_j)| < \frac{1}{2^j} \quad \text{for all } k \text{ and for } \quad j \geqslant i(x). \tag{22.26}$$

Let $\varepsilon > 0$ be any value. Then $N$ is found such that $N \geqslant i(x)$ and

$$\sum_{k=N}^{\infty} \frac{1}{2^k} < \frac{\varepsilon}{2}. \tag{22.27}$$

Let us consider the difference

$$S_{k+p}(x, f) - S_k(x, f)$$

for $k \geqslant N$ and $p > 0$. We have

$$S_{k+p}(x, f) - S_k(x, f) = \sum_{j=1}^{N-1} [S_{k+p}(x, T_j) - S_k(x, T_j)]$$

$$+ \sum_{j=N}^{\infty} S_{k+p}(x, T_j) - \sum_{f=N}^{\infty} S_k(x, T_j).$$

Due to (22.26) and (22.27)

$$\sum_{j=N}^{\infty} |S_{k+p}(x, T_j)| < \frac{\varepsilon}{2} \quad \text{and} \quad \sum_{j=N}^{\infty} |S_k(x, T_j)| < \frac{\varepsilon}{2}.$$

Consequently

$$|S_{k+p}(x, f) - S_k(x, f)| \leqslant \sum_{j=1}^{N-1} |S_{k+p}(x, T_j) - S_k(x, T_j)| + \varepsilon.$$

If $\tau$ is a trigonometric polynomial, there exists $N_0$ such that

$$S_n(\tau, x) = \tau(x) \quad \text{for} \quad n \geqslant N_0,$$

and therefore it is possible to find $N_1$ such that

$$S_n(x, T_j) = T_j(x) \quad \text{for} \quad n \geqslant N_1$$

and for all $j, j = 1, 2, \ldots, N_1 - 1$.

Therefore, if $N_2 = \max(N_1, N)$ is taken, then

$$S_{k+p}(x, T_j) - S_k(x, T_j) = 0 \quad \text{for} \quad k \geqslant N_2, \quad p > 0,$$

whence

$$|S_{k+p}(x, f) - S_k(x, f)| < \varepsilon,$$

which means that from Cauchy's criterion the series converges at the point $x$.

If $x \in CE$, then $x \in [c_j, d_j]$ for an infinite set of values of $j$. From the properties of the polynomials $T_j$, then a sequence of values $k_j(x)$ is found such that

$$|S_{k_j}(x, T_j)| > 2^j,$$

i.e. in the series there is an infinite set of sections the absolute magnitude of each of which increases with increase in $j$, and therefore the series diverges unboundedly.

The theorem is completely proved.

We now note that Zeller's theorem gives a solution of the search for a Fourier series convergent in any $E$ of type $F_\sigma$ and unboundedly divergent in $CE$.

If we pose the problem thus: what should be the structure of $E$ for a Fourier series (or in general a trigonometric series) to exist which is convergent in $E$ and divergent in $CE$, but without requiring unbounded divergence, then it seems that $E$ will be of a more complicated nature, namely of the type $F_{\sigma\delta}$. Indeed, it is easy to prove the validity of the following theorem:

THEOREM. *If the functions $f_n(x)$ are all continuous in some interval $[a, b]$, then the set of points of convergence of the sequence $f_n(x)$ is a set of type $F_{\sigma\delta}$.*

*Proof.* For any natural $n$, $m$ and $k$ we define the set

$$F^{(k)}_{n,m} = E\left\{|f_n(x) - f_m(x)| \leqslant \frac{1}{k}\right\}.$$

Due to the continuity of the functions $f_n(x)$ it is clear that $F^{(k)}_{n,m}$ is closed. If we assume that

$$F^{(k)}_m = \prod_{n=m+1}^{\infty} F^{(k)}_{n,m},$$

then $F^{(k)}_m$ will also be closed and therefore

$$E^{(k)} = \sum_{m=1}^{\infty} F^{(k)}_m$$

will be a set of type $F_\sigma$. Finally

$$E = \prod_{k=1}^{\infty} E^{(k)}$$

will be a set of type $F_{\sigma\delta}$. Let us prove that $E$ is a set of convergence for the sequence $f_n(x)$.

In fact, let $x \in E$. Then $x_0 \in E^{(k)}$ $(k = 1, 2, \ldots)$; for any $\varepsilon > 0$ it is possible to find $k_0$ such that $1/k_0 < \varepsilon$. Since $x_0 \in E^{(k_0)}$, then $x_0 \in F^{[k_0]}_m$ for some $m_0$, which means that $x_0 \in F^{(k)}_{nm_0}$ for $n > m_0$. Consequently

$$|f_n(x_0) - f_m(x_0)| < \varepsilon \quad \text{for} \quad n > m_0,$$

which means that the sequence $f_n(x)$ converges at $x = x_0$.

Conversely, if $f_n(x)$ converges at $x = x_0$, then for any $\varepsilon > 0$ it is possible to find $m_0$ such that $|f_n(x_0) - f_{m_0}(x_0)| < \varepsilon$; in particular, for any $k$ it is possible to find $m_0$ such that $|f_n(x_0) - f_m(x_0)| < 1/k$ for $n > m \geqslant m_0$. Consequently, for any $k$ we will have $x_0 \in F^{(k)}_{n,m}$ for $m > m_0$ and $n > m$, i.e. $x_0 \in F^{(k)}_m$, which also means $x_0 \in E^{(k)}$ and therefore $x \in E$.

Thus, $E$ is a set of convergence for the sequence $f_n(x)$.

It is possible to prove the reverse theorem, namely:

THEOREM. *If $E$ is an arbitrary set of type $F_{\sigma\delta}$, lying in $[a, b]$, then it is possible to find a sequence of functions continuous in $[a, b]$, which are all bounded, such that it converges to zero in $E$ and diverges boundedly everywhere outside $E$ in $[a, b]$.*

The proof can be found in reports by Hahn[1] and Sierpinski[1].

However, this problem is solved for the case when only continuity is required of the function $f_n(x)$. If we require them to be the partial sums of a trigonometric series, then this problem becomes very difficult. It has not yet been solved even for a general trigonometric series and this is all the more true for a Fourier series.

A number of interesting remarks and statements of problems concerning sets of points of convergence and divergence of a trigonometric series can be found in a report by Ul'yanov[8].

## § 23. The problem of convergence and the principle of localization for Fourier series with rearranged terms

We see in § 19 that neither the Kolmogorov example nor the Marcinkiewicz example solve the problem of whether there exists a function $f(x) \in L^p$ $(p > 1)$ for which the Fourier series diverges almost everywhere. The question of the existence of these functions remains open. But it is interesting to note that if a rearrangement of the terms of a Fourier series is permitted, then it is possible to attain divergence of these functions almost everywhere.

More precisely, we have

THE UL'YANOV[9] THEOREM. *If $f(x) \in L^p\,(0, 2\pi)$ $(1 \leqslant p < 2)$ and $f(x) \notin L^2(0, \pi)$, then in the Fourier series $\sigma(f)$*

$$\frac{a_0}{2} + \sum_{n=1}^{\infty} (a_n \cos nx + b_n \sin nx) \tag{23.1}$$

*it is possible to rearrange the terms in such a way that the newly obtained series*

$$\frac{a_0}{2} + \sum_{\nu=1}^{\infty} a_{m_\nu} \cos m_\nu x + b_{m_\nu} \sin m_\nu x) \tag{23.2}$$

*diverges† unboundedly almost everywhere in* $[0, 2\pi]$.

*Proof.* Without upsetting the generality, it is possible to suppose that $b_k = 0$ $(k = 0, 1, 2, \ldots)$. Since $f(x) \notin L^2$, then $\sum a_n^2 = +\infty$, and therefore the series

$$\frac{a_0}{2} + \sum_{n=1}^{\infty} a_n \cos nx\, \varphi_n(t_0), \tag{23.3}$$

where $\varphi_n(t)$ are Rademacher functions, for almost all values of $t_0$ is unboundedly divergent almost everywhere with respect to $x$ (see Chapter II, § 8, Note 1). We will choose only one such $t_0$ and take it to be irrational, then $\varphi_n(t_0) \neq 0$ for any $n$. Let us denote by $n_i$ those $n$ for which $\varphi_n(t_0) = +1$, and by $k_i$ those $n$ for which $\varphi_n(t_0) = -1$. Then the series (23.3) is divided into two series

$$\frac{a_0}{2} + \sum_{i=1}^{\infty} a_{n_i} \cos n_i x \quad \text{and} \quad -\sum_{i=1}^{\infty} a_{k_i} \cos k_i x. \tag{23.4}$$

Let $E$ be a set of points of $(0, 2\pi)$, in which the series (23.3) diverges unboundedly, let $A$ be a set of points in $(0, 2\pi)$ where the first of the series (23.4) diverges and $B = E - A$. It is clear that $mA + mB = mE = 2\pi$. Without upsetting the general-

† It is possible even to provide for the series (23.2) not to be summable by the Toeplitz method.

ity, we assume that $mA > 0$ and $mB > 0$. In the opposite case the proof is only simplified.

Let $\varepsilon > 0$ be an integer, $N \geqslant 0$ and $D > 0$ be arbitrary values. Let us take a perfect set $P_\varepsilon \subset A, mP_\varepsilon > mA - \varepsilon$. Since the first series in (23.4) diverges unboundedly in $A$, then for any $x \in P_\varepsilon$ it is possible to find $\varphi(x)$ such that

$$\left|\sum_{i=N+1}^{\varphi(x)} a_{n_i} \cos n_i x\right| > D. \tag{23.5}$$

But $\cos n_i x$ is a continuous function and therefore, an interval $\delta_x$ is found with centre at $x$, for each point of which (23.5) is valid. This means that the set $P_\varepsilon$ is covered by a system of intervals and according to the Heine–Borel lemma it is possible to isolate from them a finite number covering $P_\varepsilon$. Then from (23.5) the existence follows of $L(\varepsilon, N, D)$ such that

$$\left|\sum_{i=N+1}^{L(x)} a_{n_i} \cos n_i x\right| > D \quad \text{for any} \quad x \in P_\varepsilon \quad \text{and} \quad L(x) \leqslant L(\varepsilon, N, D). \tag{23.6}$$

Similarly, it is possible to take a perfect set $Q_\varepsilon \subset B, mQ_\varepsilon > mB - \varepsilon$, and to find a value $M(\varepsilon, N, D)$ such that

$$\left|\sum_{i=N+1}^{M(x)} a_{k_i} \cos k_i x\right| > D \quad \text{for any} \quad x \in Q_\varepsilon \quad \text{and} \quad M(x) \leqslant M(\varepsilon, N, D). \tag{23.7}$$

Let us take the sequence $\varepsilon_i = 1/i$, $D_i = i$. We will suppose that $N_1 = N = 0$ and let $\tau_1 = L(\varepsilon_1, 0, 1)$. From (23.6) we have

$$\left|\sum_{i=1}^{\varphi(x)} a_{n_i} \cos n_i x\right| > 1 \quad \text{for} \quad x \in P_{\varepsilon_1}, \ L(x) \leqslant \tau_1. \tag{23.8}$$

Let us assume that

$$m_\nu = n_\nu \quad \text{for} \quad 1 \leqslant \nu \leqslant \tau_1. \tag{23.9}$$

Due to (23.7) we can for the values $\varepsilon = \varepsilon_1$, $N_1 = 0$, $D = 1$ find a set $Q_{\varepsilon_1} \in B$, $mQ_{\varepsilon_1} > mB - \varepsilon_1$ and the quantity $\mu_1 = M(\varepsilon_1, 0, 1)$, such that

$$\left|\sum_{i=1}^{M(x)} a_{k_i} \cos k_i x\right| > 1 \quad \text{for any} \quad x \in Q_{\varepsilon_1} \quad \text{and} \quad M(x) \leqslant \mu_1. \tag{23.10}$$

Let us assume that

$$m_{\nu+\tau_1} = k_\nu \quad \text{for} \quad 1 \leqslant \nu \leqslant \mu_1. \tag{23.11}$$

Also, due to (23.6) for $\varepsilon = \varepsilon_2 = \frac{1}{2}$, $N = \tau_1$ and $D = 2$ we can find a set $P_{\varepsilon_2} \in A$, $mP_{\varepsilon_2} > mA - \varepsilon_2$ and the quantity $\tau_2 = L(\varepsilon_2, \tau_1, 2)$ such that

$$\left|\sum_{i=\tau_1+1}^{L(x)} a_{n_i} \cos n_i x\right| > 2 \quad \text{for any} \quad x \in P_{\varepsilon_2} \quad \text{and} \quad L(x) \leqslant \tau_2. \tag{23.12}$$

Let us suppose that

$$m_{\nu+\mu_1} = n_\nu, \quad \tau_1 + 1 \leqslant \nu \leqslant \tau_2, \tag{23.13}$$

etc. The numbers $m_\nu$ are determined by induction.

We will now consider the series

$$\frac{a_0}{2} + \sum_{\nu=1}^{\infty} a_{m_\nu} \cos m_\nu x = \frac{a_0}{2} + \sum_{k=0}^{\infty} \left( \sum_{i=\tau_k+1}^{\tau_{k+1}} a_{n_i} \cos n_i x + \sum_{i=\mu_k+1}^{\mu_{k+1}} a_{k_i} \cos k_i x \right) \tag{23.14}$$

(here $\tau_0 = \mu_0 = 0$, but within every sum in the curved brackets the indices $n_i$ and $k_i$ occur in increasing order).

The theorem will be proved, if we prove the divergence almost everywhere for the series on the left-hand side of (23.14).

We will assume that

$$A_0 = \overline{\lim_{k\to\infty}} P_{\varepsilon_k} \quad \text{and} \quad B_0 = \overline{\lim_{k\to\infty}} Q_{\varepsilon_k}.$$

It is clear that $A_0 \subset A$, $mA_0 = mA$, $B_0 \subset B$, $mB_0 = mB$, $mA_0 + mB_0 = 2\pi$. We will prove the unbounded divergence of the series

$$\frac{a_0}{2} + \sum_{\nu=1}^{\infty} a_{m_\nu} \cos m_\nu x \tag{23.15}$$

at every point of $A_0 + B_0$; then it will diverge unboundedly almost everywhere.

It is sufficient to prove this for $A_0$, since the proof for $B_0$ is similar.

If $x \in A_0$, then for an infinite set of values of $k$ we have $x \in P_{\varepsilon_k}$. But then from the very definition of the values $\tau_k$ and the sets $P_{\varepsilon_k}$ it follows that

$$\left| \sum_{i=\tau_k+1}^{L(x)} a_{n_i} \cos n_i x \right| > k, \quad \text{where} \quad \tau_k + 1 \leqslant L(x) \leqslant \tau_{k+1}.$$

Thus, for an infinite set of values of $k$ in the series (23.15) there are "sections" with modulus exceeding $k$, i.e. it diverges unboundedly for $x \in A_0$. This concludes the proof.

We will note that the series (23.15) is a Fourier series for $f(x)$ with respect to the system $\{\cos m_i x\}$. This permits the following interesting corollary to be drawn from Ul'yanov's theorem:

COROLLARY. *If instead of a normal trigonometric system, the same system is considered with the terms rearranged, then the principle of localization for Fourier series cannot hold.*

Indeed, let us construct the function $f(x)$ thus (Fig. 26):

$$f(x) = \begin{cases} \dfrac{1}{\sqrt{x}} e^{-\frac{1}{(x-1)^2}}, & 0 < x < 1, \\ 0, \; x = 0, & 1 \leqslant x \leqslant \pi, \\ f(-x), & -\pi \leqslant x < 0, \end{cases}$$

$$f(x + 2\pi) = f(x) \quad \text{for all} \quad x.$$

It is clear that $f(x) = 0$ for $x \in [1, 2\pi - 1]$,

$$f(x) \in L^p(0, 2\pi) \quad \text{for} \quad 1 \leqslant p < 2 \quad \text{and} \quad f(x) \,\bar{\in}\, L^2(0, 2\pi).$$

From Ul'yanov's theorem it follows that it is possible in the Fourier series for $f(x)$ to rearrange the terms so that the series obtained, $a_0/2 + \sum a_{m_i} \cos m_i x$, diverges unboundedly almost everywhere in $(0, 2\pi)$ which means, in particular, almost everywhere in $(1, 2\pi - 1)$. But this series will be a Fourier series of $f(x)$ with respect to the orthogonal system obtained from the trigonometric by a corresponding re-

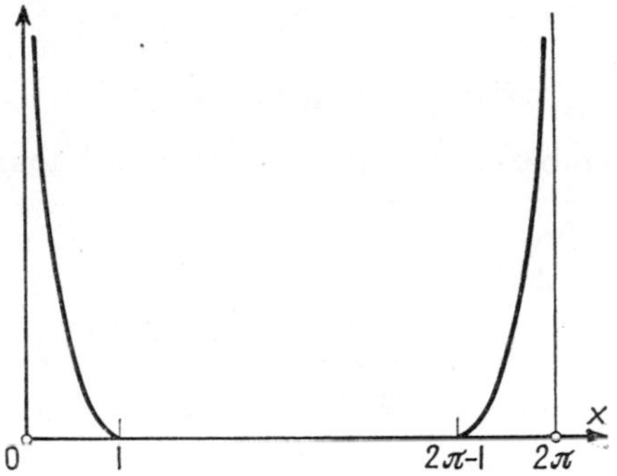


FIG. 26

arrangement of terms. On the other hand, the resolution of zero according to this system should give a series convergent everywhere to zero; the principle of localization is thus broken. In this it is interesting to note that here $f(x)$ possesses derivatives of all orders in $(0, 2\pi)$, and $p$ can be any value, provided $1 \leqslant p < 2$.

We refer the attention of the reader to the reports by Ul'yanov[12],[13], where a number of theorems are proved referring to systems obtained from a trigonometric system by rearrangement of its terms.

## § 24. Problems

1. A function $f(x) \in C(0, 2\pi)$ exists, the Fourier series of which possesses an infinite number of points of divergence in $[0, 2\pi]$ although

$$\sum_{n=1}^{\infty} [a_n^2(f) + b_n^2(f)] \ln n < \infty, \tag{24.1}$$

where $a_n(f)$ and $b_n(f)$ are Fourier coefficients of the function $f$.

[First construct the function $\varphi(x) \in C(0, 2\pi)$ with $\omega(\delta, \varphi) = O\{(\ln(1/\delta))^{-3/4}\}$, the Fourier series of which diverges at one point of $[0, 2\pi]$. Then, by the method of condensation of singularities, construct the function $f(x) \in C(0, 2\pi)$ with $\omega(\delta, f) = O\{(\ln(1/\delta))^{-3/4}\}$, the Fourier series of which possesses an infinite number of points of divergence in $[0, 2\pi]$. But if $\omega(\delta, f) = O\{(\ln(1/\delta))^{-3/4}\}$, then

$$\int_0^{2\pi}\int_0^{2\pi} \frac{|f(x+t) + f(x-t) - 2f(x)|^2}{t}\, dt\, dx < \infty,$$

which also implies (24.1) (see § 5).]

2. Construct the function $f(x) \in C(0, 2\pi)$, the Fourier series of which converges absolutely at all points $x \in (-\infty, +\infty)$ although

$$\sum_{n=1}^{\infty} [a_n^2(f) + b_n^2(f)] \ln n = \infty$$

$$\left[\text{Assume } f(x) = \sum_{n=1}^{\infty} \frac{1}{n^2} \cos 2^{2^n} x \text{ (compare with problem 7 of § 26, Chapter IV).}\right]$$

3. Prove that a measurable set $E \subset (0, 2\pi)$ exists such that

$$\sum_{n=1}^{\infty} [a_n^2(f) + b_n^2(f)] \ln n = \infty,$$

where $f(x) = 1$ for $x \in E$ and $f(x) = 0$ for $x \in [0, 2\pi] - E$.

[It is known (see Lusin, A.16, p. 464) that a characteristic function $f(x)$ exists of some set $E$ for which

$$\int_0^{\delta} \frac{|f(x+t) - f(x-t)|}{t} dt = \infty \text{ for almost all } x.$$

Therefore

$$\int_0^{2\pi} \int_0^{2\pi} \frac{|f(x+t) - f(x-t)|^2}{t} dt\, dx = \infty,$$

which proves our statement (also see § 5).]

4. Construct a measurable set $E \subset (0, 2\pi)$ such that for the characteristic function $f(x)$ ($f(x) = 1$ for $x \in E$ and $f(x) = 0$ for $x \in [0, 2\pi] - E$) the Fourier series possesses a set of points of divergence which is everywhere dense in $[0, 2\pi]$.

[The set of problem 14, Chapter I, § 73 can be taken for $E$. Use Baire's theorem and the fact that the characteristic function of our set $E$ is essentially discontinuous everywhere (i.e. it is not possible to adjust the function $f(x)$ in a set of measure zero so that it becomes continuous even at one point.]

5. Prove that whatever numerical sequence $\omega(n) \uparrow \infty$ is given, the trigonometric system $\{\cos nx, \sin nx\}$ can be enumerated in another order $\{\cos p_n x, \sin p_n x\}$ (the integers $p_n$ pass through the whole natural series of numbers) so that any series

$$\sum_{n=1}^{\infty} (a_n \cos p_n x + b_n \sin p_n x)$$

converges nearly everywhere in $[0, 2\pi]$ provided

$$\sum_{n=1}^{\infty} (a_n^2 + b_n^2)\, \omega(n) < \infty.$$

D. E. MEN'SHOV (see also Kaczmarz and Steinhaus, A. 12, p. 365 of Russian translation).

6. Let $n_k \uparrow \infty$ be some sequence of natural numbers. Then if for the series

$$\frac{a_0}{2} + \sum_{k=1}^{\infty} (a_k \cos kx + b_k \sin kx) \tag{24.2}$$

the partial sums $S_{n_k}(x)$ ($k = 1, 2, \dots$) converge in the norm of the space $L^p(0, 2\pi)$ for some $p \in [1, \infty]$, the series (24.2) is a Fourier series of some function $f(x) \in L^p(0, 2\pi)$.

[The proof is similar to the proof of the lemma in § 12 of Chapter I.]

7. Prove that whatever $\varepsilon_n \geqslant 0$ with $\lim_{n\to\infty} \varepsilon_n = 0$ are given, there exists an almost everywhere convergent Fourier series

$$\sum_{n=1}^{\infty} a_n \cos nx,$$

for which $a_n \geqslant \varepsilon_n$ for all $n = 1, 2, \dots$.

[This follows from Theorem 4, Chapter I, § 30.]

8. Construct an almost everywhere convergent Fourier series

$$\sum_{n=1}^{\infty} b_n \sin nx,$$

such that the series

$$\sum_{n=1}^{\infty} |b_n| \sin nx$$

is not a Fourier series.

[It is sufficient to take $b_n = (\sin(n\pi/3))/\ln n$ for $n \geqslant 2$ (see also problem 11, Chapter II, § 14).]

9. Construct a function $f(x) \in L^p(0, 2\pi)$ for all $p \geqslant 2$, the Fourier series of which converges to $+\infty$ in a set of the power of the continuum in any interval (but naturally the measure of this set is zero).

(Compare with problem 1, Chapter IV, § 26.)

$\left[\text{Assume } f(x) = \sum_{n=1}^{\infty} \frac{1}{n} \cos 2^{n!} x \text{ and consider the set } E = \prod_{n=10}^{\infty} E_n \text{ where } E_n = \{-\infty < \infty;\ \cos 2^{n!} x \geqslant 1/2\}.\right]$

10. Consider some number $p \in [1, \infty)$. Prove that either all the Fourier series of the function $f \in L^p(0, 2\pi)$ are convergent almost everywhere in $[0, 2\pi]$ or there exists a function $f_0(x) \in L^p(0, 2\pi)$ the Fourier series of which diverges almost everywhere in $[0, 2\pi]$.

[The proof is simpler than the proof of statement 6, Chapter IV, § 26.]

11. Consider the integers $n_k \uparrow \infty$ such that $\overline{\lim}_{k\to\infty} (n_{k+1} - n_k) = \infty$. A Fourier series exists which diverges almost everywhere in $[0, 2\pi]$ although a sub-sequence of its partial sums $S_{n_k}(x)$ converges almost everywhere in $[0, 2\pi]$.

If $\overline{\lim}_{k\to\infty} (n_{k+1} - n_k) < \infty$, the statement formulated above no longer holds (see problem 19, Chapter II, § 14).

[The proof is easily derived if the construction used is that of the example of an almost everywhere divergent Fourier series in Chapter V, § 19.]

12. Let $E \subset [0, 2\pi)$ be an arbitrary set of type $F_\sigma$. Then there exists a pair of mutually conjugate Fourier series convergent in $E$ and unboundedly divergent in $E_1 = [0, 2\pi) - E$.

L. V. TAIKOV

[The construction is achieved starting from the methods of Kolmogorov, Zeller and Hardy–Rogosinski–Sunouchi (see §§ 19, 20 and 22 of Chapter V).]

13. Construct $a_n \geqslant 0$ and $\lim_{n\to\infty} a_n = 0$ such that the series

$$\sum_{n=1}^{\infty} a_n \cos nx \quad \text{and} \quad \sum_{n=1}^{\infty} a_n \sin nx$$

diverge for all $x \in (-\infty, +\infty)$ apart from the points $x \equiv 0 \pmod{\pi}$ for the second series.

[This can be achieved by Herzog's method [1] if the polynomial $P_m(z) = 1 + \sum_{n=0}^{m/48} z^{m(8n+1)}$ is used instead of $T_m(z)$ in his example and the numbers $k_m$ used are simple and sufficiently rapidly increasing.]

14. Consider some number $\alpha \in [1, 2]$ and the Fourier series of the function $f(x) \in L(0, 2\pi)$ such that

$$\sqrt{a_n^2(f) + b_n^2(f)} \leqslant \varrho_n \downarrow 0 \quad \text{and} \quad \sum_{n=1}^{\infty} \varrho_n^{\alpha} < \infty .$$

If for a $2\pi$-periodic measurable function $\varphi(x)$ the inequality

$$|\varphi(x) - \varphi(y)| \leqslant |f(x) - f(y)|$$

holds for all $x$ and $y$, then

$$\sum_{n=1}^{\infty} (|a_n(\varphi)|^{\alpha} + |b_n(\varphi)|^{\alpha}) < \infty .$$

A. Beurling for the case $\alpha = 1$,
V. I. Prokhorenko for the case $1 < \alpha \leqslant 2$.

15. Let $S_k(x)$ be the partial sums of some trigonometric series of form (24.2). Then if for any sequence $k_k \uparrow \infty$ the partial sums $S_{k_n}(x)$ are summable $(C, 1)$ in the set $E$, i.e. a finite limit

$$\lim_{n\to\infty} \frac{1}{n} \sum_{i=1}^{n} S_{k_i}(x) \qquad (x \in E)$$

exists, the series (24.2) converges in the set $E$.

16. If for some number $\varepsilon \in (0, 2)$

$$\sum_{n=1}^{\infty} (|a_n|^{2-\varepsilon} + |b_n|^{2-\varepsilon}) < \infty ,$$

then the trigonometric series of the form (24.2) for any order of sequence of the terms is convergent almost everywhere in $[0, 2\pi]$.

D. E. Men'shov (see also Kaczmarz and Steinhaus,
A. 12, p. 200 of Russian translation).

17. Let $\varphi(t)$ be an arbitrary finite function with period 1. Then, if the series

$$\sum_{n=1}^{\infty} c_n \varphi(2^n x) \tag{24.3}$$

converges in some set $E$ with $mE > 0$, the series (24.3) converges for almost all $x \in (-\infty, \infty)$.

S. B. STECHKIN and P. L. UL'YANOV

18. Consider the real numbers $\lambda_k > 0$ and $\lambda_{k+1}/\lambda_k \geqslant q > 1$ $(k = 1, 2, \ldots)$. Then if

$$\sum_{k=1}^{\infty} |a_k|^2 < \infty \tag{24.4}$$

the series

$$\sum_{k=1}^{\infty} a_k e^{i\lambda_k x} \tag{24.5}$$

converges almost everywhere in $(-\infty, +\infty)$.

Conversely, if the series (24.5) converges in some set $E$ with $mE > 0$, then (24.4) is valid.

M. KAS and P. HARTMAN

19. Consider $\lambda_k \uparrow \infty$ and $\lim\limits_{k\to\infty}(\lambda_{k+1} - \lambda_k) > H > 0$. Then a series of the form (24.5) converges almost everywhere in $(-\infty, +\infty)$ if

$$\sum_{k=1}^{\infty} a_k^2 \ln(|\lambda_k| + 1) < \infty.$$

[The proof can be obtained with the help of an appropriate modification to Bellman's argument. Namely, for $k \geqslant k_0$ we have $\lambda_{k+1} - \lambda_k > H$ and since

$$e^{i\lambda_k x} = \frac{e^{ix}}{e^{iHx} - 1} \int\limits_{\lambda_k}^{\lambda_k + H} e^{ixt} dt,$$

assuming $f(t) = a_k$ for $\lambda_k \leqslant t \leqslant \lambda_k + H$ and $f(t) = 0$ for the remaining $x$, we find that the convergence of the series is equivalent to the convergence of the Fourier integral $\int\limits_{\lambda_{k_0}}^{\infty} f(t)\, e^{ixt}\, dt$. But $f(t) \sqrt{\ln(t + 2)} \in L^2(0, \infty)$ and therefore according to Titchmarsh's theorem (see A.31) this Fourier integral converges almost everywhere.]

20. Let $\mathop{S_n f}\limits_{k\neq p} |\lambda_k - \lambda_p| > 0$. Then a series of the form (24.5) for any order of sequence of the terms converges almost everywhere in $(-\infty, \infty)$ provided that for some $\varepsilon > 0$

$$\sum_{k=1}^{\infty} b_k^2 \ln^{2+\varepsilon} k < \infty,$$

where $b_k$ $(k = 1, 2, \ldots)$ is the sequence of the numbers $a_k$ $(k = 1, 2, \ldots)$ arranged in order of decreasing $|a_k|$.

[We can assume that $|\lambda_k - \lambda_p| > 1$ for all $k \neq p$ (this can always be proved by replacing $x$ by $Cx$). But then the system $\{e^{i\lambda_k x}\}$ is an orthogonal system in $(-\infty, \infty)$ with respect to the Hartman measure

$$\mu(E) = \frac{1}{\pi} \int\limits_E \frac{1 - \cos y}{y^2}\, dy.$$

Moreover, according to the Orlicz theorem (see Kaczmarz and Steinhaus, A.12, p. 198 of Russian translation, Theorem [5.4.1]) our series converges almost everywhere for any order of terms.]

CHAPTER VI

# "ADJUSTMENT" OF FUNCTIONS IN A SET OF SMALL MEASURE

## § 1. Introduction

This chapter is devoted to a problem which was formulated and in a sense solved completely by D.E. Men'shov. This problem can be stated thus: given a measurable function $f(x)$ and any positive quantity $\varepsilon$. Is it possible by changing the function $f(x)$ only in some set $\mathscr{E}, m\mathscr{E} < \varepsilon$, to ensure that it is transformed into a function $g(x)$ for which $\sigma(g)$ converges almost everywhere, or everywhere, or converges uniformly? What must be required of the function $f(x)$ for these questions to be answered in the affirmative? Can it be demanded not only that the "adjustment" of the function be carried out only in a set, the measure of which does not exceed $\varepsilon$, but also that $f(x)$ remain unchanged in some given set? All these problems will be examined now, using the results obtained by Men'shov.

In § 3 an important lemma will be proved, which refers to the deep and subtle properties of the Dirichlet factor; it will be described in the form in which it is possible to apply it to Men'shov's two basic theorems.

In § 4 it will be proved that any measurable $f(x)$, finite almost everywhere in $[0, 2\pi]$, for any $\varepsilon > 0$ can be changed in a set of measure less than $\varepsilon$ in order to convert it into a continuous $g(x)$ with uniformly convergent Fourier series.

But, as Men'shov showed, the set in which the change occurs cannot be chosen arbitrarily (see § 6).

However, if it is also required of the "adjusted" function that its Fourier series converge uniformly but the convergence be bounded almost everywhere, then the following result is obtained (see § 7); for any summable $f(x)$ and any perfect, nowhere-dense $P$ can change $f(x)$ outside $P$ so that a summable function $g(x)$ is obtained with a series $\sigma(g)$ convergent almost everywhere (in particular, it is possible for any $\varepsilon > 0$ to make $mP > 2\pi - \varepsilon$).

In § 6 some theorems due to Men'shov are given without proof, showing to what extent the results obtained can be strengthened and in what cases this strengthening is impossible.

## § 2. Two elementary lemmas

LEMMA 1. *Let $\lambda(x)$ be a continuous broken function in some interval $[a, b]$; if $|\lambda(x)| \leqslant M$ and the number of broken segments be $k$, then for any $n$ and $x$*

$$\left| \int_a^b \lambda(t) \frac{\sin n(t-x)}{t-x} dt \right| \leqslant 4\pi k M.$$

Indeed, if $(\alpha, \beta)$ be an interval in which $\lambda(x)$ is linear, then according to the second mean value theorem (see Introductory Material, § 2)

$$\left|\int_{\alpha}^{\beta} \lambda(t) \frac{\sin n(t-x)}{t-x} dt\right| \leqslant \left|\lambda(\alpha) \int_{\alpha}^{\xi} \frac{\sin n(t-x)}{t-x} dt\right|$$

$$+ \left|\lambda(\beta) \int_{\xi}^{\beta} \frac{\sin n(t-x)}{t-x} dt\right| \leqslant 4M\pi,$$

because

$$\left|\int_{c}^{d} \frac{\sin n(t-x)}{t-x} dt\right| \leqslant 2\pi$$

for any $c$ and $d$ (see Chapter I, § 35).

Since the interval $[a, b]$ is divided into $k$ sections, in each of which $\lambda(x)$ is linear, then the statement in the lemma is valid.

LEMMA 2. *Let $\varepsilon > 0$ and $\psi(x)$ be a periodic function with period $2\pi$ such that*

$$\left|\int_{0}^{\xi} \psi(t)\, dt\right| < \varepsilon, \quad 0 \leqslant \xi \leqslant 2\pi.$$

*Then for any $n$ and $x$*

$$\left|\int_{0}^{2\pi} \psi(t) \frac{\sin n(t-x)}{t-x} dt\right| < An^2 \varepsilon,$$

*where $A$ is an absolute constant.*

To prove this, we will note first that the function $g(y) = (\sin y)/y$ possesses a continuous derivative along the whole infinite axis, and moreover

$$\left|\frac{d}{dy}\left(\frac{\sin y}{y}\right)\right| \leqslant C, \; -\infty < y < +\infty,$$

where $C$ is constant. But from this

$$\left|\frac{d}{dt}\left(\frac{\sin n(t-x)}{t-x}\right)\right| \leqslant Cn^2 \quad \text{for any} \quad n \quad \text{and} \quad x.$$

Now, integrating by parts, we obtain

$$\int_{0}^{2\pi} \psi(t) \frac{\sin n(t-x)}{t-x} dt = H(t) \frac{\sin n(t-x)}{t-x}\Bigg|_{0}^{2\pi} - \int_{0}^{2\pi} H(t) \frac{d}{dt}\left[\frac{\sin n(t-x)}{t-x}\right] dt,$$

where we have assumed that

$$H(t) = \int_{0}^{t} \psi(u)\, du.$$

From the condition of the lemma $|H(t)| \leqslant \varepsilon$ for $0 \leqslant t \leqslant 2\pi$, and therefore

$$\left| \int_0^{2\pi} \psi(t) \frac{\sin n(t-x)}{t-x} \, dt \right| \leqslant 2n\varepsilon + Cn^2 \varepsilon \, 2\pi < An^2 \varepsilon,$$

where $A$ is a constant and the lemma is proved†.

Both the lemmas proved are very elementary and we have separated them only so as not to interrupt the description by trivial notes. Now we will continue with the lemmas which will play a decisive part in the proof of the basic theorem.

## § 3. Lemma concerning the Dirichlet factor

Here a lemma will be proved referring to the properties of an "adjusted"†† Dirichlet factor, i.e. of an expression of the type

$$\frac{\sin n(t-x)}{t-x}, \tag{3.1}$$

to which the actual Dirichlet factor

$$D_n(t-x) = \frac{\sin \left(n + \frac{1}{2}\right)(t-x)}{2 \sin \frac{t-x}{2}}.$$

is usually changed whilst investigating problems of convergence. A fact will be established which is characterized by the interference of the positive and negative waves of the function (3.1), when the argument $t$ runs through some system of intervals of equal length, situated at equal distances from one another, and $x$ runs through some set.

We use the first statement of this lemma in § 4 and the second in § 6.

LEMMA 3. *Let* $[c, d]$ *be any interval,* $\nu > 8$ *be any integer,* $r > 2$ *be any integer and* $q = r\nu$. *Let*

$$\delta = \frac{d-c}{q\nu},$$

$$c_s = c + \nu\delta s \; (s = 0, \pm 1, \pm 2, \ldots), \; (c = c_0, d = c_q),$$

$$a_s = c_s - \delta', \quad 0 < \delta' \leqslant \delta,$$

$$a = c + \frac{d-c}{\nu}, \quad b = d - \frac{d-c}{\nu},$$

$$E = \sum_{s=r}^{q-r-1} [c_s + 2\delta, \; c_{s+1} - 2\delta]$$

(see Fig. 27).

† It is easily estimated that $A < 16$.

†† *Translator's note.* The word "adjusted" has been chosen deliberately here, as this form differs from *the modified Dirichlet kernel* defined in Zygmund's book (A 35, 2nd Ed.) p. 50.

*Then we have*

$$(1)\qquad \left|\sum_{s=1}^{q}\int_{a_s}^{c_s}\frac{\sin n(t-x)}{t-x}\,dt\right| < A \quad \textit{for} \quad a \leqslant x \leqslant b, \quad n = 1, 2, \ldots,$$

$$(2)\qquad \left|\sum_{s=1}^{q}\int_{a_s}^{c_s}\frac{\sin n(t-x)}{t-x}\,dt\right| < A\,\frac{\delta'}{\delta} \quad \textit{for} \quad x \in E, \quad n = 1, 2, \ldots,$$

*where A is an absolute constant.*

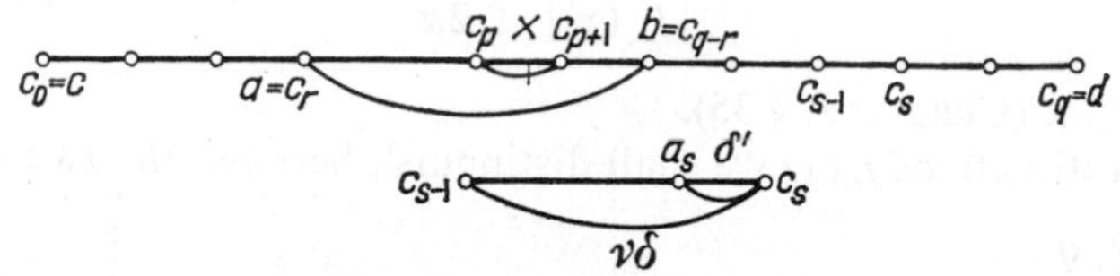


FIG. 27

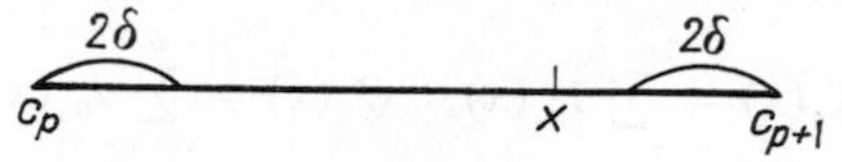


FIG. 28

*Proof.* Since $(d - c)/\nu = q\delta = r\nu\delta$, then $a = c_r$ and $b = c_{q-r}$. Therefore there exists $p$, $r \leqslant p \leqslant q - r - 1$, such that

(1) if $x \in [a, b]$, then $c_p \leqslant x \leqslant c_{p+1}$,

(2) if $x \in E$, then $c_p + 2\delta \leqslant x \leqslant c_{p+1} - 2\delta$ (see Fig. 28).

Let us denote

$$I_{n_s}(x) = \int_{a_s}^{c_s}\frac{\sin n(t-x)}{t-x}\,dt. \tag{3.2}$$

We must estimate

$$I_n(x) = \sum_{s=1}^{q} I_{n_s}(x). \tag{3.3}$$

We have for any $s \neq p$, $s \neq p \pm 1$

$$|I_{n_s}(x)| \leqslant \frac{\delta'}{\min|t-x|},$$

where min refers to all $t$ of $(a_s, c_s)$. But for $s > p + 1$

$$t - x \geqslant a_s - c_{p+1} = c_s - \delta' - c_{p+1} = (s - p - 1)\nu\delta - \delta' \geqslant (s - p - 1)(\nu - 1)\delta,$$

whence

$$|I_{n_s}(x)| \leqslant \frac{\delta'}{(\nu - 1)(s - p - 1)\delta} \quad \text{for} \quad s > p + 1, \tag{3.4}$$

and for $s < p - 1$ we have $x - t \geqslant c_p - c_s = (p - s)\nu\delta$, whence

$$|I_{n_s}(x)| \leqslant \frac{\delta'}{(p - s)\nu\delta} \quad \text{for} \quad s < p - 1. \tag{3.5}$$

Both formulae (3.4) and (3.5) give for all cases

$$|I_{n_s}(x)| \leqslant 4\frac{\delta'}{\delta}\frac{1}{\nu|p - s|} \quad \text{for} \quad |p - s| > 1, \tag{3.6}$$

because for any natural $k > 1$ it always holds that $1/(k - 1) < 2/k$. Finally

$$|I_{n_s}(x)| \leqslant 2\pi \tag{3.7}$$

for any $n$, $s$ and $x$ (Chapter I, § 35).

Now in the estimate of $I_n(x)$ we shall distinguish between the two cases

(a) $2p - 1 \leqslant q$

(b) $2p - 1 > q$.

In case (a) we suppose that

$$K_n(x) = \sum_{s=1}^{2p-1} I_{n_s}(x), \quad Q_n(x) = \sum_{s=2p}^{q} I_{n_s}(x),$$

in case (b)

$$K_n(x) = \sum_{s=2p-q}^{q} I_{n_s}(x), \quad Q_n(x) = \sum_{s=1}^{2p-q-1} I_{n_s}(x).$$

We have in both cases

$$I_n(x) = K_n(x) + Q_n(x). \tag{3.8}$$

Let us first estimate $Q_n(x)$. In the sum $Q_n(x)$ for case (a) we have $s \geqslant 2p$, which means that $s - p \geqslant p \geqslant r$, and therefore from (3.6)

$$|I_{n_s}(x)| \leqslant 4\frac{\delta'}{\delta}\frac{1}{\nu r} = 4\frac{\delta'}{\delta}\frac{1}{q}.$$

In case (b) we have $s \leqslant 2p - q - 1$, which means that

$$p - s \geqslant q + 1 - p \geqslant q + 1 - (q - r - 1) = r + 2 > r,$$

consequently, this estimate is valid; in both cases the number of terms of the sum is less than $q$, which means that

$$|Q_n(x)| \leqslant q\,4\frac{\delta'}{\delta}\frac{1}{q} = 4\frac{\delta'}{\delta}. \tag{3.9}$$

Let us continue with the estimate of $K_n(x)$. Supposing that $m = p - 1$ in case (a) and $m = q - p$ in case (b), we have in both cases

$$K_n(x) = \sum_{s=p-m}^{p+m} I_{n_s}(x). \tag{3.10}$$

We will also estimate this expression.

Supposing that $t = a_s + \tau$, we have

$$K_n(x) = \sum_{s=p-m}^{p+m} \int_0^{\delta'} \frac{\sin n(a_s + \tau - x)}{a_s + \tau - x}\, d\tau. \tag{3.11}$$

Let us suppose that

$$\lambda = \frac{a_p + \tau - x}{\nu\delta}. \tag{3.12}$$

Then $\lambda \leqslant 0$ or $a_p + \tau \leqslant c_p \leqslant x$; on the other hand

$$-\lambda = \frac{x - a_p - \tau}{\nu\delta} \leqslant \frac{c_{p+1} - c_p}{\nu\delta} = 1,$$

which means that $|\lambda| \leqslant 1$. But

$$a_s + \tau - x = (s - p)\,\nu\delta + a_p + \tau - x = (s - p + \lambda)\,\nu\delta.$$

Therefore

$$K_n(x) = \frac{1}{\nu\delta} \sum_{s=p-m}^{p+m} \int_0^{\delta'} \frac{\sin n\nu\delta(s - p + \lambda)}{s - p + \lambda}\, d\tau. \tag{3.13}$$

Let us exclude from the sum $K_n(x)$ three integrals, namely those where $s = p$, $s = p - 1$ and $s = p + 1$; we will estimate them separately. First we have for any $\alpha, \beta, x$ and $n$ (see Chapter I, § 35)

$$\left| \int_\alpha^\beta \frac{\sin n(t - x)}{t - x}\, dt \right| \leqslant 2\pi.$$

Moreover, if the distance of $x$ to any $c_s$ is not less than $2\delta$, and $a_s \leqslant t \leqslant c_s$, then $|t - x| \geqslant 2\delta - \delta' \geqslant \delta$, and therefore

$$|I_{n_s}(x)| \leqslant 2\pi \quad \text{for any} \quad s \quad \text{and} \quad x$$

and

$$I_{n_s}(x)| \leqslant \frac{\delta'}{\delta}, \quad \text{if} \quad x \in E \quad \text{and } s \text{ is any value}.$$

Thus, for $a \leqslant x \leqslant b$ the rejection of the three integrals from the sum (3.11) signifies the rejection of a magnitude, the modulus of which does not exceed $6\pi$, and for $x \in E$ this magnitude does not exceed $3\,\delta'/\delta$.

It remains to estimate

$$K_n^*(x) = \sum_{s=p-m}^{p+m}{}' \frac{1}{\nu\delta} \int_0^{\delta'} \frac{\sin Y(s - p + \lambda)}{s - p + \lambda}\, d\tau,$$

where $Y = n\nu\delta$ and where the symbol $\sum'$ signifies that $s \neq p$ and $s \neq p \pm 1$.

Supposing $s - p = v$, if $s > p$, and $p - s = v$, if $p > s$, we obtain

$$K_n^*(x) = \sum_{v=2}^{m} \left[ \frac{1}{\nu\delta} \int_0^{\delta'} \frac{\sin Y(v+\lambda)}{v+\lambda}\, d\tau + \frac{1}{\nu\delta} \int_0^{\delta'} \frac{\sin Y(v-\lambda)}{v-\lambda}\, d\tau \right].$$

If we denote

$$\sum_{v=2}^{m} \frac{\sin Y(v \pm \lambda)}{v \pm \lambda} - \sum_{v=2}^{m} \frac{\sin Y(v \pm \lambda)}{v} = R,$$

then

$$|R| \leqslant \sum_{v=2}^{m} \left| \frac{1}{v \pm \lambda} - \frac{1}{v} \right| \leqslant \sum_{v=2}^{m} \frac{1}{v(v-1)},$$

since $|\lambda| \leqslant 1$.

Therefore, for any $m$ we have $|R| \leqslant 1$, whence it follows that

$$|K_n^*(x)| \leqslant \left| \sum_{v=2}^{m} \frac{1}{\nu\delta} \int_0^{\delta'} \frac{\sin Y(v+\lambda) + \sin Y(v-\lambda)}{v}\, d\tau \right| + 2\frac{\delta'}{\delta\nu}$$

$$= \left| \frac{1}{\nu\delta} \int_0^{\delta'} 2\cos Y\lambda \sum_{v=2}^{m} \frac{\sin Yv}{v}\, d\tau \right| + 2\frac{\delta'}{\nu\delta}.$$

But

$$\left| \sum_{v=2}^{m} \frac{\sin Yv}{v} \right| \leqslant G$$

for any $Y$ and $m$, where $G$ is an absolute constant (Chapter I, § 41), therefore

$$|K_n^*(x)| \leqslant 2G\frac{\delta'}{\nu\delta} + 2\frac{\delta'}{\nu\delta} < L\frac{\delta'}{\delta}, \tag{3.14}$$

where $L$ is an absolute constant.

Considering the difference between $K_n(x)$ and $K_n^*(x)$, we conclude from this that

$$|K_n(x)| \leqslant \begin{cases} L\dfrac{\delta'}{\delta} + 6\pi & \text{for } a \leqslant x \leqslant b, \\ (L+3)\dfrac{\delta'}{\sigma} & \text{for } x \in E \end{cases} \tag{3.15}$$

and, finally, taking into account (3.8), (3.9) and (3.15)

$$|I_n(x)| \leqslant 4\frac{\delta'}{\delta} + L\frac{\delta'}{\delta} + 6\pi \leqslant A, \quad a \leqslant x \leqslant b$$

(since $\delta'/\delta < 1$) and

$$|I_n(x)| \leqslant 4\frac{\delta'}{\delta} + (L+3)\frac{\delta'}{\delta} \leqslant A\frac{\delta'}{\delta}, \; x \in E,$$

where $A$ is an absolute constant. Lemma 3 is proved in both cases.

*Note*. In view of the extensive depth of this lemma of Men'shov†, we consider it appropriate to note the fundamental idea, which could remain concealed following the calculations: the point $x$ cannot approach very closely to the end-points $c$ and $d$ of the interval $[c, d]$ under consideration, since it stands away from them at a distance not less than $(d - c)/\nu = q\delta = r\nu\delta$; therefore, there certainly exist intervals $(a_s, c_s)$ both to the left and to the right of it. Since $c_p \leqslant x \leqslant c_{p+1}$, then it is said that $2p - 1 \leqslant q$, which means to say, roughly speaking, that $x$ lies in the left half of the interval $[c, d]$ and for $2p - 1 > q$ in its right half. The sum $Q_n(x)$ is expanded into integrals with respect to these $(a_s, c_s)$ which are "comparatively far" from $x$ (since $|s - p| \geqslant r$) and therefore the estimate $Q_n(x)$ is satisfactorily rough; it is possible to replace $\sin n(t - x)$ in it by unity and to act only on the fact that the length $\delta'$ of the range of integration is not greater than $\delta$ and the distance of $t$ from $x$ is, roughly speaking, equal to the sum of the lengths of the intervals $(c_s, c_{s+1})$, situated between $t$ and $x$, i.e. $|s - p|\,\nu\delta \geqslant r\nu\delta = q\delta$. Therefore the magnitude of every $I_{n_s}(x)$ of the sum $Q_n(x)$ is of order $\delta'/q\delta$, and the magnitude of all of them is not greater than $q$, which gives the required estimate.

As regards the sum $K_n(x)$ it is quite a different matter. Here, there are the intervals $(a_s, c_s)$ which are close to the point $x$ and even for case (1) the difference $t - x$ can become equal to zero. Therefore, we require to estimate separately the integrals where $s = p - 1, p$ or $p + 1$; however, this is not too difficult, since each such integral separately does not exceed $2\pi$ (this is sufficient in case (1), since there the rejection of the constant does not change anything) and does not exceed $\delta'/\delta$ in case (2), where the estimated magnitude should be of this order.

Now in the sum $K_n(x)$ there are no integrals extending into "dangerous intervals", but of the remaining all are "close" to $x$ and therefore it is impossible to estimate them roughly. Here the fact must be used that there are as many intervals $(a_s, c_s)$ to the left of the interval $(c_p, c_{p+1})$ in which $x$ lies as to the right of it, and we will combine them in pairs (a case is given by $v = s - p$ and $v = p - s$).

This makes it possible to take into account the interference of the positive and negative sine waves by using the formula

$$\sin Y(v + \lambda) + \sin Y(v - \lambda) = 2 \sin Yv \cos Y\lambda.$$

Also, since the intervals $(a_s, c_s)$ are very small, then when the point $t$ runs through this interval, its distance from $x$ is almost the same as if it remained at $a_s$, that is, when the quantity $s$ takes different values, $(t - x)$ changes almost as a term of an arithmetic progression with difference $\nu\delta$. But as we already know

$$\sum_{k=1}^{N} \frac{\sin kx}{k}$$

is a magnitude bounded for any $N$ and $x$. In this fact too the interference of the positive and negative sinusoidal waves has already been considered. The use of this fact gives the last inequality necessary for the estimate of $K_n(x)$.

The subtlety of the estimate obtained can be demonstrated by the following considerations: let $[c, d]$ lie in $[0, 2\pi]$ and let $F(x)$ be a characteristic function for a set

---

† This is confirmed by the fact that with its help he proved a whole series of important theorems.

composed of the intervals $(a_s, c_s)$ $(s = 1, 2, \ldots, q)$. Then

$$\sum_{s=1}^{q} \int_{a_s}^{c_s} \frac{\sin n(t-x)}{t-x}\, dt = \int_0^{2\pi} F(t) \frac{\sin n(t-x)}{t-x}\, dt.$$

Since $F(t)$ is a step-function, which means that it is of bounded variation, the partial sums of its Fourier series are all bounded, and therefore it is possible to assert immediately that

$$\left| \int_0^{2\pi} F(t) \frac{\sin n(t-x)}{t-x}\, dt \right| < C,$$

where $C$ is a constant. But the fact is that, as was shown in Chapter I, § 48, if some function $F(x)$ of bounded variation possesses a maximum modulus equal to $M$ and complete variation $V$, then the partial sums of its Fourier series satisfy the condition

$$|S_n(x, F)| \leqslant M + 2V$$

which means that in the case of interest to us, where it can be readily calculated that $V = 2q$ and $M = 1$, we could only state that

$$|S_n(x, F)| \leqslant 1 + 4q.$$

And since $q$ in the lemma under consideration can be made as large as desired, then the statement

$$\left| \sum_{s=1}^{q} \int_{a_s}^{c_s} \frac{\sin n(t-x)}{t-x}\, dt \right| < A,$$

where $A$ is an absolute constant is based on the fact that the intervals $(a_s, c_s)$, where $F(x) = 1$ and outside them $F(x) = 0$, are not any $q$ intervals, but intervals selected so that in them interference of the positive and negative sinusoidal waves $\sin nt$ occurs.

COROLLARY 1. *Let* $[c, d]$ *be any interval in* $[0, 2\pi]$. *Let us maintain all the notation of the lemma. Let*

$$\varphi(x) = \begin{cases} h_s & \text{in } (a_s, c_s),\ s = 0, \pm 1, \ldots, \\ 0 & \text{outside all } (a_s, c_s). \end{cases}$$

*The numbers* $h_s$ *are chosen so that*

$$\left.\begin{array}{l} (1)\ |h_{s+1} - h_s| \leqslant \dfrac{1}{r}, \\ (2)\ 0 \leqslant h_s \leqslant 1, \end{array}\right\} \quad s = 0, \pm 1, \ldots,$$

$$(3)\ h_s = 0, \text{ if } (a_s, c_s) \text{ outside } (a, b).$$

*Then*

$$\left| \int_0^{2\pi} \varphi(t) \frac{\sin n(t-x)}{t-x}\, dt \right| < B \tag{3.16}$$

*for any* $n$ *and* $x$, *where* $B$ *is an absolute constant.*

For the proof we note first of all that

$$\int_0^{2\pi} \varphi(t)\frac{\sin n(t-x)}{t-x}\,dt = \sum_{s=1}^{q} h_s \int_{a_s}^{c_s} \frac{\sin n(t-x)}{t-x}\,dt$$

$$= \sum_{s=1}^{q} h_s I_{n_s}(x) = \sum_{s=1}^{q} (h_s - h_p)\, I_{n_s}(x) + h_p \sum_{s=1}^{q} I_{n_s}(x). \qquad (3.17)$$

If $x \bar{\in} [a, b]$, then $h_p = 0$. If $x \in [a, b]$, then according to the proved lemma

$$\left| \sum_{s=1}^{q} I_{n_s}(x) \right| < A.$$

Therefore, from formula (3.17) and considering $0 \leqslant h_s \leqslant 1$, for any $x$ in $[0, 2\pi]$, we have

$$\left| \int_0^{2\pi} \varphi(t)\frac{\sin n(t-x)}{t-x}\,dt \right| \leqslant \sum_{s=1}^{q} |h_s - h_p|\, |I_{n_s}(x)| + A. \qquad (3.18)$$

Rejecting, as we did in the proof of the lemma, those integrals for which $s = p$, $s = p - 1$ and $s = p + 1$, and noting that $|h_s - h_p| \leqslant 2$ for any $s$ and $p$ and the validity of formula (3.7) we see that (3.18) gives

$$\left| \int_0^{2\pi} \varphi(t)\frac{\sin n(t-x)}{t-x}\,dt \right| \leqslant \sum_{\substack{s \neq p \\ s \neq p \pm 1}}' |h_s - h_p|\, |I_{n_s}(x)| + 12\pi + A. \qquad (3.19)$$

We apply formula (3.6) to the integrals on the right-hand side of (3.19). We will have

$$\sum{}' |h_s - h_p|\, |I_{n_s}(x)| \leqslant 4\frac{\delta'}{\delta}\frac{1}{\nu}\sum{}' \frac{|h_s - h_p|}{|s - p|}. \qquad (3.20)$$

But $|h_s - h_p| \leqslant |s - p|/r$ due to condition (1), imposed on the numbers $h_s$, and therefore from (3.19) and (3.20)

$$\left| \int_0^{2\pi} \varphi(t)\frac{\sin n(t-x)}{t-x}\,dt \right| \leqslant 4\frac{\delta'}{\delta}\frac{1}{\nu r}q + 12\pi + A = 4\frac{\delta'}{\delta} + 12\pi + A < B,$$

where $B$ is an absolute constant.

COROLLARY 2. *Let*

$$\eta < \frac{\delta}{q} \quad \textit{and} \quad \eta < \frac{\delta'}{2}.$$

*Let us assume that*

$$a_s' = a_s + \eta; \quad c_s' = c_s - \eta$$

*and let*

$$g(x) = \varphi(x) \quad \textit{outside all} \quad (a_s', c_s')$$

*also be interpolated linearly in every* $(a_s, a_s')$ *and* $(c_s' c_s)$ *where* $\varphi(x)$ *is the function of Corollary 1. Then* $g(x)$ *is a continuous broken function in* $[0, 2\pi]$, *whilst* $g(x) = 0$ *outside* $[a, b]$,

$$\int_0^{2\pi} g(t) \frac{\sin n(t-x)}{t-x} \, dt \leqslant C \tag{3.21}$$

*for any n and x where C is an absolute constant and*

$$\int_0^{2\pi} |g(t) - \varphi(t)| \, dt \leqslant 2\delta. \tag{3.22}$$

The fact that $g(x)$ is a continuous broken function equal to zero outside $[a, b]$ is evident from its construction.

To prove the validity of (3.21), it is sufficient, using (3.16) to prove that

$$\left| \int_0^{2\pi} [g(t) - \varphi(t)] \frac{\sin n(t-x)}{t-x} \, dt \right| < B', \tag{3.23}$$

where $B'$ is an absolute constant. But in every $(a_s, c_s)$ (Fig. 29) the function $g(t) - \varphi(t)$ is a continuous broken function consisting of three segments and because $0 \leqslant h_s \leqslant 1$, we have

$$|g(t) - \varphi(t)| \leqslant 1.$$

Therefore, by virtue of Lemma 1 of § 2 we have

$$\left| \int_{a_s}^{c_s} [g(t) - \varphi(t)] \frac{\sin n(t-x)}{t-x} \, dt \right| \leqslant 12\pi. \tag{3.24}$$

Since $g(t) - \varphi(t) = 0$ outside all $(a_s, c_s)$, then

$$\left| \int_0^{2\pi} [g(t) - \varphi(t)] \frac{\sin n(t-x)}{t-x} \, dt \right| = \left| \sum_{s=1}^{q} \int_{a_s}^{c_s} [g(t) - \varphi(t)] \frac{\sin n(t-x)}{t-x} \, dt \right|$$

$$\leqslant \left| \sum_{s=1}^{q}{}' \int_{a_s}^{c_s} [g(t) - \varphi(t)] \frac{\sin n(t-x)}{t-x} \, dt \right| + 36\pi, \tag{3.25}$$

where the sign $\sum'$ signifies that we have rejected three integrals: for $s = p$, $s = p - 1$ and $s = p + 1$, each of which does not exceed $12\pi$ by virtue of (3.24).

Since in the integrals on the right-hand side of (3.25)

$$|t - x| \geqslant \delta,$$

then

$$\left|\int_{a_s}^{c_s}[g(t)-\varphi(t)]\frac{\sin n(t-x)}{t-x}\,dt\right| \leqslant \frac{1}{\delta}\int_{a_s}^{c_s}|g(t)-\varphi(t)|\,dt$$

$$= \frac{1}{\delta}\int_{a_s}^{a'_s}|\varphi(t)-g(t)|\,dt + \frac{1}{\delta}\int_{c'_s}^{c_s}|\varphi(t)-g(t)|\,dt \leqslant 2\frac{\eta}{\delta} < \frac{2}{q}$$

due to the choice of the number $\eta$.

Since the number of integrals in the formula (3.25) is less than $q$, then the right-hand side of (3.25) does not exceed $2 + 36\pi = B'$, which means that (3.23) and moreover (3.21) are proved.

Moreover, since $\varphi(x) \neq g(x)$ only in $(a_s, a'_s)$ and $(c'_s, c_s)$ and in these intervals $|\varphi(x) - g(x)| \leqslant 1$, then

$$\int_0^{2\pi}|g(t)-\varphi(t)|\,dt \leqslant \sum_{s=1}^{q}\left(\int_{a_s}^{a'_s}dt + \int_{c'_s}^{c_s}dt\right) = 2\eta q < 2\delta$$

and (3.22) is also proved.

*Note.* Subsequently, applying these results to the proof of Lemma 4, we assume during the construction of $\varphi(x)$ that $h_s = 1$ in all $(a_s, c_s)$ in some $(a', b')$ inside $(a, b)$,

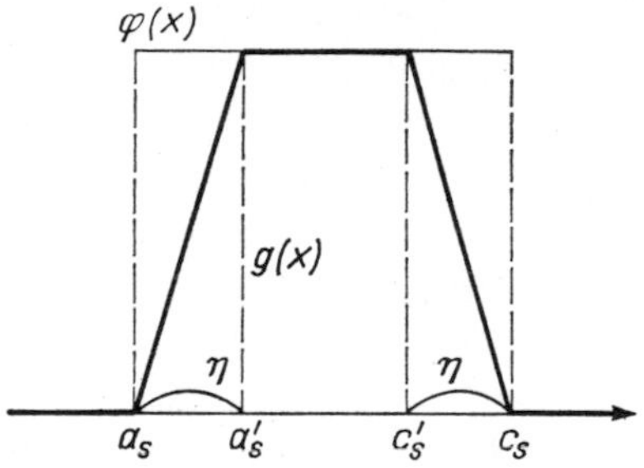


FIG. 29

that $n_s$ increases in $(a, a')$ and decreases in $(b', b)$, whilst, since the number of intervals $(c_s, c_{s+1})$ of length $\nu\delta$, which are packed in $(a, a')$ and $(b', b)$, will equal $r$, then it would be possible to arrange that the transfer from each "step ladder" (Fig. 30) to the following requires a "step" equal to $1/r$ (i.e. $h_{s+1} = h_s + 1/r$ in $(a, a')$ and $h_{s+1} = h_s - 1/r$ in $(b', b)$).

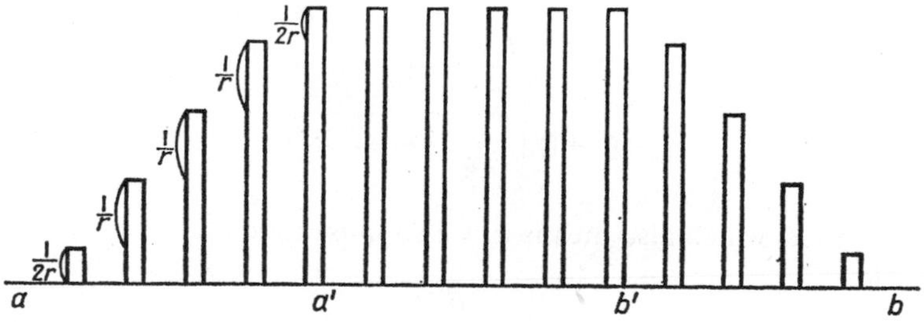


FIG. 30

However, it is more convenient for us that this should be the case for all the steps apart from the first and the last, where the "step" should be made half the size. Why this is so will be evident from Lemma 5; here we will only show the form of $\varphi(x)$ in a geometrical picture and note that for this choice of the values $h_s$ the condition $|h_{s+1} - h_s| \leqslant 1/r$ is satisfied for all $s$.

## § 4. "Adjustment" of a function to obtain a uniformly convergent Fourier series

Here we will prove the following remarkable theorem due to Men'shov[2].

THE MEN'SHOV THEOREM. *Let $f(x)$ be a measurable function, finite almost everywhere in $[0, 2\pi]$. Whatever $\sigma > 0$, it is possible to construct a function $g(x)$ coincident with $f(x)$ in some set $E$, $mE > 2\pi - \sigma$, such that the series $\sigma(g)$ converges uniformly in $[0, 2\pi]$.*

To prove the theorem the following lemma is necessary:

LEMMA 4. *Let $[c, d]$ be any segment of $[0, 2\pi]$, $\gamma$ be any real number, $\varepsilon$ be any positive number, $\nu > 8$ be any natural number.*

*Then there exist functions $\psi(x)$ and a set $\mathscr{E}$ such that*

(a) *$\psi(x)$ is a continuous broken function in $[0, 2\pi]$ and $\psi(x) = 0$ outside $[c, d]$,*

(b) $|\psi(x)| \leqslant 2\nu\,|\gamma|$ *in* $0 \leqslant x \leqslant 2\pi$,

(c) $\left|\int\limits_0^\xi \psi(x)\,dx\right| < \varepsilon, \quad 0 \leqslant \xi \leqslant 2\pi,$

(d) $\psi(x) = \gamma$ *in* $\mathscr{E}$, *where*

(e) $m\mathscr{E} > (d - c)\left(1 - \frac{5}{\nu}\right) u\mathscr{E} \subset [c, d],$

(f) $\left|\int\limits_0^{2\pi} \psi(t)\frac{\sin n(t - x)}{t - x}\,dt\right| \leqslant B\nu\,|\gamma|, \quad n = 1, 2, \ldots; \quad 0 \leqslant x \leqslant 2\pi,$

*where $B$ is an absolute constant.*

If $\gamma = 0$, then it is sufficient to suppose that $\psi(x) \equiv 0$ and all the conditions will be satisfied for $\mathscr{E} \equiv [c, d]$. Therefore, in the following argument, we will consider $\gamma \neq 0$.

We will choose the natural number $r$ so large that supposing

$$q = r\nu, \tag{4.1}$$

we have

$$4\,|\gamma|\,\frac{d - c}{q} < \varepsilon. \tag{4.2}$$

Having fixed $r$ thus, which also means $q$, we suppose that

$$\delta = \frac{d - c}{q\nu} \tag{4.3}$$

and construct the values $c_s$ and $a_s$ as in the lemma of § 3, but for $\delta' = \delta$, i.e.

$$c_s = c + \delta \nu s \quad (s = 0, \pm 1, \pm 2, \ldots),$$
$$a_s = c_s - \delta.$$

Let us assume again that

$$a = c + \frac{d-c}{\nu}, \quad b = d - \frac{d-c}{\nu}$$

and let

$$a' = c + 2\frac{d-c}{\nu}, \quad b' = d - 2\frac{d-c}{\nu}.$$

Let $\chi(x) = 1$ in $(a', b')$, $\chi(x) = 0$ outside $(a, b)$ and we will interpolate it linearly between $a$ and $a'$, and also between $b'$ and $b$ (Fig. 31).

Let us denote by $\Gamma_s$ the magnitude of the integral

$$\Gamma_s = \int_{c_{s-1}}^{c_s} \chi(t)\, dt.$$

From Fig. 31 it is clear that $\Gamma_s = 0$, if the interval $(c_{s-1}, c_s)$ lies outside $(a, b)$, that $\Gamma_s = \nu\delta$, if $(c_{s-1}, c_s)$ lies within $(a', b')$, and that, if $(c_{s-1}, c_s)$ lies within $(a, a')$ or $(b', b)$

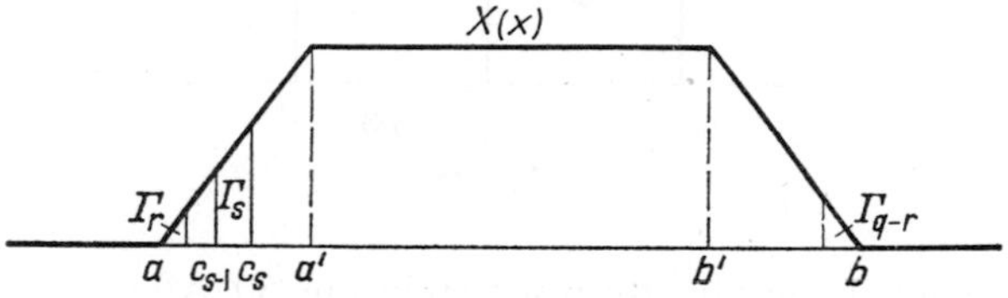


FIG. 31

then $\Gamma_s$ is the area of the trapezium or the triangle at $s = r + 1$ or $s = q - r$. Since in the interval $(a, a')$, the length of which is $(d - c)/\nu = q\delta = r\nu\delta$, there are exactly $r$ intervals of length $\nu\delta$, then in the transfer from $(c_{s-1}, c_s)$ to $(c_s, c_{s+1})$ if they both lie in $(a, a')$, the area $\Gamma_{s+1}$ is obtained from the area $\Gamma_s$ by the addition of a rectangle of height $1/r$ and base $\nu\delta$, i.e.

$$\Gamma_{s+1} - \Gamma_s = \frac{1}{r}\nu\delta$$

(Fig. 32). The argument is precisely similar if $(c_{s-1}, c_s)$ and $(c_s, c_{s+1})$ both lie in $(b', b)$, provided $\Gamma_{s+1} - \Gamma_s$ is replaced by $|\Gamma_{s+1} - \Gamma_s|$.

For the case when we transfer from the interval lying to the left of $a$ to the interval to the right of it and similarly for $a'$, $b'$ and $b$, the change in area which occurs is only $(\nu\delta/2r)$. Thus, for all cases

$$|\Gamma_{s+1} - \Gamma_s| \leqslant \frac{1}{r}\nu\delta \quad (s = 1, 2, \ldots, q-1).$$

We will now construct the function $\varphi(x)$ just as shown in Corollary 1 to Lemma 3, but assuming for all $s$

$$h_s = \frac{\Gamma_s}{\nu\delta};$$

then we will have $0 \leqslant h_s \leqslant 1$ and $|h_{s+1} - h_s| \leqslant 1/r$, as required by the definition of this function. Moreover, we note immediately that we will have for any $s$

$$\nu \int_{c_{s-1}}^{c_s} \varphi(t)\, dt = \int_{c_{s-1}}^{c_s} \chi(t)\, dt, \tag{4.4}$$

because $\varphi(t) = 0$ outside $(a_s, c_s)$ and $\varphi(t) = h_s$ in $(a_s, c_s)$, the length of which equals $\delta$, which means that

$$\nu \int_{c_{s-1}}^{c_s} \varphi(t)\, dt = \nu h_s \delta = \Gamma_s = \int_{c_{s-1}}^{c_s} \chi(t)\, dt.$$

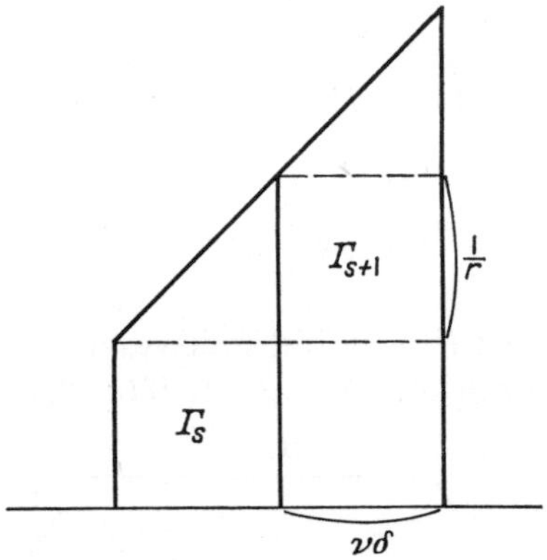


FIG. 32

It is now clear why $\varphi(t)$ has the form shown in Fig. 30. After $\varphi(t)$ has been defined, we construct $g(t)$ just as shown in Corollary 2 to Lemma 3. Finally, we suppose that

$$\psi(x) = \gamma[\chi(x) - \nu g(x)] \tag{4.5}$$

and prove that $\psi(x)$ satisfies all the conditions of Lemma 4.

Condition (a) is fulfilled, since $\chi(x)$ and $g(x)$ are both continuous broken functions in $[0, 2\pi]$ and both equal zero outside $[c, d]$.

Condition (b) follows from the fact that $|\chi(x)| \leqslant 1$, $|g(x)| \leqslant 1$ and $\nu > 1$.

To prove the validity of (c), we introduce an auxiliary function (Fig. 33)

$$\psi^*(x) = \gamma[\chi(x) - \nu\varphi(x)].$$

We have

$$\psi^*(x) - \psi(x) = \nu\gamma[g(x) - \varphi(x)],$$

and therefore due to (3.22), (4.2) and (4.3)

$$\left| \int_0^\xi [\psi^*(t) - \psi(t)]\, dt \right| \leqslant \nu\, |\gamma| \int_0^{2\pi} |g(t) - \varphi(t)|\, dt \leqslant 2\, |\gamma|\, \nu\delta < \frac{\varepsilon}{2}, \quad 0 \leqslant \xi \leqslant 2\pi.$$

Consequently (c) will be proved if we show that

$$\left| \int_0^\xi \psi^*(t)\, dt \right| < \frac{\varepsilon}{2}, \quad 0 \leqslant \xi \leqslant 2\pi. \tag{4.6}$$

But from (4.4) it immediately follows that for any $s$

$$\int_{c_{s-1}}^{c_s} \psi^*(t)\,dt = 0. \tag{4.7}$$

Let $\xi$ be any integer in $[0, 2\pi]$. If $\xi \leqslant c$, then $\psi^*(t) = 0$, because $\varphi(t)$ and $\chi(t)$ both equal zero outside $(c, d)$. If $c < \xi$, then a $k$ is found such that

$$c_k \leqslant \xi < c_{k+1}.$$

Then

$$\int_0^{\xi} \psi^*(t)\,dt = \int_0^{c_k} \psi^*(t)\,dt + \int_{c_k}^{\xi} \psi^*(t)\,dt = \int_{c_k}^{\xi} \psi^*(t)\,dt, \tag{4.8}$$

because $(c, c_k) = \sum_{s=1}^{k=1} (c_{s-1}, c_s)$ and (4.7) can be applied to every $(c_{s-1}, c_s)$.

Also we have due to (4.4), (4.2) and (4.3)

$$\left|\int_{c_k}^{\xi} \psi^*(t)\,dt\right| \leqslant |\gamma| \int_{c_k}^{c_{k+1}} \chi(t)\,dt + \nu\,|\gamma| \int_{c_k}^{c_{k+1}} \varphi(t)\,dt$$

$$\leqslant \nu\delta\,|\gamma| + \nu\delta\,|\gamma| \leqslant 2\nu\delta\,|\gamma| \leqslant \frac{\varepsilon}{2}. \tag{4.9}$$

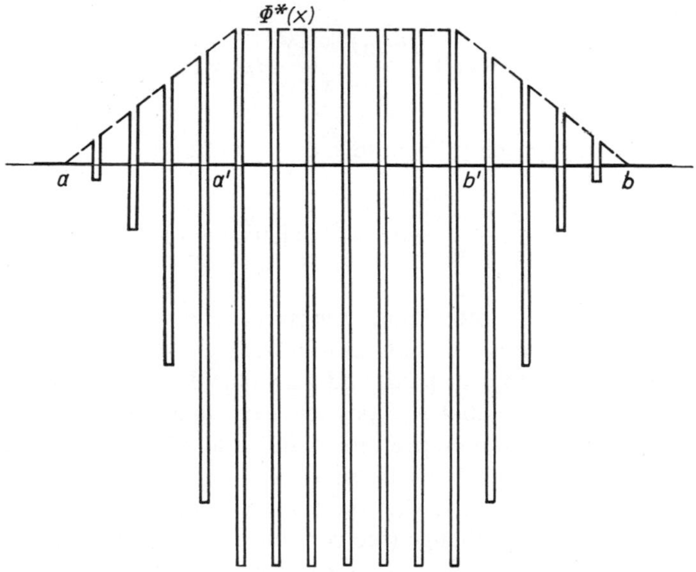


FIG. 33

From (4.8) and (4.9) it follows that (4.6) is proved, which means that condition (c) is also valid, as has already been explained above.

Let us suppose that

$$\mathscr{E} = [a', b'] - \sum_{s=2r+1}^{q-2r} (a_s, c_s),$$

i.e. we take from $[a', b']$ all the intervals $(a_s, c_s)$ lying inside it. We have

$$b' - a' = d - c - 4\frac{d-c}{\nu} = (d-c)\left(1 - \frac{4}{\nu}\right).$$

In order to obtain $\mathscr{E}$ from $(a', b')$ we have rejected the intervals of length $\delta$ and those less than $q$ sections, therefore the sum of their lengths is less than $q\delta = (d-c)/\nu$, which means that

$$m\mathscr{E} > (d-c)\left(1 - \frac{4}{\nu}\right) - \frac{d-c}{\nu} = (d-c)\left(1 - \frac{5}{\nu}\right),$$

i.e. the measure of the set $\mathscr{E}$ is what is required in condition (e) and moreover $\mathscr{E}$ lies in $[c, d]$. But in this set $\mathscr{E}$ we have $\psi(x) = \gamma$, because $g(x) = 0$ outside all $(a_s, c_s)$ and $\chi(x) = 1$ everywhere in $(a', b')$. Thus, condition (d) is also fulfilled.

Finally, it remains to prove (f). But since $\chi(x)$ is a continuous broken function in $[0, 2\pi]$ and it consists of 5 segments, then according to Lemma 1 we have, taking into account that $|\chi(t)| \leqslant 1$,

$$\left|\int_0^{2\pi} \chi(t)\frac{\sin n(t-x)}{t-x}\,dt\right| \leqslant 20\pi.$$

As regards $g(t)$, it was constructed so that Corollary 2 to Lemma 3 was satisfied, and therefore

$$\left|\int_0^{2\pi} g(t)\frac{\sin n(t-x)}{t-x}\,dt\right| < C,$$

where $C$ is an absolute constant. From this, due to (4.5)

$$\left|\int_0^{2\pi} \psi(t)\frac{\sin n(t-x)}{t-x}\,dt\right| \leqslant |\gamma|\,[20\pi + \nu c] \leqslant \nu B\,|\gamma|,$$

where $B$ is a new absolute constant and Lemma 4 is completely proved.

*Note.* The idea behind this lemma is as follows: by a "small" change we want to convert a function equal to $\gamma$ in $[c, d]$ and zero outside $[c, d]$ into a function $\psi(x)$ which is not only continuous but also possesses and integral, not exceeding a given value $\varepsilon$ in any interval $(0, \xi)$: moreover, its modulus should not exceed $2\nu|\gamma|$ where $\nu$ is given and the partial sums of its Fourier series should be of the same order as $\nu|\gamma|$. Later $\nu$ will be very large so that the change of a function in a set of measure less than $5/\nu$ will be a small change (see condition (d)). On the other hand the relationship between $\nu$ and $\gamma$ in the last constructions will be such that $\nu|\gamma|$ will also be small. Fig. 33 shows why, by subtracting from $\gamma\chi(x)$ the function $\gamma\nu\varphi(x)$, we obtain a function with a small integral: the areas bounded by the curves $\gamma\chi(x)$ and $\gamma\nu\varphi(x)$ are identical in every $(c_s, c_{s+1})$ which means that their difference equals zero, and in every section of some $(c_s, c_{s+1})$ any such area is small, because $\delta$ was chosen so small that $|\gamma|\,\nu\delta$ was less than $\varepsilon/4$.

Thus, it is possible to ensure that for a small change in the function its integral is made very small. But if it were changed in arbitrarily chosen small intervals in a large number, then the partial sum of the Fourier series of the changed function would be very great. The fact that for the construction of $\psi(t)$ condition (f) is satisfied is explained by the change being carried out in reasonably chosen intervals of length $\delta$ (operating on the lemma concerning the Dirichlet factor). As regards the change from $\varphi(t)$ to $g(t)$, this is made for the continuity of $\psi(t)$, and the properties of $\psi^*(t)$ and $\psi(t)$ are identical, because $\varphi(t)$ differs from $g(t)$ only in extremely small intervals. At this we conclude our attempt to explain the idea behind the proved lemma.

We shall now continue with the proof of the theorem. Let us note first of all that it is possible to carry out the proof for a function $\Phi(x)$, possessing the properties:

(1) $\Phi(x)$ is continuous in $[0, 2\pi]$,
(2) $\Phi(x) = 0$ outside some interval $[A, B]$, lying entirely within $(0, 2\pi)$.

Indeed, let $\sigma > 0$ be given. Let us assume that we know how to find a set $E_1$ and a function $G(x)$ such that

$$G(x) = \Phi(x) \quad \text{in} \quad E_1, \quad \text{where} \quad mE_1 > 2\pi - \frac{\sigma}{4}, \tag{4.10}$$

and $\sigma(G)$ converges uniformly.

Now let $f(x)$ be any measurable function, finite almost everywhere in $[0, 2\pi]$. Let

$$A = \frac{\sigma}{8}, \quad B = 2\pi - \frac{\sigma}{8},$$

$$A' = \frac{\sigma}{4}, \quad B' = 2\pi - \frac{\sigma}{4}.$$

Since $f(x)$ possesses a $C$-property in $[0, 2\pi]$, which also means in $(A', B')$ then it is possible to find $P \subset (A', B')$, $mP > (B' - A') - \sigma/4 = 2\pi - \frac{3}{4}\sigma$, such that $f(x) = \Phi(x)$ in $P$, where $\Phi(x)$ is a function continuous in $(A', B')$ (Fig. 34). If we assume that $\Phi(x) = 0$ in $(0, A)$ and $(B, 2\pi)$ and then we interpolate it linearly in $[AA']$ and

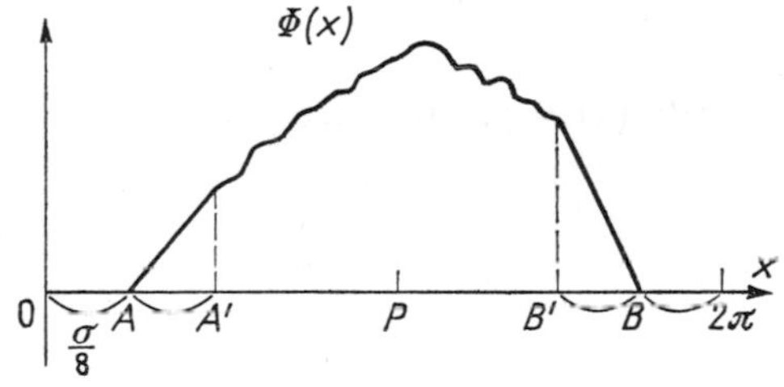


FIG. 34

$[B'B]$, $\Phi(x)$ will satisfy conditions (1) and (2). It is supposed that we already know how to find $G(x)$, satisfying condition (4.10) and with an uniformly convergent Fourier series.

Supposing that

$$E = E_1 P,$$

we see that

$$G(x) \leqslant f(x) \quad \text{in} \quad E$$

and in this case $mE > 2\pi - \sigma$ because

$$mCE \leqslant mCE_1 + mCP < \frac{\sigma}{4} + \frac{3}{4}\sigma = \sigma. \tag{4.11}$$

Thus, we have shown that it is sufficient to prove the theorem for the function $\Phi(x)$ continuous everywhere and returning to zero outside some $[A, B]$, entirely lying within $[0, 2\pi]$.

Let us return to proving the theorem for this case.

First of all, we will represent $\Phi(x)$ in the form of a series

$$\Phi(x) = \sum_{m=1}^{\infty} \Phi_m(x), \tag{4.12}$$

where all the functions $\Phi_m(x)$ are step-functions, the series converges uniformly and

$$|\Phi_m(x)| \leqslant \frac{\sigma}{2^{2m}} \quad (m = 2, 3, \ldots). \tag{4.13}$$

Due to the continuity of $\Phi(x)$ this is always possible.

Moreover, it can always be assumed that $\Phi_m(x) = 0$ in $[0, A]$ and $[B, 2\pi]$ for $m = 1, 2, \ldots$ because $\Phi(x) = 0$ in these intervals.

For every function $\Phi_m(x)$, the interval $[0, 2\pi]$ breaks up into a finite number of segments, in each of which it is constant; let $\varrho_k^{(m)}$ be these segments enumerated from left to right; in the first and the last of them $\Phi_m(x) = 0$. We will first enumerate all the $\varrho_j^{(1)}$, then all the $\varrho_j^{(2)}$ etc., then we obtain a sequence of segments

$$\Delta_1, \Delta_2, \ldots, \Delta_s, \ldots,$$

whilst, if $\nu_m$ is the number of all the intervals where the functions $\Phi_1(x), \Phi_2(x), \ldots, \Phi_m(x)$ are constant, then for $s$ satisfying the condition

$$\nu_{m-1} < s \leqslant \nu_m, \tag{4.14}$$

we have

$$\Delta_s = \varrho_j^{(m)}$$

for some value of $j$ and

$$\Phi_m(x) = \gamma_s \quad \text{for} \quad x \in \Delta_s, \tag{4.15}$$

where

$$|\gamma_s| \leqslant \frac{\sigma}{2^{2m}} \tag{4.16}$$

due to (4.13).

Now let

$$n_1 < n_2 < \cdots < n_s < \cdots \tag{4.17}$$

be a sequence of natural numbers which we will define later. Let us assume that

$$\varepsilon_s = \frac{1}{s^2 n_s^2}. \tag{4.18}$$

On the basis of Lemma 4, in which we suppose that

$$[c, d] = \Delta_s, \quad \varepsilon = \varepsilon_s, \quad \nu = 2^{m+3}\left(\left[\frac{2\pi}{\sigma}\right] + 1\right), \quad \gamma = \gamma_s, \tag{4.19}$$

we can for every $s$ satisfying condition (4.14) find a continuous broken $\psi_s(x)$ such that

(a) $\psi_s(x) = 0$ outside $\Delta_s$,

(b) $|\psi_s(x)| \leqslant 2\nu\,|\gamma_s| \leqslant 2 \cdot 2^{m+3}\left(\left[\frac{2\pi}{\sigma}\right] + 1\right)\frac{\sigma}{2^{2m}} < \frac{64\pi}{2^m}$

(due to (4.16) and (4.19))

(c) $\left|\int\limits_0^{\xi} \psi_s(t)\,dt\right| < \varepsilon_s, \quad 0 \leqslant \xi \leqslant 2\pi,$

(d) $\psi_s(x) = \gamma_s$ in $\mathscr{E}_s$, where

(e) $\mathscr{E}_s \subset \Delta_s$ and $m\mathscr{E}_s > \Delta_s\left(1 - \frac{5}{\nu}\right) > \Delta_s\left(1 - \frac{\sigma}{2\pi 2^m}\right)$,

because $\nu \geqslant 8 \times 2^m \frac{2\pi}{\sigma}$. i.e. $\frac{5}{\nu} < \frac{\sigma}{2\pi \times 2^m}$,

(f) $\left|\int\limits_0^{2\pi} \psi_s(t)\frac{\sin n(t-x)}{t-x}\,dt\right| \leqslant B\nu\,|\gamma| \leqslant \frac{A}{2^m}$

for any $n$ and $x$, where $A$ is an absolute constant because, as we have already calculated, $\nu\,|\gamma| \leqslant 32\pi/2^m$.

Let us note that if $\gamma_s = 0$, then it is possible to take $\psi_s(x) = 0$, as was shown at the beginning of the proof of Lemma 4.

Now let

$$H_m = \sum_{s=\nu_{m-1}+1}^{\nu_m} \mathscr{E}_s.$$

Then

$$mH_m = \sum m\mathscr{E}_s > \left(1 - \frac{\sigma}{2\pi \cdot 2^m}\right)\sum \Delta_s = 2\pi\left(1 - \frac{\sigma}{2\pi\, 2^m}\right) = 2\pi - \frac{\sigma}{2^m}, \tag{4.20}$$

because the intervals $\Delta_s$ for $s$ running through values from $\nu_{m-1} + 1$ to $\nu_m$ consist of all the intervals where $\Phi_m(x)$ is constant, i.e. they do not overlap and fill the interval $[0, 2\pi]$.

Supposing that

$$E = \prod_{m=1}^{\infty} H_m,$$

we have due to (4.20)

$$mE > 2\pi - \sigma. \tag{4.21}$$

If now we suppose that

$$G_m(x) = \psi_s(x) \quad \text{in } \Delta_s, \quad \nu_{m-1} < s \leqslant \nu_m, \tag{4.22}$$

then from (d) it follows that

$$G_m(x) = \gamma_s(x) \quad \text{in } \mathscr{E}_s$$

and since $\mathscr{E}_s \subset \Delta_s$, then from (4.15)

$$G_m(x) = \Phi_m(x) \quad \text{in} \quad \mathscr{E}_s$$

and consequently

$$G_m(x) = \Phi_m(x) \quad \text{in} \quad H_m,$$

whence

$$G_m(x) = \Phi_m(x) \quad \text{in} \quad E(m = 1, 2, \ldots). \tag{4.23}$$

Every $G_m(x)$ is continuous, since all the $\psi_s(x)$ are continuous and return to zero at the end-points of $\Delta_s$.

A discontinuity at the point 0 or $2\pi$ during periodic expansion can also not occur, since we have already said that $\psi_s(x) = 0$, if $\gamma_s = 0$ and in the intervals $[0, A]$ and $[B, 2\pi]$ we have $\Phi_m(x) = 0$ for any $m$.

Finally, since every $\psi_s(x)$ satisfies condition (b), then by virtue of (4.22)

$$|G_m(x)| \leqslant \frac{64\pi}{2^m},$$

and, consequently, supposing that

$$G(x) = \sum_{m=1}^{\infty} G_m(x),$$

we see that $G(x)$ is continuous, because the series converges uniformly. From (4.11) and (4.23) we then obtain

$$G(x) = \Phi(x) \quad \text{in} \quad E,$$

and because $mE > 2\pi - \sigma$ (see (4.21)), then it remains to prove that $\sigma(G)$ converges uniformly for the theorem to be proved.

Let us note, first of all, that the series $\sum_{s=1}^{\infty} \psi_s(x)$ also converges uniformly to $G(x)$. Indeed, any $G_m(x)$ can be defined as the sum of $\psi_s(x)$ for $\nu_{m-1} < s \leqslant \nu_m$, because for any $x$ only one of these functions is different from zero ($\psi_s(x) = 0$ outside $\Delta_s$ due to (a)). Moreover, every $\psi_s(x)$ satisfies (b). For this it is sufficient to prove the validity of the statement

$$G(x) = \sum_{s=1}^{\infty} \psi_s(x), \tag{4.24}$$

where the series converges uniformly.

In order to prove the uniform convergence of $\sigma(G)$ (for an appropriate choice of the numbers $n_k$ which we have not yet defined) it is sufficient to show that for any $\varepsilon > 0$ it is possible to find $N$ such that, supposing

$$S_n(x) = \frac{1}{\pi} \int_0^{2\pi} G(t) \frac{\sin n(t - x)}{t - x}\, dt,$$

we have

$$|S_n(x) - G(x)| < \varepsilon \quad \text{for} \quad n \geqslant N, \quad 0 \leqslant x \leqslant 2\pi.$$

By virtue of (4.24) we can write

$$S_n(x) = \sum_{s=1}^{\infty} \frac{1}{\pi} \int_0^{2\pi} \psi_s(t) \frac{\sin n(t - x)}{t - x}\, dt. \tag{4.25}$$

The functions $\psi_s(t)$ are completely defined only after the numbers $n_s$ have been given, which up to now have satisfied only (4.17); for these $n_s$ we construct $\varepsilon_s$ (see (4.18)) and then it is possible to define $\psi_s(t)$ according to Lemma 4 with all the conditions of (4.19) satisfied. Let us suppose that $n_1 = 1$ and let

$$n_1 < n_2 < \cdots < n_{k-1}$$

be already chosen. Then $\varepsilon_s$ and also $\psi_s$ for $s = 1, 2, \ldots, k-1$ are already constructed. Each of them is a continuous broken function, which means that their sum is too, and therefore

$$\left| \sum_{s=1}^{k-1} \frac{1}{k} \int_0^{2\pi} \psi_s(t) \frac{\sin n(t-x)}{t-x} dt - \sum_{s=1}^{k-1} \psi_s(x) \right| < \frac{1}{k}, \quad 0 \leqslant x \leqslant 2\pi, \tag{4.26}$$

provided $n$ becomes sufficiently large, since $\sigma\left(\sum_{s=1}^{k-1} \psi_s(x)\right)$ converges uniformly to this function. We will choose $n_k > n_{k-1}$ and sufficiently large for the inequality (4.26) to hold for $n > n_k$. Now all the $n_s$ are defined and all the $\psi_s(x)$ are constructed in this way.

Now let $n$ be any value; we will find a number $k$ such that

$$n_k \leqslant n < n_{k+1}. \tag{4.27}$$

Then, if $n \to \infty$, $k \to \infty$ also, which means that it is possible to take $n$ so large that

$$\frac{1}{k} < \frac{\varepsilon}{64}. \tag{4.28}$$

Moreover, we will consider $n$ to be so large that, defining $k$ from the inequality (4.27) and then finding $m$ from

$$\nu_{m-1} < k \leqslant \nu_m, \tag{4.29}$$

we have

$$\frac{A}{2^m} < \frac{\varepsilon}{4}, \tag{4.30}$$

where $A$ is a constant entering into condition (e) for the functions $\psi_s(x)$ at $\nu_{m-1} < s \leqslant \nu_m$.

Finally, due to the uniform convergence of the series $\sum_{s=1}^{\infty} \psi_s(x)$ it is possible to suppose that for this $k$

$$\left| \sum_{s=k}^{\infty} \psi_s(x) \right| < \frac{\varepsilon}{4}. \tag{4.31}$$

Now, supposing that

$$J_{n_s}(x) = \frac{1}{\pi} \int_0^{2\pi} \psi_s(t) \frac{\sin n(t-x)}{t-x} dt,$$

we have on the basis of (4.26) and (4.31)

$$|S_n(x) - G(x)| = \left| \sum_{s=1}^{\infty} J_{n_s}(x) - \sum_{s=1}^{\infty} \psi_s(x) \right|$$

$$\leqslant \sum_{s=1}^{k-1} |J_{n_s}(x) - \psi_s(x)| + |J_{n_k}(x)| + \sum_{s=k+1}^{\infty} |J_{n_s}(x)| + \left| \sum_{s=k}^{\infty} \psi_s(x) \right|$$

$$\leqslant \frac{1}{k} + \frac{\varepsilon}{4} + |J_{n_k}(x)| + \sum_{s=k+1}^{\infty} |J_{n_s}(x)|. \tag{4.32}$$

Now on the basis of property (f) of the functions $\psi_s(x)$ we have

$$|J_{n_k}(x)| \leqslant \frac{A}{2^m} < \frac{\varepsilon}{4}, \tag{4.33}$$

because $k$ satisfies (4.29) and $m$ satisfies (4.30).

Finally, on the basis of Lemma 2 for any $J_{n_s}$, due to property (c) of the functions $\psi_s(x)$, we can write

$$|J_{n_s}(x)| \leqslant 16n^2 \varepsilon_s \leqslant 16n^2 \frac{1}{s^2 n_s^2},$$

because $\varepsilon_s$ satisfies (4.18). Therefore, from (4.27) we conclude that

$$|J_{n_s}(x)| \leqslant 16n_{k+1}^2 \frac{1}{s^2 n_s^2} \leqslant \frac{16}{s^2} \quad \text{at} \quad s \geqslant k+1$$

and, consequently, due to (4.28)

$$\left| \sum_{s=k+1}^{\infty} J_{n_s}(x) \right| \leqslant 16 \sum_{s=k+1}^{\infty} \frac{1}{s^2} < \frac{16}{k} < \frac{\varepsilon}{4}. \tag{4.34}$$

Combining (4.32), (4.33), (4.34) and (4.28), we obtain

$$|S_n(x) - G(x)| < \varepsilon,$$

and the proof is concluded.

## § 5. The strengthened *C*-property

It seems to be appropriate to introduce this terminology.

DEFINITION. The function $f(x)$ possesses a *strengthened C-property* in some $E \subset [0, 2\pi]$, $mE > 0$, if for any $\varepsilon > 0$ there exists $P \subset E$, $mP > mE - \varepsilon$, in which $f(x) = g(x)$, where $g(x)$ is continuous in $[0, 2\pi]$ and its Fourier series converges uniformly in $[0, 2\pi]$.

Using this definition, we can formulate the Men'shov theorem proved in § 4 thus: *if a measurable function is finite almost everywhere in* $[0, 2\pi]$, *then it possesses a strengthened C-property in it.* However, it is easily seen that it possesses a strengthened *C*-property too in any $E$, $mE > 0$ lying in $[0, 2\pi]$. Indeed, taking $\varepsilon > 0$, it is possible to find $\mathscr{E}$, $m\mathscr{E} > 2\pi - \varepsilon$, and $g(x)$ such that $f(x) = g(x)$ in $\mathscr{E}E$ and $\sigma(g)$ converges uniformly. The intersection $E\mathscr{E}$ is a set for which $m(\mathscr{E}E) > mE - \varepsilon$, and inside it can be taken a perfect set $P$, $mP > mE - \varepsilon$; in $P$ we have $f(x) = g(x)$ and $g(x)$ possesses the necessary properties; this means that $f(x)$ possesses a strengthened $C$-property in $E$.

This permits us to state as follows:

Corollary to Men'shov's Theorem. *For any measurable $f(x)$ finite almost everywhere in* $[0, 2\pi]$ *there exists a sequence of perfect nowhere-dense sets $P_k (k = 1, 2, \ldots)$ such that*

(1) *the sets $P_k$ do not possess common points in pairs*

(2) *if $Q = \sum_{k=1}^{\infty} P_k$, then $mQ = 2\pi$,*

(3) $f(x) = f_k(x)$ *in $P_k$* $(k = 1, 2, \ldots)$

*where all $f_k(x)$ are continuous and possess uniformly convergent Fourier series in* $[0, 2\pi]$.

Indeed, we first find a perfect nowhere-dense set $P_1$, $mP_1 > 0$, in which $f(x) = f_1(x)$, where $f_1(x)$ is continuous and $\sigma(f_1)$ converges uniformly.

We will assume that $P_1, P_2, \ldots, P_{k-1}$ have already been constructed; they are all perfect, nowhere-dense and without common points in pairs and

$$f(x) = f_j(x) \quad \text{in} \quad P_j \quad \text{for} \quad j = 1, 2, \ldots, k-1,$$

where all the $f_j(x)$ are continuous and all the $\sigma(f_j)$ converge uniformly. We will assume that

$$Q_{k-1} = P_1 + P_2 + \cdots + P_{k-1}.$$

Because $Q_{k-1}$ is nowhere-dense, we have $mCQ_{k-1} > 0$; therefore, in $CQ_{k-1}$ the function $f(x)$ possesses a strengthened $C$-property which means that a perfect $P_k$ is found $mP_k > mCQ_{k-1} - 1/k$, in which $f(x) = f_k(x)$ where $f_k(x)$ is continuous and $\sigma(f_k)$ converges uniformly. The constructed $P_k$ does not possess common points with $P_1, P_2, \ldots, P_{k-1}$. It is clear that, supposing $Q = \sum_{k=1}^{\infty} P_k$, we have $mQ = 2\pi$ and the proof is concluded.

This corollary to Men'shov's theorem will be very useful later (see Chapter XV, §2).

## § 6. Problems connected with the "adjustment" of functions

We have proved that any measurable function $f(x)$ finite almost everywhere can be "adjusted" in a set of as small measure as desired so that it is converted into a continuous $g(x)$ with uniformly convergent Fourier series. In particular, this holds for any continuous function $f(x)$. But the set, in which $f(x)$ remains unchanged, depends on the function $f(x)$. Men'shov set the problem, whether it was not possible to achieve the transformation of a continuous function $f(x)$ into $g(x)$ with an uniformly convergent Fourier series, by requiring that $f(x)$ remain unchanged in some given set and it would be possible to adjust it only outside this set. He showed, above all, that his theorem (proved in § 4) can strengthen in the sense that the set $e(me < \varepsilon)$, where it is permitted to change the function, can be considered as dependent only on $\varepsilon$ and the modulus of continuity of $f(x)$ but not on the other properties of this function. More precisely, he proved a theorem (see Men'shov[11]):

*For any positive non-decreasing function* $\varrho(\delta)$ *definable for* $\delta > 0$ *and such that* $\lim_{\delta \to 0} \varrho(\delta) = 0$, *and for any* $\varepsilon > 0$ *there exists a set* $e$, $me < \varepsilon$, *such that if* $f(x)$ *is any continuous function for which the modulus of continuity* $\omega(\delta)$ *satisfies the condition*

$$\omega(\delta) \leqslant \varrho(\delta) \quad \text{for any} \quad \delta,$$

*then* $f(x)$ *can be changed in* $e$ *so that for the newly obtained* $g(x)$ *the series* $\sigma(g)$ *converges uniformly.*

But, all the same, in the preceding theorem $e$ depends on the modulus of continuity of $f(x)$. Men'shov posed the question: is it possible to choose $e$ so that it is dependent only on $\varepsilon$? It seems that this is impossible to do, even if the requirements of uniform convergence of the series $\sigma(g)$ for the adjusted function $g(x)$ is discarded and only its convergence at every point is demanded. So Men'shov[11] proved a theorem.

*For any set* $e$, $me < 2\pi$, *it is possible to define a function* $f(x)$ *continuous in* $[0, 2\pi]$ *such that: whatever the function* $\psi(x)$ *which is continuous in* $[0, 2\pi]$ *and coincides with* $f(x)$ *everywhere outside* $e$, *the series* $\sigma(\psi)$ *diverges at least at one point.*

Thus, it is already impossible to choose $E$ beforehand, $mE > 2\pi - \varepsilon$, and to require that the continuous $f(x)$ be maintained in $E$ and, changing it only outside $E$, to obtain a continuous $g(x)$ with an everywhere convergent series $\sigma(g)$.

But if it is required that $\sigma(g)$ converge only almost everywhere? This question remains open. However, if it were answered in the positive sense, it would signify that $\sigma(f)$ for any continuous $f(x)$ converges almost everywhere. Indeed, we have seen in § 21, Chapter V, that perfect nowhere-dense sets $P$ exist, possessing this property: if $f_1(x)$ and $f_2(x)$ both belong to $L^p (p > 1)$ and $f_1(x) = f_2(x)$ in $P$, then $\sigma(f_1) - \sigma(f_2)$ converges to zero almost everywhere in $P$. Therefore, if the "adjustment" of $f(x)$ outside this $P$ is possible, then this means that its Fourier series converges almost everywhere in $P$. But, choosing the sets $P_n$ of the same type in any interval $\delta_n$ adjacent to $P$, we obtain a new set $Q = P + P_1 + \cdots + P_n + \cdots$, in which $\sigma(f)$ again converges almost everywhere. Inserting suitably selected sets in each interval adjacent to $Q$ and continuing this process to infinity, we prove that $\sigma(f)$ converges almost everywhere. But the problem of the almost everywhere convergence of a Fourier series of a continuous function has not yet been solved and, evidently, is very difficult.

If it is required after the change of $f(x)$ outside a given perfect nowhere-dense set, to obtain merely a $g(x)$ for which $\sigma(g)$ converges almost everywhere but which itself is only summable, then this problem is solved in the affirmative. An even more general result which we will describe in § 7 holds.

## § 7. "Adjustment" of a summable function outside a given perfect set

In this section we will prove the following theorem due to Men'shov[13]:

THEOREM. *Let* $f(x)$ *be any function summable in* $[0, 2\pi]$ *and* $P$ *be any perfect nowhere-dense set in* $[0, 2\pi]$. *It is possible to find a summable* $g(x)$ *such that*

$$g(x) = f(x) \quad \text{in} \quad P$$

*and* $\sigma(g)$ *converges almost everywhere.*

To prove the theorem some lemmas are necessary. Lemma 5 recalls Lemma 4 and, just as the latter, is based on the properties of the Dirichlet factor discussed in § 3. The difference between them consists of the fact that in Lemma 4 continuity is required of the function $\psi(x)$ and conditions are imposed on its modulus: here it is sufficient to make it a step-function and to impose limitations not on its modulus but only on the integral of the modulus; then, instead of having a given value $\gamma$ in some set of measure approximating to the length of the interval, where $\psi(x)$ is definable, it is required that it has a given value in a set, the choice of which does not depend on us. Statement (e) of Lemma 5 is somewhat weaker than in Lemma 4, since it operates on the second half of the lemma concerning the Dirichlet factor but it is sufficient for our purpose.

LEMMA 5. *Let $[c, d]$ be an arbitrary segment, $\gamma$ be any real number, $\varepsilon$ be any positive number, $\nu > 8$ be any integer; finally, let $Q$ be any perfect nowhere-dense set, $Q \subset [c, d]$. Then there exists a function $\psi(x)$ such that*

(a) *$\psi(x)$ is a step-function in $[c, d]$,*

(b) $\int_c^d |\psi(t)|\, dt \leqslant 2|\gamma|(d-c)$,

(c) $\left|\int_c^\xi \psi(t)\, dt\right| < \varepsilon, \quad c \leqslant \xi \leqslant d$,

(d) $\psi(x) = \gamma$ *in* $Q$,

(e) $\left|\int_c^d \psi(t)\frac{\sin n(t-x)}{t-x}\, dt\right| \leqslant B\nu|\gamma|$ *for* $x \in E, \quad n = 1, 2, \ldots,$

*where*

(f) $mE > (d-c)\left(1 - \frac{6}{\nu}\right)$,

*and $B$ is an absolute constant.*

*Proof.* If $\gamma = 0$, then it is sufficient to suppose that $\psi(x) = 0$ and $E = [c, d]$. Therefore we will consider $\gamma \neq 0$.

First of all, as in the proof of Lemma 4, we choose $r$ so large that for

$$q = r\nu$$

we have

$$4|\gamma|\frac{d-c}{q} < \varepsilon. \tag{7.1}$$

Having fixed $r$ thus, which also means $q$, we again, as in Lemma 4, suppose that

$$\delta = \frac{d-c}{q\nu}. \tag{7.2}$$

Now we suppose that

$$x_s = c + \nu\delta s \quad (s = 0, 1, \ldots, q).$$

Then

$$c = x_0 < x_1 < \cdots < x_q = d.$$

In Lemma 4 these numbers are denoted by $c_s$ but now it will be more convenient to denote by $c_s$ the "slightly" displaced points. Namely, if $Q$ is nowhere-dense, then it is possible to choose $\alpha < \delta$ so that the points

$$c_s = x_s - \alpha \quad (s = 0, 1, \ldots, q)$$

all lie outside $Q$, i.e.

$$c_s \,\overline{\in}\, Q \quad (s = 0, 1, , \ldots, q).$$

Moreover, we note that

$$c_1 = x_1 - \alpha = x_0 + \nu\delta - \delta > x_0,$$

because $\nu > 8$, which means that

$$x_0 = c < c_1 < \cdots < c_q = d - \alpha < d,$$

where all $c_s$ $(s = 1, 2, \ldots, q)$ lie in $(c, d)$.

Since all $c_s$ are outside $Q$ and $Q$ is nowhere-dense, then it is possible to find $\delta' < \delta$ such that, supposing

$$a_s = c_s - \delta',$$

we have

$$[a_s, c_s] \,\overline{\in}\, Q \quad (s = 1, 2, \ldots, q). \tag{7.3}$$

Because

$$c_1 - a_1 = \delta' < \delta; \quad c_1 - c = x_1 - \alpha - x_0 \geqslant \nu\delta - \delta > \delta,$$

then we have

$$c < a_1.$$

Finally,

$$c_{s+1} - c_s = \nu\delta.$$

We will now define $\varphi(x)$ from the conditions

$$\varphi(x) = \begin{cases} -\dfrac{d-c}{q\delta'}\gamma & \text{in} \quad (a_s, c_s), \quad 1 \leqslant s \leqslant q, \\ 0 & \text{everywhere in} \quad [c, d] \quad \text{outside all} \quad (a_s, c_s). \end{cases}$$

It is clear that $\varphi(x)$ is a step-function. Moreover,

$$\int_c^{a_1} \varphi(t)\,dt = 0, \quad \int_{c_{s-1}}^{a_s} \varphi(t)\,dt = 0 \quad (s = 2, 3, \ldots, q),$$

$$\int_{a_s}^{c_s} \varphi(t)\,dt = -\delta' \frac{d-c}{q\delta'}\gamma = -\frac{d-c}{q}\gamma \quad (s = 1, 2, \ldots, q).$$

Therefore

$$\int_c^{c_1} \varphi(t)\,dt = -\frac{d-c}{q}\gamma, \quad \int_{c_{s-1}}^{c_s} \varphi(t)\,dt = -\frac{d-c}{q}\gamma \quad (s = 2, 3, \ldots, q).$$

We will suppose that
$$\psi(x) = \gamma + \varphi(x) \quad (c \leqslant x \leqslant d).$$
It is clear that $\psi(x)$ is a step-function, i.e. (a) is satisfied.

Since $\varphi(x)$ is always of the same sign as $-\gamma$, then

$$\int_c^d |\varphi(t)|\,dt = \left| \int_c^{c_1} \varphi(t)\,dt + \sum_{s=2}^{q} \int_{c_{s-1}}^{c_s} \varphi(t)\,dt + \int_{c_q}^{d} \varphi(t)\,dt \right| = (d-c)\,|\gamma|,$$

and therefore

$$\int_c^d |\psi(t)|\,dt \leqslant |\gamma|\,(d-c) + \int_c^d |\varphi(t)|\,dt \leqslant 2\,|\gamma|\,(d-c),$$

i.e. (b) is also proved.

In order to prove (c) we show first that

$$\int_{c_{s-1}}^{s} \psi(t)\,dt = 0 \quad (s = 1, 2, \ldots, q).$$

Indeed

$$\int_{c_{s-1}}^{c_s} \psi(t)\,dt = \gamma(c_s - c_{s-1}) + \int_{c_{s-1}}^{c_s} \varphi(t)\,dt = \gamma\nu\delta - \frac{d-c}{q}\gamma = 0,$$

since $\delta = (d-c)/q\nu$.

We now consider

$$\int_{c_s}^{c_s+\beta} \psi(t)\,dt \, (s = 1, 2, \ldots, q)$$

for $0 < \beta < \nu\delta$. We have

$$\int_{c_s}^{c_s+\beta} \psi(t)\,dt = \gamma\beta + \int_{c_s}^{c_s+\beta} \varphi(t)\,dt.$$

But $\beta < \nu\delta = \dfrac{d-c}{q}$, therefore $|\gamma|\beta \leqslant \dfrac{d-c}{q}|\gamma| < \varepsilon/4$ by virtue of (7.1). Moreover, $\varphi(t) \neq 0$ only in $(a_s, c_s)$ and therefore

$$\left| \int_{c_s}^{c_s+\beta} \varphi(t)\,dt \right| \leqslant \delta' \frac{d-c}{\delta' q}|\gamma| = \frac{d-c}{q}|\gamma| < \frac{\varepsilon}{4}.$$

Thus

$$\left| \int_{c_s}^{c_s+\beta} \psi(t)\,dt \right| < \frac{\varepsilon}{2} \quad \text{for} \quad 0 \leqslant \beta \leqslant \nu\delta.$$

The case $(c, c+\beta)$ is exactly similar.

Finally, let $\xi$ be any point in $[c, d]$. We will find the $c_k$ which is the closest to $\xi$ on the left (or the number $c$). Then

$$\left| \int_c^{\xi} \psi(t)\,dt \right| \leqslant \left| \int_c^{c_1} \psi(t)\,dt \right| + \left| \sum_{s=1}^{k-1} \int_{c_s}^{c_{s+1}} \psi(t)\,dt \right| + \left| \int_{c_k}^{\xi} \psi(t)\,dt \right| \leqslant \frac{\varepsilon}{2} + \frac{\varepsilon}{2} = \varepsilon,$$

since the middle sum equals zero.

Thus, property (c) is proved.

From the fact that $\varphi(t) \neq 0$ only in the segments $[a_s, c_s]$ not containing the points of $Q$, it follows that $\psi(x) = \gamma$ in $Q$ and this is condition (d).

Finally, supposing that

$$E = \sum_{s=r}^{q-r-1} [c_s + 2\delta,\ c_{s+1} - 2\delta],$$

we see that

$$mE = (q - 2r)(\nu\delta - 4\delta) = q\nu\delta\left(1 - \frac{2r}{q}\right)\left(1 - \frac{4}{\nu}\right)$$

$$= (d - c)\left(1 - \frac{2}{\nu}\right)\left(1 - \frac{4}{\nu}\right) > (d - c)\left(1 - \frac{6}{\nu}\right),$$

i.e. condition (f) is also fulfilled.

It remains to prove that (e) is fulfilled. But due to the construction of the numbers $c_s$ the set $E$ satisfies the condition of Lemma 3 and therefore

$$\left|\sum_{s=1}^{q} \int_{a_s}^{c_s} \frac{\sin n(t - x)}{t - x}\, dt\right| < A\frac{\delta'}{\delta} \quad (n = 1, 2, \ldots) \quad \text{for} \quad x \in E.$$

In every $[a_s, c_s]$ we have $\varphi(t) = -\dfrac{d - c}{q\delta'}\gamma$ and outside them $\varphi(t) = 0$, therefore for $-\infty < x < +\infty$ we have

$$\int_c^d \varphi(t)\frac{\sin n(t - x)}{t - x}\, dt = -\frac{d - c}{q\delta'}\gamma\sum_{s=1}^{q}\int_{a_s}^{c_s}\frac{\sin n(t - x)}{t - x}\, dt,$$

whence

$$\left|\int_c^d \varphi(t)\frac{\sin n(t - x)}{t - x}\, dt\right| < \frac{d - c}{q\delta'}|\gamma| A\frac{\delta'}{\delta} = A\nu|\gamma|$$

for $x \in E$. Moreover, it is known that

$$\left|\int_c^d \frac{\sin n(t - x)}{t - x}\, dt\right| < 2\pi$$

for any $c$, $d$, $x$ and $n$, which means that for $x \in E$

$$\left|\int_c^d \psi(t)\frac{\sin n(t - x)}{t - x}\, dt\right| \leqslant 2\pi|\gamma| + A\nu|\gamma| < B\nu|\gamma|,$$

where $B$ is an absolute constant, i.e. (e) is proved and the proof of Lemma 5 is concluded.

LEMMA 6. *For any functions $f(x)$ summable in $[c, d]$ and for any sequence of positive numbers $\alpha_m$ $(m = 1, 2, \ldots)$ it is possible to construct a sequence of step-functions $\Phi_m(m = 1, 2, \ldots)$ such that*

(a) *all $\Phi_m(x)$ are step-functions in $[c, d]$,*

(b) $\sum_{m=1}^{\infty} \Phi_m(x) = f(x)$ *almost everywhere in* $[c, d]$,

(c) $\int_c^d |\Phi_m(t)|\, dt < \alpha_m \quad (m = 2, 3, \ldots)$.

*Proof.* We will assume that

$$\omega_m = \min\left(\frac{\alpha_m}{2}, \frac{\alpha_{m+1}}{2}, \frac{1}{4^m}\right) \quad (m = 1, 2, \ldots).$$

Since $f(x)$ is summable, then it is possible to find for any $m$ a step-function $g_m(x)$ such that

$$\int_c^d |f(t) - g_m(t)|\, dt < \omega_m \quad (m = 1, 2, \ldots).$$

Let $E_m$ be a set of those $t \subset [c, d]$ for which

$$|f(t) - g_m(t)| < \frac{1}{2^m}.$$

Then, from the fact that

$$\int_{CE_m} |f(t) - g_m(t)|\, dt < \omega_m$$

and

$$\int_{CE_m} |f(t) - g_m(t)|\, dt \geqslant \frac{1}{2^m} mCE_m,$$

it follows that

$$mCE_m \leqslant 2^m \omega_m \leqslant \frac{1}{2^m},$$

and therefore

$$mE_m \geqslant (d - c) - \frac{1}{2^m}.$$

Supposing that

$$E = \underline{\lim}\, E_m,$$

we have, consequently

$$mE = d - c.$$

But by virtue of the definition of $E_m$ it follows from this that

$$\lim_{m \to \infty} g_m(t) = f(t)$$

in $E$, i.e. almost everywhere in $[c, d]$.

Let us suppose that

$$\Phi_1(x) = g_1(x); \quad \Phi_m(x) = g_m(x) - g_{m-1}(x) \quad (m = 2, 3, \ldots).$$

Since $g_m(x)$ were step-functions, then $\Phi_m(x)$ also possesses this property, i.e. property (a). Moreover, it is clear that

$$\sum_{m=1}^{\infty} \Phi_m(x) = \lim_{m\to\infty} g_m(x) = f(x) \quad \text{almost everywhere,}$$

i.e. (b) is also fulfilled.

Finally,

$$\int_c^d |\Phi_m(t)|\, dt \leqslant \int_c^d |g_m(t) - f(t)|\, dt + \int_c^d |f(t) - g_{m-1}(t)|\, dt$$

$$\leqslant \omega_m + \omega_{m-1} \leqslant \frac{\alpha_m}{2} + \frac{\alpha_m}{2} = \alpha_m \quad (m = 2, 3, \ldots),$$

i.e. (c) is true, and Lemma 6 is proved.

Let us return to the proof of the theorem. Let $f(x)$ be a given summable function. Supposing in Lemma 6 that the numbers $\alpha_m = 1/2^{3m}$ and $[c, d] = [0, 2\pi]$, we construct $\Phi_m(x)$, step-functions in $[0, 2\pi]$, such that

$$\sum_{m=1}^{\infty} \Phi_m(x) = f(x) \quad \text{almost everywhere in} \quad [0, 2\pi], \tag{7.4}$$

$$\int_0^{2\pi} |\Phi_m(x)|\, dx \leqslant \frac{1}{2^{3m}}. \tag{7.5}$$

For any $m$ the interval $[0, 2\pi]$ is divided into a finite number of intervals, in each of which $\Phi_m(x)$ is constant. We will enumerate from left to right all the intervals for

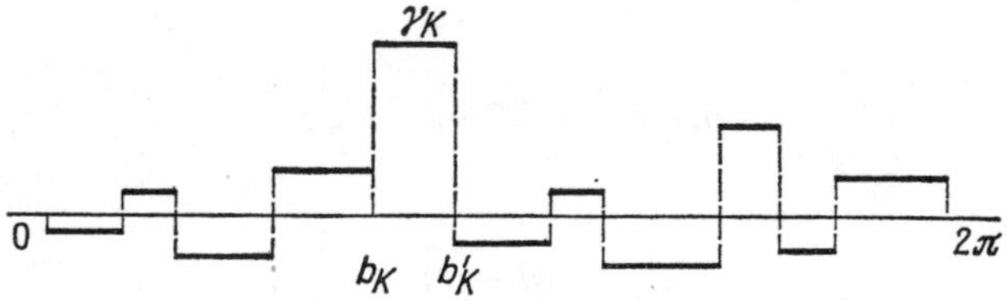


FIG. 35

$\Phi_1(x)$, then from left to right all the intervals for $\Phi_2(x)$, etc., then for $\Phi_m(x)$, etc. Supposing $\nu_0 = 0$ and denoting by $\nu_1$ the number of intervals where $\Phi_1(x)$ is constant, ..., by $\nu_m - \nu_{m-1}$ the number of intervals where $\Phi_m(x)$ is constant, ..., we have

$$\nu_0 < \nu_1 < \cdots < \nu_m < \cdots$$

and for every $k$, $\nu_{m-1} < k \leqslant \nu_m$ in the interval $(b_k, b'_k)$ the function $\Phi_m(x)$ is constant; let $\gamma_k$ be its value. The whole interval $[0, 2\pi]$ is entirely divided into non-overlapping intervals $[b_k, b'_k]$, $\nu_{m-1} < k \leqslant \nu_m$ (Fig. 35). It is clear that when $m$ is given, then for a given point $x$ there is an unique way to define the $k$ for which $x \in [b_k, b'_k]$, whilst if $m \to \infty$, then it is also known that $k \to \infty$.

Let us suppose that

$$g_k(x) = \begin{cases} \gamma_k & \text{in} \quad [b_k, b'_k], \\ 0 & \text{outside} \quad [b_k, b'_k]. \end{cases} \tag{7.6}$$

Then

$$\Phi_m(x) = \sum_{k=\nu_{m-1}+1}^{\nu_m} g_k(x), \quad m = 1, 2, \ldots,$$

apart, perhaps, from the points $b_k$ and $b'_k$.

We will show that

$$\sum_{s=1}^{\infty} g_s(x) = f(x) \quad \text{almost everywhere in} \quad [-\pi, \pi]. \tag{7.7}$$

Indeed, let $k$ be any value. We find $m$ so that $\nu_{m-1} < k \leqslant \nu_m$. Then

$$\sum_{s=1}^{k} g_s(x) = \sum_{s=1}^{\nu_{m-1}} g_s(x) + \sum_{\nu_{m-1}+1}^{k} g_s(x) = \sum_{p=1}^{m-1} \Phi_p(x) + \sum_{s=\nu_{m-1}+1}^{\nu_m} g_s(x). \tag{7.8}$$

But of all the functions $g_s(x)$ of the second term of the right-hand side of equation (7.8) only one can be different from zero at the point $x$ and since its magnitude is $\gamma_s$, and $\gamma_s$ is the value of $\Phi_m(x)$ at this point, then the second term of the right-hand side of (7.8) either equals 0 or equals $\Phi_m(x)$, which means that the whole right-hand side of (7.8) equals $\sum_{p=1}^{m-1} \Phi_p(x)$ or $\sum_{p=1}^{m} \Phi_p(x)$; but as $k \to \infty$ we have $m \to \infty$, and therefore it follows from (7.4) that

$$\lim_{k \to \infty} \sum_{s=1}^{k} g_s(x) = \sum_{s=1}^{\infty} g_s(x) = f(x) \quad \text{almost everywhere.} \tag{7.9}$$

Let us now take for every $k$ the natural $n_k$ which we will define later.

Let $P$ be a set entering into the formulation of the theorem. Let $P_k$ be the part falling in $(b_k, b'_k)$, then $P_k$ is nowhere-dense or empty.

We will assume that

$$\varepsilon_k = \frac{1}{k^2 n_k^2} \quad (k = 1, 2, \ldots). \tag{7.10}$$

In Lemma 5, choosing $m$ and $k$ from the condition $\nu_{m-1} < k \leqslant \nu_m$, we will suppose that

$$\nu = 2^{m+3}, \quad \gamma = \gamma_k, \quad \varepsilon = \varepsilon_k, \quad [c, d] = [b_k, b'_k], \quad Q = P_k.$$

This is possible since $\nu > 8$, all the remaining numbers being any values. On the basis of Lemma 5 we can find $\psi_k(x)$ and measurable $E_k$ such that

(a) $\psi_k(x)$ is a step-function in $[b_k, b'_k]$,

(b) $\int_{b_k}^{b'_k} |\psi_k(t)|\, dt \leqslant 2\,|\gamma_k|\,(b'_k - b_k)$,

(c) $\left| \int_{b_k}^{\xi} \psi_k(t)\, dt \right| < \varepsilon_k, \quad b_k \leqslant \xi \leqslant b_k'$,

(d) $\psi_k(x) = \gamma_k$ in $P_k$,

(e) $\left| \int_{b_k}^{b_k'} \psi_k(t) \frac{\sin n(t-x)}{t-x}\, dt \right| \leqslant B \cdot 2^{m+3} |\gamma_k|, \quad x \in E_k, \quad n = 1, 2, \ldots,$

(f) $mE_k \geqslant (b_k' - b_k)\left(1 - \frac{6}{2^{m+3}}\right) > (b_k' - b_k)\left(1 - \frac{1}{2^m}\right)$,

where $E_k \in [b_k, b_k']$.

We require that $\psi_k(x) = 0$ outside $(b_k, b_k')$ in $[0, 2\pi]$. Thus, the expanded $\psi_k(x)$ will be a step-function in $[0, 2\pi]$ and it will be defined completely after the numbers $n_k$, on which $\varepsilon_k$ depend, are given.

Since $P_k$ is the part of $P$ in $[b_k, b_k']$, then due to property (c) of the function $\psi_k(x)$ and by virtue of (7.6) we have

$$\psi_k(x) = \gamma_k = g_k(x) \quad \text{in} \quad P_k.$$

Moreover, from the very definition

$$\psi_k(x) = 0 \quad \text{and} \quad g_k(x) = 0 \quad \text{outside} \quad (b_k, b_k'),$$

whence

$$\psi_k(x) = g_k(x) \quad \text{in} \quad P.$$

This is true for $k = 1, 2, 3, \ldots$. This means that it follows from (7.9)

$$\sum_{k=1}^{\infty} \psi_k(x) = f(x) \quad \text{almost everywhere in} \quad P.$$

Since

$$\int_{b_k}^{b_k'} |\Phi_m(t)|\, dt = |\gamma_k|\, (b_k' - b_k),$$

then from property (b) we derive

$$\int_{b_k}^{b_k'} |\psi_k(t)|\, dt \leqslant 2 \int_{b_k}^{b_k'} |\Phi_m(t)|\, dt,$$

and therefore (since outside $(b_k, b_k')$ we have $\psi_k(t) = 0$)

$$\sum_{k=\nu_{m-1}+1}^{\nu_m} \int_0^{2\pi} |\psi_k(t)|\, dt \leqslant 2 \sum \int_{b_k}^{b_k'} |\Phi_m(t)|\, dt = 2 \int_0^{2\pi} |\Phi_m(t)|\, dt < \frac{2}{2^{3m}}$$

due to (7.5), which means that

$$\sum_{k=1}^{\infty} \int_0^{2\pi} |\psi_k(t)|\, dt < 2 \sum_{m=1}^{\infty} \frac{1}{2^{3m}} < +\infty, \tag{7.11}$$

whence it follows that $\sum_{k=1}^{\infty} \psi_k(x)$ converges almost everywhere and

$$\sum_{k=1}^{\infty} \psi_k(x) = H(x) \tag{7.12}$$

is a summable function. We have $H(x) = f(x)$ almost everywhere in $P$.

It is now necessary to prove that the numbers $n_k$ can be chosen so that the Fourier series for $H(x)$ converges almost everywhere.

Since all $\psi_k(x)$ are step-functions, then, denoting by $S_n^{(k)}(x)$ the partial sum of the Fourier series for $\sum_{j=1}^{k} \psi_j(x)$, we have

$$\lim_{n\to\infty} S_n^{(k)}(x) = \sum_{j=1}^{k} \psi_j(x) \quad \text{almost everywhere,}$$

and, moreover,

$$S_n^{(k)}(x) = \frac{1}{\pi} \int_0^{2\pi} \left[\sum_{j=1}^{k} \psi_j(t)\right] \frac{\sin n(t-x)}{t-x}\, dt + \varepsilon_{n,k}(x),$$

where

$$\lim_{n\to\infty} \varepsilon_{n,k}(x) = 0 \quad (0 \leqslant x \leqslant 2\pi, \quad k = 1, 2, \ldots).$$

Supposing that

$$J_{n,j}(x) = \frac{1}{\pi} \int_0^{2\pi} \psi_j(t) \frac{\sin n(t-x)}{t-x}\, dt,$$

we see, consequently, that

$$\lim_{n\to\infty} \sum_{j=1}^{k} J_{n,j}(x) = \sum_{j=1}^{k} \psi_j(x) \quad \text{almost everywhere.}$$

Let $n_1 = 1$. We will assume that $n_1 < n_2 < \cdots < n_{k-1}$ are already defined, then $\psi_1(x), \ldots, \psi_{k-1}(x)$ are already known and we have

$$\lim_{n\to\infty} \sum_{j=1}^{k-1} J_{n,j}(x) = \sum_{j=1}^{k-1} \psi_j(x) \quad \text{almost everywhere.}$$

On the basis of Yegorov's theorem it is possible to find a $G_k$ in which this tending to zero is uniform, whilst

$$mG_k > 2\pi - \frac{1}{k^2}, \quad G_k \subset [0, 2\pi].$$

This means that it is possible to find $n_k > n_{k-1}$ such that

$$\left| \sum_{j=1}^{k-1} J_{n,j}(x) - \sum_{j=1}^{k-1} \psi_j(x) \right| < \frac{1}{k} \quad \text{for} \quad x \in G_k \quad \text{and} \quad n \geqslant n_k. \tag{7.13}$$

Then all the $n_k$ are already defined, whilst

$$n_1 < n_2 < \cdots < n_k < \cdots$$

and all the $\psi_1(x), \ldots, \psi_k(x), \ldots$ and $G_1, G_2, \ldots, G_k, \ldots$ have been constructed. We have, supposing that

$$G = \varliminf_{k\to\infty} G_k, \quad mG = 2\pi.$$

We must now estimate $J_{n,j}(x)$ for any $x$, $0 < x < 2\pi$, any $j$ and $n \leqslant n_{k+1}$. Since

$$J_{n,j}(x) = \frac{1}{\pi}\int_0^{2\pi} \psi_j(t)\frac{\sin n(t-x)}{t-x}\,dt,$$

and $\psi_j(x)$ possesses property (c) and equals zero outside $(b_k, b_k')$, then

$$\left|\int_0^\xi \psi_j(t)\,dt\right| < \varepsilon_j \quad (0 < \xi < 2\pi),$$

and therefore it is possible to apply Lemma 2 of § 2, which gives, due to (7.10)

$$|J_{n,j}(x)| \leqslant 16n^2\varepsilon_j \leqslant 16n_{k+1}^2\frac{1}{n_j^2 j^2} \quad \text{for} \quad n \leqslant n_{k+1}.$$

From this it follows that

$$|J_{n,j}(x)| \leqslant \frac{16}{j^2} \quad \text{for any } x, \quad j \geqslant k+1, \quad n \leqslant n_{k+1}. \tag{7.14}$$

We denote by $\Omega_m$ the aggregate of all the segments $[b_k, b_k']$, $\nu_{m-1} < k \leqslant \nu_m$, for which

$$|\gamma_k| \leqslant \frac{1}{2^{2m}}.$$

We will estimate the measure of $\Omega_m$. Its complement $C\Omega_m$ is divided into sections $(b_k, b_k')$ where $|\gamma_k| > 1/2^{2m}$; in each such section $\Phi_m(x) = \gamma_k$, and therefore

$$\int_{C\Omega_m} |\Phi_m(t)|dt > \frac{1}{2^{2m}}\, mC\Omega_m.$$

But because by virtue of (7.5)

$$\int_{C\Omega_m} |\Phi_m(t)|\,dt \leqslant \int_0^{2\pi} |\Phi_m(t)|\,dt \leqslant \frac{1}{2^{3m}},$$

then

$$mC\Omega_m < \frac{1}{2^m},$$

which means that also

$$m\Omega_m > 2\pi - \frac{1}{2^m}.$$

Therefore, supposing

$$\Omega = \varliminf_{m\to\infty} \Omega_m,$$

we have

$$m\Omega = 2\pi.$$

Let us assume that

$$\delta_j = |\gamma_j'|\,(b_j' - b_j)\,2^m, \quad \nu_{m-1} < j \leqslant \nu_m \tag{7.15}$$

and

$$\Omega_m' = [0, 2\pi] - \sum_{\nu_{m-1}+2}^{\nu_m} [b_j - \delta_j, b_j + \delta_{j-1}].$$

It is clear that

$$m\Omega_m' \geqslant 2\pi - 2\sum_{\nu_{m-1}+1}^{\nu_m} \delta_j = 2\pi - 2^{m+1}\sum_{\nu_{m-1}+1}^{\nu_m} |\gamma_j|\,(b_j' - b_j)$$

$$= 2\pi - 2^{m+1}\int_0^{2\pi} |\Phi_m(t)|\,dt > 2\pi - 2^{m+1}\frac{1}{2^{3m}} = 2\pi - \frac{2}{2^{2m}},$$

whence, supposing that

$$\Omega' = \varliminf_{m\to\infty} \Omega_m',$$

we again have

$$m\Omega' = 2\pi.$$

We will assume that

$$\Omega_m'' = \sum_{k=\nu_{m-1}+1}^{\nu_m} E_k.$$

Since, due to property (f), we have

$$mE_k > (b_k' - b_k)\left(1 - \frac{1}{2^m}\right),$$

but

$$\sum_{k=\nu_{m-1}+1}^{\nu_m} (b_k' - b_k) = 2\pi,$$

then

$$m\Omega_m'' > 2\pi\left(1 - \frac{1}{2^m}\right)$$

and supposing that

$$\Omega'' = \varliminf_{m\to\infty} \Omega_m'',$$

we again have

$$m\Omega'' = 2\pi.$$

Denoting by $G'$ the set of points where the series $\sum_{k=1}^{\infty} \psi_k(x)$ converges to $H(x)$, we again have

$$mG' = 2\pi.$$

We will denote by $\mathscr{E}$ the common part of the sets $G$, $G'$, $\Omega$, $\Omega'$, $\Omega''$, and of the open interval $(0, 2\pi)$; we have

$$m\mathscr{E} = 2\pi.$$

We will prove that the Fourier series of $H(x)$ converges at every point of the set $\mathscr{E}$.

Let $S_n(x)$ be the sum of the first $n$ terms of the Fourier series for $H(x)$, then

$$S_n(x) = I_n(x) + \eta_n(x),$$

where

$$I_n(x) = \frac{1}{\pi}\int_{-\pi}^{\pi} H(t)\frac{\sin n(t-x)}{t-x}\,dt$$

and $\eta_n(x) \to 0$ in $0 < x < 2\pi$.

We shall prove that for $x \in \mathscr{E}$

$$\lim_{n\to\infty} I_n(x) = H(x).$$

From the definition of $\mathscr{E}$ it follows that for $x \in \mathscr{E}$ there are found $k_0$ and $m_0$ such that

$$\left.\begin{array}{ll} x \in \Omega_m, \quad x \in \Omega'_m, \quad x \in \Omega''_m, & m > m_0, \\ x \in G_k, & k > k_0. \end{array}\right\} \tag{7.16}$$

Moreover, $x \in G'$.

When $n$ is given, we determine $k$ from the condition

$$n_k < n \leqslant n_{k+1}$$

and then $m$ from the condition

$$\nu_{m-1} < k \leqslant \nu_m.$$

It is clear that as $n \to \infty$ we have $k \to \infty$ and then $m \to \infty$ also. It is possible to take $n_x$ so large that for it $m > m_0$ and $k > k_0$ already; then for $n \geqslant n_x$ we will always have the conditions of (7.16) fulfilled.

We have for any $x$

$$\sum_{j=1}^{\infty} \psi_j(t)\frac{\sin n(t-x)}{t-x} = H(t)\frac{\sin n(t-x)}{t-x} \tag{7.17}$$

for any $n$ and for almost all $x$ (due to (7.12)).

Since, due to (7.11)

$$\sum_{j=1}^{\infty}\int_0^{2\pi} |\psi_j(t)|\,dt < +\infty,$$

then the series

$$\sum_{j=1}^{\infty}\int_0^{2\pi} |\psi_j(t)|\left|\frac{\sin n(t-x)}{t-x}\right| dt$$

also converges for any $x$ and $n = 1, 2, \ldots$, and in this case the equality (7.17) can be integrated term by term, which means that

$$I_n(x) = \sum_{j=1}^{\infty}\frac{1}{\pi}\int_0^{2\pi}\psi_j(t)\frac{\sin n(t-x)}{t-x}\,dt = \sum_{j=1}^{\infty} J_{n,j}(x) = I'_n(x) + I''_n(x) + I'''_n(x),$$

where

$$I'_n(x) = \sum_{j=1}^{k-1} J_{n,j}(x); \quad I''_n(x) = J_{n,k}(x); \quad I'''_n(x) = \sum_{j=k+1}^{\infty} J_{n,j}(x).$$

Since it was proved that (7.14) occurs, i.e.

$$|J_{n,j}(x)| \leqslant \frac{16}{j^2}, \quad \text{if} \quad j \geqslant k+1 \quad \text{and} \quad n \leqslant n_{k+1},$$

then

$$|I_n'''(x)| \leqslant 16 \sum_{j=k+1}^{\infty} \frac{1}{j^2} < \frac{16}{k},$$

and therefore

$$\lim_{n\to\infty} I_n'''(x) = 0 \quad \text{for any } x.$$

Also, since $x \in G_k$, then due to (7.13)

$$\left| \sum_{j=1}^{k-1} J_{n,j}(x) - \sum_{j=1}^{\infty} \psi_j(x) \right| < \frac{1}{k}.$$

Because $n \geqslant n_k$ and therefore

$$\left| I_n'(x) - \sum_{j=1}^{\infty} \psi_j(x) \right| < \frac{1}{k} \quad \text{for} \quad x \in G_k. \tag{7.18}$$

But since $x \in G'$, where $\sum_{j=1}^{\infty} \psi_j(x) = H(x)$, then from (7.18) we obtain

$$\lim_{n\to\infty} I_n'(x) = H(x).$$

It remains to prove that

$$\lim_{n\to\infty} I_n'' = \lim_{n\to\infty} J_{n,k}(x) = 0.$$

If $\gamma_k = 0$, then from property (b) of the function $\psi_k(t)$ it follows immediately that $\int_{b_k}^{b_k'} |\psi_k(t)|\, dt = 0$, i.e. $\psi_k(t) = 0$ almost everywhere in $(b_k, b_k')$ and therefore $J_{n,k}(x) = 0$. Therefore, we will suppose that $\gamma_k \neq 0$.

Let us consider two cases: (1) $x \in (b_k, b_k')$ and (2) $x \bar{\in} (b_k, b_k')$. We will begin with the first case.

We know that $x \in \Omega_m$ for $m$ linked with $k$ by the condition $\nu_{m-1} < k \leqslant \nu_m$, whilst from the definition of $\Omega_m$, the interval $(b_k, b_k')$ is such that in it

$$|\gamma_k| < \frac{1}{2^{2m}}.$$

On the other hand, $x \in Q_m''$, therefore $x \in E_k$, and therefore due to property (e) of the function $\psi_k(t)$

$$|J_{n,k}(x)| \leqslant B \cdot 2^{m+3} |\gamma_k|,$$

which means that

$$|J_{n,k}(x)| < B \cdot 8 \frac{1}{2^m} \to 0 \quad \text{as} \quad n \to \infty,$$

since $m \to \infty$ in this.

We now assume that $x \bar{\in} (b_k, b_k')$; then $x \in (b_j, b_j')$ for $j \neq k$ and $\nu_{m-1} < j \leqslant \nu_m$. But $x \in \Omega_m'$, which means that $x \bar{\in} (b_k - \delta_k, b_k)$ and $x \bar{\in} (b_k', b_k' + \delta_k)$ (since $b_j' = b_{j+1}$, and $x \bar{\in} (b_j + \delta_{j-1})$ which holds for any $j$, $\nu_{m-1} < j \leqslant \nu_m$).

From this it follows that when $b_k \leqslant t \leqslant b_k'$ and $x$ is not only outside $(b_k, b_k')$ but even outside $(b_k - \delta_k, b_k' + \delta_k)$, then

$$|t - x| > \delta_k.$$

But we have assumed $\gamma_k \neq 0$, which means that $\delta_k \neq 0$ due to (7.15) and

$$|J_{n,k}(x)| \leqslant \frac{1}{\pi \delta_k} \int_{b_k}^{b_k'} |\psi_k(t)| \, dt. \tag{7.19}$$

From property (b) of the function $\psi_k(x)$

$$\int_{b_k}^{b_k'} |\psi_k(t)| \, dt \leqslant 2 \, |\gamma_k| \, (b_k' - b_k),$$

therefore, due to (7.15) and (7.19)

$$|J_{n,k}(x)| < \frac{1}{2^m}$$

which means that again $\lim J_{n,k}(x) = 0$ as $n \to \infty$.

We have proved that the Fourier series of $H(x)$ converges to it almost everywhere. If we now assume that

$$G(x) = \begin{cases} f(x) & \text{in} \quad P, \\ H(x) & \text{in} \quad CP, \end{cases}$$

then $G(x)$ is summable and the Fourier series of $G(x)$ converges to it almost everywhere, since $G(x) = H(x)$ almost everywhere, because $H(x) = f(x)$ almost everywhere in $P$.

The theorem is proved.

## § 8. Problems

1. Construct the function $f(x) \in C(0, 2\pi)$ such that a trigonometric series does not exist which would converge to $f(x)$ everywhere in $[0, 2\pi]$.

[Either the function of § 45 or that of § 46, Chapter I, can be used for $f(x)$. Apply the du Bois-Reymond–Lebesgue theorem (see Chapter I, § 72).]

2. A function $f(x)$ continuous in $[0, 1]$ exists such that whatever trigonometric series

$$\frac{a_0}{2} + \sum_{n=1}^{\infty} (a_n \cos nx + b_n \sin nx) \tag{8.1}$$

we take, a point $x_0 \in [0, 1]$ can always be found at which the series (8.1) does not converge to $f(x_0)$.

[Assume that $f(x) = F(x)$ for $0 \leqq x \leqq 1$, where the function $F(x) \in C(0, 2\pi)$ and the Fourier series of $F(x)$ diverges at the point $\frac{1}{2}$. Use the properties of the Riemann function (see Chapter I, §§ 62–72).]

3. Prove that a function $f(x)$ continuous in [0, 1] exists such that for any function $F(x) \in C(0, 2\pi)$ the Fourier series is not absolutely convergent at almost every point $x_0 \in [0, 2\pi]$, provided $F(x) = f(x)$ for $0 \leqslant x \leqslant 1$.

4. Consider the function

$$f(x) = \begin{cases} 1/x & \text{for } 0 < x < 2\pi \\ 0 & \text{for } x = 0 \text{ and } x = 2\pi. \end{cases}$$

Then a trigonometric series does not exist which would converge everywhere in $[0, 2\pi]$ to $f(x)$.

5. Let the set $F \subset (0, 2\pi)$ consist of all the points of the type $2\pi p/q$ where $0 < p < q$ and $p/q$ is an irreducible fraction.

Prove that whatever the function $f(x)$ is such that it equals $+\infty$ for $x \in E$ and $f(x)$ is finite for $x \in [0, 2\pi] - E$, then there exists a trigonometric series which would converge to $f(x)$.

[This follows from the fact that the set $E$ is not a set of the type $G_\delta$.]

6. Let $(a, b)$ be an arbitrary non-empty interval of the interval $[0, 2\pi]$ and let $E \subset (a, b)$ be some set of the second category in $(a, b)$ and $m(c, d)E > 0$ for any interval $(c, d) \subset (a, b)$. Then a trigonometric series of the form (8.1) which would converge everywhere in $E$ to $+\infty$ or to $-\infty$ does not exist.

In particular, a series of the type (8.1) does not exist which would converge to $+\infty$ or to $-\infty$ at every point of some interval $(\alpha, \beta)$.

[Use the Lusin–Privalov theorem concerning the uniqueness of analytic functions (see [19], pp. 319–320).]

7. The following problem has not been solved: can any function $f(x) \in C(0, 2\pi)$ be changed in some set of as small a measure as desired, so that the Fourier series of the new function is absolutely convergent at every point of the interval $[0, 2\pi]$?

# APPENDIX TO CHAPTER II

## § 1. The Phragmén–Lindelöf principle

Let $f(z)$, $z = x + iy$, be continuous and bounded in a strip $S$

$$\alpha \leqslant x \leqslant \beta, \quad -\infty < y < +\infty,$$

and moreover regular inside $S$. If $|f| \leqslant K$ on the boundaries of the strip, i.e. at $x = \alpha$ and $x = \beta$, then $|f(z)| \leqslant K$ also inside $S$.

Let us assume first that

$$|f(x+iy)| \to 0 \tag{1.1}$$

uniformly relative to $x$, $\alpha \leqslant x \leqslant \beta$, if $y \to \pm\infty$. If $z_0 = x_0 + iy_0$ lies inside $S$, then we take $\eta$ so large that $|f(x+i\eta)| \leqslant K$ for $\alpha \leqslant x \leqslant \beta$ and so that rectangle $\alpha \leqslant x \leqslant \beta$, $|y| \leqslant \eta$ contains the point $z_0$. Then applying the principle of the maximum modulus, which is well-known in the theory of analytic functions, we see that $|f(z_0)| \leqslant K$.

Thus, the theorem is proved for condition (1.1).

In the general case we assume that

$$f_n(z) = f(z)\, e^{\frac{z^2}{n}} = f(z)\, e^{\frac{x^2-y^2}{n}}\, e^{2i\frac{xy}{n}}.$$

Then $f_n(z)$ satisfies condition (1.1) which means that, supposing $\gamma = \max(|\alpha|, |\beta|)$ we have $|f_n(z)| \leqslant K e^{\gamma^2/n}$ on the boundary of $S$. Therefore for any $z_0$ inside $S$ we have $|f_n(z_0)| \leqslant K e^{\gamma^2/n}$ and, passing to the limit as $n \to \infty$, we obtain

$$|f(z_0)| \leqslant K.$$

It could be proved that if $f(z_0) = K$ at some internal point, then $f(z) = \text{const.}$ in $S$ but we do not require this.

*Another form of the Phragmén–Lindelöf principle.* Let $f(z)$ be continuous and bounded in the strip $S$ and also regular everywhere inside $S$ and let

$$|f(\alpha+iy)| \leqslant K_1, \quad |f(\beta+iy)| \leqslant K_2 \tag{1.2}$$

for all values of $y$. Then if $L(t)$ is a linear function taking the values 1 and 0 respectively for $t = \alpha$ and $t = \beta$, then

$$|f(x_0+iy)| \leqslant K_1^{L(x_0)} \cdot K_2^{1-L(x_0)}.$$

Although this result seems to be a strengthening of the preceding, it does however follow from it. Indeed, supposing that

$$f_1(z) = \frac{f(z)}{K_1^{L(z)} K_2^{1-L(z)}},$$

we see that $f_1(z)$ satisfies the conditions expressed in the first formulation of the Phragmén–Lindelöf principle, if we assume there $K = 1$.

## § 2. Modulus of continuity and modulus of smoothness in $L^p$ ($p \geqslant 1$)

If $f \in L^p[-\pi, \pi]$, then we assume that

$$\omega^{(p)}(\delta, f) = \sup_{0 \leqslant |h| \leqslant \delta} \left\{ \int_{-\pi}^{\pi} |f(x+h) - f(x)|^p dx \right\}^{1/p},$$

i.e.

$$\omega^{(p)}(\delta, f) = \sup_{0 \leqslant |h| \leqslant \delta} \| f(x+h) - f(x) \|_{L^p}.$$

In particular, *the quadratic modulus of continuity*

$$\omega^2(\delta, f) = \sup_{0 \leqslant |h| \leqslant \delta} \| f(x+h) - f(x) \|_{L^2},$$

and also *the quadratic modulus of smoothness*

$$\omega_2^{(2)}(\delta, f) = \sup_{0 \leqslant |h| \leqslant \delta} \| f(x+h) + f(x-h) - 2f(x) \| L^2.$$

will be useful. In the case when $f(x)$ is defined not over the whole interval $[-\pi, \pi]$ but only in some $[\alpha, \beta]$ and belongs to $L^p$ in it, then we define analogously

$$\omega^p(\delta, a, b, f) = \sup_{0 \leqslant |h| \leqslant \delta} \| f(x+h) - f(x) \|_{L^p[a,b]},$$

$$\omega_2^p(\delta, a, b, f) = \sup_{0 \leqslant |h| \leqslant \delta} \| f(x+h) + f(x-h) - 2f(x) \|,$$

if $\delta$ is such that $x \pm h \in [\alpha, \beta]$ for $x \in [a, b]$ and $0 \leqslant |h| \leqslant \delta$.

It is clear that for the modulus of continuity and the modulus of smoothness in $L^p$ the same properties hold as for the normal modulus of continuity, i.e.

(1) $\omega^{(p)}(\delta, f)$ monotonically increases,

(2) for any $\lambda > 0$

$$\omega^{(p)}(\lambda\delta, f) \leqslant C\lambda\omega^{(p)}(\delta, f),$$

where $C$ is constant and similarly for $\omega_2{}^{(p)}(\delta, f)$.

## § 3. A converse of the Hölder inequality

We know (see § 9 of the Introductory Material) that if $f(x) \in L^2$ $(p > 1)$ and $\varphi(x) \in L^q$ where $1/p + 1/q = 1$, then $f(x)\,\varphi(x) \in L$.

Similarly, if $\{a_n\} \in l^p$ and $\{b_n\} \in l^q$, then $\{a_n b_n\} \in L$.

Let us show that these statements are in a sense reversible. More precisely, we have

THEOREM. *If $\{a_n\}$ is a sequence such that*

$$\sum |a_n b_n| < +\infty,$$

*whatever the sequence $b_n$, provided $\sum |b_n|^q < +\infty$ $(q > 1)$, then*

$$\sum |a_n|^p < +\infty$$

*(where $1/p + 1/q = 1$).*

And similary, *if $f(x)\varphi(x) \in L$ for any $\varphi(x) \in L^q(q > 1)$, then $f(x) \in L^p$ (where $1/p + 1/q = 1$).*

To prove the validity of the first statement, we assume the converse, i.e. $\Sigma |a_n|^p = +\infty$. Let us assume that

$$u_n = |a_n|^p.$$

According to § 25 of the Appendix, supposing that $S_n = \sum_{k=1}^{n} u_k$, we have

$$\sum \frac{u_n}{S_n^{1+\varepsilon}} < +\infty \quad \text{and} \quad \sum \frac{u_n}{S_n} = +\infty$$

for any $\varepsilon > 0$. Let us assume that $b_n = u_n{}^{1/q}/S_n$; then

$$\sum |b_n|^q = \sum \frac{u_n}{S_n^q} < +\infty, \quad \text{since} \quad q > 1,$$

whilst

$$\sum |a_n|\,|b_n| = \sum u_n^{1/p}\frac{u_n^{1/q}}{S_n} = \sum \frac{u_n}{S_n} = +\infty.$$

This contradicts the fact that $\sum |a_n|\,|b_n| < +\infty$ for any $b_n$ for which $\sum |b_n|^q < +\infty$.

From the contradiction the validity of the theorem to be proved follows.

The argument for integrals can be reduced to the statement just proved for series. Indeed, let us assume that $f(x) \,\bar{\in}\, L^p$. Then

$$\int_a^b |f|^p\,dx = +\infty.$$

Let us take any $\varepsilon$ and divide the $Oy$ axis (in the same way as it is divided in the construction of the Lebesgue integral) into parts by points of separation $l_0 = 0, l_1, l_2, \ldots, l_n, \ldots$ situated at a distance from one another not exceeding $\varepsilon$. Let

$$E_i = \{l_i \leqslant |f(x)| < l_{i+1}\}.$$

Since

$$l_i \leqslant |f(x)| < l_i + \varepsilon,$$

then

$$l_i^p \leqslant |f(x)|^p < 2^p(l_i^p + \varepsilon^p)$$

(by virtue of the inequality of § 8 of the Introductory Material) in $E_i$ and therefore it is evident that

$$\sum l_i^p\, mE_i = +\infty.$$

If we discard from this series all the terms where $mE_i = 0$, then its divergence is not upset. Now supposing that

$$a_i^p = l_i^p\, mE_i, \quad \text{if} \quad mE_i \neq 0,$$

$$a_i = 0, \qquad \text{if} \quad mE_i = 0,$$

we see that

$$\sum a_i^p = +\infty.$$

According to what has just been proved we can find $|b_i|$ such that $\sum |b_i|^q < +\infty$, but

$$\sum |a_i b_i| = +\infty.$$

Let

$$\varphi(x) = \begin{cases} \dfrac{b_i}{(mE_i)^{1/q}}, & \text{if} \quad mE_i \neq 0, \\ 0, & \text{if} \quad mE_i = 0. \end{cases}$$

Then

$$\int_a^b f(x)\,\varphi(x)\,dx \geqslant \sum{}' \, l_i \frac{|b_i|}{(mE_i)^{1/q}}\, mE_i,$$

where the $\sum'$ indicates that all $i$ are discarded where $mE_i = 0$. But

$$\sum{}' \, l_i \frac{|b_i|\, mE_i}{(mE_i)^{1/q}} = \sum{}' \frac{|a_i|\,|b_i|}{(mE_i)^{1/p}(mE_i)^{1/q}}\, mE_i = \sum{}' \, |a_i|\,|b_i| = +\infty.$$

On the other hand

$$\int_a^b |\varphi(x)|^q\,dx = \sum{}' \frac{|b_i|^q}{mE_i}\, mE_i = \sum |b_i|^q < +\infty.$$

This means that

$$\int_a^b |f(x)\,\varphi(x)|\,dx = +\infty,$$

although

$$\int_a^b |\varphi(x)|^q \, dx < +\infty,.$$

and we arrive at a contradiction.

## § 4. The Banach–Steinhaus theorem

THEOREM. *If we have a sequence of linear functionals $U_n(x)$ in the space $L^p$ $(p > 1)$ and if*

$$|U_n(x)| < +\infty$$

*for all $x$ and $n = 1, 2, \ldots$, then there exists a constant $M$ such that*

$$\| U_n \| \leqslant M \quad (n = 1, 2, \ldots).$$

This theorem is a particular case of a more general result concerning linear functionals in Banach spaces (see, for example, Kaczmarz and Steinhaus[A. 12], Chapter I, Theorem 151).

# APPENDIX TO CHAPTER IV

## § 5. Categories of sets

Definition. *A* set $E$ is said to be *a set of the first category* in $[a, b]$ if it is the sum of a finite or denumerable number of sets, nowhere-dense in $[a, b]$.

This definition is due to Baire. Following Lusin, we shall say that $E$ is *a set of the second category* in $[a, b]$ if its complement $CE$ is a set of the first category in $[a, b]$.

Finally, if $E$ is not a set of the first category, then we shall say briefly: *E not of the first category*†.

Let $F$ be any closed set. If $\Delta$ is any closed interval then the part of $F$ falling into $\Delta$ is said to be *the portion of F*. The set $M$ is said to be *nowhere-dense in F* if in any portion of $F$ another non-empty is found which does not contain a single point of the set $M$; we call *a set of the first category in F* the set $E$ which is the sum of a finite or denumerable number of sets nowhere-dense in $F$. Sets of the second and not of the first category in $F$ are defined in the same way as in a closed interval by replacing $[a, b]$ by $F$.

*Any set of the second category in* $[a, b]$ *is a set of the power of the continuum in any closed interval* $\Delta$ *lying in* $[a, b]$ (see, for example, Lusin[A.17] § 21).

If a set $E$ of type $G_\delta$ (i.e. the intersection of a denumerable set of open sets) is everywhere dense in $[a, b]$, then it is of the second category in $[a, b]$; indeed, in this case its complement is $F_\sigma$ (i.e. the sum of a denumerable number of closed sets) and each of these closed sets should be nowhere-dense; in the opposite circumstances, they would contain a closed interval and this contradicts the fact that $E$ is everywhere dense.

We now have the following theorem due to Baire.

*Any non-empty closed set is a set of the second category in itself*††.

As a corollary of this theorem we obtain: if a non-empty closed set $F$ is contained in the sum of a denumerable set of closed sets $F_1 + F_2 + \cdots + F_n + \cdots$, then $n$ and a non-empty portion $\Delta(F)$ of the set $F$ are found such that $\Delta F \in F_n$.

Indeed, at least one of the $F_n$ cannot be nowhere-dense in $F$. But this means that amongst the closed intervals containing the points of $F$ there is a closed interval $\Delta$ such that $\Delta(F_n)$ is dense in $\Delta(F)$ and since $F_n$ is closed, then $\Delta(F) \subset \Delta(F_n) \subset F_n$.

*Note.* From the descriptive viewpoint sets of the second category are extremely "densely" arranged in the closed interval, since by removing from it a denumerable set of sets of the first category, we cannot empty the closed interval; there still remains a set of the second category. But from the metric viewpoint they could all the same be "negligible" since sets of the second category can be of measure zero (it is sufficient to construct in (0,1) the sum of a denumerable set of perfect nowhere-dense sets $P_n$ without common points and such that $mP_n = 1/2^n$, then $C(P_1 + \cdots + P_n + \cdots)$ is a set of the second category and of measure zero).

## § 6. Riemann's and Carathéodory's theorems

Theorem. *If G is a region bounded by a simple closed curve* $\Gamma$, *then there exists a function* $w = f(z)$ *giving a conformal representation of G on the circle* $|w| < 1$, *whilst between the boundaries of* $\Gamma$ *and the points of the circumference this function establishes a homeomorphic correspondence.*

This statement is the result of Riemann's theorem concerning the existence of a conformal representation on a circle for any simply connected region of an extended plane with boundaries con-

† Baire gave these sets the name "sets of the second category" but today in all reports on the descriptive theory of sets the more precise terminology of Lusin is accepted.

†† See, for example, Lusin[A.17], § 21, where although the proof is carried out for a closed interval, it can be used without change for a closed set, too.

taining more than one point (see, for example, Markushevich[A.20] p. 376) and Carathéodory's theorem concerning boundaries in conformal representation (see, for example, Markushevich[A.20] p. 409, Theorem 5 and its corollary).

## § 7. The connection between the modulus of continuity and the best approximation of a function

JACKSON'S THEOREM. *If $f(x)$ is periodic with period $2\pi$ and continuous, then*

$$E_n(f) \leqslant C\omega\left(\frac{1}{n}, f\right), \tag{7.1}$$

*where $C$ is an absolute constant* (it is possible to take $C = 12$).
(see, for example, Natanson[A.22], p. 117).

Later we shall require the following strengthening of this theorem, namely, the inequality

$$E_n(f) \leqslant C\,\omega_2\left(\frac{1}{n}, f\right). \tag{7.2}$$

To prove its validity we note that in the proof of Jackson's theorem in Natanson's book we have on p. 116 the equality (100)

$$U_n(x) - f(x) = \frac{3}{\pi n(2n^2+1)} \int_0^{\pi/2} [f(x+2t) + f(x-2t) - 2f(x)] \left(\frac{\sin nt}{\sin t}\right)^2 dt.$$

If it is written, as is done on the same page,

$$|f(x+2t) + f(x-2t) - 2f(x)| \leqslant 2\omega(2t), \tag{7.3}$$

then from this we also obtain

$$|U_n(x) - f(x)| \leqslant \left(1 + \frac{3}{2}\pi\right) \omega\left(\frac{1}{n}\right).$$

But instead of (7.3) we can write

$$|f(x+2t) + f(x-2t) - 2f(x)| \leqslant \omega_2(2t).$$

Then all the further arguments to the end of this section proceed in exactly the same way and we obtain

$$|U_n(x) - f(x)| \leqslant M\,\omega_2\left(\frac{1}{n}\right),$$

where $M$ is an absolute constant.

After this, by the same argument as in the proof of Jackson's theorem, we obtain formula (7.2) where $C$ is another absolute constant.

Similar formulae are also valid in the space $L^p$, i.e.

$$E_n^p(f) \leqslant C\omega^{(p)}\left(\frac{1}{n}, f\right), \tag{7.4}$$

$$p \geqslant 1.$$

$$E_n^{(p)}(f) \leqslant C\omega_2^{(p)}\left(\frac{1}{n}, f\right), \tag{7.5}$$

They are proved in the same way except that in all the formulae we take the norm in the space $L^p$ instead of the norm in the space $C$.

On the other hand, formulae also hold expressing the moduli of continuity in terms of the best approximations. Thus, for example, as A. F. Timan and M. F. Timan[1] proved,

$$\omega^{(2)}\left(\frac{1}{n}, f\right) \leqslant \frac{A}{n} \sum_{k=0}^{n-1} E_k^{(2)}(f), \tag{7.6}$$

and Stechkin[1] transferred this result to the space $C$ i.e. he obtained the inequality

$$\omega\left(\frac{1}{n}, f\right) \leqslant \frac{A}{n} \sum_{k=0}^{n-1} E_k(f) \tag{7.7}$$

(here $A$ is an absolute constant†).

Finally, we note that if instead of a closed interval of length $2\pi$ we consider an interval $[a, b]$, then similar formulae are valid, but the constants on their right-hand sides are not absolute but depend on $a, b$ and the norms of the functions $f(x)$ in the interval $[-\pi, \pi]$. However, when it is a matter of the same function throughout the argument, this circumstance does not prevent the necessary estimates being obtained.

We shall show, as an example, how the formula similar to (7.1) is obtained for the interval $[a, b]$. The function $f(x)$ given in $[a, b]$ must be extended in the interval $[0, 2\pi]$ in some way, provided a function $f_1(x)$ is obtained continuous over the whole interval and taking identical values at the end-points (for example, it can be assumed that $f(0) = f(2\pi) = 0$ and the function is interpolated linearly between 0 and $a$ and between $b$ and $2\pi$).

If $T_n(x)$ is the polynomial of the best approximation for $f_1(x)$ in $[0, 2\pi]$ then

$$|f_1(x) - T_n(x)| \leqslant E_n(f_1), \quad 0 \leqslant x \leqslant 2\pi,$$

and therefore

$$|f(x) - T_n(x)| \leqslant E_n(f_1), \quad a \leqslant x \leqslant b.$$

Then

$$E_n(f, a, b) \leqslant E_n(f_1). \tag{7.8}$$

But by virtue of Jackson's inequality

$$E_n(f_1) \leqslant C\omega\left(\frac{1}{n}, f_1\right). \tag{7.9}$$

From the construction of $f_1(x)$ it is clear that in $[a, b]$ its modulus of continuity coincides with $\omega[\delta, a, b, f]$ and in the intervals where it is linear we have

$$\omega(\delta, f_1) \leqslant K\delta,$$

where $K$ is a constant dependent on the norm of $f_1(x)$ in $[0, 2\pi]$ and consequently on $a, b$ and the norm of $f(x)$ in $[a, b]$. But since for any function $\varphi$ the modulus of continuity $\omega(\delta, \varphi) > a\delta$ where $a > 0$ (provided $\varphi(x)$ is not constant), then it is clear from this that

$$\omega(\delta, f_1) \leqslant B\omega(\delta, a, b, f), \tag{7.10}$$

where $B$ is a constant dependent on the norm of $f$ in $[a, b]$ and therefore from (7.8), (7.9) and (7.10)

$$E_n(f, a, b) \leqslant A\omega\left(\frac{1}{n}, a, b, f\right), \tag{7.11}$$

where $A$ is a constant dependent on the norm of $f$ in $[a, b]$.

Similarly, the formula

$$E_n(f, a, b) \leqslant A\omega_2\left(\frac{1}{n}, a, b, f\right), \tag{7.12}$$

is valid where again $A$ only depends on $a, b$ and the norm of $f$. Finally, formulae analogous to (7.6) and (7.7) are valid.

We note that the connection between the best approximations and the moduli of continuity was studied by many authors who continued the work of Jackson and Bernstein. One of their theorems is needed by us, namely:

---

† Stechkin writes the formula (7.7) somewhat differently, namely $(A/n)\sum_{k=1}^{n} E_k$ stands on the right-hand side; this is explained by the fact that he denotes by $E_n$ not the best approximation by polynomials of order not higher than $n$ but the best approximation by polynomials of order not higher than $n-1$; thus $E_n$ in our notation becomes $E_{n+1}$ in his notation.

BERNSTEIN'S THEOREM. *For $f(x) \in \operatorname{Lip} \alpha$, $0 < \alpha < 1$, it is necessary and sufficient that*

$$E_n(f) = O\left(\frac{1}{n^\alpha}\right).$$

(see, for example, Natanson[A.22], p. 132).

It is not difficult to establish that this theorem is just as strong as the statement:

If $0 < \alpha < 1$, then the conditions

$$E_n(f) = O\left(\frac{1}{n^\alpha}\right) \quad \text{and} \quad \omega(\delta, f) = O(\delta^\alpha)$$

are equivalent, i.e. each of them implies the other.

For $\alpha = 1$ this is not valid, but here, as Zygmund[14] showed, the modulus of smoothness must be taken instead of the modulus of continuity, i.e.

*The conditions*

$$E_n(f) = O\left(\frac{1}{n}\right) \quad \text{and} \quad \omega_2(\delta, f) = O(\delta)$$

*are equivalent.*

(see, for example, Natanson[A.22], p. 142).

With respect to other reports in this connection see Bary and Stechkin[1].

# APPENDIX TO CHAPTER V

## § 8. $\mu$-measures and integrals

Some class $K$ of sets definable in the space $\mathscr{E}$ is said to be *completely additive* if

(1) an empty set lies in $K$,

(2) if $E$ belongs to $K$, then its complement $CE$ (relative to $\mathscr{E}$) belongs to $K$,

(3) if all $E_n$ belong to $K$, then $\sum_{n=1}^{\infty} E_n$ also belong to $K$.

The function $\mu(E)$ is said to be a *measure* if it is determinate and non-negative for every $E$ of class $K$ and if

$$\mu\left(\sum_{n=1}^{\infty} E_n\right) = \sum_{n=1}^{\infty} \mu(E_n)$$

for any sequence of sets $E_n$ of $K$, not having pairs of common points. The value $\mu(E)$ is said to be the $\mu$-measure of the set $E$. If at every point of $E$ with the exception, perhaps, of the points belonging to $E$ of $\mu$-measure zero, some property $V$ holds, we shall say that the property $V$ is fulfilled almost everywhere in measure $\mu$ in $E$.

The Lebesgue integral defined as in the classical case but using $\mu$-measure instead of the Lebesgue measure is denoted by

$$\int_E f\,d\mu. \tag{8.1}$$

As regards its properties see, for example, Saks[A.30], Chapter I. In particular, in § 12 there it is proved that all the theorems noted in § 14 of the Introductory Material and referring to the integration of sequences of functions remain valid if integrals in measure $\mu$ are used instead of the normal Lebesgue integral.

Later we encounter integrals of the form

$$\int_E f\,dF(x), \tag{8.2}$$

where $F(x)$ is some function of bounded variation in some interval $[a, b]$. If a number $F(\beta) - F(\alpha)$ is set up to correspond with every interval $[\alpha, \beta] \subset [a, b]$, then we have an additive function of segments. If the function $F$ is monotonic, then this function is non-negative. In § 6 of Chapter III of Saks' book[A.30] a detailed explanation is given of what measure defined with the help of a non-negative additive function of a segment means. Thus, the definition of the integral (8.2) reduces to the definition of the integral (8.1) if $\mu$-measure is defined starting from monotonic $F(x)$. If $F(x)$ is not monotonic, then it is first represented in the form $F(x) = F_1(x) - F_2(x)$ where $F_1(x)$ and $F_2(x)$ are monotonic functions chosen in an appropriate way and then the integral (8.2) is defined as the difference of integrals of the same type but for the functions $F_1$ and $F_2$ (see Saks[A.30], Chapter III, §§ 4, 5 and 13).

Thus, for integrals of the type (8.2) the theorems cited above concerning the integration of sequences of functions are also valid.

# BIBLIOGRAPHY

## A. BOOKS

Fizmatgiz = State Physics and Mathematics Publishing House. GONTI = State United Scientific and Technical Publishing House. Gostekhizdat = State Technical Publishing House. GTTI = State Theoretical and Technical Publishing House. IL = Foreign Literature Publishing House. ONTI = United Scientific and Technical Press. Uchpedgiz = State Training and Pedagogical Publishing House. AN SSSR = Academy of Sciences of the U.S.S.R.


1. AKHIEZER, N.I. and M.G. KREIN, On some problems of the theory of moments *(O nekotorykh voprosakh teorii momentov)*. GONTI, Kharkov (1938).
2. ALEKSANDROV, P.S., and A.N. KOLMOGOROV, Introduction to the theory of functions of the real variable *(Vvedeniye v teoriyu funktsii deistvitel'nogo peremennogo)*. GONTI (1938).
3. BANACH, S., *Théorie des opérations linéaires*, Warsaw (1932).
4. BERNSTEIN, S.N., Collected works *(Sobraniye sochinanii)*, published by A. N. SSSR, Vol. I (1952), Vol. II (1954).
5. BERNSTEIN, S.N., Extremal properties of polynomials *(Ekstremal'nyye svoistva polinomov)*, Moscow (1937).
6. DENJOY, A., *Calcul des coefficients d'une série trigonométrique*, Paris (1941–1949).
7. FIKHTENGOL'TS, G.M., Course in differential and integral calculus *(Kurs differentsial'nogo i integral'nogo ischisleniya)*, Vol. II.
8. HARDY, G.H., *Divergent series*, Oxford (1949); Russian translation, IL, Moscow (1951).
9. HARDY, G.H., J.E. LITTLEWOOD and G. PÓLYA, *Inequalities*, Cambridge (1934); 2nd ed. (1952); Russian translation, IL, Moscow (1948).
10. HARDY, G.H., and W.W. ROGOSINSKI, *Fourier Series*, Cambridge Tracts, no. 38 (1950).
11. HOBSON, E.W., *Theory of functions of a real variable and the theory of Fourier series*, Cambridge (1921).
12. KACZMARZ, S., and H. STEINHAUS, *Theorie der Orthogonalreihen*, Monografje Matematyczne, Warsaw (1935); Russian translation including amendments and review, Fizmatgiz, Moscow (1958).
13. LEBESGUE, H., *Leçons sur l'intégration et sur la recherche des fonctions primitives*, Paris, 2nd ed. (1928); Russian translation, GTTI (1934).
14. LEBESGUE, H., *Leçons sur les séries trigonométriques*, Paris (1906).
15. LUSIN, N.N., The integral and trigonometric series *(Integral i trigonometricheskii ryad)*, Moscow (1915).
16. LUSIN, N.N., The integral and trigonometric series *(Integral i trigonometricheskii ryad)*. With critical and historical annotations by N. Bary and D.E. Men'shov. 2nd ed. Gostekhizdat, Moscow (1951).
17. LUSIN, N.N., The theory of functions of the real variable *(Teoriya funktsii deistvitel'nogo peremennogo)*. Uchpedgiz (1940).
18. LYUSTERNIK, L.A., and V.I. SOBOLEV, The elements of functional analysis *(Elementy funktsional'nogo analiza)*. Gostekhizdat, Moscow (1951).
19. MANDELBROJT, S., *Séries de Fourier et classes quasi-analytiques de fonctions*, Paris (1935); Russian translation, ONTI (1937).
20. MARKUSHEVICH, A.I., Theory of analytical functions *(Teoriya analiticheskikh funktsii)*, Gostekhizdat, Moscow (1950).
21. MINKOWSKI, H., *Diophantische Approximationen*, Leipzig (1907).
22. NATANSON, I.P., Constructional theory of functions *(Konstructivnaya teoriya funtksii)*, Gostekhizdat (1949).
23. NATANSON, I.P., Theory of functions of the real variable *(Teoriya funktsii veshchestvennoi peremennoi)*, Gostekhizdat (1957).

24. Nevanlinna, R., *Eindeutige analytische Funktionen*, Berlin (1936); 2nd ed. (1953); Russian translation, Gostekhizdat, Moscow–Leningrad (1950).
25. Plessner, A., *Trigonometrische Reihen* in Pascal's "Repertorium der höheren Analysis", Vol. 13, Berlin and Leipzig (1929).
26. Privalov, I. I., Cauchy Integral *(Integral Cauchy)*, Saratov (1919).
27. Privalov, I. I., Boundary properties of analytic functions *(Granichnyye svoistva analiticheskikh funktsii)*, Gostekhizdat, Moscow–Leningrad (1941).
28. Riemann, B., Collected works *(Sochineniya)*, Gostekhizdat, Moscow–Leningrad (1948); Russian translation.
29. Riesz, F., and Sz. Nagy B., *Leçons d'analyse fonctionelle*, Budapest (1952); Russian translation, IL, Moscow (1954).
30. Saks, S., *Theory of the Integral.* English translation, Monografje Matematyczne, II, Warsaw and New York (1937); Russian translation, IL, Moscow (1949).
31. Titchmarsh, E. C., *Introduction to the Theory of Fourier Integrals*, Oxford (1937); Russian translation, Gostekhizdat (1948).
32. Tonelli, L., *Serie trigonometriche*, Bologna (1928).
33. de la Vallée-Poussin, Ch. J., *Leçons sur l'approximation des functions d'une variable réelle*, Paris (1919).
34. de la Vallée-Poussin, Ch. J., *Cours d'analyse infinitésimale*, Louvain-Paris, ed. 5 (1923); Russian translation, GTTI, Moscow (1933).
35. Zygmund, A., *Trigonometrical series*, 1st English ed. (1935); *Trigonometric series*, 2nd ed., Cambridge (1959); Russian translation of 1st edition, GONTI (1939).

## B. ORIGINAL PAPERS

*AEN* = Annales scientifiques de l'Ecole Normale Supérieure (Paris). *AJM* = American Journal of Mathematics (Baltimore). *AM* = Acta Mathematica (Uppsala). *Ann. di M.* = Annali di Mathematica pura ed applicata (Bologna). *Ann. M.* = Annals of Mathematics (Princeton). *Ac. Sz.* = Acta Litterarum ac Scientiarum Regiae Universitatis Hungaricae (Szeged). *Ann.-Sc. N.P.* = Annali di Scuola Normale Superiore di Pisa. *At. A.L.* = Atti Accademia Nazionale dei Lincei (Rome). *BAMS* = Bulletin of the American Mathematical Society. *BSMF* = Bulletin de la Société Mathématique de France (Paris). *CR* = Comptes rendus de l'Académie des Sciences à Paris. *DAN* = Doklady Akademii Nauk SSSR. *DMJ* = Duke Mathematical Journal (Durham). *FM* = Fundamenta Mathematicae (Warszawa). *GN* = Nachrichten der Akademie der Wissenschaften in Göttingen. *IAN* = Izvestiya Akademii Nauk SSSR, seriya matematicheskaya. *JEP* = Journal de l'École Polytechnique (Paris). *JIMS* = The Journal of the Indian Mathematical Society (Madras). *JLMS* = Journal of the London Mathematical Society. *J.M.Ph.* = Journal of Mathematics and Physics (Massachusetts Institute of Technology). *J.r.a.M.* = Journal für die reine und angewandte Mathematik (Berlin). *MA* = Mathematische Annalen (Berlin–Göttingen–Heidelberg). *Mat.* = Matematica (Cluj). *MC* = Matematicheskii Sbornik. *MZ* = Mathematische Zeitschrift (Berlin–Göttingen–Heidelberg). *Pr.A.M.S.* = Proceedings of the American Mathematical Society. *PKNA* = Proceedings Koninklijke Nederlandse Akademie van Wetenschappen (Amsterdam). *PLMS* = Proceedings of the London Mathematical Society. *PNAS* = Proceedings of the National Academy of Sciences of the United States of America (Washington). *QJ* = Quarterly Journal of Mathematics (Oxford). *RCMP* = Rendiconti del Circolo Matematico di Palermo. *St.M.* = Studia Mathematics (Wroclaw). *TAMS* = Transactions of the American Mathematical Society. *TLI* = Trudy Leningradskogo industrial'nogo instituta, razdel fiziko-matematicheskii. *TMIC* = Trudy Matematicheskogo instituta im. V.A. Steklova. *TMJ* = Tôhoku Mathematical Journal. *TMMO* = Trudy Moskovskogo matematicheskogo obshchestva. *UMN* = Uspekhi matematicheskikh nauk. *UZM* = Uchenyye zapicki Moskovskogo gosudarstvennogo universiteta.

Alexits, G., [1] Über den Einfluß der Struktur einer Funktion auf die Konvergenz fast überall ihrer Fourierreihe, *Ac. Sz.*, **4** (1953), 95–101.

Arbault, J., [1] Sur l'ensemble de convergence absolue d'une série trigonométrique, *BSMF*, **80** (1952), 253–317.

Baiada, E., [1] Il corpo convesso di Carathéodory, *Ann. di M.* (4) **39** (1955), 75–85.

BANACH, S., [1] Über einige Eigenschaften der lakunären trigonometrischen Reihen, *St.M.*, Vol. II (1930), 207–220.

BARY, N.K., [1] Sur l'unicité du développement trigonométrique, *CR*, **177** (1923), 1195–1197; *FM*, **9** (1927), 62–118.

[2] Mémoire sur la représentation finie des fonctions continues, *MA*, **103** (1930), 145–248; 598–653.

[3] Sur le rôle des lois diophantiques dans le problème d'unicité du développement trigonométrique, *MC*, **2** (44) (1937), 699–722.

[4] The uniqueness problem of the representation of functions by a trigonometric series (in Russian) *UMN*, **4**, no. 3 (31) (1949), 3–68; English translation, *AMS*, no. 52, New York (1951), 1–89.

[5] Supplement to above Reference [4], *UMN*, **7**, no. 5 (51) (1952), 193–196.

[6] On primitive functions and trigonometric series convergent almost everywhere (in Russian), *MC*, **31** (73) (1952), 687–702.

[7] Generalization of the inequalities of S.N.Bernstein and A.A.Markov (in Russian), *IAN*, **18** (1954), 159–176.

[8] On the best approximation of two conjugate functions by trigonometric polynomials (in Russian), *IAN*, **19** (1955), 285–302.

[9] On the locally best approximation of periodic functions by trigonometric polynomials (in Russian), *UZM*, no. 181, Matematika, Vol. VIII (1956), 107–138.

BARY, N.K., and D.E. MEN'SHOV, [1] Sur l'intégrale des Lebesgue–Stieltjes et les fonctions absolument continues de fonctions absolument continues, *Ann.di M.*, Series IV, Vol. V (1927–28), 19–54.

BARY, N.K., and S.B. STECHKIN, [1] Best approximations and differential properties of two conjugate functions (in Russian), *TMMO*, Vol. V (1956), 485–522.

BELLMAN, R., [1] Random summability and Fourier series, *BAMS*, **49** (1943), 732–733.

[2] A note on a theorem of Hardy on Fourier constants, *BAMS*, **50** (1944), 741–744.

BERNSTEIN, S.N., [1] On the best approximation of continuous functions by polynomials of a given degree (in Russian). *Collected Works* (see No. A4 of Books Bibliography), Vol. I, 11–104; French translation, *Mem. Acad. Roy. Belgique,* 2me serie, **4** (1912), 1–104.

[2] On the absolute convergence of trigonometric series (in Russian), *Collected Works,* Vol. I, 217–223; see also *CR*, **158** (1914), 1661–4.

[3] On a method of summation of trigonometric series (in Russian). *Collected works*, Vol. I, 523 to 525; French translation, *CR*, **191** (1930), 976–9.

[4] Comments regarding a note of R.Salem (in Russian). *Collected works*, Vol. II, 159–160.

[5] On the absolute convergence of trigonometric series (in Russian). *Collected works*, Vol. II, 166–169.

[6] On periodic functions for which the best convergent series is a Fourier series (in Russian) *Collected works*, Vol. II, 178–183.

BESICOVITCH, A.S., [1] On a structural property of a function and ensemble (in Russian). *MC*, **31** (1922), 128–147.

[2] A general metric property of summable functions, *JLMS*, **1** (1926), 120–128.

BEURLING, A., [1] Ensembles exceptionnels, *AM*, 72 (1940), 1–13.

BOAS, R.P., [1] Integrability of trigonometric series, III, *QJ*, ser. (2) **3** (1952), 217–221.

BOHR, H., [1] Über einen Satz von J.Pal, *Ac.Sz.*, **7** (1935), 129–135.

DU BOIS-REYMOND, *P.*, [1] Untersuchungen über die Konvergenz und Divergenz der Fourierschen Darstellungsformen, *Abh. Akad. Wiss.*, München, XII (1876), 1–103.

[2] Beweis über die Koeffizienten der trigonometrischen Reihen, *Abh. Akad. Wiss.*, München, XII (1876), 117–166.

BOKS, T.J., [1] Sur le rapport entre les méthodes d'intégration de Riemann et de Lebesgue, *RCMP* **45** (1921), 211–264.

BROWMAN, A., [1] On two classes of trigonometrical series. *Thesis*, University of Uppsala (1947).

BYKOV, YA.V., [1] On the theory of trigonometric series (in Russian). *Report at Kazan University*, 98:7 (1939), 47–51.

CALDERÓN, A.P., [1] On theorems of M.Riesz and A.Zygmund, *PAMS*, **1** (1950), 533–535.

CALDERÓN, A.P., and A.ZYGMUND, [1] On the theorem of Hausdorff–Young and its extensions, *Annals of Math. Studies*, **25** (1950), 166–188.

CANTOR, G., [1] Über die Ausdehnung eines Satzes aus der Theorie der trigonometrischen Reihen, *MA*, **5** (1872), 123–132.

CARATHÉODORY, C., [1] Über den Variabilitätsbereich der Koeffizienten von Potenzreihen, die gegebene Werte nicht annehmen, *MA*, **64** (1907), 95–115.
[2] Über den Variabilitätsbereich der Fourier'schen Konstanten von positiven harmonischen Funktionen, *RCMP*, **32** (1911), 193–217.
CARLEMAN, T., [1] Über die Fourierkoeffizienten einer stetigen Funktion, *AM*, **41** (1918), 377–384.
[2] A theorem concerning Fourier series, *PLMS*, **21** (1923), 483–492.
[3] Sur les équations intégrales singulières à noyau réel et symétrique, *Uppsala Universitets Arsskrift* (1923), 1–228.
CHEREISKAYA, V. I., [1] Theorem on the uniform convergence of Fourier series (in Russian), *UZM*, Matem., Vol. VIII (1956), 159–164.
CIVIN, P., and H. E. CHRESTENSON, [1] The multiplicity of a class of perfect sets, *Pr.A.M.S.*, **4** (1953), 260–263.
DELONE, B. N., [1] The geometry of positive quadratic forms (in Russian), *UMN*, Vol. III (1937), 16–62.
DENJOY, A., [1] Sur quelques propriétés des séries à termes positifs, *BSMF*, **40,** 3 (1912), 223–228.
[2] Sur l'absolue convergence des séries trigonométriques, *CR*, **156** (1912), 135–136.
[3] Mémoire sur la totalisation des nombres dérivés non sommables, *AEN* (3), XXXIV (1916), 127–222; (3) XXXV (1917), 181–236.
[4] Sur l'intégration riemannienne, *CR*, **169** (1919), 219–221.
DZHVARSHEISHVILI, A. G., [1] On a convergence test of Fourier series (in Russian). *Report of Akad. Nauk Georgian SSR*, **11** (1950), 403–407.
ERDÖS, P., [1] On the convergence of trigonometric series. *J.M.Ph.*, **22** (1943), 37–39.
FADDEYEV, D. K., [1] On the representation of summable functions by singular integrals at Lebesgue points (in Russian). *MC*, I (43) (1936), 351–368.
FATOU, P., [1] Séries trigonométriques et séries de Taylor, *AM*, **30** (1906), 335–400.
[2] Sur la convergence absolue des séries trigonométriques, *BSMF*, **41** (1913), 47–53.
FEJÉR, L., [1] Lebesguesche Konstanten und divergente Fourierreihen, *J.r.a.M.* **139** (1910), 22–53.
[2] Sur les singularités de la série de Fourier des fonctions continues, *AEN*, **28** (1911), 63–103.
[3] La convergence sur son cercle de convergence d'une série de puissances effectuant une représentation conforme du cercle sur le plan simple, *CR*, **156** (1913), 46–49.
[4] Über die arithmetischen Mittel erster Ordnung der Fourierreihen, *GN* (1925), 13–17.
FROSTMAN, O., [1] Potential d'équilibre et capacité des ensambles, *Lund* (1935).
GEL'FAND, I. M., D. A. RAIKOV and G. E. SHILOV, [1] Commutative normal rings (in Russian). *UMN*, 1:2 (12) (1946), 48–146.
GEL'FOND, A. O., [1] Distribution of fractional parts and convergence of functional series with gaps (in Russian *UZM*, issue 148, Matematika Vol. IV (1951), 60–68.
GERGEN, J. J., [1] Convergence and summability criteria for Fourier series, *QJ* (Oxford) **1** (1930) 252–275.
GERMEIER, YU. B., [1] The derivatives of Riemann and de la Vallée-Poussin and their application to some problems of the theory of trigonometric series (in Russian). *Dissertation*, Moscow (1946).
GHIZZETTI, A., [1] Ricerche sui momente di une funzione limitata compressa fra limiti assegnati, *At.A.L.* (7) **13** (1942), 1165–1199.
[2] Sui coefficienti di Fourier di una funzione limitata compressa fra limit assegnati. *Ann. Sc. N.P.* (3) **4** (1950), 131–156.
[3] Ricerche abeliane e tauberiane compiute nell'Instituto Nazionale per le Applicazioni del calcolo, *Ann. di M.* (4) **34** (1953), 113–132.
GIBBS, W., [1] Fourier series, *Nature* **59** (1908), 200.
HAHN, H., [1] Über die Menge der Konvergenzpunkte einer Funktionfolge, *Arch. d. Math. u. Phys.*, **28** (1919), 34–35.
HARDY, G. H., [1] On the summability of Fourier series, *PLMS*, 2, **12** (1913), 365–372.
[2] Notes on some points in the integral calculus. *Mess. for Maths.*, **49** (1919), 149–155; **58** (1928), 50–52.
[3] Remarks on three recent notes in the Journal, *JLMS*, **3** (1928), 166–169.
[4] On certain criteria for the convergence of a Fourier series of a continuous function, *Mess. for Maths.*, **47** (1918), 149–156.
HARDY, G. H., and J. E. LITTLEWOOD, [1] Sur la série de Fourier d'une fonction à carré sommable, *CR*, **156** (1913), 1307–1309.

[2] Some problems concerning Diophantine approximation, *AM*, **37** (1914), 193–238.
[3] Some problems of Diophantine approximation: a remarkable trigonometrical series, *PNAS*, **2** (1916), 583–586.
[4] Abel's theorem and its converse, *PLMS*, **18** (1919), 205–235.
[5] Solution of the Cesàro summability problems for power series and Fourier series, *MZ*, **19** (1923), 67–96.
[6] On the strong summability of Fourier series, *PLMS*, **26** (1926), 273–286.
[7] On the absolute convergence of Fourier series, *JLMS*, **3** (1928), 250–253.
[8] Some new properties of Fourier constants, *MA*, **97** (1926), 159–209; *JLMS*, **6** (1931), 3–9.
[9] Some new convergence criteria for Fourier series, *JLMS*, **7** (1932), 252–256; *Ann. Sc. N.P.*, **3** (1934), 43–62.
[10] On the strong summability of Fourier series, *FM*, **25** (1935), 162–189.
[11] Notes on the theory of series, XX; Generalization of a theory of Paley, *QJ*, **8** (1937), 161–171.
[12] The allied series of a Fourier series, *PLMS* (2), **24** (1925), 211–246.

Hartman, Ph., and A. Wintner, [1] On sine series with monotonic coefficients. *JLMS*, **28** (1953), 102–104.

Hausdorff, F., [1] Eine Ausdehnung des Parsevalschen Satzes über Fourierreihen, *MZ*, **16** (1923), 163–169.

Helson, H., [1] Proof of a conjecture of Steinhaus, *PNAS*, **40** (1954), 205–206.
[2] On a theorem of F. and M. Riesz, *Colloq. Math.*, **3**, No. 2 (1955), 113–117.

Herzog, F., [1] A note on power series which diverge everywhere on the unit circle, *Michigan Math. J.*, **2**, No. 2 (1953–1954), 175–177.

Herzog, F., and J. Piranian, [1] Sets of convergence of Taylor series. *DMJ*, **16** (1949), 529–534.

Heywood, Ph., [1] A note on a theorem of Hardy on trigonometrical series, *JLMS*, **29** (1954), 373–378.
[2] On the integrability of functions defined by trigonometric series, *Q J*, Oxford, series (2), **5** (1954), 71–76; **6** (1955), 77–79.

Hille, E., and J. D. Tamarkin, [1] Remarks on a known example of a monotone continuous function, *Am. Math. Monthly*, **36** (1929), 255–264.

Hille, E., and G. Klein, [1] Riemann's localization theorem for Fourier series, *DMJ*, **21** (1954), 587–591.

Hobson, E. W., [1] On the convergence of series of orthogonal functions, *PLMS* (2) **12** (1913), 297–308.

Ivashev–Musatov, O. C., [1] On the Fourier–Stieltjes coefficients of singular functions (in Russian), *IAN*, **20** (1956), 179–196.
[2] On the coefficients of trigonometric null-series (in Russian), *IAN*, **21** (1957), 559–578.

Izumi, S., [1] Some trigonometrical series, X, *TMJ* (2), **6** (1954), 69–72.

Izumi, S., N. Matsuyama and T. Tsuchikura, [1] Some negative examples, *TMJ* (2), **5** (1953), 43–51.

Izumi, S., and M. Satô, [1] Some trigonometrical series, XVIII, *Proc. Jap. Acad.*, **32** (1956), 20–23.

Jurkat, W., and A. Peyerimhoff, [1] Der Satz von Fatou–Riesz und der Riemannsche Lokalisationssatz bei absoluter Konvergenz, *Arch. Math.*, **4** (1953), 285–297.

Kaczmarz, S., [1] Integrale vom Dinischen Typus, *St.M.* III (1931), 189–199.

Kahane, J. P., [1] Sur certaines classes de séries de Fourier absolument convergentes, *J. Math. pures et appl.*, **35** (1956), 249–259.
[2] Sur un problème de Littlewood, *PKNA*, Indag. meth., A. 60, No. 3 (1957), 268–271.

Kaidash, N. M., [1] On the almost everywhere convergence of Fourier series (in Russian). *Dissertation, MGU*, Moscow (1954).

Kennedy, P. B., [1] Fourier series with gaps, *QJ*, **7** (1956), 224–230.
[2] Remark on a theorem of Zygmund, *JLMS*, **33,** No. 1 (1958), 71–72.

Kerschner, R., [1] On singular Fourier–Stieltjes transforms, *AJM*, **58** (1936), 450–452.

Kharshiladze, F. I., [1] On a method of summation by S. N. Bernstein of Fourier series (in Russian) *MC*, **11** (53) (1942), 121–148.

Khinchin, A. Ya., [1] Sur une extension de l'intégrale de M. Denjoy, *CR*, **162** (1916), 287–290.
[2] Über die diadischen Brüche, *MZ*, **18** (1923), 109–116.

Khinchin, A., and A. Kolmogorov, [1] Über Konvergenz von Reihen, deren Glieder durch den Zufall bestimmt werden, *MC*, **32** (1925), 668–677.

Kolmogorov, A. N., [1] Une série de Fourier–Lebesgue divergente presque partout, *FM*, **4** (1923), 324–329.

[2] Sur les fonctions harmoniques conjuguées et les séries de Fourier, *FM*, **7** (1925), 23–28.
[3] Une série de Fourier–Lebesgue divergente partout, *CR*, **183** (1926), 1327–1239.
[4] Über die Summen durch den Zufall bestimmten Größen, *MA*, **99** (1928), 309–318.
[5] Sur un procédé d'intégration de M. Denjoy, *FM*, **11** (1928), 27–28.
[6] Une contribution à l'étude de la convergence des séries de Fourier, *FM*, **5** (1924), 96–97.
[7] Fundamental concepts in the theory of probability (in Russian), *M-L.*, *ONTI* (1936).

Kolmogorov, A. N., and G. A. Seliverstov, [1] Sur la convergence des séries de Fourier, *CR*, **178** (1925), 303–305.

Konyushkov, A. A., [1] On the Lipschitz classes (in Russian). *IAN*, **21** (1957), 423–448.
[2] Best approximations by trigonometric polynomials and Fourier coefficients (in Russian), *MC*, **44** (86) (1958), 53–84.

Kozlov, V. Ya., [1] On the connection between absolute convergence and the uniqueness of expansion of a function into a trigonometric series (in Russian), *DAN*, **15** (1937), 417–420.
[2] On complete systems of orthogonal functions (in Russian). *MC*, **26** (68) (1950), 351–364.

Kuttner, B., [1] A theorem on trigonometric series, *JLMS*, **10** (1935), 131–135.

Kuz'min, R. O., [1] On some trigonometric inequalities (in Russian). *Journal of the Leningrad Physics and Maths. Society*, **1** (1927), 233–239.
[2] On trigonometric series divergent everywhere (in Russian). *TLI*, department of Physics and Maths., **10**, no. 3 (1936), 53–56.

Landau, E., [1] Über das Vorzeichen der Gausschen Summe, *GN* (1928), 19–20.
[2] Über eine trigonometrische Summe, *GN* (1928), 21–24.

Lebesgue, H., [1] Recherches sur la convergence des séries de Fourier, *MA*, **61** (1905), 251–280.
[2] Sur les intégrales singulières, *Ann. Fac. Sc. Univ. Toulouse* (3), I (1909), 25–117.

Leibenzon, Z. L., [1] On the ring of functions with absolutely convergent Fourier series, *UMN*, **9** no. 3 (61), (1954), 157–162.

Lévy, P., [1] Sur la convergence absolue des séries de Fourier, *Comp. Math.*, **1** (1934), 1–14.
[2] Sur quelques problèmes actuellement irrésolus et sans doute insolubles dans les théories des séries et des intégrales de Fourier, *JEP*, **145** (1939), 179–194.

Littlewood, J. E., [1] On mean values of power series, *PLMS*, **25** (1924), 328–337; *JLMS*, **5** (1930), 179–182.
[2] On a theorem of Kolmogorov, *JLMS*, **1** (1926), 229–231.
[3] On the Fourier coefficients of functions of bounded variation, *QJ*, **7** (1936), 219–226.
[4] Mathematical notes (14). On a theorem of Hardy and Littlewood, *JLMS*, **13** (1938), 194–195.
[5] On a theorem of Paley, *JLMS*, **29** (1954), 387–395.

Littlewood, J. E., and R. Paley, [1] Theorems on Fourier series and power series, *JLMS*, **6** (1931), 230–233.

Lorentz, G. G., [1] Fourier-Koeffizienten und Funktionenklassen, *MZ*, **51** (1948), 135–149.

Lozinskii, S. M., [1] On convergence and summability of Fourier series and interpolation processes, *MC*, **14** (56) (1944), 175–268.
[2] On a theorem of N. Wiener (in Russian), *DAN*, **49** (1945), 562–565; *DAN*, **53** (1946), 691–694.
[3] Treatment of the Jackson theorem (in Russian), *DAN*, **83** (1952), 645–647.

Lukacs, F., [1] Über die Bestimmung des Sprunges einer Funktion aus ihrer Fourier-Reihe, *J.r.a.M.*, **150** (1920), 107–112.

Lusin, N. N., [1] Concerning a certain Taylor series (in Russian), *Collected Works*, Vol. I, 25–30,
[2] Concerning a basic theorem of integral calculus (in Russian), *Collected Works*, Vol. I, 5–24.
[3] Concerning the absolute convergence of trigonometric series (in Russian), *Collected Works*. Vol. I, 31–40.
[4] Functions (in mathematics) (in Russian). *Great Soviet Enc. (1st ed.)* (1934), Vol. 59, 314–334.

Lusin, N. N., and I. I. Privalov, [1] On the uniqueness and multiplicity of trigonometric series (in Russian). *Lusin's Collected Works*, Vol. I, 280–318; French translation *AEN*, **42** (1925), 143–91.

Marcinkiewicz, J., [1] Sur les séries de Fourier, *FM*, **27** (1936), 38–69.
[2] Quelques théorèmes sur les séries et les fonctions. *Bull. Sém. Math. Univ. Wilno*, no. 1 (1938), 19–24.
[3] Sur quelques intégrales du type de Dini, *Ann. Soc. Polonaise Math.*, **17** (1938), 42–50.
[4] Sur une nouvelle condition pour la convergence presque partout des séries de Fourier, *Ann. Sc. N.P.*, **8** (1939), 239–240.
[5] Sur la sommabilité forte des séries de Fourier, *JLMS*, **14** (1939), 162–168.

[6] Sur la convergence absolue des séries de Fourier, *Mat.*, **16** (1940), 66–73.
[7] Sur la convergence des séries orthogonales, *St.M.*, **6** (1936), 39–45.

MARCINKIEWICZ, J., and A. ZYGMUND, [1] On the behaviour of trigonometric series and power series, *TAMS*, **50** (1941), 407–453.
[2] On the differentiability of functions and summability of trigonometric series, *FM*, **26** (1936), 1–43.
[3] Two theorems on trigonometric series, *MC*, **2** (44), (1937), 733–738.
[4] Some theorems on orthogonal systems, *FM*, **28** (1937), 309–335.

MAZURKIEWICZ, S., [1] Sur l'intégrale $\int_0^1 \frac{f(x+t)+f(x-t)-2f(x)}{t}\,dt$, *St.M.*, III (1931), 114–118.

MEN'SHOV, D.E., [1] Sur l'unicité du développement trigonométrique, *CR*, **163** (1916), 433–436.
[2] Sur les séries de Fourier des fonctions continues, *MC*, **8** (50) (1940), 493–518.
[3] Sur la représentation des fonctions mesurables par des séries trigonométriques, *MC*, **9** (51) (1941), 667–692.
[4] Sur la convergence uniforme des séries de Fourier, *MC*, **11** (53) (1942), 69–76.
[5] Sur les sommes partielles des séries de Fourier des fonctions continues, *MC*, **15** (57) (1944), 385–432.
[5a] On universal trigonometric series (in Russian), *DAN*, **49** (1945), 79–82.
[6] On the partial sums of trigonometric series (in Russian), *MC*, **20** (62) (1947), 197–237.
[7] On the convergence in measure of trigonometric series (in Russian), *TMIS*, **32** (1950), 3–97.
[8] On the convergence of trigonometric series (in Russian), *Ac.Sz.*, **12,** Pars A (1950), 170–184.
[9] On the limits of indetermination of trigonometric series (in Russian), *DAN*, **74** (no. 2) (1950), 181–184.
[10] On certain problems in the theory of trigonometric series (in Russian). *Report of Moscow University*, Physics and Maths., series, no. 8 (1950), 3–10.
[11] On Fourier series of continuous functions (in Russian), *UZM*, **148** (1951), Matematika, Vol. IV, 108–132.
[12] On the limits of indetermination of Fourier series (in Russian), *MC*, **30** (72) (1952), 601–650.
[13] On Fourier series of summable functions (in Russian), *TMMO*, **1** (1952), 5–58.
[14] On certain properties of Fourier series (in Russian), *IAN*, **18** (1954), 379–388.
[15] On the limits of indetermination of the partial sums of universal trigonometric series (in Russian), *UZM*, no. 165, Matematika, **7** (1954), 3–33.
[16] On the limits of indetermination in measure of partial sums of trigonometric series (in Russian) *MC*, **34** (76) (1954), 557–574.
[17] On almost convergent trigonometric series (in Russian), *MC*, 37 (79) (1955), 265–292.
[18] On the limits of sequences of partial sums of trigonometric series (in Russian), *DAN*, **106** (1956), 777–780.

MORSE, M., and W. TRANSUE, [1] A new application of the Young–Pollard convergence criteria for a Fourier series, *DMJ*, **18** (1951), 563–571.

SZ. NAGY, B., [1] Méthodes de sommation des séries de Fourier, I, *Ac. Sz.*, **12** (1950), 204–210.

NASH, J.P., [1] Uniform convergence of Fourier series, *The Rice Inst. Pamphl.* (1953), Spec. Issue Nov., 31–57.

NATANSON, I.P., [1] On the summation of Fourier series by the method of C.N. Bernstein and W. Rogosinski (in Russian), *TLI*, no. 4, rep. 2 (1937), 39–44.

NEDER, L., [1] Zur Theorie der trigonometrischen Reihen, *MA*, **84** (1921), 117–136.
[2] Ein Satz über die absolute Konvergenz der Fourier-Reihe, *MZ*, **49** (1944), 644–646.

NEMYTZKII, V.V., [1] On certain classes of linear sets in connection with the absolute convergence of trigonometric series (in Russian with French summary), *MC*, **33** (1926), 5–32.

NERSESOVA, E.A., [1] Sur la multiplicité du développement trigonométrique, *CR*, **202** (1936), 195–197.

NIKOL'SKII, S.M., [1] On linear methods of summation of Fourier series (in Russian), *IAN*, **12** (1948), 259–278.

NOBLE, M.E., [1] Coefficient properties of Fourier series with a gap condition, *MA*, **128,** 55–62; correction (1954), 256.

ORLICZ, W., [1] Über Konjugierte Exponentenfolgen, *St.M.*, **3** (1931), 200–211.
[2] Beiträge zur Theorie der Orthogonalentwicklungen (III), *Bull. Acad. Pol.*, Sér. (1932), 229–238.

[3] Über unbedingte Konvergenz in Funktionenräumen (I), *St.M.*, IV (1933), 33–37.

Pagni, M., [1] Un osservazione sui coefficienti di Fourier di funzione crescenti, *At.A.L.* (8), **4** (1948), 672–675.

Pál, J., [1] Sur des transformations de fonctions qui font converger leurs séries de Fourier, *CR*, **158** (1914), 101–103.

Paley, R., [1] Some theorems on orthogonal functions, *St.M.*, **3** (1931), 226–238.

[2] On Fourier series with positive coefficients, *PLMS*, **7** (1932), 205–208.

[3] A note on power series, *JLMS*, **7** (1932), 122–130.

Paley, R., and A. Zygmund, [1] On some series of functions, *Proc. Cambr. Phil. Soc.*, **26** (1930), 337–357, 458–474; **28** (1932), 190–205.

Pisot, C., [1] La répartition modulo 1 et les nombres algébriques, *Ann. Sc. N. P.* (2), **7** (1928), 205–248

Plancherel, M., [1] Sur la convergence des séries de fonctions orthogonales, *CR*, **157** (1913), 539–541

Plessner, A. I., [1] Über Konvergenz von trigonometrischen Reihen, *J.r.a.M.*, **155** (1925), 15–25.

[2] On conjugate trigonometric series (in Russian), *DAN*, **4** (1935), 235–238.

Polya, G., and G. Szegö, [1] Über den transfiniten Durchmesser (Kapazitätskonstante) von ebenen und räumlichen Punktmengen, *J.r.a.M.*, **165** (1931), 4–48.

Privalov, I. I., [1] Sur les fonctions conjuguées, *BSMF*, **44** (1916), 100–103.

[2] Generalization of Paul du Bois-Reymond's theorem (in Russian), *MC*, **31** (1923), 229–231.

[3] On the differentiation of Fourier series (in Russian), *MC*, **30** (1915), 320–324.

Pyatetskii-Shapiro, I. I., [1] On the uniqueness problem of the expansion of functions into a trigonometric series (in Russian), *DAN*, **85** (1952), 497–500.

[2] On the uniqueness problem of the expansion of functions into a trigonometric series (in Russian), *UZM*, no. 155, Matematika, Vol. V (1952), 54–72.

[3] Supplement to the report "On the uniqueness problem of the expansion of functions into a trigonometric series" (in Russian), *UZM*, no. 165, Matematika, Vol. VII (1954), 79–97.

Rademacher, H., [1] Einige Sätze über Reihen von allgemeinen Orthogonalfunktionen, *MA*, **87** (1922), 112–138.

Rajchman, A., [1] Sur le principe de localisation de Riemann, *C.R. de la Soc. Sci. de Varsovie*, **11** (1918), 115–122.

[2] Sur l'unicité du développement trigonométrique, *FM*, **3** (1922), 287–301.

[3] Rectification et addition à ma Note "Sur l'unicité du développement trigonométrique", *FM*, IV (1923), 366–367.

[4] Sur la multiplication des séries trigonométriques et sur une classe d'ensembles fermés, *MA*, **95** (1926), 388–408.

Riemann, B., [1] On the possibility of representing a function by means of a trigonometric series (in Russian), *Collected works*, Gostekhizdat (1948), 225–261.

Riesz, F., [1] Über die Fourier-Koeffizienten einer stetigen Funktion von beschränkter Schwankung, *MZ*, **2** (1918), 312–315.

[2] Über eine Verallgemeinerung der Parsevalschen Formel, *MZ*, **18** (1923), 117–124.

[3] Über die Randwerte einer analytischen Funktion, *MZ*, **18** (1922), 87–95.

Riesz, M., [1] Sur les fonctions conjugúees, *MZ*, **27** (1927), 218–244.

Riesz, M., and F. Riesz, [1] Über Randwerte einer analytischen Funktion, *Quatr. Congrès des Math. Scand.* (1916), 27–44.

Rogosinski, W., [1] Über die Abschnitte trigonometrischer Reihen, *MA*, **95** (1925), 110–134.

[1a] Über die Abschnitte der Fourierreihen. *Jahresb. der Deutsch. Math. Vereinigung* **33,** H. 9–12, 2 Abt. (1925), 87–88.

[2] Reihensummierung durch Abschnitts-Koppelungen, *MZ*, **25** (1926), 132–149.

[3] Abschnittsverhaltungen bei trigonometrischen und insbesondere Fourierschen Reihen, *MZ*, **41** (1936), 75–136.

Rudin, W., [1] Transformations des coefficients de Fourier, *CR*, **243** (1956), 638–640.

Salem, R., [1] Essais sur les séries trigonométriques, *Actual. Sci. et Industr.*, no. 862, Paris (1940).

[2] On some properties of symmetrical perfect sets, *BAMS*, **47** (1941), 820–828.

[3] On trigonometrical series whose coefficients do not tend to zero, *BAMS*, **47** (1941), 899–901.

[4] On the absolute convergence of trigonometric series, *DMJ*, **8** (1941), 317–334.

[5] On sets of multiplicity for trigonometrical series, *AJM*, **64** (1942), 531–538.

[6] On singular monotonic functions of Cantor type, *J.M.Ph.*, **21** (1942), 69–82.

[7] A singularity of the Fourier series of continuous functions, *DMJ*, **10** (1943), 711–716.

[8] On a theorem of Zygmund, *DMJ*, **10** (1943), 23–31.
[9] Sets of uniqueness and sets of multiplicity, *TAMS*, **54** (1943), 218–228, **56** (1944), 32–49.
[10] On a theorem of Bohr and Pál, *BAMS*, **50** (1944), 579–580.
[11] Sur les transformations des séries de Fourier, *FM*, **33** (1945), 108–114.
[12] Corrections to the papers "Sets of uniqueness and sets of multiplicity I and II", *TAMS*, **63** (1948), 595–598.
[13] New theorems on the convergence of Fourier series, *PKNA*, Indeg. Math., **16** (1954), 550–555.
[14] On a problem of Smiethies, *PKNA*, Indeg. Math., **16** (1954), 403–407.
[15] On strong summability of Fourier series, *AJM*, **77** (1955), 393–403.

SALEM, R., and A. ZYGMUND, [1] Capacity of sets and Fourier series, *TAMS*, **59** (1946), 23–41.
[2] On a theorem of Banach, *PNAS*, **33** (1947), 293–295.
[3] On lacunary trigonometric series, *PNAS*, USA, **33** (1947), 333–338, part II; also **34** (1948), 54–62.
[4] Sur un theorème de Piatetski-Shapiro, *CR*, **240** (1955), 2040–2042.
[5] Sur les ensembles parfaits dissymétriques à rapport constant, *CR*, **240** (1955), 2281–2283.
[6] Some properties of trigonometric series whose terms have random signs, *AM*, **91** (1954), 245 to 301.

SATÔ MASAKA, [1] Uniform convergence of Fourier series, *Proc. Japan. Acad.*, **30** (1954), 528–531, 668–701, 808–813; **31** (1955), 261–263, 600–605; **32** (1956), 99–104.

SCHAEFFER, A. C., [1] The Fourier–Stieltjes coefficients of a function of bounded variation, *AJM*, **61** (1939), 934–940.

SHILOV, G. E., [1] On the Fourier coefficients of a class of continuous functions (in Russian), *DAN*, **35** (1942), 3–7.

SHIROKOV, F. V., [1] On conjugate trigonometric series (in Russian). *Dissertation, Moscow State University* (1956).

SHNEIDER, A. A., [1] On sets which are a generalization of H-sets (in Russian), *MC*, **34** (76) (1954), 249–258.

SIERPINSKI, W., [1] Sur l'ensemble des points de convergence d'une suite de fonctions continues, *FM*, **2** (1921), 41–49.

SMIRNOV, V. I., [1] Sur les valeurs limites des fonctions analytiques, *CR*, **188** (1929), 131–133.

STECHKIN, S. B., [1] Generalization of some inequalities of S. N. Bernstein (in Russian), *DAN*, **60** (1948), 1511–1514.
[2] Best approximations of functions represented by lacunary trigonometric series (in Russian), *DAN*, **76** (1951), 33–36.
[3] On the absolute convergence of orthogonal series (in Russian), *MC*, **29** (71) (1951), 225–232.
[4] On the convergence and divergence of trigonometric series (in Russian), *UMN*, VI, no. 2 (1951), 148–149.
[5] On the order of the best approximation of continous functions (in Russian), *IAN*, **15** (1951), 219–242.
[6] On the Kolmogorov–Seliverstov theorem (in Russian), *IAN*, **17** (1953), 499–512.
[7] On the absolute convergence of Fourier series (in Russian), *IAN*, **17** (1953), 87–98; **19** (1955), 221–246; **20** (1956), 385–412.
[8] On the absolute convergence of orthogonal series (in Russian), *DAN*, **29** (71) (1951), 225–231; *DAN*, **102** (1955), 37–40.
[9] On the best approximation of conjugate functions by trigonometric polynomials (in Russian), *IAN*, **20** (1956), 197–206.
[10] An extremal problem for polynomials (in Russian), *IAN*, **20** (1956), 765–774.
[11] On Fourier coefficients of continuous functions (in Russian), *IAN*, **21** (1957), 93–116.
[12] On trigonometric series divergent at every point (in Russian), *IAN*, **21** (1957), 711–728.

STEIN, P., [1] On a theorem of M. Riesz, *JLMS*, **8** (1933), 242–247.

STEINHAUS, H., [1] Sur une série trigonométrique divergente, *C. R. de la Soc. sci. de Varsovie*, V, Fasc. 3 (1912) 223–227
[2] Sur un problème de MM. Lusin et Sierpinski, *Bull. Acad. Sci. Cracovie* (1913), 335–350.
[3] Sur le développement du produit de deux fonctions en une série de Fourier, *Bull. Intern. de l'Acad. de Cracovie* (1913), 113–116.
[4] Sur quelques propriétés des séries trigonométriques et de celles de Fourier, *Roczprawy Akad. Unietnoszi Cracow*, **56** (1925), 175–225.

[5] A divergent trigonometrical series, *JLMS*, **4** (1929), 86–88.

[6] A new property of G. Cantor's set (in Polish), *Wektor*, **7** (1917).

SUNOUCHI, G., [1] On the convergence test of Fourier series, *Math. Japon.*, **1** (1948), 41–44.

[2] Convergence criteria for Fourier series, *TMJ*, **4** (1953), 187–193.

[3] A Fourier series which belongs to the class *H* diverges almost everywhere, *Kodai Math. Sem. Rep.*, **1** (1953), 27–28.

[4] On the strong summability of Fourier series, *Proc. Amer. Math. Soc.*, **1** (1950), 526–533.

SZÁSZ, O., [1] Über den Konvergenzexponent der Fourierschen Reihen, *Münch. Sitzungsber.* (1922), 135–150.

[2] Zur Konvergenztheorie der Fourierschen Reihen, *AM*, **61** (1933), 185–201.

[3] On the partial sums of certain Fourier series, *AJM*, **59** (1937), 696–708.

[4] On the absolute convergence of trigonometric series, *Ann.M.*, **47** (1946), 213–220.

SZIDON, S., [1] Reihentheoretische Sätze und ihre Anwendungen in der Theorie der Fourierschen, Reihen, *MZ*, **10** (1921), 121–127.

[2] Ein Satz über die absolute Konvergenz von Fourier-Reihen, in denen sehr viele Glieder fehlen, *MA*, **96** (1926), 418–419.

[3] Verallgemeinerung eines Satzes über die absolute Konvergenz von Fourier-Reihen mit Lücken *MA*, **97** (1927), 675–676.

[4] Ein Satz über trigonometrische Polynome mit Lücken und seine Anwendung in der Theorie der Fourierreihen, *J.r.a.M.*, **163** (1930), 251–252.

[5] Ein Satz über Fouriersche Reihen stetiger Funktionen, *MZ*, **34** (1932), 485–486.

[6] Einige Sätze und Fragestellungen über Fourier-Koeffizienten, *MZ*, **32** (1934), 477–480.

[7] Ein Satz über Fouriersche Reihen mit Lücken, *MZ*, **32** (1934), 481–482.

[8] Über orthogonale Entwicklungen, *Ac.Sz.* **10** (1943), 206–253.

TALALYAN, A. A., [1] On the convergence of orthogonal series (in Russian), *DAN*, **110** (1956), 515–516.

[2] Convergence almost everywhere of orthogonal series (in Russian), *Dissertation, Math. Inst., Akad. Nauk USSR* (1956).

TANDORI, K., [1] Bemerkung zur Divergenz der Fourierschen Reihen stetiger Funktionen, *Publ. Math.*, **2**, Debrecen (1952), 191–193.

TAUBER, A., [1] Ein Satz aus der Theorie der unendlichen Reihen, *Monatsh. f. Math. u. Phys.*, **8** (1897), 273–277.

TEMKO, K. V., [1] Convex capacity and Fourier series (in Russian), *DAN*, **110,** no. 6 (1956); *UZM*, Matematika, **9,** no. 186 (1959), 83–108.

[2] On the absolute convergence of Fourier series (in Russian), *MC*, **43** (85) (1957), 401–408.

TIMAN, A. F., [1] On a method of approximating continuous functions by trigonometric polynomials (in Russian), *IAN*, **11** (1947), 263–282.

[2] On certain methods of summation of Fourier series (in Russian), *IAN*, **14** (1950), 85–94.

[3] Note on trigonometric polynomials and Fourier–Stieltjes series (in Russian), *UMN*, XII, no. 2 (74) (1957), 175–183.

TIMAN, A. F., and M. F. TIMAN, [1] Generalized modulus of continuity and the best approximation in mean (in Russian), *DAN*, **71** (1950), 17–20.

TITCHMARSH, E. C., [1] On conjugate functions, *PLMS*, **29** (1929), 49–80.

TOEPLITZ, O., [1] Über allgemeine lineare Mittelbildungen, *Prace Math. Fyzicne*, **22** (1911), 113–119.

TOLSTOV, G. P., [1] Note on a theorem of D. F. Yegorov (in Russian), *DAN*, **22** (1939), 309–311.

[2] On points of density of linear measurable sets (in Russian), *MC*, **10** (52) (1942), 249–264.

TSUCHIKURA, T., [1] Remark on a theorem of Erdös and a problem of Zalcwasser, *J. Math. Tokyo*, **1** (1951), 27–31.

TURÁN PAL, [1] Egy Steinhausfele problémárol. *Mat. Lapok*, **4** (1953), 263–275.

[2] On the strong summability of Fourier series, *J. Ind. Math. Soc.* (N.S), **12** (1948), 8–12.

UL'YANOV, P. L., The generalization of a theorem of Marcinkiewicz (in Russian), *IAN*, **17** (1953), 513–524.

[2] On some equivalent conditions of the convergence of series and integrals (in Russian), *UMN*, VIII, no. 6 (1953), 133–141.

[3] On trigonometric series with monotonically decreasing coefficients (in Russian), *DAN*, **90** (1953), 33–36.

[4] Application of *A*-integration to a class of trigonometric series (in Russian), *MC*, **35** (77) (1954), 469–490.

[5] On the expansion of functions (in Russian), *DAN*, **105** (1955), 913–915.
[6] On an *A*-integral of Cauchy I (in Russian), *UMN*, XI, no. 5 (1956), 223–229.
[7] The *A*-integral and conjugate functions (in Russian), *UZM*, no. 181, Matematika, vol. VIII (1956), 139–157.
[8] On the divergence of Fourier series (in Russian), *UMN*, vol. XII (75) (1957), 75–132.
[9] On rearrangements of a trigonometric system (in Russian), *DAN*, **116** (1957), 568–571.
[10] On localized properties of convergent Fourier series (in Russian), *UZM*, Matematika, **9**, no. 186 (1959), 71–82.
[11] Basic integrals and Fourier series (in Russian). *Reports of Moscow University*, Maths. series no. 5 (1959), 33–42.
[12] On series for a rearranged trigonometric system (in Russian), *IAN*, **22,** no. 4 (1958), 515–542
[13] On unconditional convergence and summability (in Russian), *IAN*, **22** (1958), 811–840.

DE LA VALLÉE-POUSSIN, CH. J., [1] Un nouveau cas de convergence des séries de Fourier, *RCMS*, XXXI (1911), 296–299.
[2] Sur l'unicité du développement trigonométrique, *Bull. Acad. Roy. de Belg.* (1012), 702–718.
[3] Capacité des ensembles, Paris (1937).

VERBLUNSKY, S., [1] On a class of perfect sets, *AM*, **65** (1935), 283–305.

VIOLA, T., [1] Sull'insieme dei punti di convergenza delle serie trigonometriche generali, *Ann. Sc. N. P.* (2), **4** (1935), 155–162.

WANG, F. T., [1] Note on $H_2$ summability of Fourier series, *JLMS*, **19** (1944), 208–209.

WEYL, H., [1] Über die Konvergenz von Reihen, die nach Orthogonalfunktionen fortschreiten, *MA*, **67** (1909), 225–245.
[2] Über die Gleichverteilung von Zahlen mod. Eins., *MA*, **77**, 3 (1916), 313–352.

WIENER, N., [1] The quadratic variation of a function and its Fourier coefficients, *Massachusetts Journal of Math.*, **3** (1924), 72–94.
[2] Tauberian theorems, *Ann. M.*, **33** (1932), 1–100.

WIENER, N., and A. WINTNER, [1] Fourier–Stieltjes transforms and singular infinite convolutions, *AJM*, **40** (1938), 513–522.

YANO, SH., [1] Notes on Fourier analysis (XV). On the absolute convergence of trigonometrical series, *TMJ*, **1** (1949), 46–49.

YOUNG, FR., [1] Transformations of Fourier coefficients, *PAMS*, **3** (1952), 783–791.

YOUNG, L. C., [1] Sur une généralisation de la notion de variation de puissance *p*-ième bornée au sens de M. Wiener, et sur la convergence des séries de Fourier, *CR*, **204** (1937), 470–472.a

YOUNG, W. H., [1] A note on trigonometrical series, *Mess. for Maths.*, **38** (1909), 44–48.
[2] Konvergenzbedingungen für die verwandte Reihe von Fourierschen Reihe, *Münch. Sitzungsberichte*, **41** (1911), 361–371.
[3] Sur la généralisation du théorème de Parseval, *CR*, **155** (1912), 30–33.
[4] On the multiplication of successions of Fourier constants, *Proc. Roy. Soc.* (A), **87** (1912), 331–339.
[5] On the determination of the summability of a function by means of its Fourier coefficients, *PLMS*, **12** (1913), 71–88.
[6] Sur la convergence des séries de Fourier, *CR*, **163** (1916), 187–190.
[7] On the convergence of the derived series of Fourier series, *PLMS*, **17** (1916), 195–236.

ZELLER, K., [1] Über Konvergenzmengen von Fourierreihen, *Arch. Math.*, **6** (1955), 335–340.

ZYGMUND, A., [1] O module ciagloci sumy szeregu sprezonego z szeregiem Fouriera, *Pracc Math. fiz.*, **33** (1924), 125–132.
[2] Contribution à l'unicité du développement trigonométrique, *MZ*, **24** (1926), 40–46.
[3] Über die Beziehungen der Eindeutigkeitsfragen in den Theorien der trigonometrischen Reihen und Integrale, *MA*, **99** (1928), 562–589.
[4] Sur la convergence absolue des séries de Fourier, *PLMS*, **3** (1928), 194–196.
[5] Sur les fonctions conjugées, *FM*, **13** (1929), 284–303; **18** (1932), 312.
[6] Quelques théorèmes sur les séries trigonométriques et celles de puissances, *St.M.*, III (1931), 77–91.
[7] On the convergence of lacunary trigonometric series, *FM*, **16** (1930), 90–107.
[8] On lacunary trigonometric series, *TAMS*, **34** (1932), 435–446.
[9] A remark on conjugate series, *PLMS*, **34** (1932), 392–400.
[10] Sur le caractère de divergence des séries orthogonales, *Mat.*, **9** (1935), 86–88.
[11] Proof of a theorem of Paley, *Proc. Cambr. Phil. Soc.*, **34** (1938), 125–133.

[12] Note on the formal multiplication of trigonometrical series, *Bull. Sem. Math. Univ. Wilno*, **2** (1939), 62–66.
[13] On the convergence and summability of power series on the circle of convergence, *FM*, **30** (1938), 170–196; ***PLMS*, 47** (1942), 326–350.
[14] Smooth functions, *DMJ*, **12** (1945), 47–76.
[15] On the theorem of Fejér–Riesz, *BAMS*, **52** (1946), 310–318.
[16] An example in Fourier series, *St.M.*, **10** (1948), 113–119.

# INDEX

Made in Great Britain